INTEGRATED INTRODUCTION
TO
CHEMISTRY AND BIOLOGY

Volume 2

Beth Abdella and Gary Meissler

Printed in the United States of America
ISBN 978-1-7339033-9-4

TABLE OF CONTENTS

Chapter 12: Water, Aqueous Solutions, and Biochemical Implications....................................1

Chapter 13: Matter and Reactions...69

Chapter 14: Chemical Stoichiometry..110

Chapter 15: Gases...146

Chapter 16: Equilibrium I: Reaction Quotients and Equilibrium Constants.......................178

Chapter 17: Equilibrium II: Equilibrium Stresses and Equilibrium Calculations...............224

Chapter 18: The Characteristics of Acids and Bases..261

Chapter 19: Understanding Weak Acids and Bases Concept and Calculations.................301

Chapter 20: Applications of Acids and Bases: Buffers, Titrations, Indicators..................337

Glossary of Terms..386

Answers to Exercises...429

iv

CHAPTER 12: WATER, AQUEOUS SOLUTIONS, AND BIOCHEMICAL IMPLICATIONS

Water is essential to life. It plays crucial biological and biochemical roles for all known life forms. It is surmised that the first life forms developed in aqueous environments. This chapter explores the unique properties of water with particular emphasis on water as a solvent. Many different substances dissolve in water, so many that water has been called a "universal solvent." And yet, there are many substances that do not dissolve well in water, and this can be a problem. Consider, for instance, the development of a promising new drug molecule that is not sufficiently soluble in water to enter the bloodstream. It is our goal in this chapter to understand the properties of water at a molecular level. What is it about the structure of water molecules that leads to its particular and unique set of properties?

12-1. SUBSTANCES, MIXTURES , AND SOLUTIONS

The word **substance** implies either a pure **element** (a sample of helium gas, He, or a chunk of zinc metal, Zn) or a pure **compound** (a spoonful of sugar, $C_{12}H_{22}O_{11}$, or a tank of propane gas, C_3H_8). Any material that consists of a single element or a single compound is a *substance*.

Water is a substance, but it is most often found as **mixtures** with other substances. If you scoop a sample of water out of a typical ocean, lake or river you'll get a mixture of substances, not just H_2O. There might be particles of sand, loam, wood and plant debris. There will likely be algae and bacteria. There will also be dissolved minerals, salts and gases that won't be visible. Maybe you'll get a fish! This "water sample" is a very complex mixture of substances, especially considering that the loam, wood, algae, bacteria, plant debris and fish are already incredibly complex mixtures of a huge variety of substances. Likewise, if you get a glass of water out of your faucet, you will also have a mixture. There will be a variety of dissolved species in the water sample, the exact composition of which depends on the source of your community's water and any water treatments applied in your home. "Hard" water contains more dissolved 2+ metal ions such as Ca^{2+} and Mg^{2+} than "soft" water. Water softeners replace these **divalent cations** with twice as many monovalent cations (such as Na^+ and K^+). This minimizes issues caused by the poor interaction between divalent cations and detergent molecules, as well as other hard water maladies.

Just what does the word **mixture** imply? A *mixture* of substances can be described by listing a chemical formula (or name) for each substance and an amount of that substance in the mixture. Mixtures are typically made by stirring different components together or allowing them to mix naturally. Air is a mixture of different gases; see Figure 12-1. Steel is a mixture of iron atoms and carbon atoms. Gasoline is a mixture of many different hydrocarbon molecules, along with detergents, oxygenators and other specialty chemicals.

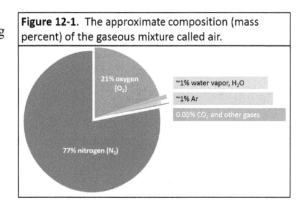

Figure 12-1. The approximate composition (mass percent) of the gaseous mixture called air.

21% oxygen (O₂)
~1% water vapor, H₂O
~1% Ar
0.05% CO₂ and other gases
77% nitrogen (N₂)

Some mixtures are **heterogeneous** and others are **homogeneous**. Different samples of a *heterogeneous mixture* have different relative compositions. Consider stirring together 100.0 g of sugar crystals and 100.0 g of salt crystals in your kitchen. You will have a mixture that, overall, is 50.0% sugar and 50.0% salt by mass. If you spoon out two samples of your mixture, each spoonful will have a composition of its own, maybe 48.4% sugar and 51.6% salt in one and 56.8% sugar and 43.2% salt in the other. Your sugar and salt mixture is *heterogeneous*. Good stirring might increase the *homogeneity* of this mixture, but it will never be perfect; it will always be heterogeneous. On the other hand, different samples of a *homogeneous mixture* have exactly the same composition. These mixtures are also called **solutions**.

Solution = Homogeneous Mixture

If you pour your 50% sugar and 50% salt mixture into a pitcher of water and stir until it all dissolves, your mixture will become homogeneous. Now your mixture contains three components instead of the original two: sugar, salt, and water. Each component separately is a pure substance (all of these happen to be *compounds*). In a *solution*, the component present in largest amount is often called the **solvent**, while the other components are called **solutes**. In our example, water is the solvent and sugar and salt are both solutes. Each sample of this solution will have a composition identical to any other sample of the solution; the solutes are evenly distributed throughout the solvent.

We are most familiar with solutions that have a liquid solvent and solid solutes, but there are many other options. Steel is a solid solution (solvent = iron, solute = carbon), air is a gaseous solution (solvent = nitrogen, solutes = other gases), soda pop is a solution in water (solvent) that contains both solid solutes (such as sugar) and a gaseous solute (carbon dioxide) to make it bubbly once the bottle is opened. Water and methanol are said to be **miscible** liquids. This means that they dissolve in each other in ANY relative composition. Consider a solution of 1.0 mL water in 50.0 mL of methanol; the solvent is methanol, the solute is water. On the other hand, a solution of 1.0 mL methanol in 50.0 mL of water changes the roles so that water is now the solvent! Gasoline is a complex solution of approximately 75 substances, none of which is present in a particularly large proportion. The most prevalent component (isopentane, see structure at right) is present only as about 10% of the total. Gasoline is a solution for which the idea of a solvent and solutes is not particularly helpful.

$$H_3C \overset{\overset{\displaystyle CH_3}{|}}{\underset{\underset{\displaystyle H}{|}}{C}} \overset{}{} CH_2 \overset{}{} CH_3$$

What makes a mixture different than a compound? The hallmark of a *mixture* is that its components can be mixed in a seemingly endless variety of compositions. Steel can be any iron and carbon mixture with a carbon composition between 0.02% and 2.14% (by mass). Salt water (NaCl in H_2O) can be made in an infinite variety of compositions, the upper bounds of which is determined by the overall solubility on NaCl in water. *Compounds*, on the other hand, have only one possible composition, as denoted by their chemical formula. Carbon monoxide (CO) is 43% carbon and 57% oxygen by mass while carbon dioxide (CO_2) is 27% carbon and 73% oxygen by mass. You can see calculations of this type in Example 12-1.

Example 12-1.

Determine the composition, by mass percent, of each of the following *compounds*. Notice that for a compound, the formula provides the "recipe"!

a. CO   **b.** CH_4

<u>Solutions</u>:

a. It is convenient to assume one mole of CO, which contains one mole of carbon atoms and one mole of oxygen atoms. The total mass of the carbon is 12.01 g, the mass of the oxygen is 16.00 g and the mass of the whole sample is 12.01 + 16.00 = 28.01 g. We calculate the mass percent of a particular element in a compound by comparing the mass of the element to the mass of the whole. In our case:

$$\text{mass \% carbon} = \frac{12.01 \text{ g C}}{28.01 \text{ g total}} \times 100\% = 42.88\% \text{ carbon}$$

$$\text{mass \% oxygen} = \frac{16.00 \text{ g O}}{28.01 \text{ g total}} \times 100\% = 57.12\% \text{ oxygen}$$

b. Assume one mole of CH_4, which contains one mole of carbon atoms and four moles of hydrogen atoms. The total mass of the sample is $12.01 + 4(1.008) = 16.04$ g. In this case:

$$\text{mass \% carbon} = \frac{12.01 \text{ g C}}{16.04 \text{ g total}} \times 100\% = 74.88\% \text{ carbon}$$

$$\text{mass \% hydrogen} = \frac{4 \text{ mol H} \times \frac{1.008 \text{ g H}}{\text{mol H}}}{16.04 \text{ g total}} \times 100\% = 25.14\% \text{ hydrogen}$$

Note that the sum of these two percentages (100.02%) is not exactly 100% due to rounding of values.

Example 12-2.

Determine the composition, by mass percent, of each of the following *mixtures*.

a. salt water made by dissolving 23.0 g NaCl in 150.0 g water
b. salt water made by dissolving 1.9 g NaCl in 35.6 g water

Solutions:

a. Notice that in describing the mixture of salt water, one has to provide a recipe. For a mixture, the recipe can be widely variable!

$$\text{mass \% H}_2\text{O} = \frac{150.0 \text{ g H}_2\text{O}}{173.0 \text{ g solution}} \times 100\% = 86.7\% \text{ water}$$

$$\text{mass \% salt} = \frac{23.0 \text{ g NaCl}}{173.0 \text{ g solution}} \times 100\% = 13.3\% \text{ salt}$$

b. Here we have a different recipe for salt water.

$$\text{mass \% H}_2\text{O} = \frac{35.6 \text{ g H}_2\text{O}}{37.5 \text{ g solution}} \times 100\% = 94.9\% \text{ water}$$

$$\text{mass \% salt} = \frac{1.9 \text{ g NaCl}}{37.5 \text{ g solution}} \times 100\% = 5.1\% \text{ salt}$$

The only limit on the possible recipes of salt water is the solubility of sodium chloride in water!

Another common difference between compounds and mixtures is that, while forming a compound from its elements always results in the creation of new ionic or covalent bonds, forming a mixture rarely does. Consider making a covalent compound (such as water) from its elements (hydrogen and oxygen):

$$2H_2(g) + O_2(g) \longrightarrow 2H_2O(\ell)$$

The chemical formulas change, so we could say that there is a **chemical change**. There are new covalent bonds. Similarly, making sodium chloride from its elements

$$2Na(s) + Cl_2(g) \longrightarrow 2NaCl(s)$$

results in the loss of metallic and covalent bonds and the formation of ionic bonds. Because formulas change, this is also a chemical change.

Making most mixtures does not result in new chemical bonds, although it may certainly result in new intermolecular attractions. Consider placing both hydrogen gas and oxygen gas in a balloon. You will just get a mixture of the two gases. In the gas phase, there are no important intermolecular attractions to worry about. Each gas goes from being pure to being impure, but no chemical reaction occurs (unless someone provides a spark of energy and water is produced!) Note: making a mixture is a **physical change**; chemical formulas are not altered. Physical changes involve change of phase (melting, vaporization, dissolution, etc.) During these processes the formulas of the chemical substances do not change (but the phase tags do!)

$$H_2O(s) \longrightarrow H_2O(\ell) \qquad\qquad \text{melting (or } fusion)$$

$$H_2O(\ell) \longrightarrow H_2O(g) \qquad\qquad \text{vaporization}$$

$$CH_3OH(\ell) \longrightarrow CH_3OH(aq) \qquad\qquad \text{dissolution}$$

Consider mixing liquid water with liquid methanol to produce a *solution* (see third **phase change** reaction equation, above). The solution has different hydrogen bonds than in the pure substances because a methanol molecule can hydrogen bond to a water molecule; see Figure 12-2. Note that the chemical formulas of water and methanol do not change upon mixing; there are no changes to the covalent bonds. Again, this is a physical change, not a chemical change. A mixture made by stirring sodium chloride (NaCl) and potassium bromide (KBr) crystals together results in no new ionic bonds and no changes in the formulas of the substances present. Likewise, when mixing iron shavings (Fe) with zinc dust (Zn), no new metallic bonds form.

Figure 12-2. One of the possible hydrogen bonds between a methanol molecule (CH_3OH, blue) and a water molecule.

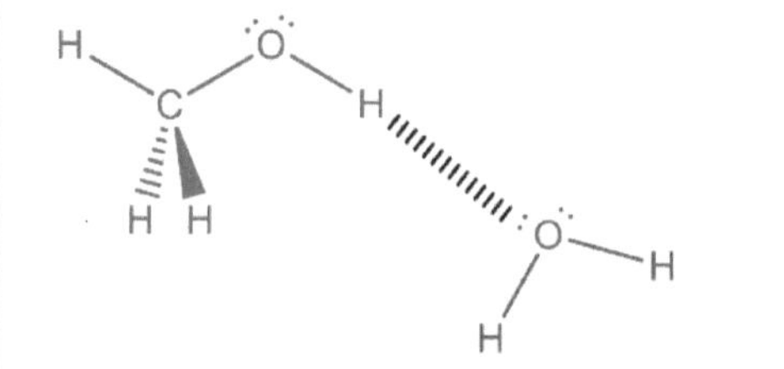

Some *mixtures* do allow the formation of new metallic bonds or new ionic bonds (but making a mixture never results in new covalent bonds). **Alloys** are solid solutions of metals, usually produced by mixing molten metals together and then solidifying. In an alloy, new metallic bonds form between neighboring atoms of different elements. However, because an alloy does not have one particular composition (you can mix the same two metals together in an endless variety of compositions),

Table 12-1. Stainless Steel "304" is the most commonly used variety because it offers good corrosion resistance, has good formability and is readily welded.

Elemental component	Mass percent
C	0.08
Si	0.75
Mn	2.0
P	0.045
S	0.030
Cr	18.0-20.0
Ni	8.0-10.5
N	0.10
Fe (solvent)	The remainder, to 100%

it is a mixture, not a compound. There is no chemical formula for an alloy, so it cannot be a compound. Instead, a list of components and their compositions is necessary to describe an alloy. Stainless steel is an alloy having a variety of different recipes based on the intended use of the material. You can see the composition of the most commonly used stainless steel in Table 12-1.

Not only are various solutions a big part of our everyday lives, a substantial portion of chemical and biochemical laboratory work is carried out in solutions, particularly **aqueous solutions** (meaning that the solvent is water). Examples include some types of soil analyses, water quality tests, forensic investigations, medical lab tests, and immunizations. The remainder of this chapter provides an introduction to water, its solutions, and important related concepts. Water will also be a focus of some chapters yet to come; it's a little molecule with lots of complications!

Example 12-3.

Label each of the following as an element, compound, solution, or heterogeneous mixture. Use your life experiences and perhaps a little internet research to help in your decision-making.

    a. ammonia   **b.** leaf   **c.** swimming pool water   **d.** ketchup

    e. solid silver teapot   **f.** laughing gas   **g.** windshield washer fluid

Solutions:

    a. a compound (A pure substance with a particular chemical formula, NH_3)

    b. a heterogenous mixture (Different parts of the leaf have different structures and therefore different components)

    c. a solution (There are lots of dissolved chemicals in swimming pools)

    d. heterogeneous mixture (That's why you shake it up before squeezing it on your fries!)

    e. an element (Ag)

    f. a compound (N_2O)

    g. a solution (Look this up if necessary. There are a variety of components and recipes).

12-2. WATER

As an award-winning actor may play many roles effectively, water is a "molecule of a thousand faces." Chemically it can act as an acid or a base (Bronsted-Lowry definitions); can be oxidized or reduced; can be a ligand to metal ions; can play a variety of crucial roles in living organisms; and can show its versatility in numerous other ways. It can also act as a solvent, a role that we will focus on in this chapter.

A. Unique Characteristics

To understand water's role as a solvent we first need to consider its unique characteristics. Water is probably the liquid with which people are most familiar; we bathe in it, drink it, swim in it, and watch it fall from the sky as rain. Your body is approximately 60% water by mass! Our high degree of familiarity with water might lead to the assumption that the properties of water are similar to the properties of most similarly sized molecules. However, when water is compared to other substances we learn that water has many unusual characteristics. For example, the solid form of almost all substances sinks in the liquid form, but ice floats on water. Solid water has an unusually low density. Also, molecules as light as water are expected to be gases at room temperature due to having weak intermolecular attractions. However, the boiling point of water is unusually high; see Table 12-2. Clearly, water is a substance that deserves close study!

Table 12-2. Boiling points of substances having low molar mass

Substance	Mass (g/mol)	Boiling point (°C)	State (at 25 °C)
H_2	2.0	−252.8	gas
He	4.0	−268.9	gas
CH_4	16.0	−164	gas
NH_3	17.0	−33.4	gas
H_2O	**18.0**	**100.**	**liquid**
HF	20.0	19.5	gas
Ne	20.2	−245.9	gas

As we have seen previously, H₂O has very polar bonds due to the large electronegativity difference between the oxygen and hydrogen atoms. Because it is a bent molecule, these polar bonds result is a polar molecule. As we saw in Chapter 11, water has a particularly large dipole moment of 1.84 D. For comparison, the dipole moments of water and some other simple polar molecules are given in Table 12-3. Water is very polar! Remember, from Chapter 11, that water (and HF and NH₃) display boiling points that are much higher than would be expected based on molar masses.

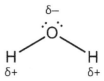

Table 12-3. The dipole moments of selected molecules in units of debye, D.	
molecule	Dipole moment (D)
H₂O	1.84
HF	1.82
NH₃	1.42
HCl	1.08
H₂S	0.97
HBr	0.82
HI	0.44

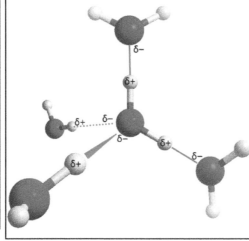

Figure 12-3. The tetrahedral arrangement of four hydrogen bonds (blue) around the central water molecule.

In a sample of pure water, each water molecule can hydrogen bond with four of its neighboring molecules; see Figure 12-3. In liquid water these relatively weak attractions (compared to a covalent bond) are numerous[1], but transient. In liquid water, the ideal geometry (linear around the connecting hydrogen atom) is not routinely achieved. On the other hand, in solid water (ice) each water molecule maintains 4 stable hydrogen bonds over time due to the lack of energy in the system (the cold temperature!) The impact of this relatively small structural difference on the density of the substance is amazing; see Figure 12-4.[2] This figure shows approximately the same number of water molecules, first in the solid phase and then in the liquid phase. The ideal 180° OHO bond angles of

the hydrogen bonds of ice require that the molecules of water be further apart from one another than in liquid water. For most substances, the solid form is more dense than the liquid form and the solid sinks in the liquid. For water the opposite is true, and ice floats.

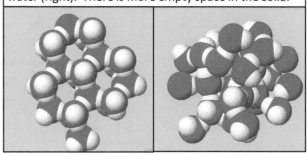

Figure 12-4. The bulk structures of ice (left) and liquid water (right). There is more empty space in the solid.

In summary, we can point to hydrogen bonding as the root cause of many of the unusual properties of water. Given that hydrogen bonding is a particularly strong intermolecular attraction, water molecules have a particularly strong attraction for one another. This attraction must be overcome in the boiling process as molecules move into the gas phase. Thus hydrogen bonding gives water its unusually high boiling point. Remember that other small molecules that are capable of hydrogen bonding (HF and NH₃) also have higher than expected boiling points, just not high enough to be liquids at room temperature! Most light molecules have very weak attractions for each other because dispersion forces are particularly weak for small molecules.

---

[1] Water molecules in liquid water (at room temperature) average being involved in 3.6 hydrogen bonds at any given point in time.

[2] The structures in this figure can be manipulated at http://www.edinformatics.com/interactive_molecules/ice.htm

B. Water as a Solvent

We mentioned in the opening paragraph of this chapter that water is sometimes referred to as the "universal solvent." While water can dissolve a wide range of chemical compounds, some substances are essentially insoluble in water. One simplistic rule to keep in mind states that "like dissolves like." What does this mean? Is it strictly true?

Because water is polar *and* can form hydrogen bonds, other substances that are polar and/or that can participate in hydrogen bonding can be considered to be "like" water. The essence of the "like dissolves like" statement is that polar solvents will be able to dissolve polar solutes and non-polar solvents will be able to dissolve non-polar solutes.

Many salts dissolve well in water because the ionic nature of a salt guarantees polarity; there is a separation of charge. In water, cations attract the negative (oxygen) end of water molecules and anions attract the positive end. In addition, some ions, such as hydroxide ion (OH^-) or oxalate ion ($C_2O_4^{2-}$) can participate in hydrogen bonding with water; see Figure 12-5. These attractions cause a **solvation shell** (or in the specific case of water, a **hydration shell**) to form around the dissolved ions. The geometry of water molecules around an ion in solution depends on the ion, but an octahedral arrangement, such as what is shown in Figure 12-6 for the sodium ion (Na^+) is very common.

Figure 12-5. A. A hydroxide ion donating a hydrogen bond to a water molecule. B. The oxalate ion accepting a hydrogen bond from a water molecule.

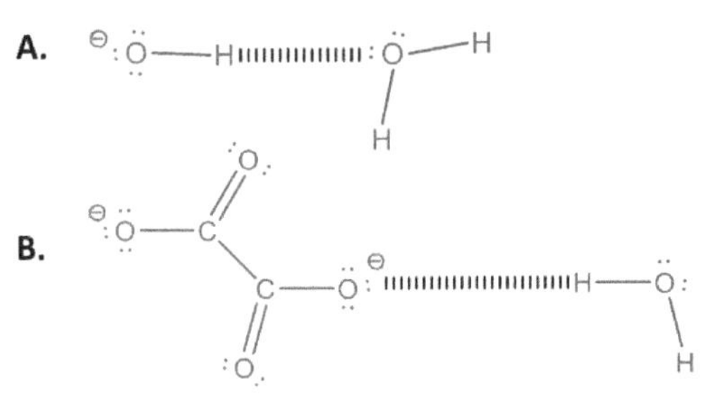

Figure 12-6. The octahedral *hydration shell* around a dissolved sodium ion. Note that the cation attracts the electron rich oxygen atoms of the water molecules. The wedges and dotted lines are <u>not</u> covalent bonds; they are there to help visualize the geometry of these attractions.

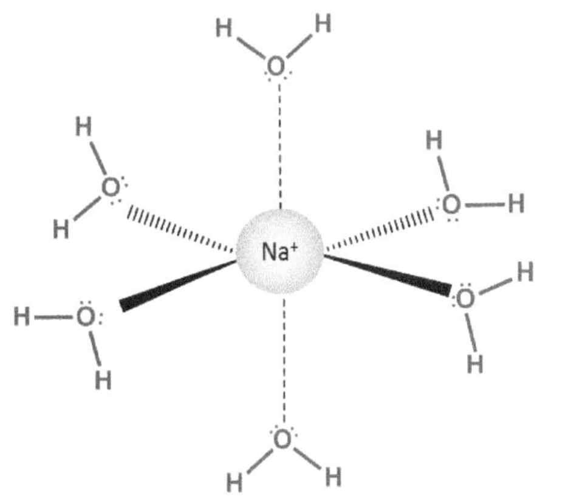

The water molecules of the *hydration shell* are not rigidly held in place; the system is dynamic. The solvent molecules and the ions are in continual motion, so that these attractions are constantly breaking and reforming with different water molecules. When a salt dissolves, the anions and cations are separated from one another (the ionic bonds are broken), but new **ion-dipole attractions** form. Ions in solution move independently of other dissolved ions.

Many polar molecules can dissolve in water for the same reasons as a salt: there is a separation of charge in the polar molecule, and perhaps the ability to form hydrogen bonds, as well. Either **dipole-dipole attractions** or **hydrogen bonding** can be associated with polar solutes in water. In Figure 12-2 we showed one possible hydrogen bond between a methanol molecule and a water molecule.

Exercise 12-1.

Sketch a *different* hydrogen bond between a water molecule and a methanol molecule than the one shown in Figure 12-2. Make sure to use an appropriate hydrogen atom in your sketch!

All solute particles in aqueous solutions are surrounded by an inner sphere of water molecules making up the hydration shell of the solute. Successful solute particles have characteristics similar to those of the water molecule and can form hydrogen bonds, dipole-dipole attractions or ion-dipole attractions with the closest water molecules.

C. Electrolytic Characteristics

Electrolytes are solutes that, when dissolved, form a solution that can conduct an electric current. The discussion of electrolytic character works best if one sticks to soluble compounds. Solutes that are electrolytes provide ions in solution. When an external voltage is applied, the ions travel independently through solution, cations in one direction and anions in the other, thus establishing an electrical current. All soluble compounds can be classified into three categories according to their relative abilities to provide ions in solution (and, accordingly, their relative abilities to carry a current): strong electrolytes, weak electrolytes and nonelectrolytes.

1. Strong electrolytes

Strong electrolytes are soluble substances that provide a **stoichiometric**[3] number of ions in solution. These ions are either <u>liberated</u> from an ionic network when a salt dissolves, or they are <u>formed</u> when a very polar molecule reacts with water molecules to produce ions. Strong electrolytes include the soluble salts[4] and strong acids. When soluble salts dissolve, the ions **dissociate** from one another and become independently hydrated. Strong acids, unlike strong bases, are <u>not</u> salts. Rather, strong acids are *molecules* made up of non-metal elements using covalent bonds, such as HCl, HNO_3, and H_2SO_4. When strong acids are dissolved in water, a chemical reaction occurs that generates ions from molecules. Reactions of this type, where new ions are made from neutral molecules, are called **ionizations**. Let's look at how to represent dissociations and ionizations with chemical symbolism.

a. Dissociations of Soluble Salts (including the soluble strong bases)

We can write balanced reaction equations for the dissolution (dissolving) of a salt in water. Calling these "reaction" equations is a misnomer because dissolving a solute is a *physical change*, not a *chemical reaction*! For the dissolution of potassium hydroxide in water, we can write any of the following, and <u>they all mean the same thing</u>!

A. $KOH(s) \longrightarrow KOH(aq)$ B. $KOH(s) \xrightarrow{H_2O} KOH(aq)$

C. $KOH(s) \longrightarrow K^+(aq) + OH^-(aq)$ D. $KOH(s) \xrightarrow{H_2O} K^+(aq) + OH^-(aq)$.

Let's break this down.

1. All four reaction equations make the physical change apparent by using (s) for "solid" on the "reactant" side and (aq) for "aqueous" on the "product" side.

2. Don't fall into the trap of thinking that C and D show chemical reactions because it looks as if the formulas have changed. They haven't. KOH is always comprised of K^+ ions and OH^- ions. When written as a neutral formula the charges cancel and don't explicitly show.

---

[3] Relating to quantities of particles in simple integer ratios, as prescribed by a reaction equation's coefficients and/or a chemical formula's subscripts. No fancy math is needed, for instance, 100 $MgCl_2$ formula units dissolve to supply 100 Mg^{2+} ions and 200 Cl^- ions.

[4] Remember that the definition of a salt is that the formula includes cations and anions. Usually the cation is a metal ion, but it could also be the ammonium ion, NH_4^+ (or a positively charged complex ion). Strong bases such as NaOH and KOH are salts.

3. Lines C and D make the dissociation events explicit. Lines A and B must be interpreted by the reader to indicate the dissociation of the ions. It is the <u>phase tag</u>, (aq), along with the <u>ionic nature</u> of the substance (as signified by its formula) that provide the necessary hints.

4. Water (the solvent) can be shown over the reaction arrow (B and D), but this is not necessary; the (aq) phase tag also tells us that water is the solvent.

5. All of these reaction equations include a single, forward-pointing arrow, telling a scientist that the process "goes to completion." These are soluble salts where large amounts dissolve. Dissociation is inherent to the dissolution process and we assume that the ions remain dissociated from one another over time.

So, reaction equations C and D more obviously describe the solubility process by making the *dissociation* process visible. We are more easily reminded that the ions go from a solid crystal structure (on the left side of the arrow) to aqueous and *separately solvated* ions (on the right). Again, any of these equations, A–D, are correct. We might call equations A and B **neutral formula equations**, while calling equations C and D **ionic equations**. Note that in the case of the <u>solid</u> salt (on the left), we never show the separated ions. That's because the ions are not separated from one another until they dissolve! Scientists often have a preference for ionic equations, because these show the processes in a more realistic fashion.

Different salts provide different numbers of cations and anions per formula unit, as shown by their formulas. Table 12-4 offers some additional examples. Note that you must be able to recognize the ion identities in a salt formula in order to write the dissolution equations! The dissolution processes in Table 12-4 are notated in the often preferred ionic form. If you are asked to write dissociation reaction equations, you should use an ionic equation in order to convince your instructor that you understand the process as completely as possible!

Table 12-4. A Variety of Dissolution Reaction Equations	
<u>Dissociation reaction equation</u>	Number of ions per <u>formula unit of salt</u>
$NaCl(s) \longrightarrow Na^+(aq) + Cl^-(aq)$	2 ions per formula unit
$K_3PO_4(s) \longrightarrow 3K^+(aq) + PO_4^{3-}(aq)$	4 ions per formula unit
$Pb(NO_3)_2(s) \longrightarrow Pb^{2+}(aq) + 2NO_3^-(aq)$	3 ions per formula unit
$NH_4SCN(s) \longrightarrow NH_4^+(aq) + SCN^-(aq)$	2 ions per formula unit

Example 12-4.

Write a dissociation reaction equation for each of the following soluble salts in water. Use an ionic equation form (explicitly dissociate the ions).

a. calcium acetate   **b.** iron(III) sulfate   **c.** lithium sulfide

<u>Solutions</u>:

a. First we must determine the chemical formula of the salt. Calcium only forms the Ca^{2+} ion; acetate is $C_2H_3O_2^-$. So the neutral formula of the salt must be $Ca(C_2H_3O_2)_2$.

Second, we write the reactant side of the equation using the designation for a solid salt and providing the single forward arrow: $Ca(C_2H_3O_2)_2(s) \longrightarrow$

Third, on the right, we indicate the formulas and numbers of each aqueous ion liberated from a formula unit of the solid: $Ca(C_2H_3O_2)_2(s) \longrightarrow Ca^{2+}(aq) + 2C_2H_3O_2^-(aq)$

Finally, we check our work, by making sure that phase tags are in place, that charges of the ions are displayed correctly, and that the reaction is properly balanced:

- same set of atoms on both sides of arrow; and
- same overall charge on both sides of arrow (neutral in this particular case).

b. Iron(III) sulfate is composed of the Fe^{3+} ion and the SO_4^{2-} ion. We will need two cations and three anions to make the neutral salt formula. After the steps listed in part a, we can write: $$Fe_2\left(SO_4\right)_3(s)\longrightarrow 2Fe^{3+}(aq)+3SO_4^{2-}(aq)$$

c. Lithium sulfide is composed of the Li^+ ion and the S^{2-} ion. We need two cations for every anion to make the neutral salt formula. After the steps listed in part a, we can write:
$$Li_2S(s)\longrightarrow 2Li^+(aq)+S^{2-}(aq)$$

b. Ionizations of the Strong Acids

We can write balanced reaction equations for the chemical reactions that occur when strong acid <u>molecules</u> *ionize* in water. Each of the reactions features the strong acid molecule reacting with a water molecule to create a hydronium ion (H_3O^+) and a left-over anion. The *ionization reactions* of three of the seven common strong acids are written below.[5] Look for the patterns in the reaction equations. Each of the balanced reaction equations offered here starts with the strong acid molecule already in aqueous solution; we are not showing the dissolving process of the original strong acid molecules, such as

$$HBr(\ell)\longrightarrow HBr(aq)$$

Single, forward arrows remind us that the number of molecules dissolved is the number of molecules that *ionize* (produce <u>new ions</u>). We could say that there is a **stoichiometric** formation of ions, because every aqueous HBr molecule produces a Br^- ion; no fancy math is needed; 100 HBr(aq) gives 100 Br^-(aq). Note that there are neutral molecules on the reactant side of the arrow and new ions on the product side.

These reactions are all of the same form: one H^+ ion moves from the neutral acid molecule to the neutral water molecule. <u>The very useful definition of an acid molecule is that it is an H^+ ion donor</u>; it gives an H^+ to some other species.

Ionization Reactions of Selected Strong Acids

$$HBr(aq)+H_2O\left(\ell\right)\longrightarrow Br^-(aq)+H_3O^+(aq)$$

$$HNO_3(aq)+H_2O\left(\ell\right)\longrightarrow NO_3^-(aq)+H_3O^+(aq)$$

$$H_2SO_4(aq)+H_2O\left(\ell\right)\longrightarrow HSO_4^-(aq)+H_3O^+(aq)$$

---

[5] It would be inaccurate to write ionization reactions for $HClO_3$ and $HClO_4$ because these molecules are not stable. Solutions of these strong acids are produced in other ways.

We could view this process with Lewis dot structures, using curved arrows to show the rearrangement of valence electron pairs; see Figure 12-7. Essentially, a lone pair of electrons on the partially negative oxygen atom of water "steals" an H^+ ion (a proton) away from the acid molecule. One could equally well describe the process as the acid molecule forcing the water molecule to accept the proton. In either case, the result is the formation of two ions: when H^+ leaves a neutral molecule, the molecule becomes a −1 ion; when H^+ adds to a neutral molecule,

Figure 12-7. On the left, the curved red arrow shows an oxygen lone pair of electrons (also red) attacking the partially charged hydrogen of the nitric acid molecule. When the new covalent bond between the water molecule and the hydrogen ion forms (the red bond in the H_3O^+ ion), the original bonding electrons (blue) stay behind on the nitrate ion (as shown by the blue curved arrows). Curved arrows show us what electrons are doing!

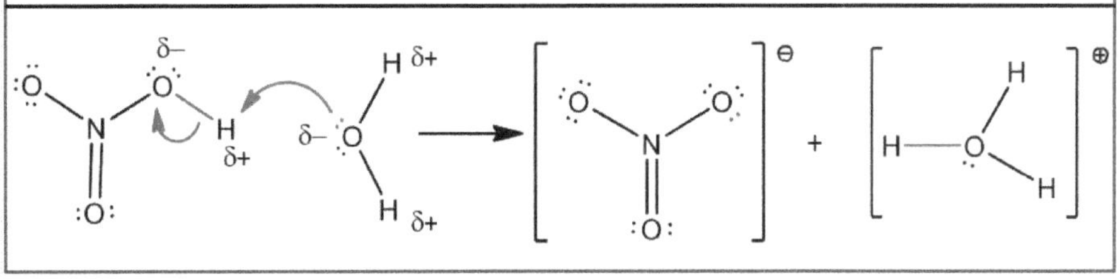

the molecule becomes a +1 ion. You should be able to draw similar diagrams for any of the other strong acids, as long as the Lewis dot structures are provided. NOTE: sulfuric acid is a little different in that there are two acidic hydrogen atoms in the structure. You should just transfer one of them to a water molecule, for now.[6]

Two notes about Figure 12-7:

1. A large number of chemical reactions follow a similar pattern to this one. Note that the reaction centers around a region of partial negative charge on one molecule (water) and partial positive charge on the other (acidic H). Reactions are often driven by +/− interactions!

2. We have not shown all possible resonance structures in Figure 12-7. The original acid molecule has two important resonance structures (double bond pointing down or to the left), while the product nitrate ion has three important resonance structures (double bond in any of the three positions). You should be able to draw these.

Example 12-5.

Write reaction equations to show how the following strong electrolytes place ions into aqueous solution:

a. KI   **b.** Na_2SO_4 **c.** HCl   **d.** aluminum perchlorate

Solutions:

a. $KI(s) \longrightarrow K^+(aq) + I^-(aq)$
b. $Na_2SO_4(s) \longrightarrow 2\,Na^+(aq) + SO_4^{2-}(aq)$
c. $HCl(aq) + H_2O(\ell) \longrightarrow Cl^- + H_3O^+(aq)$
d. $Al(ClO_4)_3(s) \longrightarrow Al^{3+}(aq) + 3\,ClO_4^-(aq)$

Exercise 12-2.

Write reaction equations to show how the following strong electrolytes place ions into aqueous solutions:

a. $Ba(OH)_2$ **b.** nickel(II) sulfate   **c.** HI   **d.** $Na_2S_2O_3$

---

[6] The second hydrogen atom on H_2SO_4 is also acidic, but it is a weak acid rather than a strong acid. We will discuss this circumstance in a later chapter.

2. Weak electrolytes

Weak electrolytes are soluble species that yield only a comparatively small number of ions in solution. We say that these ionizations do NOT "go to completion." These ionization reactions produce a **sub-stoichiometric** number of ions (meaning that not all of the molecules produce ions). Instead, the reactant species and the ion products are said to be in **chemical equilibrium** with one another. The two types of weak electrolytes are weak acids and weak bases.

a. Weak Acids

Weak acids, like strong acids, are molecules that donate H^+ ions to other species (such as water molecules). For strong acids, 100% of the dissolved molecules are assumed to be successfully ionized. For weak acids, ionization is an incomplete process, resulting in many fewer ions in solution. Most of the weak acid molecules exist in solution as the un-ionized (but polar) molecule. The small number of ions in a weak acid solution allows only a weak electrical current to be sustained. Hydrogen fluoride, HF, is a weak acid molecule.[7] HF is similar to other acid molecules in that it is a highly polar molecule with the hydrogen atom carrying considerable partial positive charge. We can show the acidic character of HF:

$$HF(aq) + H_2O(\ell) \longrightarrow F^-(aq) + H_3O^+(aq)$$

But, as the dissolved molecules ionize and the number of ions in solution increases, the reverse reaction begins to play an important role:

$$HF(aq) + H_2O(\ell) \longleftarrow F^-(aq) + H_3O^+(aq)$$

At some relatively small concentration of ions in the solution, the forward and reverse processes occur at the same rate. At this point, called **chemical equilibrium**, the net concentration of species in the solution does not change over time because for every HF molecule that ionizes (forward reaction) another HF molecule is re-formed (via the reverse reaction). Chemical equilibrium is **dynamic**, the forward and reverse processes are both occurring, but are exactly balanced in rate. We indicate *dynamic equilibrium* by showing both processes in one equation; we use a "reversible reaction" arrow, as shown here.[8]

$$HF(aq) + H_2O(\ell) \rightleftharpoons F^-(aq) + H_3O^+(aq)$$

Because only a small percentage of the acid molecules are ionized at any point in time[9], there are a considerably larger number of molecules of acid in the solution than ions. Sometimes this imbalance between the reactant side of the arrow and the product side of the arrow is emphasized with a lop-sided reversible arrow, as shown here.

$$HF(aq) + H_2O(\ell) \rightleftharpoons F^-(aq) + H_3O^+(aq)$$

This arrow indicates that the system has only a small propensity toward ion formation; the larger arrow points toward the more prevalent form of the material. If you think about it, that means that the reverse reaction is more successful than the forward reaction; a successful reaction produces product!

---

[7] This seems odd, given that F is more electronegative than Cl, Br or I. However, the size of a fluorine atom is more similar to that of a hydrogen atom than any of the other halogen atoms. This creates a more extensive bonding orbital overlap and, therefore, a stronger covalent bond than in HCl, HBr, or HI. The stronger bond in HF limits its acidity.

[8] Do not use a double-headed arrow ($\leftrightarrow$). Those are reserved for resonance structures!

[9] The percentage depends on many variables including the identity and concentration of the acid.

b. Weak Bases

As we have seen, an acid is a proton, H⁺, donor. Because acids react with bases, one can guess that a base is defined as a **proton acceptor**. The **weak bases**, when dissolved in water, react by taking a proton away from a water molecule (water acts as the acid, by donating an H⁺!) Ammonia is a common weak base. We can write:

$$NH_3(aq) + H_2O(\ell) \rightleftharpoons NH_4^+(aq) + OH^-(aq)$$

Weak bases establish *dynamic equilibria* with incomplete ionizations, similar to the equilibria established by weak acids. Thus we use reversible arrows. Substantially fewer ions are formed than the molecules of ammonia that remain, so we can use lop-sided reversible arrows if desired:

$$NH_3(aq) + H_2O(\ell) \rightleftharpoons NH_4^+(aq) + OH^-(aq)$$

Note, in Figure 12-8, that ammonia uses the lone pair of electrons (red curved arrow and red electron pair) on its nitrogen atom to form a new bond (red) to the transferred proton. The original bonding electrons (blue) stay with the oxygen atom of the water molecule. Only the H⁺ is transferred from the water molecule to the ammonia molecule.

Figure 12-8. The ionization reaction of the weak base, ammonia. The curved arrows show the rearrangements of the red and blue pair of electrons.

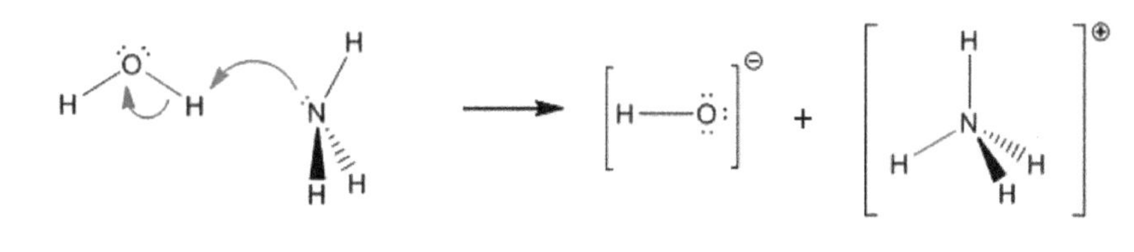

Table 12-5. Examples of weak acids and weak bases.

Weak Acids:	Formula	Name
	CH_3CO_2H	acetic acid
	HCO_2H	formic acid
	HF	hydrofluoric acid
	H_3PO_4	phosphoric acid
	$HC_6H_7O_6$	vitamin C (ascorbic acid)
	$R\text{-}CH_2CO_2H$	side chain of amino acid Asp
Weak Bases:	Formula	Name
	NH_3	ammonia
	NH_2NH_2 (or N_2H_4)	hydrazine
	CH_3NH_2	methylamine
	C_5H_5N	pyridine
	$C_6H_5NH_2$	aniline
	$R\text{-}CH_2CH_2CH_2CH_2NH_2$	side chain of amino acid Lys

Example 12-6.

Write balanced chemical equations for ionizations of the following species. Make sure to show the water molecule involved!

  a. the weak acid, HOCl

  b. the weak base, CH_3NH_2 (Draw a Lewis dot structure to help determine where the only lone pair of electrons resides. Use this pair to make the new bond!)

Solutions:

  a. A weak acid gives a proton (H^+) to a water molecule (H_2O is acting as a base!) in a reaction that does not go to completion. We write:

$$HOCl(aq) + H_2O(\ell) \rightleftharpoons OCl^-(aq) + H_3O^+(aq)$$

  b. A weak base accepts a proton from a water molecule (H_2O is acting as an acid!) in a reaction that does not go to completion. The lone pair of electrons is on the nitrogen atom.

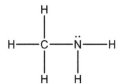

We add the proton to the nitrogen atom and write:

$$CH_3NH_2(aq) + H_2O(\ell) \rightleftharpoons CH_3NH_3^+(aq) + OH^-(aq)$$

Many nitrogen-containing molecules are weak bases due to the lone pair on the nitrogen atom; see Table 12-5!

3. Nonelectrolytes

Many soluble covalent compounds (molecules) dissolve without the formation of ions; such compounds are classified as **nonelectrolytes**. While many of these molecules are polar, having positive and negative regions, these charges are constrained by covalent bonds to travel together. Without the ability for positive and negative charges to migrate independently, polar molecules in solution cannot conduct electrical currents. Tap water is a weakly electrolytic solution due to small amounts of dissolved salts, not due to the water molecules! Distilled water does not support a measurable electrical current.

Writing dissolution equations for soluble nonelectrolytes only requires that we show a **phase change** from the original (solid, liquid, or gas) to the final (aq). Do not ionize molecular compounds in aqueous solution unless they are acids or bases! Here are some examples of dissolution equations (**phase changes**) for nonelectrolytes:

Glucose (an important metabolic sugar): $C_6H_{12}O_6(s) \longrightarrow C_6H_{12}O_6(aq)$

Ethanol (ethyl alcohol): $C_2H_5OH(\ell) \longrightarrow C_2H_5OH(aq)$

carbon dioxide: $CO_2(g) \longrightarrow CO_2(aq)$

None of these molecules ionizes in aqueous solution. Solubilities in 25 °C water are:

glucose	909 g/L	5.05 mol/L
ethanol	miscible[10]	
carbon dioxide[11]	1.45 g/L[12]	0.033 mol/L

Structures of these molecules are shown in Figure 12-9. Glucose and ethanol are polar molecules with obvious structural similarities to water molecules, including at least one –OH group. It is easy to rationalize "like dissolves like" for molecules such as these because they are dipoles that also have the ability to participate in hydrogen bonding. Indeed, ethanol is *miscible* with water and glucose has a solubility of over 5 mol/L! Carbon dioxide, however, is not a dipole and it has a correspondingly lower solubility in water. We can rationalize the solubility of CO_2 based on the existence of polar C=O bonds (the overall molecule is not polar due to the geometry of these two bonds causing their individual

Figure 12-9. Structures and space-filling models of water, glucose, ethanol, and carbon dioxide. Note the –OH groups on the first three molecules.

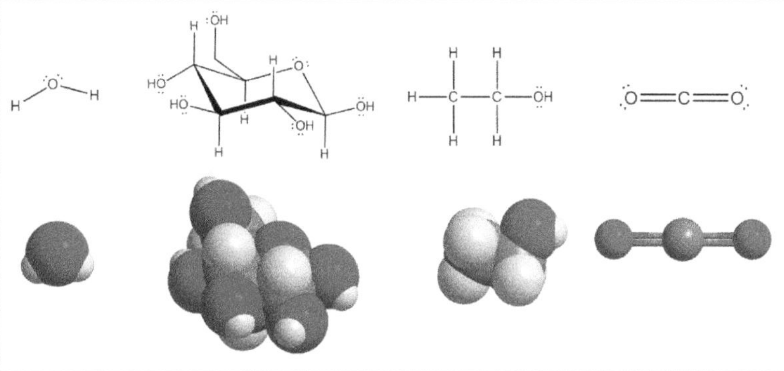

polarities to cancel). Nonetheless, the partial negative charge carried by the oxygen atoms of CO_2 allows them to serve in the acceptor role of hydrogen bonds. Carbon dioxide molecules cannot form hydrogen bonds with each other (there is no donor site), but they can hydrogen bond with water molecules.

Exercise 12-3.

Draw the Lewis dot structure of carbon dioxide with as many hydrogen bonds to surrounding water molecules as possible. Use the most ideal hydrogen bond geometries. Label the donor and acceptor sites for each hydrogen bond.

Unlike CO_2, many non-polar molecules have very little in common with a water molecule. Not surprisingly, this greatly limits their ability to dissolve in water. While water has been called the "universal solvent," it certainly cannot solubilize all substances to a reasonable extent!

Consider the halogen molecules, Cl_2, Br_2, and I_2. Each of these molecules is nonpolar and offers no possibility for hydrogen bonding. While not particularly soluble in water, these substances are soluble enough to be useful in some laboratory applications. Bromine is the most soluble of the three (~0.22 mol/L). Iodine has an unexpectedly low water solubility (~0.0011 mol/L). The solubility of Cl_2 is intermediate at ~0.046 mol/L. As we will see, the expected periodic trend would be based on size with $I_2 > Br_2 > Cl_2$. However, this trend is confused, in part by reactions between the halogen molecules and water (F_2 reacts quite violently).

Why would any of these nonpolar molecules dissolve into the very polar water environment? Before answering that question, let's lay a foundation by considering the halogens as pure substances. In liquid bromine, Br_2, neighboring molecules interact with one another through dispersion forces. We expect dispersion forces to be stronger when molecules are larger, and I_2 is larger than Br_2 which

---

[10] Ethanol and water are soluble in each other in any ratio.

[11] Carbon dioxide does react with water to a small degree, producing the weak acid, H_2CO_3, which then ionizes to a small extent. A large majority of dissolved CO_2 molecules remain CO_2 in solution.

[12] The solubility of gases depends on the pressure of the gas above the solution. These data are at a CO_2 pressure of 1.0 bar.

is larger than Cl_2.[13] Thus it makes sense that, at room temperature, iodine is a solid, bromine is a liquid, and chlorine is a gas.

In Chapter 11 we introduced the concept of **polarizability**, the ability of a nonpolar molecule to become dipolar. Dispersion forces are weak in part because both dipoles involved are very temporary. Consider the similar situation caused by placing a nonpolar molecule (such as Br_2) into a polar (aqueous) environment. A neighboring water molecule is a permanent dipole and thus can have a larger effect on the electron cloud of the Br_2 than any instantaneous dipole.

Figure 12-10 shows how the electron cloud of bromine can be repelled by the negative end of a water molecule resulting in a dipolar bromine molecule. The bromine molecule thus attracts solvent molecules in a **dipole-induced dipole** fashion. This effect can be stronger and longer-lived than a dispersion force situation due to the involvement of the water molecule which is both particularly polar and a permanent dipole.[14] Because dipole-induced dipole attractions are not as

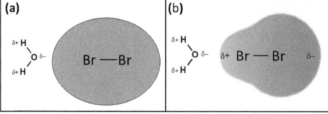

Figure 12-10. (a) The nonpolar (purple) bromine molecule next to the very polar water molecule. (b) The partially negative oxygen atom induces dipolar character (blue and red) in the bromine molecule. This provides an increased attraction between the solvent molecule and the solute.

favorable (strong) as a water-water hydrogen bonds, bromine still has a low solubility; water prefers a structure that is not interrupted by bromine molecules!

Because I_2 is more polarizable (larger, more electrons) than Br_2 which is more polarizable than Cl_2, we expect that the trend in water solubility should be $I_2 > Br_2 > Cl_2$. Iodine, however, is the least soluble of the three, for reasons that are beyond the scope of this book. Regardless of occasional rule-breakers, such as I_2 in this case, it is worthwhile to understand the role of polarizability in the solubility of non-polar molecules in water.

If we wish to emphasize the poor solubility of a nonelectrolyte, we can use a reversible arrow in the dissolution reaction equation. We could have done this for carbon dioxide earlier in this section, for instance. It is a very good idea to correctly determine the appropriate phase tag for the reactant side of the reaction equation. For the halogens we could write:

$$I_2(s) \rightleftharpoons I_2(aq) \qquad Br_2(\ell) \rightleftharpoons Br_2(aq) \qquad \text{and} \qquad Cl_2(g) \rightleftharpoons Cl_2(aq)$$

4. What about the essentially insoluble (or minimally soluble) salts?

Definitions for strong, weak and non-electrolytes apply well as long as one is considering only soluble substances. Then we can say that a strong electrolyte provides a stoichiometric number of ions in water solution; a weak electrolyte provides a sub-stoichiometric number of ions in water solution; and a non-electrolyte does not provide ions in solution. The definitions focus on the behavior of the solute, not on how much of it is present. Naturally, if we put only a tiny amount of a strong electrolyte in solution, the solution will not support a large current because there won't be enough ions; this doesn't make it a weak electrolyte.

---

[13] Remember that dispersion forces depend on the relative ability of electrons of the molecule to become unbalanced, either on their own (resulting in an instantaneous dipole) or due to the influence of a neighboring dipole (resulting in an induced dipole). While both neighboring molecules are briefly dipolar, they attract one another.

[14] As opposed to an *instantaneous dipole-induced dipole* situation where the dipole moments are small and very short-lived.

The salts that are poorly soluble (we can call them **minimally soluble**, or **slightly soluble**, or **essentially insoluble**)[15] are troublesome if one is interested in classifying according to electrolytic characteristics. What do we mean by minimally soluble? So little of these salts dissolves that if you determine the mass of the dry salt before trying to dissolve it, and then determine the mass of the recovered, undissolved portion of the salt (after drying), you would not be able to tell that any dissolved at all! And yet analytical tests on the water could determine that a small number of ions from the salt had indeed dissolved.

As far as electrolytic character goes, these slightly soluble salts are not easy to classify.[16] We will not try to subject these essentially insoluble substances to electrolyte definitions. Instead, let's clarify how they behave and how we notate their dissolution processes.

The dissociation of ions from a minimally soluble salt follows the same principles as dissociations of the soluble salts. This time, however, we need a way to show that only a small amount of the salt dissolves. Silver chloride is an essentially insoluble salt that we can use for an example. The ions Ag^+ and Cl^- are liberated from the solid in tiny amounts (solubility of AgCl = 1.3 $\times$ 10^{-5} mol/L). We can show the dissociation process as usual:

$$AgCl(s) \longrightarrow Ag^+(aq) + Cl^-(aq) \qquad \textbf{dissociation}$$

But, once some silver ions and chloride ions are dissociated, they have a tendency to find each other and re-solidify. The formation of a solid in this situation can be called either **precipitation** (always appropriate) or **crystallization** (if the solid is produced in an orderly crystalline form). We can show the crystallization process as the reverse of the dissociation:

$$AgCl(s) \longleftarrow Ag^+(aq) + Cl^-(aq) \qquad \textbf{precipitation} \text{ or } \textbf{crystallization}, \textit{the formation of}$$
$$\textit{solid from dissolved species.}$$

When the rates of these two processes balance each other, we say the system is *at dynamic equilibrium*. At this point, a maximum amount of the salt is dissolved and all of the dissolved salt exists as solvated ions. As we did for the weak acids and bases, we indicate dynamic equilibrium by writing both processes in one equation, using a reversible reaction arrow:

$$AgCl(s) \rightleftharpoons Ag^+(aq) + Cl^-(aq)$$

or a lop-sided, reversible reaction arrow:

$$AgCl(s) \rightleftharpoons Ag^+(aq) + Cl^-(aq)$$

Additional examples of slightly soluble salts include barium sulfate and iron(III) hydroxide:

$$BaSO_4(s) \rightleftharpoons Ba^{2+}(aq) + SO_4^{2-}(aq) \qquad\qquad Fe(OH)_3(s) \rightleftharpoons Fe^{3+}(aq) + 3OH^-(aq)$$

Note that the reaction equations are exactly the same as for dissociations of soluble salts except for the use of a reversible arrow instead of a single, forward arrow.

---

[15] This contradicts the "like dissolves like" rule! These salts tend to have large lattice energies (see Chapter 5) so that the solid phase interactions of the ions are preferred over the interactions between individual ions and water molecules. Poor solubility spans a large range of solubilities, none of which are zero. Some sources classify the poorly soluble salts as any with solubilities less than 0.01 mol/L.

[16] Some classify these substances as *strong electrolytes*, because the (tiny) amount that <u>does</u> dissolve places a stoichiometric number of ions into solution. Others categorize these substances as *weak electrolytes*, because the solutions formed can (at best) conduct weak currents and, after all, <u>some</u> ions are always placed into solution.

5. Making decisions about dissolution processes

The biggest difficulties in the successful writing of dissolution (dissolving), dissociation, and ionization processes is deciding which one you need for a given substance, and whether or not the process goes to completion. If it's a salt, is it soluble, or not? If it's a covalent molecule, is it a strong acid, weak acid, a weak base, or a nonelectrolyte molecule? Here are some guidelines and helpful information.

For the salts, a table of "solubility rules" will be helpful to you in determining the solubility (or not) of a particular salt. Table 12-6 is one example of such a table. Tables such as this are meant to be references; there is no need to memorize all of the information. It is <u>convenient</u> to know the first two bullet points in the table, as these are blanket statements with no exceptions.

Table 12-6. Solubility Rules for Salts.

Ions that promote <u>solubility</u>:

- All salts of the ammonium ion (NH_4^+), and of Group 1 cations, are *soluble*.
- All nitrates (NO_3^-), perchlorates (ClO_4^-), and acetates ($C_2H_3O_2^-$) are *soluble*.
- All chlorides (Cl^-), bromides (Br^-), and iodides (I^-), are *soluble* **EXCEPT** those of silver (Ag^+), lead(II), and mercury(I) (and also mercury(II) for bromides and iodides).
- All sulfates (SO_4^{2-}) are soluble **EXCEPT** Ag_2SO_4, Hg_2SO_4, $BaSO_4$, $SrSO_4$, and $CaSO_4$, $PbSO_4$. (*Ag_2SO_4 is the most soluble of these low-solubility sulfates.)

Ions that promote <u>insolubility</u>:

- All carbonates (CO_3^{2-}), sulfites (SO_3^{2-}), and phosphates (PO_4^{3-}) are *insoluble* **EXCEPT** those of ammonium (NH_4^+) and Group 1 cations (see first rule, above).
- All hydroxides (OH^-) are *insoluble* **EXCEPT** those of ammonium, Group 1 cations, barium and strontium. (Calcium hydroxide is slightly soluble.)
- All sulfides (S^{2-}) are *insoluble* **EXCEPT** those of ammonium, Group 1 cations and Group 2 cations.
- All oxides (O^{2-}) are *insoluble* **EXCEPT** those of Group 1 cations, calcium, and barium. *Note:* ammonium oxide does not exist! *Note:* the soluble oxides actually react with the solvent water to form hydroxides: O_2^{2-} (aq) + $H_2O(\ell)$ → 2 OH^-(aq)

Notice that the top half of the table focuses on salt compositions that offer <u>high solubility</u> while the bottom half focuses on compositions that limit solubility. In this table, only one rule focuses on the salt's <u>cation</u> (see first rule), while all others focus on the <u>anion</u> of a salt. Specific exceptions to the rules are noted as necessary. The word "insoluble" in a table such as this should not be taken literally. None of these salts are absolutely insoluble. In a lab setting, they will appear to be insoluble because not enough will dissolve to be easily noticeable. These are the "essentially insoluble" salts.

Table 12-7 offers a summary of helpful hints for writing dissolution reaction equations.

Table 12-7. Summary of Hints for Writing Appropriate Dissolution Reaction Equations

<u>Simple dissolution</u>: *molecules* that dissolve without producing ions.
    1. Formulas include only nonmetal or semimetal atoms.
    2. The molecule is <u>not</u> a strong acid or weak acid or weak base.
    3. If information is not readily available, use sources such as Safety Data Sheets, NIST webbook, Chemicalbook.com and/or Wikipedia, for information on
        a. original phase tag (is it a solid, liquid or gas at room temp?)
        b. level of solubility ($\rightarrow$ for soluble species and $\rightleftharpoons$ for relatively insoluble species)
        c. making sure that the molecule is not an acid or base.

<u>Dissolution via dissociation</u>: solid *salts* release aqueous ions (strong bases are salts).
    1. Formulas of salts include cations (metal ion or NH_4^+) and anions (simple or polyatomic).
    2. Remember to include charges on formulas of ions!
    3. Solubility table will help to determine which arrow to use
        ($\rightarrow$ for soluble species and $\rightleftharpoons$ for insoluble species).

<u>Dissolution followed by ionization</u>: molecules that are *strong or weak acids, weak bases*
    1. Formulas usually include only nonmetal atoms
    2. These molecules all react with water molecules
        acids donate a proton to water molecule; $H_3O^+(aq)$ is one of the products
        bases accept a proton from water molecule; $OH^-(aq)$ is one of the products
        first the acid or base has to undergo simple dissolution; we start the ionization reaction equation with the acid or base already in the aqueous phase.
    3. Memorize the seven strong acids HCl, HBr, HI, HNO_3, H_2SO_4 (and $HClO_4$, $HClO_3$) use single, forward arrow for these.[17]
    4. Weak acids <u>may</u> have H atoms listed first in formula (HF, HCN, HOCl)
        use reversible arrow
    5. Weak bases <u>may</u> have a nitrogen atom (with a lone pair of electrons)
        (NH_3, CH_3NH_2, N_2H_4)
        use reversible arrow
    6. Consult Safety Data Sheets for guidance on
        acidity/basicity of molecules if you are unsure

[17] Solutions of the parenthetical strong acids ($HClO_3$ and $HClO_4$) must be produced via methods that are beyond the scope of this text; the molecules are not stable.

Example 12-7.

Write the appropriate equation for the dissolution of butanol (or 1-butanol or *n*-butanol) in water. Use a Safety Data Sheet (SDS) to determine the nature of this solute.

Solution:

There are many different sources of information available online. Safety Data Sheets list chemical and physical properties in Section 9. For acids and bases, a pH value for the material may be presented in that section. For butanol, we found the following information:

appearance: "colorless liquid"
pH: "No data available" which often means that it is not an acid or a base.
solubility in water: "moderate" at one source, "soluble" at another source
CAS-No.: 71-36-3

(If you don't know the chemical formula of the substance and the SDS sheet doesn't list it, search the CAS number on the internet. Every chemical substance has a unique CAS number, so you need not worry about the correct name to search. The CAS-No is likely listed in Section 1 or 3 of an SDS.

The first two findings convince us that on the "reactant" side of the equation we should use the liquid phase tag, (ℓ). The pH entry saying "no data available" often indicates a molecule that is neither an acid nor a base. Both statements about solubility indicate that this molecule is more soluble than something that we would consider to be essentially insoluble, so we use a single, forward arrow:

$$C_4H_9OH(\ell) \longrightarrow C_4H_9OH(aq)$$

Example 12-8.

Write appropriate balanced chemical equations for the dissolution of each of the following species. Your first step must be to decide the type of substance, and where necessary, determine the chemical formula.

a. CaS   **b.** barium hydroxide   **c.** H_3PO_4
d. HNO_3 **e.** CH_3OCH_3, dimethyl ether   **f.** CH_3CO_2H
g. silver phosphate   **h.** N_2H_4

Solutions:

a. This is a soluble salt (see solubility rules). We write:
$$CaS(s) \longrightarrow Ca^{2+}(aq) + S^{2-}(aq) \quad \text{(Note the single forward arrow.)}$$

b. This is a soluble salt (that is also a strong base). We write:
$$Ba(OH)_2(s) \longrightarrow Ba^{2+}(aq) + 2OH^-(aq)$$

c. Phosphoric acid is a weak acid from Table 12-5. Weak acids require reversible arrows.
We write: $H_3PO_4(aq) + H_2O(\ell) \rightleftharpoons H_2PO_4^-(aq) + H_3O^+(aq)$
(This acid has three acidic protons, but it is enough for now to show the first ionization!)

d. This is one of the strong acids. We write:
$$HNO_3(aq) + H_2O(\ell) \longrightarrow NO_3^-(aq) + H_3O^+(aq)$$

e. CH_3OCH_3 (dimethylether) is not a strong acid or strong base or salt. It is not one of the weak acids or weak bases that we recognize from Table 12-5. We suspect that it is a molecule that simply dissolves as a nonelectrolyte. An online SDS indicates that dimethyl ether is a gas at room temperature, that it is not acidic or basic, and that it is somewhat soluble. We write:

$$CH_3OCH_3(g) \longrightarrow CH_3OCH_3(aq) \qquad \text{or} \qquad CH_3OCH_3(g) \rightleftharpoons CH_3OCH_3(aq)$$

depending on how we interpret the solubility statement. If in doubt, the reversible arrows are technically correct in essentially all situations with non-electrolytes.

f. Acetic acid is a weak acid. The final H in the formula is the acidic H.[18] (Sometimes its formula is written $HC_2H_3O_2$ instead, to emphasize the ONE acidic hydrogen, which is listed first.) We write: $CH_3CO_2H(aq) + H_2O(\ell) \rightleftharpoons CH_3CO_2^-(aq) + H_3O^+(aq)$

or $\qquad HC_2H_3O_2(aq) + H_2O(\ell) \rightleftharpoons C_2H_3O_2^-(aq) + H_3O^+(aq)$

g. This is an essentially insoluble salt (see solubility rules). We write:

$$Ag_3PO_4(s) \rightleftharpoons 3Ag^+(aq) + PO_4^{3-}(aq) \quad \text{(Note the reversible arrows.)}$$

h. This molecule is a weak base found in Table 12-5. A search for "N_2H_4 SDS" turned up several that gave no information about pH, but two that listed the pH as "> 12" which also indicates that it is a base. It reacts with water by accepting a proton. Weak base ionizations require reversible arrows. We write:

$$N_2H_4(aq) + H_2O(\ell) \rightleftharpoons N_2H_5^+(aq) + OH^-(aq)$$

12-3. QUANTITATIVE ASPECTS OF SOLUTIONS

A. Molarities of Dissolved Species

The most commonly used measure of concentration is **molarity**, symbolized M and defined as the number of moles of solute per liter of *solution* (NOT per liter of *solvent*!)

$$\boxed{\textbf{molarity (M)} = \frac{\text{moles solute}}{\text{L solution}}}$$

It is not at all uncommon for solutions with concentrations much smaller than 1 M to be used in the laboratory, especially in biochemical applications. Be aware that metric prefixes such as mM and μM are often applied to molarity units. These units arise from the use of millimole (mmol) and micromole (μmol) units:

$$10^3 \text{ mmol} = 1 \text{ mol} \quad \text{or} \quad 1 \text{ mmol} = 10^{-3} \text{ mol}$$

$$10^6 \text{ μmol} = 1 \text{ mol} \quad \text{or} \quad 1 \text{ μmol} = 10^{-6} \text{ mol}$$

So that $\qquad \text{mM} = \frac{\text{mmol solute}}{\text{L solution}} \quad \text{and} \quad \text{μM} = \frac{\text{μmol solute}}{\text{L solution}}$

Square brackets are also used to indicate molarity. For example, if a solution of NaCl contains 0.264 moles of NaCl per liter of solution we may write:

Concentration of NaCl = 0.264 M or [NaCl] = 0.264 M

When reading a concentration, the M is not read as "molarity" but as "molar;" the sodium chloride concentration is 0.264 molar.

---

[18] Sometimes its formula is written $HC_2H_3O_2$, to emphasize the ONE acidic hydrogen, which is listed first. In this case, the acetate ion would be written as $C_2H_3O_2^-$.

To determine the molarity of a solution having a known mass of solute dissolved in a known volume, we must determine the number of moles of solute, then divide by the volume, in liters. For example, suppose an aqueous solution contains 6.82 g of glucose ($C_6H_{12}O_6$) dissolved in water to a total volume of 1.25 L. Using the definition of molarity:

$$\left[C_6H_{12}O_6\right] = \frac{\text{moles } C_6H_{12}O_6}{\text{L solution}} = \frac{\left(6.82\,\text{g}\,C_6H_{12}O_6\right)\left(\dfrac{1\,\text{mol}\,C_6H_{12}O_6}{180.16\,\text{g}\,C_6H_{12}O_6}\right)}{1.25\,\text{L}} = 0.0303\text{M}$$

Example 12-9.

A solution is prepared by dissolving 0.9863 g potassium nitrate in water and **diluting** to a final volume of 250.0 mL. What is the concentration of the solution?

Solution:

$$\text{molarity} = \frac{\text{moles of solute}}{\text{liters of solution}} \quad \text{so} \quad \left[KNO_3\right] = \frac{\text{moles } KNO_3}{\text{L solution}}$$

$$\left[KNO_3\right] = \frac{0.9863\,\text{g}\,KNO_3\left(\dfrac{1\,\text{mol}\,KNO_3}{101.10\,\text{g}\,KNO_3}\right)}{250.0\,\text{mL}\left(\dfrac{1\,\text{L}}{1000\,\text{mL}}\right)} = 0.03902\,\text{M}\,KNO_3$$

Note that the volume must be converted from milliliters to liters!

Alternate solution:

Using dimensional analysis often leads to a more straight-forward statement of your method. In other words, dimensional analysis is a excellent way to communicate your work. Start by listing the concentration in whatever units you have. We have grams KNO_3 per mL solution, then use conversion factors to achieve the units of molarity (moles/L solution):

$$\frac{0.9863\,\text{g}\,KNO_3}{250.0\,\text{mL solution}} \times \frac{1\,\text{mol}\,KNO_3}{101.10\,\text{g}\,KNO_3} \times \frac{1000\,\text{mL}}{1\,\text{L}} = 0.3902\,\text{M}$$

If both numerator and denominator need to be converted, the order of writing the conversion factors is unimportant, because one does not logically follow the other.

To prepare a solution of a desired concentration, we can rearrange the definition of molarity:

$$\text{molarity} = \frac{\text{moles solute}}{\text{L solution}} \Rightarrow \text{moles solute} = (\text{L solution}) \times (\text{molarity})$$

If we multiply the desired concentration (molarity) by the volume of solution needed, we obtain the number of moles of solute necessary. The molar mass is then necessary to convert from moles to mass, as shown in the following example.

Example 12-10.

What mass of mercury(I) nitrate is necessary to prepare 400.0 mL of a 0.0100 M solution?

Solution:

Because $\text{molarity} = \dfrac{\text{moles of solute}}{\text{L of solution}}$, we know that moles solute = (L solution) × (molarity).

The solute is $Hg_2(NO_3)_2$. After we compute the number of moles of the solute needed, we can convert to the mass needed by using the solute's molar mass. *Note that it is imperative that a quantity with units of "M" be written as a quantity with units "mol(of what)/L" in order for units to cancel correctly during calculations.*

$$\text{moles } Hg_2(NO_3)_2 = (400.0\,mL)\left(\frac{1\,L}{1000\,mL}\right) \times \left(\frac{0.0100 \text{ mol } Hg_2(NO_3)_2}{L}\right)$$

$$= 0.00400 \text{ mol } Hg_2(NO_3)_2$$

Converting from moles to grams:

$$0.00400 \text{ mol } Hg_2(NO_3)_2 \left(\frac{525.2 \text{ g } Hg_2(NO_3)_2}{\text{mol } Hg_2(NO_3)_2}\right) = 2.10\,g$$

This problem can be solved with one string of calculations. It is always a good idea to begin your string of conversions with a value that is not a ratio (if there is one). In this example, we begin with the volume desired, 400.0 mL:

$$(400.0\,mL)\left(\frac{1\,L}{1000\,mL}\right)\left(\frac{0.0100 \text{ mol } Hg_2(NO_3)_2}{1\,L}\right)\left(\frac{525.2 \text{ g } Hg_2(NO_3)_2}{1 \text{ mol } Hg_2(NO_3)_2}\right) = 2.10 \text{ g } Hg_2(NO_3)_2$$

Notice that after each "conversion factor," above, the units are sensible: L, then moles salt, then grams of salt.

Exercise 12-4.

Determine the molarities of the following solutions:

a. A solution prepared by dissolving 1.2344 g of sodium chromate in water and diluting to a final volume of 500.0 mL.

b. A solution prepared by dissolving 0.3269 g of $CuSO_4 \cdot 5\,H_2O$ in water and diluting to a final volume of 250.0 mL.

Exercise 12-5.

Determine the mass of solute necessary to prepare:

a. 2.000 L of 0.500 M potassium permanganate.
b. 100.0 mL of 0.800 M nickel(II) nitrate.

B. Molarities of Ions in Solutions of Strong Electrolytes

To this point we have described the concentrations of solutions on the basis of the number of moles of compound dissolved per liter of solution. For example, the label on a bottle might say "0.226 M Co(NO$_3$)$_2$". Such a solution contains 0.226 moles of Co(NO$_3$)$_2$ per liter, but we must be savvy enough to know that the cations and anions are separately solvated in the solution. Sometimes it is useful to describe the concentrations of individual ions in a solution of a strong electrolyte. We can write the dissolution reaction equation for the cobalt(II) nitrate solution:

$$Co(NO_3)_2(s) \longrightarrow Co^{2+}(aq) + 2\,NO_3^-(aq)$$

Each mole of Co(NO$_3$)$_2$ gives one mole of aqueous Co^{2+} ions and two moles of aqueous NO$_3^-$ ions. In 0.226 M Co(NO$_3$)$_2$:

$$\left[Co^{2+}\right] = \left(\frac{0.226\ mol\ Co(NO_3)_2}{L}\right)\left(\frac{1\ mol\ Co^{2+}}{1\ mol\ Co(NO_3)_2}\right) = 0.226\ M\ Co^{2+}$$

$$\left[NO_3^-\right] = \left(\frac{0.226\ mol\ Co(NO_3)_2}{L}\right)\left(\frac{2\ mol\ NO_3^-}{1\ mol\ Co(NO_3)_2}\right) = 0.452\ M\ NO_3^-$$

The concentration of nitrate is double that of Co(NO$_3$)$_2$ because two NO$_3^-$ ions are released for every mole of Co(NO$_3$)$_2$ that dissolves. This is an example of the common situation in which the molarity of an individual ion is greater than the molarity of the compound itself (because the compound dissolves to give multiple ions).

Example 12-11.

Determine the concentration of each ion present in:

a. 0.26 M sodium phosphate   **b.** 0.0588 M aluminum bromide

c. A solution prepared by dissolving 0.200 mol of sodium sulfate and 0.150 mol of nickel(II) sulfate in water and diluting to a final volume of 0.500 L.

Solutions:

a. Sodium phosphate provides aqueous ions as it dissolves in water:

$$Na_3PO_4(s) \longrightarrow 3\,Na^+(aq) + PO_4^{3-}(aq)$$

$$\left[Na^+\right] = \left(\frac{0.26\ mol\ Na_3PO_4}{L}\right)\left(\frac{3\ mol\ Na^+}{1\ mol\ Na_3PO_4}\right) = 0.78\ M\ Na^+$$

$$\left[PO_4^{3-}\right] = \left(\frac{0.26\ mol\ Na_3PO_4}{L}\right)\left(\frac{1\ mol\ PO_4^{3-}}{1\ mol\ Na_3PO_4}\right) = 0.26\ M\ PO_4^{3-}$$

More simply we could recognize that because Na$_3$PO$_4$ provides three sodium ions and one phosphate ion, the concentration of aqueous Na$^+$ ions is triple the concentration of Na$_3$PO$_4$, and the concentration of PO$_4^{3-}$ ions is the same as that of Na$_3$PO$_4$.

b. Aluminum bromide provides ions as follows:

$$AlBr_3(s) \longrightarrow Al^{3+}(aq) + 3\,Br^-(aq)$$

The number of aqueous Al^{3+} ions formed is the same as the number of $AlBr_3$ formula units dissolved. Therefore:

$$[Al^{3+}] = [AlBr_3] = 0.0588\ M$$

The number of aqueous Br^- ions formed is triple the number of $AlBr_3$ formula units dissolved:

$$[Br^-] = 3 \times [AlBr_3] = 3 \times 0.0588\ M = 0.176\ M$$

c. This problem is complicated by having two solutes in the same solution, with each solute providing the same anion, but different cations.

0.200 mol: $Na_2SO_4(s) \rightarrow 2\,Na^+(aq) + SO_4^{2-}(aq)$
0.150 mol: $NiSO_4(s) \rightarrow Ni^{2+}(aq) + SO_4^{2-}(aq)$

In this situation, to find the final concentration in mol/L, we must find the total number of moles of each ion, then divide by the total solution volume in which the ions are found. Sodium and nickel ions are straightforward, because there is only one source of each:

Na^+ (aq):   each formula unit of $Na_2SO_4(s)$ provides **2** Na^+, so
               0.200 mol $Na_2SO_4(s)$ provides <u>0.400 mol Na^+</u>

Ni^{2+} (aq):   each formula unit of $NiSO_4(s)$ provides **1** Ni^{2+}, so
               0.150 mol $NiSO_4(s)$ provides <u>0.150 mol Ni^{2+}</u>

For sulfate we must take into account both sources of this ion:

SO_4^{2-} (aq): Determine the number of moles from each source, then add:

From Na_2SO_4:   0.200 mol
From $NiSO_4$:   <u>0.150 mol</u>
Total <u>moles SO_4^{2-}</u> = **0.350 mol**

Finally, divide the number of moles of each ion by the total volume of solution to determine the concentrations:

$$[Na^+] = \frac{0.400\ mol}{0.500\ L} = 0.800\ M \qquad\qquad [Ni^{2+}] = \frac{0.150\ mol}{0.500\ L} = 0.300\ M$$

$$[SO_4^{2-}] = \frac{0.350\ mol}{0.500\ L} = 0.700\ M$$

Exercise **12-6.**

Determine the concentration of each ion present in:

a. 0.0989 M strontium chlorate

b. 0.0552 M mercury(I) nitrate

c. A solution prepared by dissolving 0.120 mol of potassium oxalate and 0.080 mol potassium chloride in water and diluting to a final volume of 750.0 mL

C. Other Concentration Units

There are many ways to convey information about the concentration of a solution. For future reference, we define two additional concentration units here:

$$\text{Molality } (m) = \frac{\text{moles solute}}{\text{kg solvent}}$$

$$\text{Mole fraction } (\chi) = \frac{\text{moles of one solution component}}{\text{total moles of all solution components}}$$

Molality (symbolized by a lowercase, italics m) is used in the study of **colligative properties** of solutions, properties that depend on how many solute particles are present for a fixed amount of solvent. Note that the denominator is "kg of solvent" rather than "kg of solution"! Examples of colligative properties are the elevation of a boiling point, or the lowering of a freezing point, of a solution (compared to the pure solvent) via the inclusion of one or more solutes.

Mole fractions (symbolized by the Greek letter, chi, χ) are particularly useful with solutions that have no obvious solvent. This occurs in solutions wherein there is no single component that is present in much larger quantities than the other components. At the beginning of this chapter, we mentioned that gasoline is a solution for which the idea of a solvent and solutes is not particularly helpful. In addition, many gaseous mixtures also lack a component that is in large enough relative abundance to be considered a solvent. In Chapter 15, we will consider the use of mole fractions to account for the pressures of mixtures of gases (Dalton's law of partial pressures).

D. Dilutions

Dilution of a solution is the act of adding additional solvent, so that the concentration decreases. If a large concentration decrease is desired (say from 2.0 M to 0.00010 M, a serial dilution will generally result in considerably less error than a simple, one-step dilution. Let's explore both.

1. Simple dilution (one step)

Let's return to the definition of molarity:

$$\text{molarity} = \frac{\text{moles solute}}{\text{L solution}}$$

and rearrange this equation to solve for the number of moles of solute:

$$\text{moles solute} = \text{molarity} \times \text{L solution} = MV$$

Suppose we have a solution of a known concentration, M_i (we will use the subscript "i" to indicate characteristics of the *initial* solution) and known volume, V_i. If we add solvent to this solution, the number of moles of solute will not change; however, because the volume will obviously change, the concentration must also change. The concentration will decrease because the numerator of the molarity stays the same while the denominator increases (fewer moles of solute per unit volume)

Initially: moles solute = $M_i V_i$

After dilution: moles solute = $M_f V_f$
                    (the subscript "f" indicates the *final* solution)

Because the number of moles of solute is the *same* both before and after dilution, we may write:

$$\text{moles solute} = M_i V_i = M_f V_f \quad \text{i = initial, f = final}$$

We can use the expression in the box, above, to relate the initial molarities and volumes to the final molarities and volumes whenever a dilution is done. This process is illustrated in the following examples.

Example 12-12.

What volume of 1.00 M HCl solution is necessary to prepare 250. mL of 0.200 M HCl?

Solution:

The initial solution contains 1.00 M HCl; we know its concentration (M_i) but not the volume needed (V_i). For the final solution, the one to be prepared, we know both the volume and concentration (V_f and M_f):

Initial:	Final:
$M_i = 1.00$ M	$M_f = 0.200$ M
$V_i = ?$	$V_f = 250.$ mL

Beginning with the expression $M_iV_i = M_fV_f$ we can solve for V_i:

$$(1.00 \text{ M}) \times V_i = (0.200 \text{ M}) \times (250. \text{ mL})$$

$$V_i = \textbf{50.0 mL}$$

Note that *any set of units* for concentration and volume can be used, as long as they are the same for both the initial and final cases!

Example 12-13.

   a. Determine the concentration of sodium sulfite in a solution that has been prepared by using a pipet to withdraw 20.00 mL from 500.0 mL of stock solution containing 0.258 M sodium sulfite, draining the pipet into a 250.0 mL volumetric flask, and diluting to the mark.

Solution:

Make sure you visualize the process described. A dilution is being made. We can begin with $M_iV_i = M_fV_f$. What do we know?

Initial:	Final:
$M_i = 0.258$ M	$M_f = ?$
$V_i = 20.00$ mL	$V_f = 250.0$ mL

We can solve for the unknown M_f as follows:

$$(0.258 \text{ M}) \times (20.00 \text{ mL}) = M_f \times (250.0 \text{ mL})$$

$$M_f = 0.0206 \text{ M} \quad (0.02064 \text{ rounded to 3 significant figures})$$

[Note: The 500.0 mL volume of the stock solution is irrelevant to the calculations in this problem. We only used 20.00 mL of it!]

   b. What are the concentrations of sodium ions and sulfite ions in the diluted solution?

Solution:

Sodium sulfite is a strong electrolyte that forms ions as follows:

$$Na_2SO_3(s) \longrightarrow 2\,Na^+(aq) + SO_3^{2-}(aq)$$

Because two moles of Na^+ and one mole of SO_3^{2-} are released per mole of sodium sulfite, we can conclude:

$[Na^+] = 2 \times 0.02064\ M = 0.0413\ M$ (using the result from
part **a** before rounding)

$[SO_3^{2-}] = 0.0206\ M$

Exercise 12-7.

A 2.000 L solution containing 1.2293 M nitric acid is available in the stockroom. What volume of this solution would be necessary to prepare 250.0 mL of 0.500 M acid?

Exercise 12-8.

The concentration of $KMnO_4$ in a 500.0 mL volumetric flask is unknown. A 5.00 mL pipet was used to transfer a sample from this flask into a 25.00 mL volumetric flask, which was then diluted to the mark with water. Chemical analysis of this sample determines that the concentration of permanganate ions is 0.106 M. What is the concentration of permanganate in the 500.0 mL volumetric flask?

2. Serial dilutions (multiple steps)

As a lead-in to the use of serial dilutions for some lab tasks, consider Example 12-14, below.

Example 12-14.

What volume of a 2.0 M solution of NaOH is required to make 100. mL of 0.00020 M NaOH?

Solution:

Setting out to make this dilution in one step, we consider $M_iV_i = M_fV_f$. What do we know?

Initial:

$M_i = 2.0\ M$
$V_i = ?\ mL$

Final:

$M_f = 0.00020\ M$
$V_f = 100.\ mL$

We can solve for the unknown V_i:

$(2.0\ M) \times V_i = 0.00020\ M \times (100.\ mL)$

$V_i = 0.010\ mL$ or 10. µL!   (This is approximately 1/5 of a drop!)

Well? What do you think? How are we going to measure 0.010 mL of the original solution? At a minimum, we need some specialty equipment (with microliter-sized volumetric capabilities). Even if the proper equipment is available, we can expect our percent error to be relatively high; small errors on small measurements make for much larger percent errors than small errors on large measurements. Scientists have determined that they are better off doing a series of less drastic dilutions rather than one very drastic dilution.

So we use a **serial dilution**: a consecutive set of dilutions, usually of identical proportions. For instance, the original solution could be diluted by a factor of 10. Then that new solution (call it dilution #1) is diluted by a factor of 10 to produce dilution #2. Then dilution #2 is diluted by a factor of 10, etc.

The calculations associated with serial dilution often focus on a factor that, when applied to the initial concentration of the solution, yields the final molarity. This is just another ramification of the $M_iV_i = M_fV_f$ relationship. A simple rearrangement of this equation yields

$$M_i \times \frac{V_i}{V_f} = M_f$$

where the ratio of volumes (V_i/V_f) is called a **concentration factor**, which is the reciprocal of the **dilution factor**. If a dilution factor of 10 is desired, the concentration factor should be 1/10, or 0.10. *Dilution factors* have values greater than 1, while *concentration factors* have values less than 1. Return to Example 12-13 part a, where the mathematics was presented as:

We can solve for the unknown M_f: $(0.258 \text{ M}) \times (20.00 \text{ mL}) = M_f \times (250.0 \text{ mL})$

This really amounts to the use of a *concentration factor*, which we see if we simply re-write:

We can solve for the unknown M_f: $M_f = (0.258 \text{ M}) \times \frac{(20.00 \text{ mL})}{(250.0 \text{ mL})}$

The *concentration factor* in this problem is 20.00/250.0 = 0.0800.
The *dilution factor* is the reciprocal of the concentration factor: 250.0/20.00 = 12.5,
                                                                      or   1/0.0800 = 12.5

Notice that because another simple rearrangement of $M_iV_i = M_fV_f$ gives $\frac{V_i}{V_f} = \frac{M_f}{M_i}$
the *concentration factor* can be obtained as either a ratio of the volumes (initial/final) or a ratio of molarities (final/initial). Notice that these ratios both give a value less than 1 (for a dilution).

Returning to our original problem (from Example 12-14) of the 2.0 M stock solution and the 0.00020 M (or 0.20 mM) desired solution, we can see that the overall concentration factor required is

$$\frac{M_f}{M_i} = \frac{0.00020}{2.0} = 0.00010$$

Because this factor is so small, we think about doing a serial dilution instead of a simple dilution. We could break this *concentration factor* up into a series of 0.10 dilutions. Because we want to end up with at least 100. mL of the final solution, we envision each of these dilutions as being 10.00 mL of original solution ending in 100. mL of final solution. A 10.00 mL volumetric pipet is certainly handy to use!

If we see this as a series of simple dilutions, we might show our calculations as follows:

$(2.0 \text{ M}) \times \frac{(10.00 \text{ mL})}{(100.0 \text{ mL})} = \textbf{0.20 M}$

$(0.20 \text{ M}) \times \frac{(10.00 \text{ mL})}{(100.0 \text{ mL})} = \textbf{0.020 M}$

$(0.020 \text{ M}) \times \frac{(10.00 \text{ mL})}{(100.0 \text{ mL})} = \textbf{0.0020 M}$

$(0.0020 \text{ M}) \times \frac{(10.00 \text{ mL})}{(100.0 \text{ mL})} = \textbf{0.00020 M}$

It is much more convenient and efficient to string the dilutions together mathematically:

$(2.0 \text{ M}) \times \frac{(10.00 \text{ mL})}{(100.0 \text{ mL})} \times \frac{(10.00 \text{ mL})}{(100.0 \text{ mL})} \times \frac{(10.00 \text{ mL})}{(100.0 \text{ mL})} \times \frac{(10.00 \text{ mL})}{(100.0 \text{ mL})} = \textbf{0.00020 M}$

Notice that this string of dimensional analysis clearly shows the reader what was done in the laboratory.

Example 12-15.

Consider a **saturated**[19] stock solution of ethylenediaminetetraacetic acid, or EDTA, a critical component of many protein solutions in the laboratory because it coordinates stray metal ions to protect the protein from interacting with the metal ion and probably becoming unfolded. The saturated solution of EDTA has a concentration of 0.260 M. You have been asked to prepare 1.00 L of an EDTA solution by making a three-step serial dilution of 50.0 mL to 1.00 L. What is the final concentration of the EDTA solution (in units of μM)?

Solution:

What do we know from the problem?

$M_i = 0.260$ M EDTA $\qquad\qquad$ $V_i = 50.0$ mL $= 0.0500$ L
$M_f =$ unknown $\qquad\qquad\qquad$ $V_f = 1.00$ L

We use the plan: $\qquad\qquad M_i \times \dfrac{V_i}{V_f} \times \dfrac{V_i}{V_f} \times \dfrac{V_i}{V_f} = M_f$

Because the final concentration is desired in units of μM, we add an initial conversion of the stock solution concentration to μM.

$$0.260 \text{ M} \times \frac{1\times10^6\,\mu\text{M}}{1\text{ M}} \times \frac{0.0500\text{ L}}{1.00\text{ L}} \times \frac{0.0500\text{ L}}{1.00\text{ L}} \times \frac{0.0500\text{ L}}{1.00\text{ L}} = \mathbf{32.5\ \mu M}$$

Exercise 12-9.

Consider a stock solution of 3.60 M HCl and the desire to have a solution that is between 2.00 and 10.0 mM, with a precisely known concentration.

a. How many 10.0 mL/50.0 mL dilution steps will be necessary?

b. What will be the concentration of the final solution (in mM)?

E. Titrations

Titrations are chemical analyses in which the amount of a solute, or the concentration of a solution, is determined by performing a chemical reaction involving the solute of interest. Because we are *analyzing* this solute of interest, we could call it the **analyte**. Let's say that you have a solution of a chemical (call it **A**) of unknown concentration. Additionally, let's say that **A**, our *analyte*, has a red color in aqueous solution. Finally, imagine that there is a chemical reaction between **A** and **Y** that yields the colorless product **Z**:

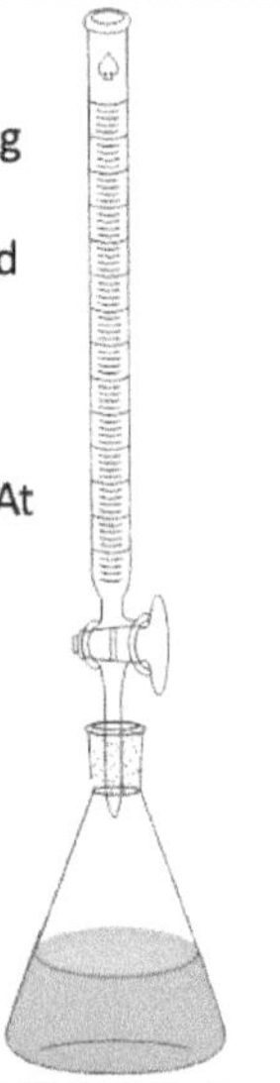

Figure 12-11. A buret for measuring the volume of titrant (Y) used; and the titration flask, originally holding the solution to be analyzed (A, red). At the equivalence point, the flask holds the product (Z, colorless).

$$2\ \text{A(aq)} + \text{Y(aq)} \longrightarrow \text{Z}\big(\text{aq}\big)$$

$\qquad$ red $\qquad$ colorless $\qquad\qquad$ colorless

We could use a buret to deliver the titrant (**Y**) into the solution of **A** in the flask (see Figure 12-11). As the titration reaction takes place, red **A** is converted to colorless **Z**. As more and more **Y** is added, the red color in the Erlenmeyer flask fades to pink. Just when the last pink color disappears (assuming our eyes are very, very good!), we have reached the **equivalence point**, where we have added just the right amount of **Y** to completely react with A, leaving just colorless **Z** in solution.

---

[19] A "saturated" solution is one in which the solvent cannot hold any more of that particular solute.

How does this process translate into a successful analysis?

First, in order to quantify the *analyte*, we use what is known about the titrant, **Y**. We must know both its concentration (molarity of **Y**, M_Y) and the volume used (V_Y). We can make the solution of **Y** to the desired molarity. The buret markings will inform us about the volume of **Y** used. Because $M_Y \times V_Y = moles(Y)$, we can calculate the moles of **Y** used to reach the equivalence point.

Second, the balanced reaction equation: $2\,A(aq) + Y(aq) \longrightarrow Z(aq)$ allows us to convert from moles of **Y** to moles of **A**. In our example, 2 moles of **A** reacts for every mole of **Y** used. So,

$$mol(Y) \times \frac{2\,mol\,A}{1\,mol\,Y} = mol(A)$$

Finally, if we know the original volume of the solution of **A**, we can determine the original concentration of **A**:

$$[A] \; = \; M_A = \frac{mol_A}{V_{A\,solution}}$$

Here are some keys to success with a titration:

1. In order for the calculations outlined above to be successful, volumes must be measured accurately and precisely. Transferring the solution of **A** into the Erlenmeyer flask via a volumetric pipet would be an excellent way to make sure that we have a known volume of the analyte solution. The markings on the buret will allow the volume of the titrant solution to be precisely known.

2. The chemical reaction between **A** and **Y** must be sufficiently fast. If the reaction is too slow, it is very likely that too much titrant will be added because of the lag time between addition and complete reaction.

3. There must be some kind of signal (color change, **precipitate**[20] formation, pH change, etc.) to alert us that the equivalence point between the two reactants has been reached. In our example, the loss of A was visible due to its red color. In a titration, the point at which the signal occurs is called the **end point** of the titration (because, for the researcher, that is when the titration comes to an end). If the end point does not coincide with the chemical **equivalence point**, the titration calculations will not be accurate.

In a later chapter, we will go into more detail about acid-base titrations. For now, we want to focus on the types of data collected and the types of calculations done in order to analyze a solution by titration.

1. Simple titrations: 1:1 mole ratio of reactants

Titration calculations are the least complicated when the titration reaction equation involves only coefficients of 1, so that moles of analyte equals moles of titrant at the equivalence point. This simple 1:1 stoichiometry is very common in acid and base reactions.

---

[20] A **precipitate** is a solid that arises from species that were previously in solution. The solid is usually "amorphous" in character (without order), rather than crystalline. In the case of crystal production (which is more difficult) the process is may be called **crystallization** instead of precipitation.

Example 12-16.

What volume of 0.150 M NaOH solution must be added to neutralize 50.0 mL of 0.200 M HCl solution?

Solution:

We know that NaOH is a strong base in aqueous solution and HCl is a strong acid. As we have seen in our study of strong electrolytes in this chapter, the important part of NaOH is the OH^- ion, and HCl will be ionized to form the H_3O^+ ion.[21] The sodium ion of NaOH and the chloride ion of HCl are unimportant to the acid-base reaction that occurs (ions such as these are sometimes called **spectator ions**, because they are uninvolved in the action, or reaction, in this case.)

One way, therefore, that this reaction equation could be written is:

$$H_3O^+(aq) + OH^-(aq) \longrightarrow 2H_2O(\ell)\,^{[22]}$$

At the point of neutralization, there must be a 1:1 ratio of H_3O^+ ions to OH^- ions; the number of moles of OH^- ions added must equal the number of moles of H_3O^+ ions initially present. We can make convenient use of the definition of molarity:

$$\text{molarity} = \frac{\text{moles solute}}{\text{L solution}} \quad \text{or} \quad \text{moles solute} = \text{molarity} \times \text{L solution} = MV$$

For the HCl solution: moles $H_3O^+ = M_a V_a$ ("a" is for acid)

For the NaOH solution: moles $OH^- = M_b V_b$ ("b" is for base)

Because of the 1:1 stoichiometry, the number of moles of OH^- added must equal the number of moles of H_3O^+ ions initially present:

$$\text{moles } H_3O^+ = \text{moles } OH^-$$

Substituting: $\boxed{M_a V_a = M_b V_b}$ [23]

Now we can substitute into this equation the quantities that are known:

Acid	Base
$M_a = 0.200$ M	$M_b = 0.150$ M
$V_a = 50.0$ mL	$V_b = ?$

Using $M_a V_a = M_b V_b$: $(0.200 \text{ M}) \times (50.0 \text{ mL}) = (0.150 \text{ M}) \times V_b$

Solving for the volume of base gives $V_b = \mathbf{66.7 \text{ mL}}$

The expression in the box in this example, $\boxed{M_a V_a = M_b V_b}$, can be used in general for calculations at the **equivalence point** for simple acid-base reactions in which the acid contributes one H_3O^+ ion and the base contributes one OH^- ion. If moles of acid DO NOT EQUAL moles of base in the balanced reaction equation, we could not use this expression! The exercise, below, is a classic titration data exercise. Make sure you can solve problems of this type; seek help, if necessary.

---

[21] Or, just as H^+ for simplicity's sake. Your instructor may have a preference for how you notate a strong acid.

[22] It could also be written as $HCl(aq) + NaOH(aq) \longrightarrow H_2O(\ell) + NaCl(aq)$. The shorter, simpler form shown up above is called a *net ionic reaction equation*. More on these in Chapter 13.

[23] Note that this is not the $M_i V_i = M_f V_f$ of a dilution, although the mathematics is the same. In a dilution, initial moles (before dilution) = final moles (after dilution). In a titration of 1:1 stoichiometry, moles acid = moles base in the balanced reaction equation, thus $M_a V_a = M_b V_b$.

Exercise 12-10.

Addition of 24.68 mL of 0.1066 M sodium hydroxide solution neutralized the acid in a 30.00 mL sample of aqueous HNO_3. What was the original concentration of the HNO_3 solution?

2. Titrations having a more complex mole ratio of reactants

Many other titrations do not have a 1:1 ratio between reactants—and not all titrations involve acids and bases. A classic example is a reaction that was once commonly used to determine the concentration of permanganate solutions:

$$5 \, C_2O_4^{2-} + 2 \, MnO_4^- + 16 \, H^+ \rightarrow 10 \, CO_2 + 2 \, Mn^{2+} + 8 \, H_2O$$

oxalate   permanganate   manganese(II)
(colorless)   (violet)   (colorless)

This example has similarities to our **A** and **Y** example, in that one of the reactants is richly colored and can serve as the end point signal, but this time the colored species is typically in the buret.[24] If a solution of the dark violet permanganate ion is added from a buret to a solution of oxalate ion (which is colorless), the purple color of permanganate disappears as long as the oxalate has not yet been used up. When 2 moles of permanganate ion have been added for every 5 moles of oxalate ion, the reaction has reached its **equivalence point**.[25] The next drop of permanganate solution added will result in the presence of unreacted permanganate in the flask, because it has nothing with which to react. The very light pink color in the flask serves as the end point for the titration. Think about this; clearly the lighter the pink color, the better, because the oxalate ion was used up BEFORE the pink appeared.

Calculations in situations with more complicated mole relationships must take these mole ratios into account. Here is a typical problem:

Example 12-17.

A 25.00 mL solution containing 0.208 M oxalate ion (could be from any soluble oxalate salt, such as $Na_2C_2O_4$) has been prepared. Permanganate ion solution (usually from the salt $KMnO_4$) is placed in the buret and is added slowly to the oxalate solution. When 18.76 mL of permanganate solution has been added to the flask, the solution in the flask changes from colorless to pale pink. This color change indicates that the reaction has gone to completion. What is the concentration of the permanganate solution?

<u>Solution:</u>

We base our approach on the definition of molarity, in this case the molarity of permanganate:

$$\left[MnO_4^- \right] = \frac{\text{moles } MnO_4^-}{\text{L } MnO_4^- \text{ solution}}$$

We already know the value for the denominator: the volume of the MnO_4^- solution added is 18.76 mL. All we need to find out is the number of moles of MnO_4^- contained in that volume.

We do have one useful piece of information from the chemical equation: when the reaction has gone to completion, we know that 2 moles of MnO_4^- must be added for every 5 moles of $C_2O_4^{2-}$. So if we can find the moles of oxalate used, we can convert to moles of

---

[24] The analyte can be either in the flask or the buret, depending on what suits the purposes better.

[25] The *equivalence point* does not necessarily mean moles analyte = moles titrant, but means instead that according to the stoichiometry of the reaction equation, neither the analyte nor the titrant is in excess.

permanganate using this 5:2 relationship. To find moles of oxalate ion, and then permanganate ion, we can begin a string of conversions by starting with the 25.00 mL volume of the oxalate solution:

$$25.00\,mL\,C_2O_4^{2-}\,sln \times \frac{1\,L}{1000\,mL} \times \frac{0.208\,mol\,C_2O_4^{2-}}{1\,L\,C_2O_4^{2-}\,sln} \times \frac{2\,mol\,MnO_4^-}{5\,mol\,C_2O_4^{2-}} = 0.00208\,mol\,MnO_4^-$$

The molarity of MnO_4^- is

$$\left[MnO_4^-\right] = \frac{moles\,MnO_4^-}{L\,MnO_4^-\,sln} = \frac{0.00208\,moles\,MnO_4^-}{18.76\,mL\left(\frac{1\,L}{1000\,mL}\right)} = 0.111\,M$$

Exercise 12-11.

Silver ions react with sulfate to form a precipitate:

$$2\,Ag^+\,(aq) + SO_4^{2-}\,(aq) \longrightarrow Ag_2SO_4\,(s)$$

A 0.200 M solution of sodium sulfate is added dropwise to a 25.00 mL solution of silver nitrate. Precipitation of silver sulfate is complete after addition of 5.76 mL of the sodium sulfate solution. What is the concentration of silver ions in the original sample?

3. Titrations and dissolved solids

Finally, we can consider situations in which a material, typically a solid, is dissolved (perhaps in acid), and then titrated. We do not need to know the molarity of the dissolved material; as long as we know how many moles of it are present. In a titration, the concentration of the solution in the buret can be determined without knowing the concentration of the solution in the flask. Such a situation is best illustrated using an example:

Example 12-18.

Potassium dichromate, $K_2Cr_2O_7$, reacts with iodide ions in acidic aqueous solution as follows:

$$K_2Cr_2O_7(aq) + 6\,I^-(aq) + 14\,H^+(aq) \longrightarrow 2\,K^+(aq) + 2\,Cr^{3+}(aq) + 3\,I_2(aq) + 7\,H_2O\,(\ell)$$

Consider a solution of 0.1367 g of potassium dichromate dissolved in sulfuric acid. A solution of potassium iodide is added using a buret. If 23.28 mL of KI solution is necessary for complete reaction, what was the concentration of the potassium iodide solution?

Solution:

In setting up this problem we should note that the potassium dichromate is serving as the **primary standard**, the reactant whose amount is accurately known (by mass) and on which all the calculations are based.

Once again we use the definition of molarity: $[KI] = [I^-] = \dfrac{moles\,I^-}{volume\,I^-\,solution}$

The volume of I^- solution is already known: 23.28 mL = 0.02328 L

To find the number of moles of I^- we can relate them to the moles of $K_2Cr_2O_7$ present. A convenient way to set up the calculation is to treat it as a conversion factor problem:

$$\left(0.1367\, g\, K_2Cr_2O_7\right)\left(\frac{1\, mol\, K_2Cr_2O_7}{294.18\, g\, K_2Cr_2O_7}\right)\left(\frac{6\, mol\, I^-}{1\, mol\, K_2Cr_2O_7}\right)=0.002788\, mol\, I^-$$

mass of sample   *molar mass*   *ratio of moles from*
                          of $K_2Cr_2O_7$ *balanced equation*

We can now calculate the molarity of I^-:

$$\left[I^-\right]=\frac{moles\, I^-}{volume\, I^-\, solution}=\frac{0.002788\, mol\, I^-}{0.02328\, L}=0.1198\, M$$

12-4. ABSORPTION OF LIGHT BY SOLUTIONS

An important, and often useful, aspect of many solutions is that they absorb light and other electromagnetic radiation. This characteristic can be used in some cases to determine the concentration of solutions and to gain insight into the nature of the solutes themselves—for example, in helping to understand why some solutes absorb light of particular energies (giving rise to characteristic colors) while others do not.

A. The Logarithmic Relationship Between Absorbance and Light Intensities

If light of intensity I_o ("o" for *original*) at a given wavelength passes through a solution containing a chemical species (molecule or ion) with the capability of absorbing that wavelength of light, the light emerges with a lesser intensity, I. This process is diagrammed in Figure 12-12.

As seen in the boxed equation, below, the degree to which a particular wavelength of light is absorbed (its **absorbance, A_λ**) may be described either as a logarithmic dependence on the ratio of incident and **transmitted** light intensities (in pink in the box, below) or as a product of three factors, as seen on the right in the box, below. The latter relationship is often called the Beer-Lambert Law, or just Beer's Law for short.

$$\log\frac{I_o}{I}=A_\lambda=\varepsilon_\lambda\ell c$$

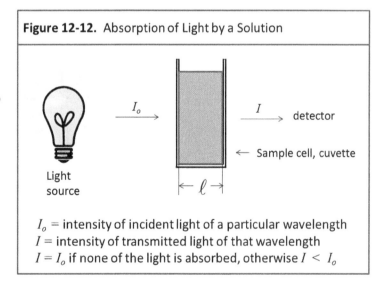

Figure 12-12. Absorption of Light by a Solution

I_o = intensity of incident light of a particular wavelength
I = intensity of transmitted light of that wavelength
$I = I_o$ if none of the light is absorbed, otherwise $I < I_o$

We focus first on the equivalency in pink. This equation includes three variables:

1. Intensity of incoming light (I_o)

This is the amount of light that is entering the sample cell; see Figure 12-12. In any given experiment, this light will have a particular wavelength, λ. We won't worry about the units of light intensity, because in our equation, two intensities will allow the units to cancel.

2. Intensity of transmitted light (I)

This light is of the same wavelength, λ, as I_o. (See Figure 12-12). The transmitted light makes it through the solution without being absorbed. If $I = I_o$, then none of this wavelength of energy was absorbed. In all other cases, I will be less than I_o. Absorbed light (energy) is used to excite something (such as an electron), so absorbed energy is "missing" from the transmitted light.

3. Absorbance (A) of a particular wavelength (λ) of light, A_λ

Chemical species can absorb energy. When visible energy is absorbed, an electron in the species is energized to jump into an orbital of higher energy. In this way, the absorbed energy "disappears" during its travel through the solution. The lowest energy of absorption occurs if an electron jumps from the HOMO (highest occupied molecular orbital) to the LUMO (lowest unoccupied molecular orbital). Depending on the energy spacing of the orbitals, this jump requires different amounts of energy. So, different solutes will absorb different wavelengths.

While atomic absorptions result in line spectra, visible absorptions by molecules tend to occur in broad bands (as we saw in Chapter 3). When some parts of the visible spectrum are missing (absorbed) the remaining light will be comprised only of the transmitted (un-absorbed) wavelengths. The color seen is approximately the complementary color[26] to the color most absorbed. For example, because blue and orange are complementary colors, a blue solution will absorb strongly in the orange (and surrounding) parts of the visible spectrum and an orange solution will absorb strongly in the blue (and surrounding) parts of the visible spectrum.[27]

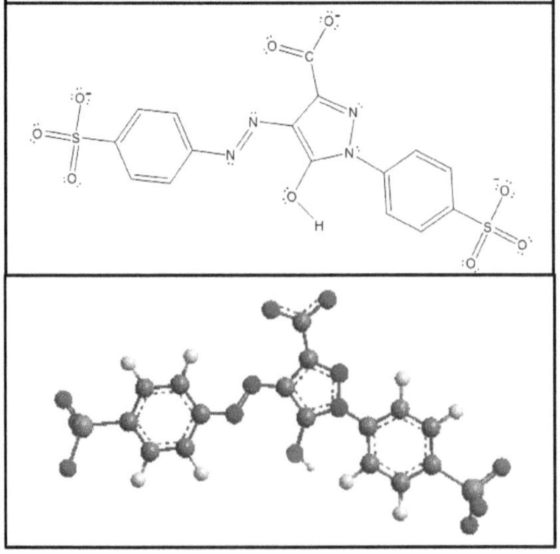

All molecules absorb UV wavelengths, as these wavelengths typically carry amounts of energy that can excite bonding electrons from their ground state orbital into higher energy orbitals. Two categories of chemical entities that often absorb visible light are:

a. Coordination complexes between metal ions and associated ligands, as we studied in Chapter 10. The e_g-t_{2g} energy gap is often similar to the energies of visible wavelengths.

b. Molecules/ions with highly delocalized pi electrons, such as the dye molecule, tartrazine, in Figure 12-13. Highly delocalized pi systems have more closely spaced orbitals than more localized systems, so it takes less energy to excite delocalized electrons. Normal bonding electrons absorb UV radiation, the delocalized electrons absorb radiation from the less energetic visible region of the spectrum.

Figure 12-13. Two views of the food color tartrazine (Yellow 5), which is highly *conjugated*. Some H atoms are "understood" in the (abbreviated) Lewis dot structure (top); all atoms are shown in the ball and stick structure (bottom).

Structurally, delocalization is prevalent when the molecule contains a relatively large sequence of alternating single and double bonds; systems such as this are said to be highly **conjugated**. Conjugated systems have sp^2 hybridized atoms, are largely planar through the conjugated region (due to all of the trigonal planar atoms), and have unhybridized, perpendicular-to-the-plane p orbitals that

---

[26] Complementary colors are found straight across a "color wheel" from one another: Blue and Orange, Red and Green, Yellow and Violet. See Figure 9-15 for a visual reminder.

[27] If you want to know approximate wavelengths for different colors of light, simply remember that ROYal Goats Can Be Violent, which localizes colors over the visible spectrum every 50 nm: Red (700 nm), Orange (650 nm), Yellow (600 nm), Green (550 nm), Cyan (500 nm), Blue (450 nm) and Violet (400 nm).

overlap to produce the delocalized pi-system. It is these pi-electrons that can absorb visible light. Make sure you can identify a continuous set of sp^2 atoms in tartrazine, between the two sulfur atoms.

One atom (the lower nitrogen atom in the 5-membered ring) looks as if it has a steric number of 4, but in this molecule it is trigonal planar due to the existence of a resonance structure in which the lone pair has moved into a pi-bonding situation between that nitrogen atom and the neighboring carbon atom of the benzene ring. See the resonance hybrid view at the bottom of Figure 12-13 and Exercise 12-12!

Exercise 12-12.

    a. Draw one resonance structure of tartrazine (see Figure 12-13) wherein the lone pair of electrons on the nitrogen atom at the "bottom" of the 5-membered ring has shifted to become a pi bond between that nitrogen and the carbon atom to its right (part of the benzene ring). You will have to move additional electron pairs in order that all carbon atoms continue to be involved in 4 bonds. (It is OK to "abbreviate" the structure by ignoring anything to the left of the 5-membered ring.)

    b. Draw at least two resonance structures of some other part of the tartrazine molecule. (And consider the very large number of resonance forms available to this ion!)

An absorbance value must specify a wavelength, usually in units of nm, and often designated by a subscript. For example, A_{420} means absorbance of light having a wavelength of 420 nm. ("A" has no units, because it is derived from a ratio of two intensities.) This wavelength matches that of the light used in the experiment.

Scientists refer to both **transmitted** and **absorbed** light. These are two parts of a whole. The original light passing through a sample can either be transmitted (pass all the way through) or absorbed (get used up by exciting electrons). We are not interested here in **emission**, which is light given off by a chemical sample under conditions where excited electrons are releasing light energy. Most energy given off by excited electrons in molecules is heat energy (IR) rather than visible light.

Because the transmitted light plus the absorbed light make up the total of the light intensity, we can write:

$$\frac{I}{I_o} = \text{the fraction of the light that is transmitted}$$

$$1 - \frac{I}{I_o} = \text{the fraction of the light that is absorbed}$$

Note: fraction absorbed + fraction transmitted = 1, and
               percent absorbed + percent transmitted = 100%

Calculation of Percent Absorbed from an Absorbance Value

Let's determine how an absorbance value translates into a fraction of light transmitted (or absorbed). If, for some wavelength, $A = 1.0$, we can write:

$$\log \frac{I_o}{I} = 1.0$$

A "logarithm" is an "exponent of 10." Saying that the log of the ratio is 1.0 is just a way to say that the ratio has a value of $10^{1.0}$.

So, we can rewrite the statement as: $\dfrac{I_o}{I} = 10^{1.0}$

resulting in the statement
$$\frac{I_o}{I} = 10$$

We can let $I_o = 100\%$, a convenient way to indicate the initial intensity of the light, (initially it's all there!) and write

$$\frac{100\%}{I} = 10$$

requiring that
$$I = 10\%$$

Because I is the transmitted light, the rest, 90%, is absorbed.

Alternatively, we could let $I_o = 1.0$ and write $\frac{1.0}{I} = 10$ so that $I = 0.10$. This is the same result: when the fraction of light transmitted is 0.10, the percent of light transmitted is 10%. It does not matter what we choose as the I_o value, but 100% and 1.0 are convenient choices.

Example 12-19.

What percentage of 580 nm light has been absorbed when $A_{580} = 0.72$?

Solution:

We know the A value, but not the relative intensities. We can always set $I_o = 100\%$. That way, the calculated I value will automatically be the percent transmitted:

$$A_{580} = 0.72 = \log\left(\frac{I_o}{I}\right) = \log\left(\frac{100\%}{I}\right)$$

applying the definition of logarithm : $10^{0.72} = \left(\frac{100\%}{I}\right)$

$$5.248 = \left(\frac{100\%}{I}\right), so \ I = \left(\frac{100\%}{5.248}\right) = 19.05\%$$

If the transmitted light, I, is 19.05%, the absorbed light is 100-19.05 = **81%**

The percent of light absorbed increases rapidly at small A values, and then slowly approaches 100%, as shown at right. Note that "3.0" is a very large absorbance value! In experiments concerned with measuring absorbances, it is best to work at "A" values no higher than 1.5.

Absorbance (A)	Percent of light absorbed
0	0
0.5	68%
1.0	90%
2.0	99%
3.0	99.9%

Example 12-20.

a. Calculate the percentage of 660 nm light absorbed and transmitted for a solution having $A_{660} = 0.25$.

Solution:

If $A = 0.25$, then $\log\frac{I_o}{I} = 0.25$.

We can write:

$$\frac{I_o}{I} = 10^{0.25} = 1.778$$

Letting $I_o = 100\%$ provides us with

$$\frac{100\%}{I} = 1.778$$

$$\frac{100\%}{1.778} = I \quad and \quad I = 56.2\%$$

If **56.2%** of the 660 nm light is transmitted, the rest of it, **43.8%**, is absorbed. (Note that the wavelength value is not involved in the calculation!)

b. Bonus question: assuming that 660 nm is near the maximum of the absorbance band, what color do you expect this solution to be?

Solution:

From **ROY**al **G**oats **C**an **B**e **V**iolent: 700 nm = red and 650 nm = orange; 660 nm is very near orange. We expect that a solution that absorbs in the orange (and surrounding) regions will likely appear to be some shade of blue (the complementary color to orange!)

Exercise 12-13.

Show that $A = 2.0$ corresponds to absorption of 99% of a particular wavelength of light entering a solution.

B. The Beer-Lambert Law

The Beer-Lambert law (pink, below) is the more commonly used relationship in the equivalency introduced earlier:

$$\log\frac{I_o}{I} = A_\lambda = \varepsilon_\lambda \ell c$$

This relationship correlates concentrations of solutions (c) to the absorbance of a particular wavelength, A_λ. This relationship is useful for the analysis of solution concentration; if you can measure the absorbance, you can, perhaps, calculate the concentration:

$$c = \frac{A_\lambda}{\varepsilon_\lambda \ell}$$

1. The variables

It is useful to examine this equation term by term. **Absorbance, A,** has previously been discussed. So we are left with the three variables on the right side of the equation, above. The most common units for each of these three quantities is included, parenthetically, in the list below. Remember that A is unitless!

a. Concentration, c $\left(M, \frac{mol}{L}\right)$

Absorbance is proportional to concentration. In Figure 12-14, you can imagine the concentration of the solute to be related to the number of red solute particles in the solution. The darker the color, the closer the solute particles are to each other. It may be helpful to think of the light in terms of its particulate nature, as a photon.[28] The greater the concentration of the solute, the greater the chance that a given photon of the light will collide with a solute particle and be absorbed before it makes it through the cell.

Figure 12-14. Effect of concentration on absorbance. A red solute absorbs green photons. Twice as many solute particles gives twice the absorbance value, A_{550}. Relative numbers of absorbed photons (green bursts) are shown.

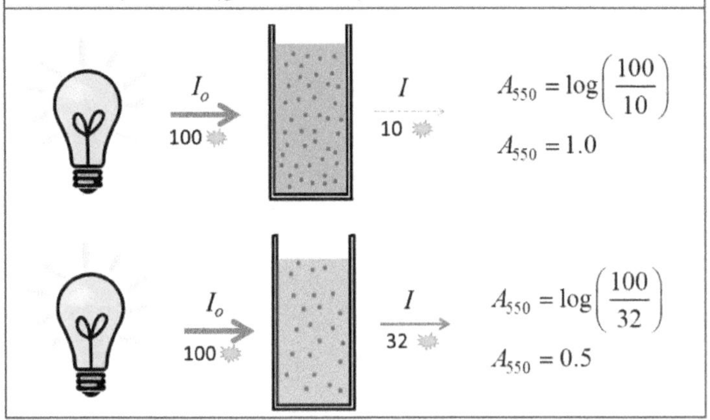

$$A_{550} = \log\left(\frac{100}{10}\right)$$
$$A_{550} = 1.0$$

$$A_{550} = \log\left(\frac{100}{32}\right)$$
$$A_{550} = 0.5$$

b. Path length, ℓ (cm)

Absorbance is proportional to **path length**; see Figure 12-15. This seems reasonable, especially thinking in terms of photons of light. If a photon must travel a greater distance through a solution, there is more opportunity for it to collide with a solute particle and be absorbed. Normal sample cells (**cuvettes**) for making absorption measurements on solutions have a 1.00 cm path length (inside dimension). Sample cells for making absorption measurements on gases have path lengths up to 10.0 cm, in order that the light encounters enough particles to be significantly absorbed.

Figure 12-15. Effect of path length on absorbance. A red solute absorbs green photons. Both solutions are the same concentration. When the path length is twice as long, the absorbance value, A_{550}, is twice as big.

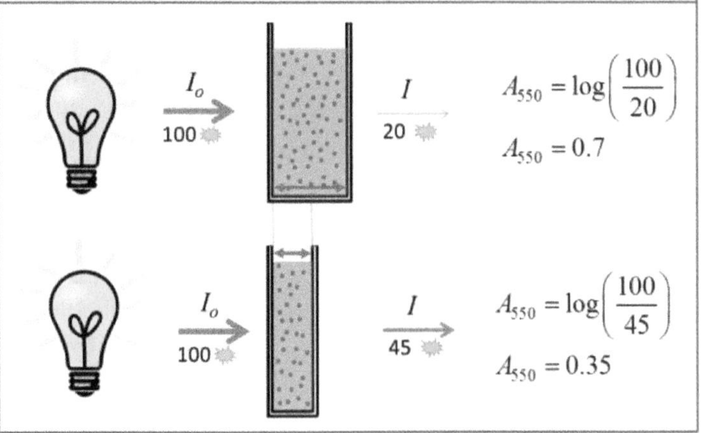

$$A_{550} = \log\left(\frac{100}{20}\right)$$
$$A_{550} = 0.7$$

$$A_{550} = \log\left(\frac{100}{45}\right)$$
$$A_{550} = 0.35$$

c. Molar absorptivity, ε_λ $\left(\frac{L}{mol \cdot cm}\right)$ (at a particular wavelength, λ)

The **molar absorptivity** is a measure of how well a solute absorbs a particular wavelength of light, which has to do with the energy gaps between orbitals (especially the HOMO-LUMO gap). Photons must be able to boost an electron into an available orbital in order to be absorbed. Thus, photons must have the "right" wavelength. In the Beer-Lambert law, the wavelengths for A_λ and ε_λ must be the same; the absorbance of 550 nm light depends on the solute's ability to absorb 550 nm light.

---

[28] A photon is a packet of energy (or light) that has both particle and wave characteristics.

The chemical structure of a solute determines the wavelengths of light that it can best absorb. If a solute absorbs light strongly at a particular wavelength, its value of ε at that wavelength is high; if it absorbs weakly, its value of ε is low. Each solute has its own characteristic pattern of absorbing light of different wavelengths. In Figure 12-16, we isolate information about a mythical red solute and three particular wavelengths. As you can see from the ε_λ values at the top of the figure:

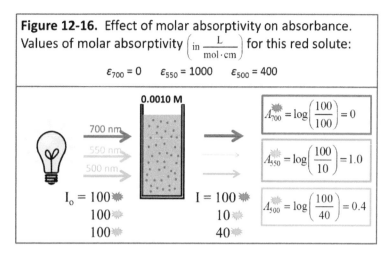

Figure 12-16. Effect of molar absorptivity on absorbance. Values of molar absorptivity $\left(\text{in }\dfrac{L}{mol \cdot cm}\right)$ for this red solute:

$$\varepsilon_{700} = 0 \qquad \varepsilon_{550} = 1000 \qquad \varepsilon_{500} = 400$$

$$A_{700} = \log\left(\frac{100}{100}\right) = 0$$

$$A_{550} = \log\left(\frac{100}{10}\right) = 1.0$$

$$A_{500} = \log\left(\frac{100}{40}\right) = 0.4$$

> green (550 nm) is absorbed best,
> cyan (500 nm) is absorbed, but not as well as green;
> red (700 nm) is not absorbed at all.

Incoming (I_o) and outgoing (I) intensities for each of these wavelengths are noted in the figure by counting relative numbers of incoming and transmitted photons (colored "bursts"). Exercise 12-14 will help you make connections between the two mathematical definitions of absorbance:

$$\log\frac{I_o}{I} = A_\lambda = e_\lambda \ell c$$

Exercise 12-14.

Using data from Figure 12-16 and assuming that the cuvette has a standard 1.00 cm path length, show that $A_\lambda = \varepsilon_\lambda \ell c$ agrees with $A = \log(I_o/I)$ for each wavelength in Figure 12-16.

2. The spectrum

Plotting either ε vs. λ or A vs. λ gives plots of the same general shape, because A is big when ε is big, etc. See an example in Figure 12-17. Either of these plots can be called the solute's **absorption spectrum**. Keep in mind that while an absorption spectrum is being measured, the sample cell doesn't change (path length) and the solution doesn't change (concentration), so during a particular experiment A changes as ε changes!

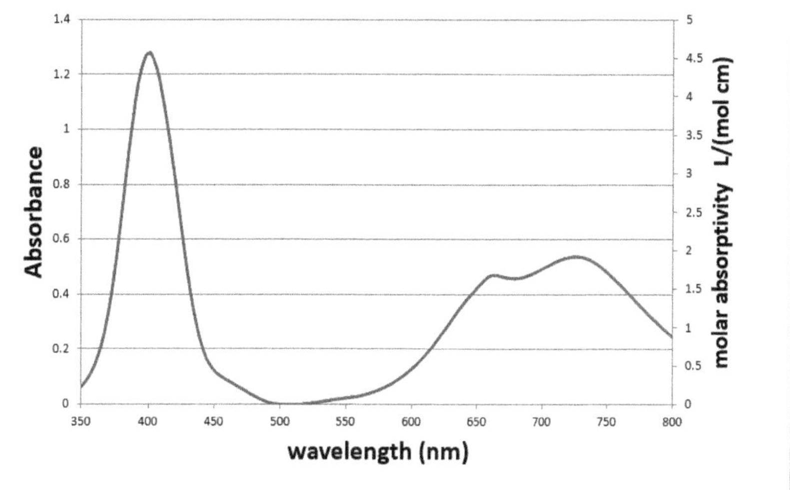

The example shown in Figure 12-17 is the absorption spectrum of $[Ni(H_2O)_6]^{2+}$. This green complex ion forms spontaneously in aqueous

Figure 12-17. Absorption spectrum of $[Ni(H_2O)_6]^{2+}$ (aq). A vs. λ and ε vs. λ plots are identical except for the values (and units) on the y-axes.

solutions of nickel(II).[29] In this spectrum, the left side y-axis is absorbance (A) and the right side y-axis is molar absorptivity (ε). Both are a function of wavelength (thus we often write A_λ and ε_λ). The peaks show which wavelengths are well-absorbed (larger A and larger ε) and the valleys show which wavelengths are transmitted best through the solution (smaller A and smaller ε). Note that because

$$\varepsilon_\lambda = \frac{A_\lambda}{\ell c}$$

and $\ell = 1.00$ cm, the values of A_λ and ε_λ are related by a factor of c. If a spectrum could be obtained for a 1.00 M solution,[30] A_λ and ε_λ would have the same values (although not the same units)!

This spectrum shows us that the molar absorptivity (and absorbance!) of aqueous Ni^{2+} maximizes around 390 nm and 730 nm. The broad absorption from about 800-625 nm (red) causes the solution to look green (the complementary color of red). We see that the yellow-green-cyan-blue portion of the spectrum (600-450 nm) is mostly transmitted. Altogether, our eyes see a shade of green.

3. How wavelength fits in

The wavelength of absorption is not involved in any calculations related to the Beer-Lambert law. However, because magnitudes of both A and ε depend on wavelength, it is important to always record the wavelength at which any measurement of light absorption is made.

4. Units

The most common units of the quantities in the Beer-Lambert law have been discussed, above. The path length is chosen for convenience; most commonly a cell having a path length of 1.00 cm is used for liquid samples. If concentration is measured in moles per liter and the path length in centimeters, this gives the molar absorptivity, ε, the relatively unusual units of $\frac{L}{mol\cdot cm}$. Remember that absorbance values have no units, so the units of $\varepsilon\ell c$ must cancel!

$$\left(\frac{L}{mol\cdot cm}\right)(cm)\left(\frac{mol}{L}\right)$$

Example 12-21.

At a wavelength of 450 nm a 0.0256 M solution of a copper(II) compound has an absorbance of 0.826 when measured in a cell having path length of 1.00 cm. What is the molar absorptivity of the compound at this wavelength?

Solution:

Using the expression $A = \varepsilon\,\ell\,c$ from the Beer-Lambert law:

$$A_{450} = 0.826 \qquad \ell = 1.00 \text{ cm} \qquad c = 0.0256 \text{ M}$$

$$\varepsilon_{450} = \frac{A_{450}}{\ell c} = \frac{0.826}{(1.00\,cm)(0.0256\,M)} = 32.3\frac{L}{mol\cdot cm}$$

(The wavelength value is not used in the calculation, but describes the origin of these data!)

---

[29] We dissolved nickel(II) sulfate, $NiSO_4$, to obtain this spectrum.

[30] The solute may not be soluble enough to obtain a 1.00 M solution. If it is soluble enough, the absorptions at that concentration may exceed the instrument's scale.

Exercise 12-15.

At a wavelength of 402 nm, a solution of the $[Mn(H_2O)_6]^{2+}$ ion has a molar absorptivity of 0.038 L $mol^{-1}cm^{-1}$. What concentration of this ion would be necessary to give an absorbance of 0.020 at this wavelength, measured in a cell having a path length of 10.00 cm?

12-5. WEAK INTERACTIONS IN PROTEINS

In Chapter 7 we introduced proteins as polymers of amino acids. The primary structure of a protein is the order in which the amino acids occur in a particular working protein molecule. Now that we've studied weak intermolecular forces, ionization, and the associations of water with its solutes, we can begin to make sense of higher levels of protein structure, aspects concerned with the conformations (shape), folding and association of multiple chains into a working whole. These levels are called **secondary**, **tertiary**, and **quaternary** structures of proteins.

A. Secondary Structures and Hydrogen Bonds

We start this section by returning to the concept of a hydrogen bond. Remember that, essentially, hydrogen bonds are particularly strong dipole-dipole attractions that feature a partially positive hydrogen atom bridging a gap between two highly electronegative atoms.[31] The hydrogen atom is covalently bonded to one O or N and non-covalently attracted to the other.

Notice, in Figure 12-18, that the backbone of a protein polymer has hydrogen bond donating sites (the N-H) and accepting sites (the C=O groups). While viewing Figure 12-18, don't forget to think about the resonance of the peptide bonds, which we remind you of in Figure 12-19. The right-hand resonance structure helps to enhance hydrogen bonding; the oxygen carries more of a negative charge and the positively charged nitrogen pulls additional electron density away from the hydrogen atom, enhancing its partial positive charge. Another potential acceptor site, the lone pair on the nitrogen atom (left-hand structure), is not likely to form hydrogen bonds due to its resonance delocalization. It does not have enough of a presence in any one spot to serve as a hydrogen bond acceptor.

Figure 12-18. A tetra-peptide showing the backbone atoms in blue. Note the pattern of hydrogen bond donors ("H" of N-H) and acceptors ("O" of C=O).

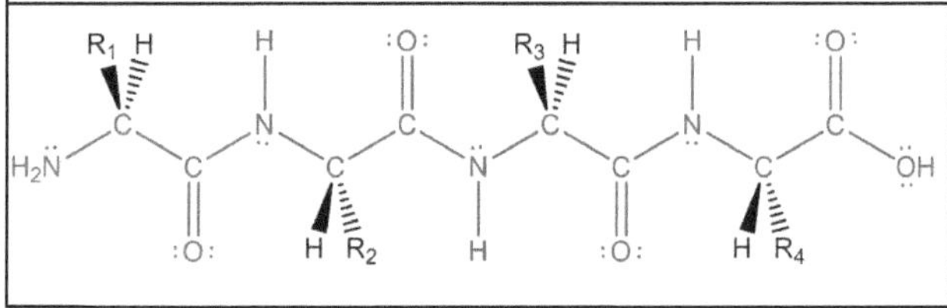

Figure 12-19. Reminder of the resonance of a peptide bond (amide). These "R" groups are the rest of the polymeric structure of a protein. Pi electron density is delocalized over three atoms (N, C, O).

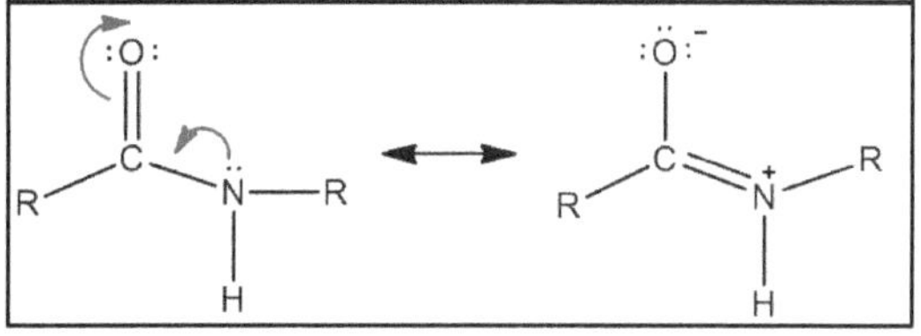

There are certainly more hydrogen bonding sites available in a protein (the serine side chain, $-CH_2OH$, for example), but as it turns out, the backbone positions detailed above are the most important to the major **secondary structures** found in biological proteins. Geometric considerations do not allow hydrogen bonding to occur between consecutive amide bonds. If hydrogen bonds are to form, they will involve amino acids that are NOT NEIGHBORS of each other.

---

[31] Biological systems generally do not include fluorine atoms, so hydrogen bonds (H-FON attractions) are limited to "H-ON attractions."

Myoglobin contains seven helical regions which are rendered quite obvious in the ribbon-style structure of Figure 12-20. These helices, called **α-helices**, arise when the hydrogen bonding of backbone groups (as discussed above) assumes a repeating pattern and geometry. As the backbone spirals, creating the helix, **amino acid residues** that are 4 positions apart in the primary sequence become helical neighbors and the hydrogen atom of the N-H group from

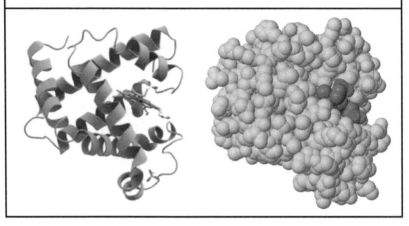

Figure 12-20. Two views of oxygenated myoglobin. **Left:** A ribbon-style view that emphasizes secondary and tertiary structures. **Right:** A space-filling rendition that details the positions of individual atoms within the protein structure. Protein data bank file **1MBO**.

one of these residues hydrogen bonds to the C=O oxygen of the other. Every amino acid residue of the helix is involved in two of these attractions, one with the residue 4 positions earlier and one with the residue 4 positions beyond.

Figure 12-21 offers various views of the hydrogen bonding that stabilizes an α-helix. The first view shows a stretched out protein chain with two of the eventual positions of hydrogen bonds mapped on to it; each hydrogen bond involves two amino acid residues that are separated by 3 other residues. The hydrogen bonds cannot be as long as they look in the left view! The coiling of the helix brings these groups into close proximity and then the formation of the hydrogen bonds stabilizes that helical form. Close investigation of these hydrogen bonds shows that they do not quite have ideal geometries; the bond angle from N-H-O is less than 180°. Even though each hydrogen bond is weak, the sum total of all of these weak attractions stabilizes the helical form of the protein chain. The **α-helix** is a ubiquitous secondary structure found in almost all working proteins. It greatly reduces the overall "floppiness" of the structure by minimizing the ability of many backbone bonds to rotate.[32]

Figure 12-21. Hydrogen bonding in an α-helix. **Left:** Backbone O-H-N pattern involves two amino acid residues that are separated by three other residues. **Right:** Two side-views showing how the coiling of the helix brings the residues into close proximity for the formation of the hydrogen bonds; the nitrogen end is blue and the oxygen end is red.

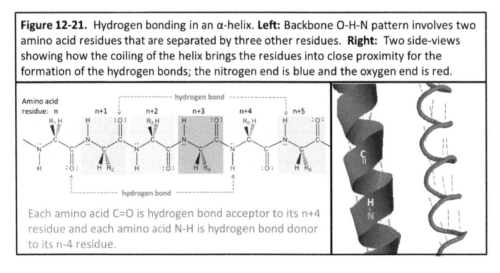

---

[32] Remember that the peptide bonds were already rigid due to partial double bond character. The helical structure limits rotations around the remaining single bonds in the helical regions.

Another secondary structure common to proteins is the **β-strand** (beta-strand). Each green diagonal ribbon in the protein of Figure 12-22A represents a β-strand. While hydrogen bonding is not necessary to stabilize the strand, it is very common for multiple strands to associate as **β-sheets**, as also seen in Figure 12-22A. Figure 12-22B shows the hydrogen bonding that stabilizes the β-sheet structure. Note that this style of hydrogen bonding uses the same donor and acceptor groups as the α-helix, but the amino acid residues that are bonded to each other are now much more distant from one another in the primary sequence of the protein. The **antiparallel**[33] β-sheet in Figure B shows essentially ideal hydrogen bond geometry, 180° around the hydrogen atom.

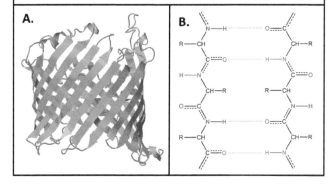

Figure 12-22. A. A porin protein with a β-sheet structure. Sheets arise from the association of neighboring β-strands (the flat ribbons, arrows at the end of ribbons show the N→C direction of the primary structure).
B. The association of β-strands into a sheet utilizes hydrogen bonds, as shown here. Blue atoms are donors and acceptors. Long green dotted line shows hydrogen bond attractions.

We have learned that hydrogen bonds are much weaker attractions than covalent bonds. Protein-protein hydrogen bonds, such as the ones we have been discussing here, are particularly weak in an aqueous environment. Why? Because water molecules can easily substitute for any of the hydrogen bonding partners. If a protein can lose its desired secondary structure while maintaining the same net number of bonds, there is no driving force to maintain the structure. Fortunately, this problem is moderated by the fact that even soluble proteins have a limited surface contact with water. In the next section, we explore how a **globular**[34] **protein** achieves and maintains its shape.

B. Tertiary Structures

As seen in Figure 12-20, the seven α-helices of myoglobin fold back on each other to achieve a compact, three-dimensional structure. The folding sites occur between the helical segments and result in the close contact of various helix surfaces. This folding defines the **tertiary structure** of myoglobin and other globular proteins. Amino acids that are far from each other in the primary sequence can become near neighbors, through space, in the tertiary structure. What are the driving forces for this kind of folding? Does a protein fold spontaneously, or does it need some kind of help to get it right? These, and many more questions about protein folding, are the basis of many ongoing research inquiries.

1. Hydrophobic Interactions

One of the forces that drives proteins to fold into tertiary structures is called the **hydrophobic effect**, and results in interactions that might be called **hydrophobic interactions**. *Hydrophobic* literally means "water-hating." Hydrophobic molecules are those that are *non-polar* with low *polarizability*. Water molecules do not want to be next to these molecules. These molecules are essentially insoluble in water.

Imagine using vigorous stirring (maybe even shaking) to combine a hydrophobic substance with water. You have likely done this by shaking-up an oil and vinegar salad dressing. Why do the layers re-separate? Let's think about this on a molecular scale. The layer of water molecules closest

---

[33] Where one strand is running the opposite direction as the other, often with a hairpin turn between them. (See the arrowheads on the green ribbons in Figure 12-22A.

[34] "Globular" means spherical or bulbous. A globular protein is one whose chain is folded back on itself until the whole length of the protein polymer is bundled into a small, roughly spherical shape.

to a stirred-in hydrophobic molecule[35] is similar to a solvent cage, but has an important difference from the solvent cages we introduced earlier for soluble particles:

The solvent cage molecules (H_2O) around a hydrophobic particle
do NOT make any bonding interactions with the particle.

Instead, the solvent cage molecules become <u>rigidly arranged</u> in order to try to avoid interactions with the hydrophobic material. The only way for this <u>unfavorable rigidity</u> to be minimized is for the water molecules to "push" the hydrophobic particles into close proximity with one another. As the hydrophobic regions coalesce into larger globules, the total surface contact area between the hydrophobic substance and water decreases, so there are fewer "unhappy" water molecules. As the hydrophobic substance collects into larger and larger globules within the bulk water, the density difference between the hydrophobic substance and liquid water will either cause the hydrophobic substance to float above the water or sink to the bottom of the container. In your salad dressing, the oil floats on the water.

So, *hydrophobic interactions* are commonly understood as being the result of unfavorable arrangements of water molecules next to hydrophobic surfaces. The phrase, *hydrophobic interaction*, is a misnomer, in that implies that the hydrophobic particles are driving the effect through some kind of favorable interaction with one another. Make sure to understand that the coming together of the hydrophobic particles is not due to an attractive force, but rather to water's attempt to alleviate, as much as possible, unfavorable arrangements of its own molecules. It is certainly true that once the hydrophobic particles are pushed close to one another, dispersion forces between them will develop. However, these dispersion forces are not strong enough to drive the process.

Figure 12-23. A cross-section through the middle of myoglobin, a small soluble, globular protein.
Red = (−) charged amino acids, Blue = (+) charged amino acids, Gray = non-polar amino acids.

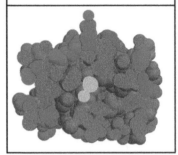

How is this important to the adoption of globular structures by many proteins? The 20 amino acids found in biological proteins were introduced in Chapter 7. You will find them, again, in Table 12-8. Note that the side chain characteristics vary considerably, from nonpolar, to polar, to ionizable (having the potential to carry positive or negative charges). Figure 12-23 shows a cross-section of a typical soluble, globular protein, colored to highlight polar and nonpolar regions. Notice that the interior of the globule is nonpolar, while the exterior surface carries multiple charged amino acid residues (we discuss ionizations in the next section!). We can imagine that water pushed the polymer into this globular form in order to eliminate the need for water molecules to be in contact with hydrophobic portions of the polymer. Hydrophobic interactions are a major factor in protein folding.

---

[35] An oil molecule is a triacylglyceride; we studied these fats and oils in Chapter 11. Most of the structure is hydrocarbon. Thus it is non-polar and not particularly polarizable due to the small sizes of the atoms.

Table 12-8. The Side Chain Structures of the Twenty Traditional Proteinogenic Amino Acids.

Nonpolar	Name, Symbol	Polar	Name Symbol	Ionizable (acidic/basic)[c]	Name Symbol
 H	Glycine **Gly, G**	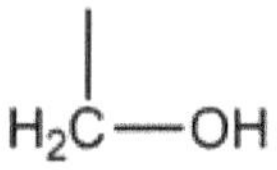 H_2C—OH	Serine **Ser, S**	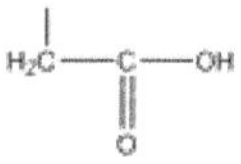 H_2C—C—OH ($\parallel$ O)	Aspartic acid **Asp, D**
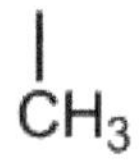 CH_3	Alanine **Ala, A**	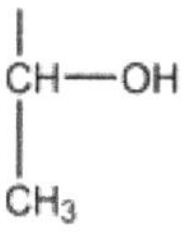 CH—OH, CH_3	Threonine **Thr, T**	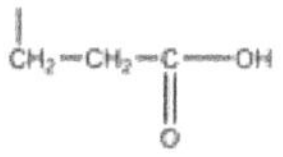 CH_2—CH_2—C—OH ($\parallel$ O)	Glutamic acid **Glu, E**
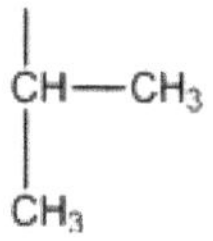 CH—CH_3, CH_3	Valine **Val, V**	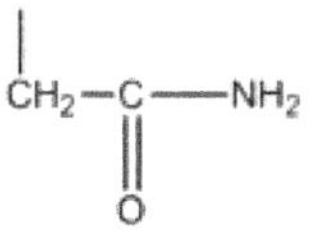 CH_2—C—NH_2 ($\parallel$ O)	Asparagine **Asn, N**	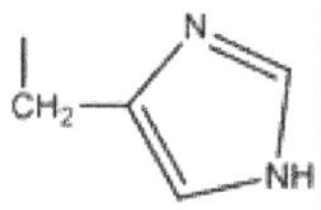 CH_2 (imidazole ring with N, NH)	Histidine **His, H**
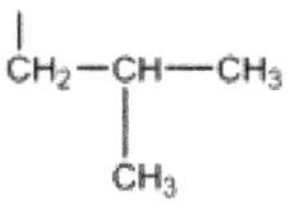 CH_2—CH—CH_3, CH_3	Leucine **Leu, L**	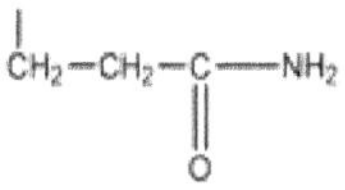 CH_2—CH_2—C—NH_2 ($\parallel$ O)	Glutamine **Gln, Q**	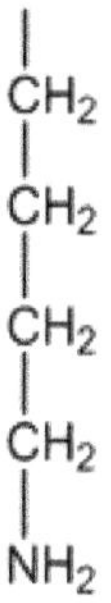 CH_2 CH_2 CH_2 CH_2 NH_2	Lysine **Lys, K**
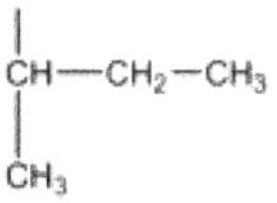 CH—CH_2—CH_3, CH_3	Isoleucine **Ile, I**	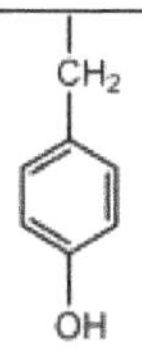 CH_2 (benzene ring with OH)	Tyrosine **Tyr, Y**		
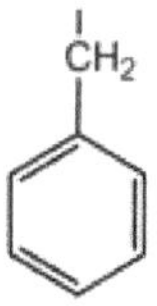 CH_2 (benzene ring)	Phenylalanine **Phe, F**			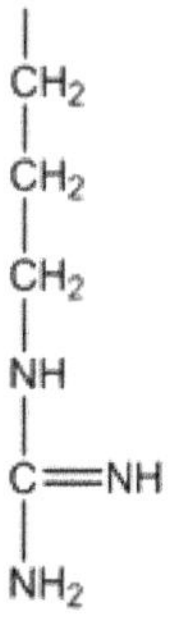 CH_2 CH_2 CH_2 NH C=NH NH_2	Arginine **Arg, R**
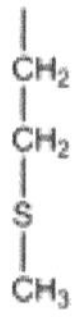 CH_2 CH_2 S CH_3	Methionine **Met, M**				
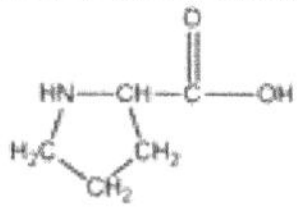 (proline cyclic structure)	Proline[a] **Pro, P**				
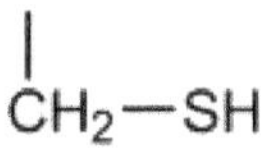 CH_2—SH	Cysteine[b] **Cys, C**				
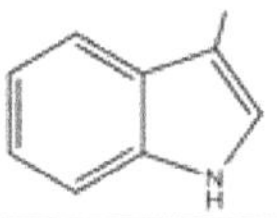 (indole ring structure)	Tryptophan, **Trp, W**				

[a]Notice that the entire structure of proline is shown. Proline is the only one of the 20 amino acid monomers for which the generic structure in Figure 7-11 does not apply. Proline's side chain bonds to both the α-carbon (normal) and the nitrogen of the amine, creating a cyclic amine structure.

[b]The top two entries in this column are acids and the next three are bases. Remember that acids are proton donors and bases are proton acceptors. Acidic side chains give protons away, thus becoming negatively charged ions. The basic side chains (specifically a nitrogen atom) pick up protons using its lone pair of electrons, thus becoming positively charged ions.

2. Ion-ion Attractions

Some of the big folds in a protein's tertiary structure are stabilized by attractions of positively and negatively charged amino acid side chains. These interactions are often called **salt bridges** because they utilize anion-cation attractions, similar to a salt. We begin by considering the ionizable sites common to all individual amino acids.

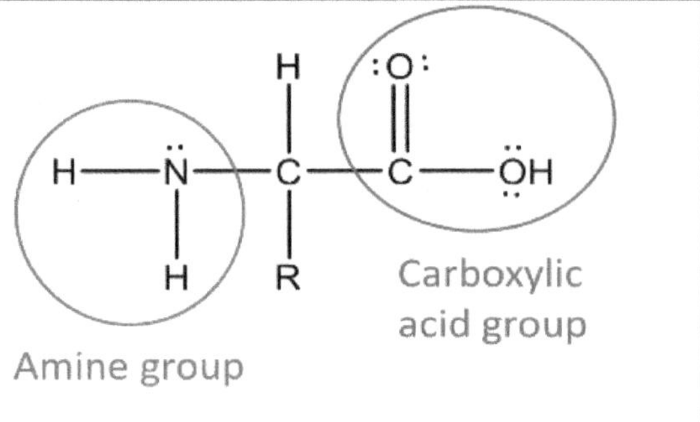

Amino acids carry both a weak acid group (carboxylic acid) and a weak base group (amine); see Figure 12-24. We have seen that weak acids and bases ionize via H+ transfer with water molecules. The carboxylic acid of the amino acid glycine (side chain = H) ionizes according to this chemical reaction equation:

Figure 12-24. A generic amino acid with the amine group circled in blue and the carboxylic acid group circled in red.

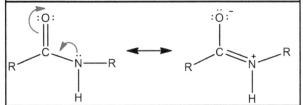

$$H_2NCH_2CO_2H(aq) + H_2O(\ell) \rightleftharpoons H_2NCH_2CO_2^-(aq) + H_3O^+(aq)$$

Additionally, the weak base amine group of glycine ionizes:

$$H_2\ddot{N}CH_2CO_2H(aq) + H_2O(\ell) \rightleftharpoons H_3\overset{+}{N}CH_2CO_2H(aq) + OH^-(aq)$$

Figure 12-25. The zwitterionic form of a generic amino acid. The ionized carboxylate group has two equivalent resonance structures.

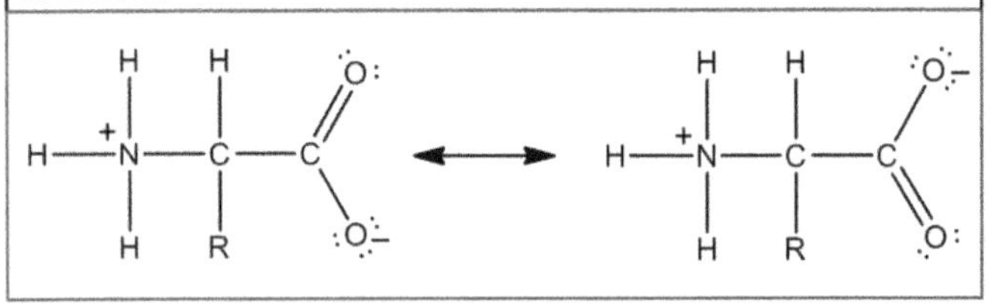

Note that an acid must have a very polar bond to the acidic H (it is lost as H+). A base must have a lone pair of electrons[36] with which to make a new bond to an H+ ion. Because an amino acid can do both, in solution it usually carries a positive charge on the nitrogen atom and a negative charge shared (via resonance structures) by the two oxygen atoms of the carboxylate group. We say that an amino acid such as glycine exists as a **zwitterion** in aqueous solution. A *zwitterion* is a molecule that may be neutral[37] overall, but contains multiple ionized sites; see Figure 12-25.

An important aspect of peptide bond formation that we did not discuss in Chapter 7 is that most of the ionizable groups of the original amino acids are lost upon peptide bond formation. For instance, once the amine has reacted to form an amide, the lone pair of electrons on the nitrogen becomes unavailable for ionization due to delocalization; see resonance of the amide in Figure 12-26. While most amines are basic, amides are not. More obviously, perhaps, the formation of a peptide bond also causes the carboxylic acid group of the amino acid to lose its ability to serve as an acid, the acidic hydrogen is expelled as part of a water molecule during peptide bond formation.[38]

Figure 12-26. Resonance of an amide minimizes the presence of the lone pair of electrons on the nitrogen atom, making this nitrogen atom much less basic (unable to make a new bond to H+).

---

[36] We show it on the blue nitrogen atom in the reactant.

[37] Zwitterions can carry a net charge if, for instance, there are three ionized groups.

[38] This reaction is detailed in Figure 7-12.

Thus, by the time a protein is built from its component amino acids, the only ionizable groups remaining are those on ionizable side chains and the N-terminal amine group and the C-terminal **carboxylate** group[39]. Table 12-7 identifies several amino acids as "ionizable." Figure 12-27 shows these amino acid side chains in their ionized forms; the basic side chains of His, Lys, and Arg have picked up an H⁺ (utilizing a nitrogen atom lone pair of electrons) and the carboxylic acid side chains of Asp and Glu have

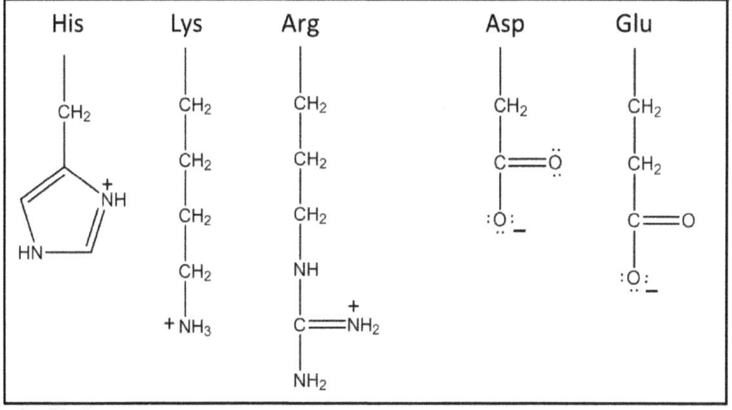

Figure 12-27. The ionizable amino acid side chains in their ionized forms. The bases (His, Lys, Arg) have picked up an additional proton on a nitrogen atom. The acids, Asp and Glu, have lost a proton from the carboxylic acid group. All of these except lysine have resonance structures available.

lost an H⁺. Compare the structures in Table 12-8 to those in Figure 12-27. These acid and base groups are predominantly in their charged forms at biological pH's.[40]

Protein molecules, then, carry far fewer charged groups than the unreacted set of amino acids from which they come. The charged groups on the surface of myoglobin in Figure 12-23, come from the ionization of acidic and basic sidechains. Acidic side chains become negatively charged (shown in red in Figure 12-23, the conjugate base structure) and basic side chains become positively charged (shown in blue, the conjugate acid structure). Thus these hydrophilic groups play a role in the hydrophobic effect that encourages folding, as discussed in the previous section.

As we mentioned at the beginning of this section, **salt bridges** (the attraction of a negatively charged protein site with a positively charged protein site) help to stabilize some tertiary structures. These attractions are much weaker than the ionic bonding attractions that we studied in Chapter 6. The lattice energies for the formation of solid ionic networks from *gas-phase ions* are variable, but large. Now, in Chapter 12, we run into ion-ion attractions again, but this time we are in an *aqueous system* (the cell!) and the attractions are much weaker because of the competition with attractions to the very polar water molecule. Gas-phase ions (Chapter 6) are very unstable; they quickly find one another and deposit as a solid. However, as we know, many solid ionic networks are unstable in an aqueous environment—they dissolve! In an aqueous environment we cannot expect the +/– attractions to be as strong as in the gas phase. Aqueous ions can be stabilized by interactions with water molecules instead of interactions with each other, thus they are attracted less strongly to each other.

Nonetheless, the attraction of a negative charge on one stretch of protein polymer with a positive charge on a nearby stretch can help to stabilize the folded structure. Note that the attractive force of any *salt bridge* will be maximized if it occurs in the interior of a globular protein. Any individual ion is reasonably stable on the globule's surface, where water molecules can easily interact with it. However, in the "greasy" hydrophobic interior, any individual ion may be unable to attract a suitable counter ion. Without such a partner it is unstabilized and lies at high energy. If it does find an ionic bonding partner in the greasy interior, the salt bridge formed will be very stable, because neither of the partner ions has any other good bonding alternatives.

---

[39] The *carboxylic acid* group –CO₂H becomes the *carboxylate* group –CO₂⁻ once it is ionized; *-ate* is a common ending for the names of anions (compare to *acetic acid* and the *acetate ion*).

[40] We will learn more about this in Chapters 18 and 19.

Figure 12-28 shows a *salt bridge* in the interior of a globular protein. On the left, most of the protein polymer chain is stylized to simplify the picture; only the two involved amino acid side chains are shown in atomic detail. You can see the three nitrogen atoms of Arg10 side chain (blue) and the two oxygen atoms of the Glu35 side chain (red, compare to structures in Figure 12-27). Note that both side chains end in a trigonal planar geometry. Make sure that makes sense to you! These two amino acids are the 10th and 35th residues in the primary structure. The image on the right in Figure 12-28 is a space-filling rendition that more realistically portrays the crowded conditions in a folded-up protein. Backbone atoms are purple, sidechains are gray, except for Arg10 and Glu35 sidechains (you can see the blue nitrogen atoms of Arg and the red oxygen atoms of Glu).

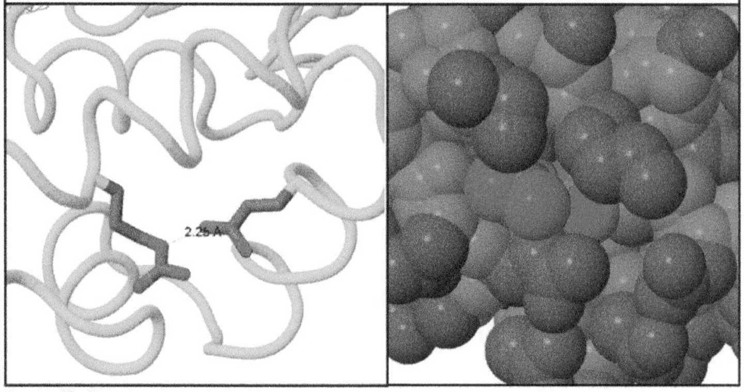

Figure 12-28. Two views of a *salt bridge* in phage repressor 434. The two ions come from the side chains of Arg10 and Glu35. **Left:** Simplified view showing that the salt bridge connects two α-helices. **Right:** Space-filling view of the same salt bridge.

C. Quaternary Structures

The final "level" of protein structure, called **quaternary structure**, exists when multiple protein chains come together into a single working mega-molecule. Not all proteins have quaternary structure; myoglobin, for example, is comprised of just one protein chain and this makes quaternary structure impossible. Hemoglobin (Figure 12-29) is an example of a working protein that makes use of quaternary structure. Four globin protein chains (each one a different color in the figure) fold up independently and then associate into the tetrameric working molecule. We described hemoglobin, in Chapter 7, as a polymer of polymers, but did not explore the types of attractions involved in the association of independent subunits beyond classifying them as relatively weak attractions. These attractions commonly include hydrophobic interactions, hydrogen bonding, dispersion forces and salt bridges. The most important force for the generation of quaternary structures is usually the hydrophobic effect. Any potential hydrogen bonding sites or ionized sites on the surfaces of a subunit are easily stabilized by interactions with water molecules, so they do not become a lot more stable upon association with another protein chain. However, any hydrophobic patches on the surface of subunits will tend to be pushed against one another via the

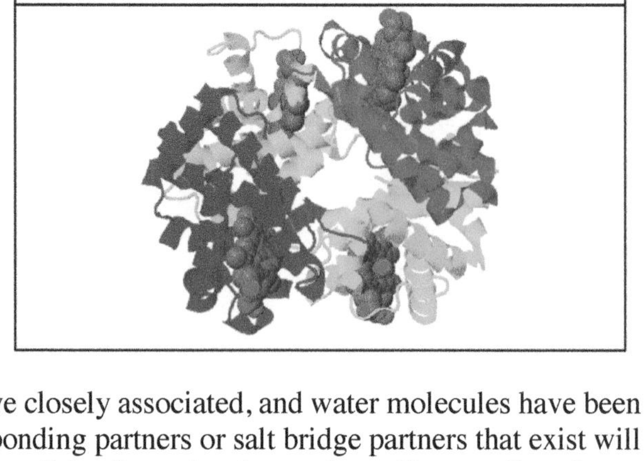

Figure 12-29. The quaternary structure of hemoglobin. Each colored polymer ribbon is a distinct protein chain. Each working hemoglobin molecule has a tetrameric subunit structure.

surrounding water molecules. Once subunits have closely associated, and water molecules have been expelled from the contact region, any hydrogen bonding partners or salt bridge partners that exist will provide a stabilizing influence over and above that of the dispersion forces that will naturally exist when atoms of the two subunits are snuggled next to one another.

12-6. PHOSPHOLIPIDS AND BIOLOGICAL MEMBRANES

Every living cell is surrounded by a cell membrane. Additionally, the **organelles** within a cell (nucleus, golgi body, mitochondria, peroxisomes, vacuoles, etc.) are each surrounded by a membrane. Clearly, membranes must have a very important role in life processes. This section introduces membrane structure and function in terms of fundamental chemical principles. Cell membranes are complex mixtures of a variety of components; see Figure 12-30.[41]

Figure 12-30. A cartoon of a working cell membrane, the main structure of which is a lipid bilayer. Other components include proteins and carbohydrates.

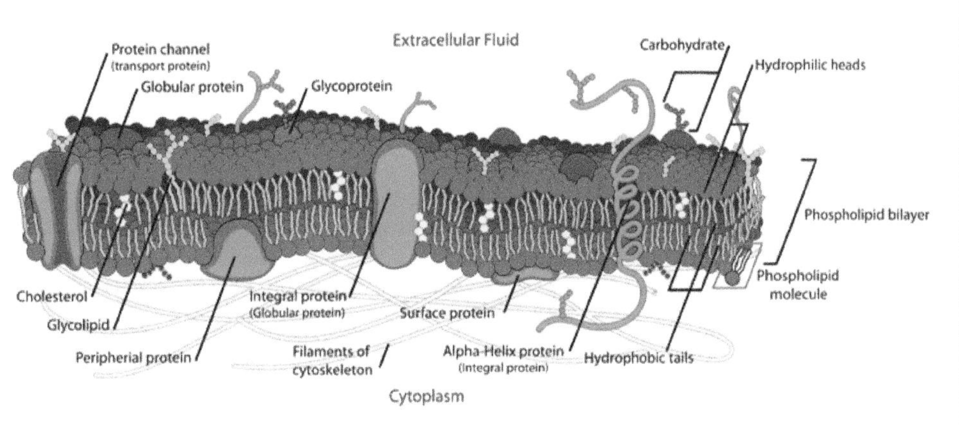

The membrane bilayer is the major structural unit of a membrane. However, much of the work of a membrane is done by molecules that are associated with the bilayer in a variety of ways. We will start our exploration by taking a close look at the molecules from which the membrane bilayer is constructed.

A. Amphiphiles

We have studied the behaviors of both soluble and essentially insoluble particles[42] in water. Soluble particles interact with surrounding water molecules via various types of weak attractions. Insoluble particles do not interact with the water molecules around them, but rather cause unfavorable arrangements of those molecules. What happens when a molecule is large enough to have both a polar region and a nonpolar region? The polar region is hydrophilic (interacts well with water molecules), while the nonpolar region is hydrophobic (water molecules avoids interacting with these regions as much as possible). Molecules and ions of this type are called **amphiphiles**; they have the characteristic of being **amphiphilic** or **amphipathic**. The prefix *amphi-* means "of both kinds."

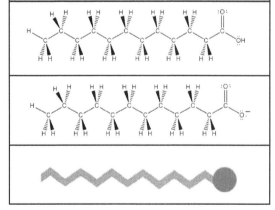

Figure 12-31. **Top:** Acidic form of a 12-carbon fatty acid. **Middle:** The anionic form of the same fatty acid. **Bottom:** A cartoon showing the polar head group (red) and the hydrophobic tail (gray).

Some of the simplest amphiphiles are detergent molecules. **Fatty acids** are an example of these. The structure of a typical *fatty acid* in both its acid form and its ionized form is shown in Figure 12-31. A typical cartoon of the structure is presented in the bottom pane of the figure. There

---

[41] "Cell membrane detailed diagram en" by LadyofHats Mariana Ruiz - Own work. Licensed under Public Domain via Wikimedia Commons http://commons.wikimedia.org/wiki/File:Cell_membrane_detailed_diagram_en. svg#/media/File:Cell_membrane_detailed_diagram_en.svg.

[42] The word "particle" is used when one wishes to include atoms, ions and molecules in the discussion.

are two naming systems for molecules of this type: common names and systematic names. Acet*ic* acid (CH_3CO_2H) and the acet*ate* ion ($CH_3CO_2^-$) are the common names for 2-carbon version of these structures. With the much longer carbon-12 version, we have the common names laur*ic* acid and the laur*ate* ion. Notice the consistent use of *–ic* endings (for the acids) and *–ate* endings (for the ions).[43]

Molecules or ions of these types have a polar region (the carboxylic acid/carboxylate group) and a non-polar region (the hydrocarbon chain). The polar end is often called the **polar head group** and the non-polar region is often referred to as the **hydrophobic tail**.

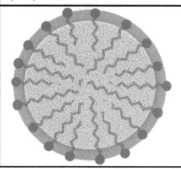

Figure 12-32. Two-dimensional view of a spherical micelle. The outer layer is comprised of polar head groups, the interior is hydrophobic.

The hydrophobic effect plays a huge role in what happens to detergent molecules in water. For relatively small detergent molecules, the super-structure created is called a micelle; see Figure 12-32. In order to avoid contact with hydrophobic regions of the amphiphile, water molecules push the hydrophobic regions together into a globule. The outer surface of this globule is lined with the polar head groups, so water molecules end up interacting only with hydrophilic regions of the amphiphile. The spherical micelle can solubilize greasy dirt, thus the prevalence of these types of molecules in soaps and detergents. Any hydrophobic species stirred into an aqueous solution of detergent micelles will prefer to move into the interior of the micelle, and thus be stabilized in the aqueous solution and flushed down the drain; see Figure 12-33.

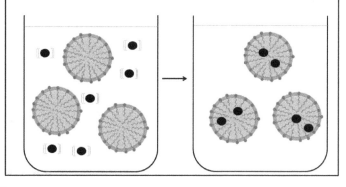

Figure 12-33. Left: Detergent micelles and greasy dirt in water. Brackets indicate poor solvent-solute interactions. **Right:** The greasy dirt dissolves better in the hydrophobic environment of the interior of the micelle. The micelle stabilizes the hydrophobic material in solution.

B. Phospholipids

Phospholipids are more complex amphiphiles than the simple fatty acids. Each phospholipid molecule is constructed from 5 smaller species using covalent bonds: a glycerol molecule, a phosphate ion, two fatty acid molecules, and one polar **alcohol**[44] molecule. The structure of a typical phospholipid molecule is shown in Figure 12-34;[45] here the polar alcohol molecule is ethanolamine ($HOCH_2CH_2NH_3^+$). Note that phospholipid molecules are often

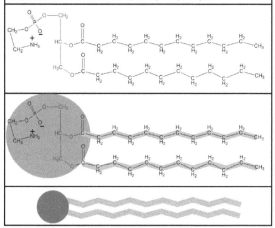

Figure 12-34. Top: the structure of one possible phospholipid. The glycerol backbone is in blue. **Middle:** The polar head group (red) and the hydrophobic tails (gray). **Bottom:** A cartoon rendition of a phospholipid.

[43] The systematic names of these species also use –ic and –ate endings. Acetic acid = ethanoic acid; acetate ion = ethanoate ion; lauric acid = dodecanoic acid; laurate ion = dodecanoate ion.

[44] "Alcohol" molecules contain one or more –OH groups, such as methanol: CH_3OH. Because the O-H bond is polar, alcohol molecules tend to be polar.

[45] You should compare this to the structure of a triacylglyceride (fat or oil) from Chapter 11. The glycerol backbone and fatty acid portions are the same (but now we use two fatty acids instead of three).

zwitterions, having both a positive and negative charge in the polar head group. Individual phospholipid molecules differ from one another by the identity of the polar alcohol and by the large assortment of different fatty acids that may be used, both **saturated** and unsaturated.

The cartoon of a phospholipid is similar to the cartoon of a detergent molecule. One difference is that there is a much more complicated structure within the polar head group. Another difference is the number of hydrophobic tails, two instead of just one. This makes the hydrophobic region of this amphiphile a lot bulkier than that of a detergent. While the polar head group is also larger than that of the case pictured in Figure 12-34, a positive nitrogen atom tends to curl back to the negative oxygen thus making the area taken up by the polar head group smaller than expected. These structural characteristics leave us with an amphiphile that cannot form micelles in water; the tails are too bulky, making it impossible for the head groups to adequately coat the surface of the globule.

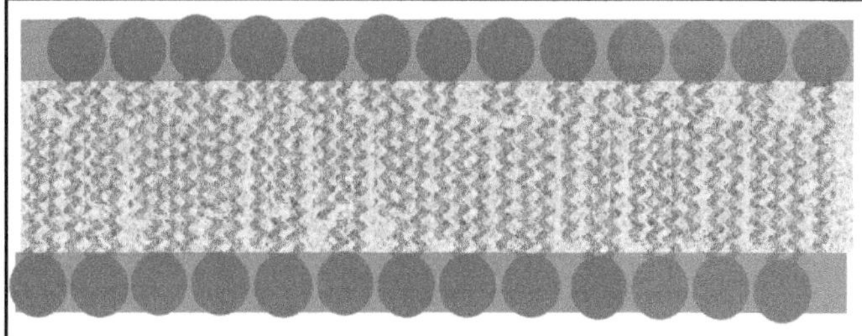

Instead of micelles, phospholipids tend to form **bilayers** in aqueous solution; see Figure 12-35. These structures are called <u>bi</u>-layers because there are <u>two</u> layers of phospholipid. Lipid bilayers form via the **self-assembly** of the individual phospholipid molecules, driven by the hydrophobic effect. There are only weak forces holding neighboring lipid molecules to each other. One layer of

Figure 12-35. A lipid bilayer. Water molecules do not interact with the hydrophobic tails.

the bilayer (maybe the top in Figure 12-35) faces out of the cell and the other layer (bottom in Figure 12-35) faces the interior of the cell. As a bilayer reaches large enough dimensions, it can **self-seal** into a spherical, membrane-like system called a **vesicle**; see Figure 12-36. Picture a water balloon floating in a swimming pool, the latex of the balloon is playing the role of "bilayer" by separating the interior solution from the exterior solution. Notice that vesicle formation eliminates the need for any water molecules to interact with the hydrophobic interior of the membrane. Remember, even though it's called <u>self</u>-assembly and <u>self</u>-sealing, these processes are driven by the surrounding bulk water, not by the amphiphiles themselves.

Bilayer structures are not polymeric; there are no covalent bonds connecting individual phospholipid molecules to their neighbors. Individual lipid molecules in a bilayer system can travel independently within their half (**outer leaf** or **inner leaf**) of the bilayer. It is difficult for an individual lipid molecule to be able to move from one leaf to the other (this is called a **trans bilayer movement**, or a **flip-flop**) because this would require the polar head group (red) to move through the hydrophobic interior (gray) of the bilayer, and polar groups prefer to be in **hydrophilic**[46] environnments. In a biological membrane the two leafs of a membrane are able to have different compositions of the various phospholipids. This would not be possible if individual molecules could easily flip-flop to the other leaf. If flip-flops were easy, the compositions of the two leafs would equalize (equilibrate) over time.

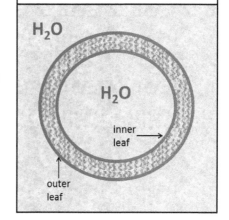

Figure 12-36. A sealed bilayer can sequester one aqueous solution from another. A sealed bilayer created in the lab is called a *vesicle*.

H_2O

H_2O

inner leaf

outer leaf

C. Membrane Functions

What is the purpose of a membrane? There are many answers to this question, depending on the particular membrane, but we can generalize to cover many bases here.

---

[46] water-loving

1. Membranes create compartments that keep two solutions from mixing.

Membranes are the beakers of living systems. Why is this important? Imagine an amoeba in a pond. Its cell membrane defines the organism's <u>self</u> as opposed to its <u>environment</u>. Additionally, its cell membrane keeps unwanted molecules out of the <u>self</u> while allowing desired molecules to enter.

Different cell organelles have different functions. For instance, ribosomes synthesize proteins and lysosomes digest (break-down) a variety of no longer needed molecules, including proteins. Clearly, it doesn't make sense to synthesize new molecules in the same environment that might break them right back down. The organelle membranes sequester these activities, similar to how a scientist would use separate beakers.

Finally, membranes allow the use of **concentration gradients** as biological energy sources. Many cells actively pump sodium ions, Na^+, across the membrane and out of the cell. With the Na^+ concentration high outside and low inside, we say that we have a *concentration gradient* across the membrane. Because there is a natural drive to equalize concentrations, a concentration gradient amounts to an energy source. The membrane can control the re-entry of Na^+, perhaps requiring that it carry some other needed component with it as it re-crosses the membrane. Thus concentration gradients power some of the work of the cell.

2. Membranes can be used to keep an organelle to a reasonable size.

This is very much the case for mitochondria; see Figure 12-37. This energy harvesting organelle requires an expansive membrane to accomplish the task. On the other hand, the requirements for dissolved contents within that very large membrane are relatively small. In Figure 12-37, we see that in order to save space, the working membrane of the mitochondrion (brown) is enclosed by an outer membrane (orange) that has a much smaller surface area. Imagine stuffing a large under-inflated balloon into a small balloon! The work of the mitochondrion is primarily accomplished by components of the inner membrane and its contents, the **mitochondrial matrix** (blue). An important part of the job of the outer membrane is to contain the organelle to a reasonably compact size.

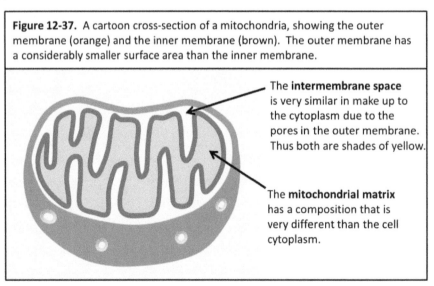

Figure 12-37. A cartoon cross-section of a mitochondria, showing the outer membrane (orange) and the inner membrane (brown). The outer membrane has a considerably smaller surface area than the inner membrane.

The **intermembrane space** is very similar in make up to the cytoplasm due to the pores in the outer membrane. Thus both are shades of yellow.

The **mitochondrial matrix** has a composition that is very different than the cell cytoplasm.

3. Cell membranes allow communication with the outside environment

The chemical make-up (especially the sugar residue sequences) on the surface of the outer bilayer leaf identifies the type of cell present. This is similar to putting labels on beakers.

4. Cell membranes enable cell propagation

Cell membranes enable cell propagation via the pinching off of one cell membrane to obtain two cells. The fluidity of the bilayer is essential in this process. Additionally, no covalent bonds have to be broken in order to turn one bilayer into two independent bilayers.

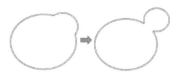

D. Membrane Proteins

It is important to understand that most of the work of a membrane is accomplished by membrane-associated proteins, not by phospholipid molecules. Membrane-spanning proteins determine which ions and molecules can get into and out of a membrane. They can do this either in an active fashion (as pumps that utilize an energy source) or in a passive fashion (as pores that allow diffusion).

A cartoon of a section of working cell membrane is found in Figure 12-38.[47] Scientists think about membranes in terms of the so-called **fluid mosaic model**. Membrane molecules including lipids and proteins "float" in the bilayer and can diffuse throughout the area of the membrane. Consider membrane-spanning proteins, such as the blue globular protein near the middle of Figure 12-38 and the protein channel on the left. After a little time, these proteins will be found in different positions in the membrane. In some cases multiple membrane-associated proteins must associate with one another in the membrane in order to do their jobs. The ability to diffuse throughout the bilayer is important in order that binding partners be located.

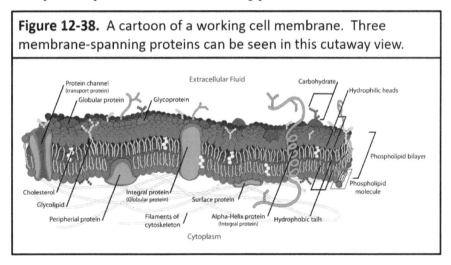

Figure 12-38. A cartoon of a working cell membrane. Three membrane-spanning proteins can be seen in this cutaway view.

Should the surface features of a membrane-spanning protein be hydrophilic or hydrophobic? Water-soluble globular proteins have hydrophilic surfaces, as we discussed earlier. As seen in Figure 12-38, some of the membrane-spanning protein's outer surface must interact with the hydrophobic portion of the membrane rather than the aqueous system on either side of the membrane. Because a membrane's hydrophobic interior is about 30 Å thick, a membrane-spanning protein must have a hydrophobic "belt" on its surface that is about that wide.

1. Channels

Let's consider, again, the smaller *outer* membrane of a mitochondrion (orange bilayer in Figure 12-37). We said, earlier, that a major part of its job is to confine the much larger inner membrane to a reasonable volume. Additionally, it is part of the job of the outer membrane to be

---

[47] "Cell membrane detailed diagram en" by LadyofHats Mariana Ruiz - Own work. Licensed under Public Domain via Wikimedia Commons http://commons.wikimedia.org/wiki/File:Cell_membrane_detailed_diagram_en.svg#/media/File:Cell_membrane_detailed_diagram_en.svg.

more **permeable**[48] than most membranes. Most membranes carefully police which molecules (sugars, amino acids, metabolites, etc.) can move across. The outer mitochondrial membrane, however, is well-stocked with a class of proteins called **porins** that allow "small" molecules (anything up to about 5000 g/mol!) to diffuse across the membrane. This means that, as far as small molecules go, the volume between the two mitochondrial membranes contains the same array of molecules at the same concentrations as the cell **cytoplasm**, the complex gel-like solution making up most of the cell contents.

On the other hand, the outer membrane must block the movement of many larger molecules. For instance, it is essential that the protein, **cytochrome c**, not be able to cross the outer membrane. Cytochrome c is a small protein (about 12,000 g/mol) that travels along the *outer* surface of the *inner* membrane. In the case that it loses contact with the inner membrane, it is important that it not be able to escape into the cytoplasm. The outer membrane does not let cytochrome c get across, thus encouraging it to re-engage with the surface of the inner membrane.

Figure 12-39. Two views of membrane-associated porin molecules. **Left:** A porin molecule sitting in a lipid bilayer. **Right:** Four porin molecules viewed from outside of the membrane.

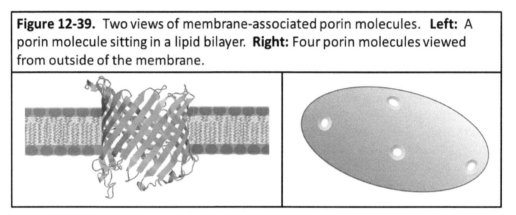

Figure 12-39 introduces the structural features of a typical porin. Many channel-like proteins have what is called a **β-barrel** structural **motif**.[49] We see β-strands associated into a hollow, barrel-like tertiary structure. The diameter of the pore is defined by the number of β-strands involved in the barrel-like structure. Basically, the porin protein produces a hole (a pore) in the bilayer of the membrane, as seen in the right-hand image of Figure 12-39. Whereas a typical soluble globular protein is hydrophobic on the interior and hydrophilic on the exterior surface, porins are essentially the opposite. Polar amino acid groups line the pore side of the barrel while hydrophobic amino acid side chains form a hydrophobic belt along the exterior surface, allowing the porin to sit in the membrane environment.

Channels, such as those created by the porin-class of proteins, allow simple diffusion to occur across a membrane for molecules that are otherwise too polar to pass through. Channels allow molecules to attain <u>equal concentrations</u> across the membrane. The next section introduces proteins that we think of as pumps. These are the ones that can, for instance, create a concentration gradient across a membrane.

2. Pumps

A concentration gradient is an unstable (and therefore, high energy) situation. There is a natural driving force to equalize concentrations. Consider pouring a solution of blue food color into a pot of water and stirring[50] until the new, diluted solution is homogeneous and a much lighter blue. What are the odds that at some moment you find that the blue dye molecules have re-congregated into a small, dark blue portion of the pot of water? Basically, what are the odds that the stirring has been

---

[48] Permeability is the characteristic of allowing the passage of other molecules from one side to the other.

[49] A "motif" is a distinctive and recurring form or structure.

[50] We could wait for diffusion to occur, the result would be the same as with stirring. Stirring is only an aid to speed up the very natural process.

un-done? As you might guess, because you've never witness this occurring, the odds are astronomically set against it. So we know that concentration gradients are not favored by nature.

Living cells produce concentration gradients as a way to store energy; the gradient is a high energy situation that can be used to drive certain processes. How does a cell produce a concentration gradient? Because the gradient is a high energy situation, it will take an energy input to make it happen. Normal cell membranes incorporate a substantial amount of a membrane-spanning protein called **sodium-potassium adenosine triphosphatase** (in symbols: **Na^+-K^+ ATPase**). The name of this protein clues us in on some aspects of its function. The protein "acts" on sodium and potassium ions. Specifically, it moves them across the cell membrane. Additionally, the protein requires ATP as an energy source, and enzyme action results in the hydrolysis of the ATP. Na^+-K^+ ATPase is an energy-requiring pump for sodium and potassium ions; it creates and maintains their concentration gradients.

Typically, concentration gradients exist across the cell membrane for both sodium (Na^+) and potassium ions (K^+). The sodium ion concentration is higher outside the cell and the potassium ion concentration is higher inside the cell. You can see a sodium ion gradient in the box, below. Cell membranes also maintain a **charge gradient** such that there is overall more (+) charge outside the cell and more (−) charge inside the cell. This helps in the establishment of the potassium ion gradient because K^+ ions will, quite naturally, want to flow to the side of the membrane containing more negative charge, even if its own concentration there is relatively high. However, moving sodium ion out of the cell is an extremely difficult task, because its concentration is already higher out there, plus there is already excess positive charge out there.

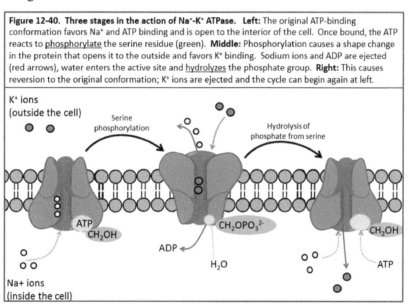

Figure 12-40. Three stages in the action of Na^+-K^+ ATPase. Left: The original ATP-binding conformation favors Na^+ and ATP binding and is open to the interior of the cell. Once bound, the ATP reacts to <u>phosphorylate</u> the serine residue (green). **Middle:** Phosphorylation causes a shape change in the protein that opens it to the outside and favors K^+ binding. Sodium ions and ADP are ejected (red arrows), water enters the active site and <u>hydrolyzes</u> the phosphate group. **Right:** This causes reversion to the original conformation; K^+ ions are ejected and the cycle can begin again at left.

Figure 12-40 shows an artist's rendition of the pumping process. Each of the three images of the protein in Figure 12-40 shows a different stage in the pumping process. Let's consider the steps that need to occur to move Na^+ ions out and K^+ ions in.

1. In the left-most protein cartoon in Figure 12-40, we see the protein in a conformation (shape) that is open to the interior of the cell (the cytoplasm, below the membrane) and closed to the exterior (extracellular fluid, above the membrane). This conformation allows the binding of

ATP (see structure of ATP in Figure 12-41) to an **intracellular**[51] site and also has three sites that are just the right size for the chelation of Na^+ by amino acid side chain groups.

2. With 3 Na^+ bound, a chemical reaction between the ATP molecule and a serine side chain of the protein (green, Figure 12-40) becomes favorable. The result of the chemical reaction is that the terminal phosphate of the ATP molecule becomes covalently bonded to the side chain oxygen of the serine residue. See Figure 12-40, noting the transition from the left-most cartoon to the middle cartoon labeled "serine phosphorylation." Adding a phosphate group to a molecule is called **phosphorylation**.

Figure 12-41. Top: The structure of ATP. Bottom: An abbreviated structure (emphasizing the triphosphate portion of ATP) used in Figure 12-42 in order to simplify things a bit.

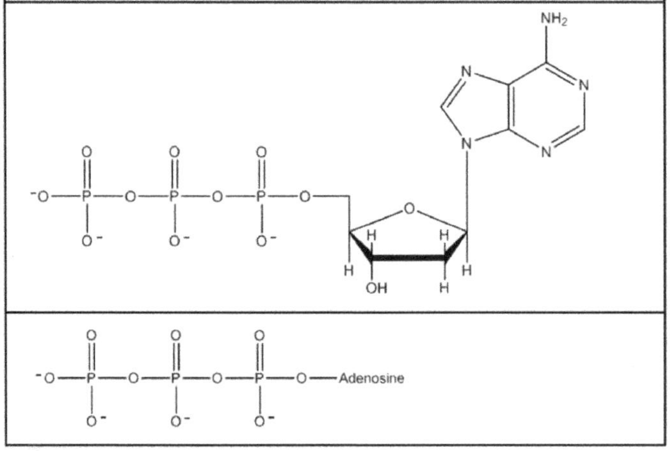

Details of the phosphorylation reaction are shown in Figure 12-42. The transferred atoms are in blue. Note that both the atoms and the overall charge are are the same in the reactants and the products (–4 on the left and –4 on the right). This is the hallmark of all balanced reaction equations regardless of the level of complexity of the reaction.

Figure 12-42. Phosphorylation. A lone pair of electrons on the serine oxygen makes a new bond to the third phosphorus atom of ATP (blue arrow). ADP is expelled, taking a bonding pair of electrons (red arrow) with it. The third phosphate group is now bonded to the serine side chain. The serine side chain replenishes its missing lone pair by allowing the H^+ ion to leave (green arrow). Note that the uncharged serine side chain becomes highly negatively charged.

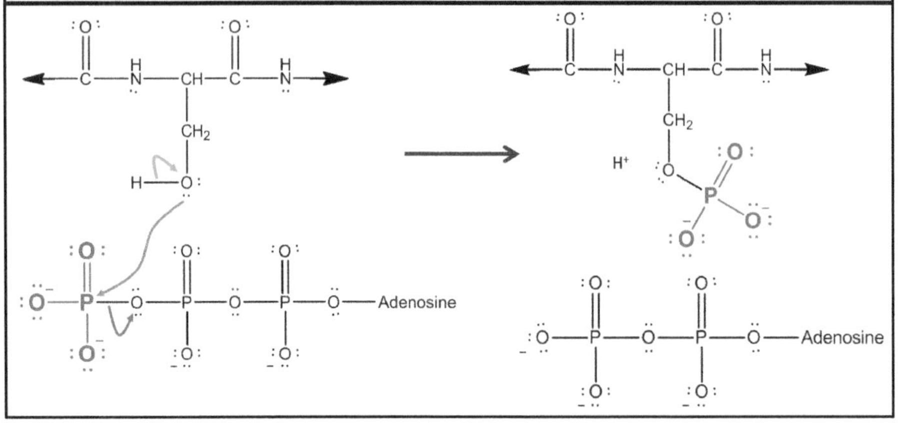

3. The change in the serine side chain from uncharged to highly negative causes an adjustment in the protein conformation. See the middle cartoon in Figure 12-40. The protein is now open to the extracellular side of the membrane and it no longer offers binding sites fitting the geometry of sodium ions, so the 3 Na^+ are ejected to the extracellular fluid. This step *increases the sodium ion concentration gradient*. ADP is released into the cytosol.

4. Ejection of the sodium ions makes room for the now favorable chelation of two potassium ions. The preference for potassium ions over sodium ions at this point is due to the new

---

[51] Intracellular means "inside" the cell; remember that "intramural" means inside the institution!

geometry of the binding site and the larger size of the potassium ions. Ejection of the ADP allows water to enter the active site. See the middle cartoon in Figure 12-40.

5. With potassium ions bound and water in the active site, another reaction at the site of the phosphorylated serine residues occurs; see the transition from the middle to right hand cartoons in Figure 12-40. This time, the phosphate group on the serine residue is **hydrolyzed** (removed via reaction with a water molecule). Details of the hydrolysis are shown in Figure 12-43. The serine residue is regenerated in its original form and a hydrogen phosphate ion is liberated into the cytosol.

6. The protein now converts back to its original conformation due to the lack of charge on the serine residue. This re-opens the protein to the interior of the cell, and *expels the bound potassium ions, thus increasing their concentration gradient.* (This is the conformation that prefers the smaller sodium ions.) The cycle can begin again.

Figure 12-43. Hydrolysis. The removal of the phosphate group from the serine side chain. A lone pair of electrons on a water molecule forms a new bond with the phosphorus atom of the phosphate group (blue arrow). The bonding pair between the phosphate and the serine oxygen is used to pick up a new H^+ ion for the serine side chain (green arrow). The missing lone pair on water's oxygen atom is replaced by loss of a hydrogen ion (red arrow). The original serine residue is regenerated along with a hydrogen phosphate ion, HPO_4^{2-}.

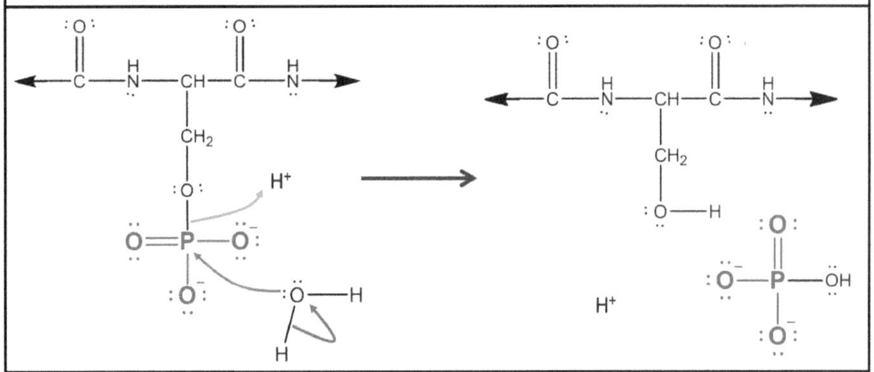

This section of the chapter has attempted to help you understand how a membrane can build a concentration gradient by using the chemical energy inherent in the relatively unstable ATP molecule.[52] We say that the hydrolysis of the ATP molecule is **coupled** to the transport of the ions across the membrane; each process requires the other. Inspection of Figures 12-42 and 12-43 will convince you that the ATP molecule is never <u>directly</u> hydrolyzed; ATP never reacts with water. Nonetheless, the overall reaction equation catalyzed by Na^+-K^+ ATPase could be written as:

$$3\ Na^+ \text{ (inside)} + 2\ K^+ \text{ (outside)} + ATP^{4-} \text{ (aq)} + H_2O(\ell) \longrightarrow$$

$$3\ Na^+(\text{outside}) + 2\ K^+(\text{inside}) + ADP^{3-} + HPO_4^{2-} + H^+$$

Part of this overall process (blue) amounts to the hydrolysis of ATP:

$$ATP^{4-} \text{ (aq)} + H_2O(\ell) \longrightarrow ADP^{3-} + HPO_4^{2-} + H+$$

Savvy biochemists know that the coupling of the processes means that things are not as simple as they might appear. In this case, the terminal phosphate of ATP spent some time bonded to a serine side chain of the protein. Because the protein starts and ends a cycle without any bonding changes, it doesn't appear in the balanced reaction equation. In general, catalysts (such as Na^+-K^+ ATPase) do not appear in balanced reaction equations because they are regenerated in their original form during the reaction process.

---

[52] If it didn't want to react according to Figures 12-42 and 12-43, we would have a problem!

In sections 12-5 and 12-6 of the chapter we have seen how weak attractive forces such as dispersion forces, hydrogen bonds, and ionic interactions help proteins achieve their active conformations. In addition we have introduced another weak interaction, called the hydrophobic effect, which is an important player whenever non-polar species or amphipathic species find themselves in aqueous environments. We have seen how some of these same types of interactions are responsible for the formation and stability of membrane bilayers and for the ability of proteins to associate with the bilayer. Finally, we explored a variety of membrane-associated functions in living cells.

CHAPTER 12 PROBLEMS

1. Give the correct classification (solution, heterogeneous mixture, element, or chemical compound):

    a. Table sugar (sucrose)   d. Ammonium chloride
    b. Lemonade (with pulp)   e. Steel
    c. Sulfur   f. Fizzing soda pop

2. Give the correct classification (solution, heterogeneous mixture, element, or chemical compound):

    a. Sugar dissolved in water   d. Sodium bromide
    b. Aspirin (the molecule, not the pill)   e. Orange juice (unfiltered)
    c. Bronze   f. Air

3. Give the correct classification (solution, heterogeneous mixture, element, or chemical compound):

    a. Gasoline   d. Baking soda (sodium bicarbonate)
    b. Copper   e. Nordic gold
    c. Gravy   f. Sample removed from Ganges River

4. Give the correct classification (solution, heterogeneous mixture, element, or chemical compound):

    a. Black ink   d. Potting soil
    b. Filtered coffee   e. Calcium carbonate
    c. Diamond   f. Salsa

5. Calculate the mass percent of each of the following:

    a. oxygen in SO_2 c. carbon in caffeine ($C_8H_{10}N_4O_2$)
    b. Al in aluminum chloride   d. hydrogen in caffeine ($C_8H_{10}N_4O_2$)

6. What is the mass percent NaCl in each of the following mixtures?

    a. 10.0 g NaCl in 120 g water
    b. 0.50 g NaCl and 1.50 g sugar
    c. 10.0 g NaCl, 10.0 g KI in 120. g water
    d. 2.55 g NaCl, 4.10 g buckyballs, 3.82 g sand

7. Draw pictures to show each of the following.

    a. a hydrogen bond between a sulfate ion and a water molecule
    b. a hydrogen bond between a hydrogencarbonate ion and a water molecule
    c. same as part b, but switch the donor/acceptor roles.

8. Draw an octahedral hydration cage around a chloride ion. Are the interactions primarily due to hydrogen bonds, dipole-dipole attractions, dipole-ion attractions or dispersion forces?

9.   Write dissolution reaction equations in an "ionic" form for each of the following soluble salts.

    a.   KOH   **d.** $Sc(NO_3)_3$

    b. NH_4Cl **e.** $Fe(C_2H_3O_2)_2$

    c. $Na_2Cr_2O_7$ **f.** $Al_2(SO_4)_3$

10.   Write dissolution reaction equations in an "ionic" form for each of the following essentially insoluble salts.

    a.   silver chromate   **d.**   manganese(IV) sulfide

    b. $AlPO_4$ **e.** Hg_2Cl_2

    c. $Fe(OH)_2$ **f.** $CoCO_3$

11.   Write dissolution reaction equations in an "ionic" form for each of the following salts. Use a table of solubility rules to decide which arrow to use.

    a. $BaSO_4$ **d.**   potassium sulfide

    b. $Ni_3(PO_4)_2$ **e.**   mercury(II) perchlorate

    c. $LiOH$ **f.** $Mn_3(PO_4)_4$

12.   Write ionization reaction equations for each of the following acids or bases. Remember to consider the charges on ions!

    a. N_2H_4 **d.**   HI

    b. $HClO_4$ **e.** C_5H_5N

    c. $HC_2H_3O_2$ **f.** H_3PO_4 (remove only one hydrogen)

13.   Label each species as a strong, weak, or nonelectrolyte when dissolved in water and write an appropriate dissolution or ionization reaction equation for each one. Formulas are written such that leading H atoms are acidic. If there are diprotic or triprotic acids, remove only one hydrogen atom.

    a. C_3H_6O (acetone)   **f.** NH_3

    b. $AgNO_3$ **g.** $H_2C_2O_4$

    c.   HCN   **h.** $C_3H_8O_3$ (glycerol)

    d.   KCl   **i.**   NaOH

    e. $C_6H_{12}O_6$ (glucose)   **j.** H_2SO_4

14.   Add curved arrows to show how the electrons rearrange as the ionization reaction between the two molecules takes place. What are the Lewis dot structures of the products?

    a. 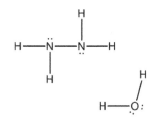   **b.**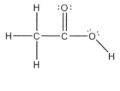

15.   Sodium chloride (2.375 g) is dissolved in water and diluted to a final volume of 500.0 mL. What is the molarity of the resulting solution?

16. Potassium nitrate (1.026 g) is dissolved in water and diluted to a final volume of 250.0 mL. What is the molarity of the resulting solution?

17. How many moles of bromide ions are in 10.00 mL of a 0.265 M solution of lithium bromide? How many mmols? How many μmols?

18. How many mmols of perchlorate ions are in 25.00 mL of a 0.4445 M solution of ammonium perchlorate?

19. Sodium dichromate ($Na_2Cr_2O_7$, 1.5729 g) was dissolved in water and diluted to the mark in a 500. mL volumetric flask. In the resulting solution what are the concentrations of:

    a. Sodium dichromate   **b.** Sodium ions   **c.** Dichromate ions

20. Ammonium phosphate, $(NH_4)_3PO_4$, (0.4103 g) was dissolved in water and diluted to the mark in a 250. mL volumetric flask. In the resulting solution what are the concentrations of:

    a. Ammonium phosphate   **b.** Ammonium ions   **c.** Phosphate ions

21. What mass of sodium sulfite (Na_2SO_3) is necessary to prepare 250.0 mL of a solution that is 0.125 M in sodium ion concentration?

22. Describe how you would prepare 1.00 L of 0.250 M ammonium dichromate from solid ammonium dichromate using any appropriate glassware.

23. Describe how you would prepare 0.500 L of 0.150 M sodium hydrogen carbonate from solid sodium hydrogen carbonate using any appropriate glassware.

24. It is necessary to prepare 250.0 mL of a 0.100 M sodium thiosulfate ($Na_2S_2O_3$) solution from solid sodium thiosulfate, using any appropriate glassware. What mass of sodium thiosulfate would be needed, and what procedure would you follow in preparing this solution?

25. It is necessary to prepare 500.0 mL of a potassium sulfite solution having a potassium ion concentration of 0.200 M. What mass of potassium sulfite would be needed, and what procedure would you follow in preparing this solution?

26. A 25.00 mL aliquot (portion) of 0.500 M $CaCl_2$ is diluted to a final volume of 0.500 L. What are the concentrations of calcium and chloride ions in the final solution?

27. **a.** A 10.00 mL aliquot of 0.350 M Na_3PO_4 is diluted to a final volume of 250.0 mL. What are the concentrations of sodium and phosphate ions in the final solution?

    b. What volume of 0.250 M NaCl is necessary to prepare 500.0 mL of 0.110 M solution?

28. Suppose you had a flask containing 1.0 L of 0.9000 M potassium chloride. How would you prepare 250.0 mL of a solution of KCl of concentration 0.3600 M? (Assume that you have the necessary glassware to measure out volumes to the nearest 0.1 mL.)

29. Suppose you had a 500 mL volumetric flask containing 0.1524 M $K_2Cr_2O_7$ solution. How would you prepare 100 mL of a solution having a dichromate ion concentration of 0.0500 M? (Assume that you have the necessary glassware to measure out volumes to the nearest 0.1 mL.)

30. A solution has been prepared by dissolving 0.5000 g of potassium sulfate in water and diluting to a final volume of 500.0 mL.

   a. What are the concentrations of potassium and sulfate ions in the final solution?

   b. The solution in part a is then used to prepare 250.0 mL of a solution having a potassium ion concentration of 0.00100 M. What volume of the original solution would be needed to prepare this solution?

31. 1.000 L of a "stock" solution containing 0.8000 g of dissolved ammonium nitrate has been prepared. How would you prepare 250.0 mL of 0.00400 M ammonium nitrate using the appropriate amount of stock solution?

32. Assuming a density of 1.00 g/mL, what is the molarity of pure water?

33. Isopropanol, C_3H_8O, is commonly known as "rubbing alcohol." It has a density of 0.7581 g/mL at 20°C. What is the molarity of an isopropanol solution prepared by adding water to 10.00 mL of isopropanol until a final volume of 500.0 mL is reached at this temperature?

34. A solution of isopropanol, C_3H_8O, has a concentration of 2.50 M. A three step serial dilution with a dilution factor of 40 is performed. What is the concentration of the final solution obtained (in M and mM)?

35. A solution of formaldehyde, CH_2O, has a concentration of 0.56 M. A five step serial dilution with a concentration factor of 0.12 is performed.

   a. What volume of the stock solution must be added to a 100.0 mL volumetric flask to obtain this concentration factor (for each step)?

   b. What is the concentration of the final solution (in M, mM and µM)?

36. A 6.00 mL aliquot of 1.80 M stock solution of $CuSO_4$ is diluted to 50.0 mL. This step is repeated as per a serial dilution for a total of 4 dilutions.

   a. What is the value of the individual dilution factors?
   b. What is the value of the individual concentration factors?
   c. What is the concentration of the final solution (in M and mM)?

37. A 10.00 mL aliquot of 20.5 mM stock solution of EDTA is diluted to 150.0 mL. This step is repeated as per a serial dilution for a total of 3 dilutions.

   a. What is the value of the individual dilution factors?
   b. What is the value of the individual concentration factors?
   c. What is the concentration of the final solution (in µM)?

38. Addition of 36.88 mL of 0.2046 M HCl solution neutralized the base in a 25.00 mL sample of aqueous NaOH. What was the original concentration of the NaOH solution?

39. A 40.00 mL sample of 0.144 M HNO_3 is titrated with aqueous KOH. The equivalence point of the titration occurs when 42.33 mL of KOH solution has been added to the base. What is the concentration of the KOH solution in the buret?

40. A 20.00 mL sample of 0.108 M NaOH is titrated with aqueous HCl. The equivalence point of the titration occurs when 21.69 mL of HCl solution has been added to the base. What is the concentration of the HCl solution in the buret?

41. Oxalic acid ($H_2C_2O_4$) is a diprotic weak acid that reacts with strong base according to the reaction equation:

$$H_2C_2O_4(aq) + 2OH^-(aq) \longrightarrow C_2O_4^{2-}(aq) + 2H_2O(\ell)$$

A 25.00 mL sample of 0.212 M oxalic acid is titrated with aqueous NaOH. The equivalence point of the titration occurs when 30.46 mL of NaOH solution has been added to the acid. What is the concentration of the NaOH solution in the buret?

42. The concentration of $KMnO_4$ solutions can be determined by titrating known amounts of oxalate ion. The reaction equation for the titration is

$$5\,C_2O_4^{2-}(aq) + 2\,MnO_4^-(aq) + 16\,H^+(aq) \longrightarrow 10\,CO_2(aq) + 2\,Mn^{2+}(aq) + 8\,H_2O(\ell)$$

A 0.4076 g sample of $Na_2C_2O_4$ is dissolved in 40.0 mL of water and then is titrated with a solution of $KMnO_4$. According to the buret, 23.12 mL of the permanganate solution was used when the endpoint of the titration (unreacted, purple permanganate ions) was reached. What is the concentration of the $KMnO_4$ solution?

43. Potassium permanganate, $KMnO_4$, solutions react with oxalate ion according to this balanced reaction equation.

$$5\,C_2O_4^{2-}(aq) + 2\,MnO_4^-(aq) + 16\,H^+(aq) \longrightarrow 10\,CO_2(aq) + 2\,Mn^{2+}(aq) + 8\,H_2O(\ell)$$

If you suspect that your $KMnO_4$ solution is approximately 0.12 M, what approximate volume of the solution will be required to titrate 0.5000 g $Na_2C_2O_4$?

44. The concentration of an EDTA solution (actually $EDTA^{4-}$) can be determined by titration of magnesium ion. As we saw in Chapter 10, EDTA serves as a hexadentate ligand to divalent metal ions according to the following reaction equation:

$$EDTA^{4-}(aq) + Mg^{2+}(aq) \longrightarrow \left[Mg(EDTA) \right]^{2-}(aq)$$

An indicator that changes color in the presence/absence of free magnesium ion can be used as an equivalence point signal. A stock solution of $Mg(NO_3)_2$ (1.362 g per 2.000 L of solution) is prepared. A 20.00 mL aliquot of the stock solution is titrated with EDTA and a color change is noted when 43.46 mL of EDTA has been added. What is the concentration of the EDTA solution?

45. The water hardness (concentrations of divalent metal ions) of a tap water sample can be determined by titration with a solution of EDTA of known concentration. EDTA (actually $EDTA^{4-}$) reacts with divalent metal ions (especially Ca^{2+} and Mg^{2+}) according to this reaction equation, where M^{2+} signifies any 2+ cation:

$$EDTA^{4-}(aq) + M^{2+}(aq) \longrightarrow \left[M(EDTA) \right]^{2-}(aq)$$

If a 2.554 mM EDTA solution is used to titrate a 50.00 mL tap water sample and the indicator changes color after 27.33 mL of the titrant is used, what was the concentration of divalent metal ions in the water sample in mM units?

46.   The analysis in number 45 was completed to assess whether or not the water softener in your home was working properly. Water hardness is defined as follows, where 1 mM = 100.1 ppm (parts per million).

	ppm M^{2+}
soft	<60
moderately hard	60-120
hard	120-180
very hard	>180

What is the hardness level of the tap water from number 45 in ppm? Is the water softener working properly?

47.   Use the Beer-Lambert law to answer the following:

   a. What is the absorbance, A_λ, if 12.3% of light of a particular wavelength is absorbed?

   b. If $A_{482} = 0.25$, what percent of 482 nm light is being absorbed?

48.   At a wavelength of 620 nm, a solution has an absorbance of only 0.014 when measured in a cell having a path length of 1.00 cm. In order to obtain a more accurate measurement, the absorbance is determined again, this time using a cell having a path length of 10.00 cm. Predict the absorbance of the solution in this longer cell.

49.   A 0.264 M solution of cobalt(II) nitrate has an absorbance of 1.29 at a wavelength of 510 nm when measured in a cell having a path length of 1.00 cm. What is the molar absorptivity of cobalt(II) nitrate at this wavelength?

50.   A coordination compound of iron has formula $Fe(dtc)_3$ where *dtc* is a ligand named diethyldithiocarbamate with formula $S_2CN(C_2H_5)_2$.

$$Fe(dtc)_3 = 500.68 \frac{g}{mol} \qquad \text{Molar absorptivity } (\varepsilon_{350}) = 11,700 \frac{L}{mol \cdot cm}$$

A solution is prepared by dissolving a small amount of $Fe(dtc)_3$ in a 1.000 L flask and diluting to the mark. A sample is removed from the flask, and the absorbance of this sample in a 1.00 cm path length cell at 350 nm is found to be 0.468.

   a. Calculate the molarity of $Fe(dtc)_3$ in your solution.

   b. Calculate the original mass of $Fe(dtc)_3$ in the 1.000 L flask.

51.   **a.** You are asked to graph the absorbance of a solution vs. the path length of the solution. Draw the axes and their labels.

   b. What will the slope of the graph tell you?

   c. Will the slope of a plot be positive or negative, assuming an absorbing solution?

52.   **a.** You are asked to graph the absorbance of a solution vs. the concentration of the solution. Draw the axes and their labels.

   b. What will the slope of the graph tell you?

   c. Will the slope of a plot be positive or negative, assuming an absorbing solution?

53.   You are studying a colored solute via spectrophotometry in the lab. Your cuvette has a 1.00 cm path length and you are working at $\lambda_{max} = 452$ nm. A graph of A_{452} vs. molarity gives a linear plot with equation $y = 0.0722x - 0.0040$.

   a. What is the value of ε_{452} for the solute being studied?

   b. What is the likely color of the solutions you studied?

54. In lab, you perform a three-step serial dilution of a blue solution utilizing a dilution factor of 3.00. If the stock solution has an absorbance of 0.983, what do you expect will be the absorbance values of the three dilutions? Explain your work.

55. You complete the process of obtaining absorption readings for your dilutions from problem 54. The results are as follows:

    stock: 0.983
    dilution 1:   0.330
    dilution 2:   0.228
    dilution 3:   0.077

    What conclusion can you draw from these results?

56. Hydrogen bonding is important in stabilizing secondary structures such as α-helices and β-sheets in proteins. In which case (α-helices or β-sheets) are the hydrogen bonds linking amino acids that are farther from one another in the primary sequence of the protein? Explain.

57. What is the distinction between secondary and tertiary protein structure?

58. Why might hydrophobic interactions be a better strategy for maintaining tertiary structure than hydrogen bonding?

59. If an α-helical stretch of protein has a primary structure:

    Leu-Ile-Ala-Gly-Ile-Phe-Leu-Phe-Val-Ile-Ala-Gly-Phe-Trp-Ile-Leu-Val

    Do you expect this helix to be found on the surface or in the interior of the tertiary structure, why?

60. Explain why the zwitterion of alanine is neutral, overall, while the zwitterion of aspartic acid is likely to carry a negative charge, overall.

61. Proteins called *enzymes* catalyze (speed up) chemical reactions in cells. In order to do that, the reactant(s) (called *substrates* in this biological context) bind to specific surface sites of the enzyme. These *enzyme-substrate* binding interactions utilize many of the same types of weak bonds responsible for secondary and tertiary protein structure: hydrogen bonds, ion-ion attractions, hydrophobic interactions. Based on this information, explain why the bonding of a substrate to an enzyme often causes the release of water molecules from the enzyme surface.

62. SDS (sodium dodecylsulfate) is often used in the analysis of protein solutions via a method called electrophoresis. Look up sodium dodecylsulfate on the internet and answer the following questions:

    a. Is SDS a salt or a neutral molecule?
    b. How many carbon atoms are present in a "*dodecyl*" group?
    c. Would it be best to characterize SDS as polar, nonpolar, or amphiphilic? Explain.
    d. What is the effect of SDS on proteins in solution?
    e. What sources did you use for this investigation?

63. If membranes serve as the beakers of living systems, what is analogous to the labels on the beakers?

64.   Explain the function(s) of the outer mitochondrial membrane and describe how it performs these functions.

65.   Explain how the outer surface of a trans-membrane protein differs from the outer surface of a water-soluble protein.

66.   **a.** What is an important structural similarity between channel proteins and pump proteins?

       b. What is the most striking difference between the activities of channels and pumps?

67.   **a.** Explain why the phosphorylation of a serine side chain might cause a shift in the tertiary structure of the protein.

       b. Is a change in tertiary structure upon phosphorylation of a serine side chain more likely if the serine residue is on the exterior surface of a soluble enzyme or inside an otherwise hydrophobic binding site? Explain.

68.   The phosphorylation of serine could be categorized as a Lewis acid/Lewis base reaction. Which atom serves as the Lewis acid? Which atom serves as the Lewis base?

69.   The hydrolysis of a phosphate group on serine could be categorized as a Lewis acid/Lewis base reaction. Which atom serves as the Lewis acid? Which atom serves as the Lewis base?

CHAPTER 13: MATTER AND REACTIONS

So far in this book we have built an understanding of the structures of matter, from the electronic structure of the atom to modern views of bonding:

- Chapters 3-5 were concerned with the structures and properties of atoms;
- Chapter 6 introduced metals, salts, and molecular substances.
- Chapters 7-10 concerned various aspects of covalent bonding, from Lewis dot structures to the hybrid orbital approach to molecular orbital theory to coordinate covalent bonding.
- Chapter 11 introduced weak bonding and
- Chapter 12 extended our thinking about weak bonding to include solutions.

Physics is largely the science of energy and motion while biology is largely the science of life. In the same mode, chemistry could be described as the science of matter and its changes. There are, of course, many intersections of these sciences with one another. Physics certainly includes the study of atomic structure, and biology includes the study of chemical changes within biological systems. Nuclear reactions are often thought of as the purview of physics while chemical reactions are the purview of chemistry. In this chapter we will touch on both nuclear and chemical changes in order that the distinction between them is clear. In this chapter we also look at physical changes and biochemical reactions, in order to round out our treatment of the scope of the types of changes that matter can undergo.

13-1. CLASSIFICATION OF MATTER

An important objective shared by many sciences is the classification of phenomena into various categories. For example, an astronomer may classify stars into types based on brightness, color, temperature, or other characteristics; a biologist may classify plants and animals according to their phylum, class, and order; and a physicist classifies behaviors in terms of classical mechanics or quantum mechanics. The "fire, water, earth, and air" concept of the ancient Greeks was a crude way of classifying matter. There are many schemes by which matter can be classified; this activity is generally considered to be within the purview of chemistry, but has obvious ramifications for any of the sciences. In this section we will consider some of the most general ways of classifying matter, the properties of matter, and the changes which matter undergoes.

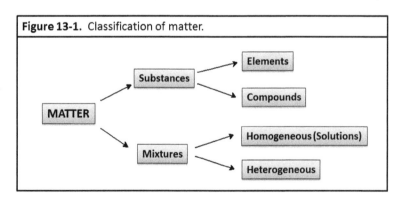

Figure 13-1. Classification of matter.

Suppose we are given a sample of material. We can ask a variety of questions in our attempt to describe it:

Does it consist of one element or more than one?
Does it consist of one substance or more than one?
Is it the same (homogeneous) throughout?
What are its physical characteristics?
What are its chemical characteristics?
How can it be changed by physical or chemical means?

In dealing with these types of questions, we will find it useful to begin by classifying matter according to the flow chart of Figure 13-1.

A. Classification as Pure Substance or Mixture

All matter can be classified as either a **pure substance** or a **mixture**. A pure substance is often just called a substance. Substances can be subdivided into either **elements** or **compounds**. Elements and compounds can be sub-classified according to their structural types, as we indicate below.

Elements are recognizable by having chemical formulas that include only the symbol of one element from the Periodic Table. Elements can be classified by their structures. There are **monatomic elements** such as neon (Ne) or xenon (Xe). These are gases at normal temperatures and pressures and contain no strong chemical bonds. There are **molecular elements** such as nitrogen (N_2), phosphorus (P_4), and carbon (C_{60}) that utilize covalent bonding between relatively small numbers of atoms. These molecular elements can be gases, liquids, or solids under normal conditions of temperature and pressure, depending primarily on molecular mass and polarizability. We have seen previously, for instance, that under normal atmospheric conditions Cl_2 is gaseous, Br_2 is liquid, and I_2 is solid. There are many **metallic elements** (such as Fe or Na) that utilize metallic bonding. These are network or crystalline style structures of indeterminate size. Most metals are solids under normal atmospheric conditions. As seen earlier in this book, a single element may have more than one available bonding structure, or **allotropic form**. Carbon is an excellent example; it exists as either molecules (C_{60} and other fullerenes), or as covalent networks (diamond or graphene). We have seen that graphene sheets can weakly bond to each other through pi-stacking interactions to produce a material called graphite.

Compounds are recognizable by having chemical formulas that include the symbols of more than one element, for example, NaCl, or CH_2Cl_2. We have already seen how we can use the formulas to help us determine whether the compound is an ionic one (contains a metal ion or ammonium ion) or a covalent compound (contains only non-metals or semi-metals). We have explored coordination complexes, wherein metals may be bonded to ligands using covalent bonds. Compounds must be neutral, overall.

Ionic compounds are structured as a "network" or as crystalline solids at normal temperatures and pressures. They may include monatomic ions (such as Fe^{3+} or Br^-), polyatomic ions (such as NH_4^+ or SO_4^{2-}), or complex ions from the field of coordination chemistry. For example, the salt $K_4[V(CN)_6]$, utilizes monatomic cations (K^+) and a complex anion, $[V(CN)_6]^{4-}$. Some salt structures contain only ionic bonds (NaCl), while others, such as NH_4NO_3 and $K_4[V(CN)_6]$, contain both ionic and covalent bonds.

Covalent compounds are usually molecular and can be solids (sugar, $C_{12}H_{22}O_{11}$), liquids (water, H_2O), or gases (CO_2) at normal room temperature conditions. A neutral coordination complex is also a covalent molecular substance, for example $Fe(CO)_5$. The physical state of molecular substances is controlled by the strength and number of intermolecular attractions available to the particular molecule, for instance, whether it is polar or nonpolar, how polarizable it is, and whether or not it can hydrogen bond to its neighbors.

If a sample of matter is not a pure substance it must be a **mixture**, a combination of more than one substance. While substances have definite compositions, mixtures do not. Mixtures, then, cannot be represented by a chemical formula. Instead, they must be described by the relative amounts of various substances present, perhaps by mass percent. Mixtures are sub-classified as either **homogenous** or **heterogeneous**.

Homogeneous mixtures can also be called **solutions**. Solutions have exactly the same composition throughout. "Uniform" and "unvaried" are synonyms of "homogeneous." While we are most familiar with solutions composed of liquid **solvent** and solid **solute** (such as salt water), solutions can be composed in a wide variety of ways. We explored alloys in Chapter 6; an alloy is a solid phase solution. Soda pop is an aqueous solution containing both solid and gaseous solutes. Air, in the absence of particulate matter such as dust, is often considered essentially a homogeneous mixture. However, samples of air taken from different locations may differ in their water content (humidity), and the composition of air changes significantly with altitude. Mixtures of gases confined in sealed vessels become homogeneous and therefore satisfy the definition of a solution.

Heterogeneous mixtures, then, are mixtures whose compositions vary within the mixture. For instance, a mixture of sugar and salt crystals is a heterogeneous mixture. The mixture has an overall composition, perhaps 61.0% sugar and 39.0% salt by mass, but an individual scoop taken from the mixture will likely have a different composition than that, perhaps 59.2% sugar and 40.8% salt. Some heterogeneous mixtures will become homogeneous with stirring; initially pouring solid sugar into water will make a heterogeneous mixture. Either stirring (or waiting for diffusion to do the stirring for you) can result in homogeneity. Other mixtures, such as the mixture of salt and sugar crystals already mentioned, will never be homogeneous. A living cell is a heterogeneous mixture. It contains a variety of different organelles, the cell membrane, maybe a cell wall, etc. Any sub-sample of the cell will have a different overall makeup than the whole cell.

Examples of heterogeneous mixtures are numerous. Samples of dirt, plants, meat, smoke (which contains small solid particles) are clearly heterogeneous. Paper is heterogeneous; back-light a plain piece of paper and you will see that it is not as uniform as you first thought! Although at first glance milk may seem homogeneous, on magnification it is seen to contain small globules of fat suspended in aqueous solution. Samples removed at random could have more or fewer fat globules. *Most animal and vegetable products are heterogeneous.* Examples include fruits and vegetables, margarine, yogurt, ketchup, mustard, and spices.

Some heterogeneous mixtures can be separated into their components by filtration; a filter paper (such as a coffee filter) allows liquid solutions to pass through, while retaining solids. Orange juice starts out heterogeneous; it contains solid pulp as well as liquid solution. If the juice is sufficiently filtered, the solids can be removed and the solution sold as "pulp-less" orange juice.

While we often think of the air in our homes as a homogeneous mixture, in fact this air is usually carrying a lot of tiny solid "dust" particles. Un-idealized air is a heterogeneous mixture. The filter on your car engine or your home's furnace traps particulates out of the air before allowing the air to pass into the burning chamber of the engine or furnace.

Example 13-1.

Classify the following as element, compound, solution, or heterogeneous mixture.

a. Potassium chloride — **Compound.** Contains ions in definite ratio (KCl).

b. Rose gold — **Solution.** An alloy of gold with about 21% copper and 4% silver, giving a rose-hued metal, often for use in jewelry.

c. Water — **Compound.** Contains atoms in definite ratio (H_2O).

d. Sample taken from a river — **Heterogeneous mixture.** Likely to contain solid particles, bubbles, fish, etc.

e. Mayonnaise — **Heterogeneous mixture.** Similar to milk, it contains fat globules in addition to aqueous solution.

f. Copper — **Element.**

g. Carbonated soft drink — **Heterogeneous mixture.** The "fizz" consists of bubbles of carbon dioxide (CO_2) rising through the liquid.

Exercise 13-1.

Classify the following as element, compound, solution, or heterogeneous mixture.

    a. Gold   **c.** Wood   **e.** Silver bromide

    b. Butter   **d.** Ice   **f.** Hummingbird "nectar": sugar + water + red dye

---

B. Classification by Physical Properties

Matter can be classified by its physical state, or phase. Pure substances are usually either solids, liquids, or gases, or perhaps a mixture of these phases. Even a pure substance can be present in a mixture of phases, for example, a glass of ice water.[53] Homogeneous mixtures utilizing water as the solvent (such as salt water) are said to be in the **aqueous** phase. Scientists often show the phase of a substance in a reaction equation with a subscript. This is necessary to convey what is often vital scientific information about a sample. For instance, a 10.0 g sample of $H_2O(g)$ holds a higher energy content than a 10.0 g sample of $H_2O(\ell)$! Or, if someone says they utilized $Cu(\ell)$ instead of $Cu(s)$ in a chemical reaction, you know you have to melt the copper first and all of a sudden it may not be so straightforward to try that same reaction yourself.

There are other physical states, such as **semi-solid** and **plasma**. Semi-solids are encountered in the kitchen as shortenings such as butter or margarine. They are solid enough to hold their shape, but liquid enough to change shape when small amounts of pressure are applied. A plasma is similar to a gas in that it has no particular shape or volume, but rather takes the shape and volume of its container. However, many properties of plasmas are unlike those of a gas. Most of the differences arise because the particles of plasmas are largely ionic and thus there are many new ramifications of having a large number of charge-carrying particles. While we are not very familiar with plasmas through ordinary life experiences, plasma is probably the most prevalent state of matter in the universe. Stars, for instance, are plasmas. The glowing "gas" in an energized discharge tube (such as the ones we use to see the line spectra of elements) is a plasma. Figure 13-2 shows the plasma made by energizing neon gas; many of the atoms are ionized!

Figure 13-2. Neon gas becomes a plasma when ionized.

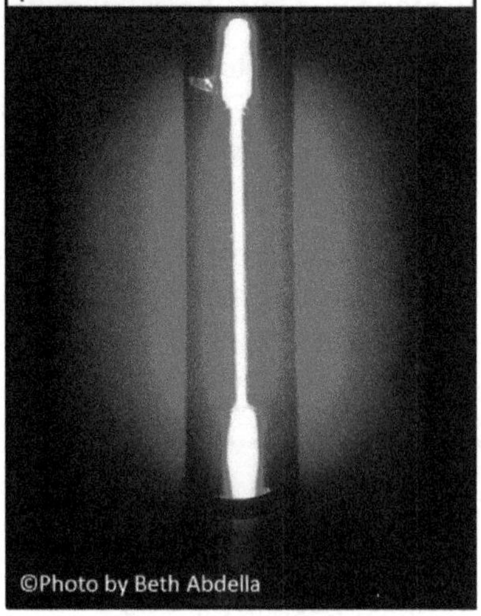

©Photo by Beth Abdella

Physical properties include any property that involves physical state, such as a boiling point or degree of solubility in a particular solvent. Physical properties also include other properties, as long as they do not describe the chemical reactivity of a substance. Examples include the color of the substance (I_2 is a dark purple solid), the ability of a substance to conduct heat or electricity, or the size of the particles of the substance: chunk of iron (could be a nugget in your hand or an I-beam for a building) vs. iron filings (small dust-like particles) vs. nanoparticles of iron (invisible to the naked eye, diameter ~20nm). Density (introduced in Chapter 2) is a physical property of a substance because it has nothing to do with its reactivity. The density of a substance may well change at different temperatures and pressures, but the formula of the substance remains unchanged.

C. Classification by Chemical Properties

Chemical properties are those that describe the chemical reactivity of a substance. In a chemical reaction, one or more substance(s) become some other set of substances through bonding

---

[53] Technically speaking, a glass of ice water prepared from a normal kitchen water tap is a mixture because there are sure to be dissolved substances in the water. We are often thinking a bit "ideally" in order to simplify the circumstances!

rearrangements. Matter can be classified based on the chemical properties it has, or doesn't have. Because acids react with bases, whether a substance is an acid or a base is a chemical property. Ammonia (NH_3), for instance, is basic while acetic acid (CH_3CO_2H) is acidic. Because combustion (burning) is a chemical reaction, whether or not a substance is flammable is a chemical property. Acetone (CH_3COCH_3) is flammable, but water (H_2O) is not. Substances that are toxic react chemically with biological molecules, thus toxicity is a chemical property. Cyanide salts (such as NaCN) are toxic, while table salt (NaCl) would not generally be described as toxic. Toxicity is a property that is controlled by the size of the dose; immense doses of an otherwise nontoxic substance might be toxic. For instance, people have died from drinking too much water in too short a time and developing a condition called *hyponatremia*. The kidneys cannot keep up with a very fast influx of too much water. Blood becomes too dilute; too much water moves into cells. Neurons in the brain have no room in which to swell. Victims experience excruciating headaches, seizures, coma and death. The science of toxicology is an interdisciplinary science concerned with understanding and describing toxic behaviors and doses. Toxicologists work in many different settings including clinical labs, forensic labs, industrial corporations, pharmaceutical industries, and regulatory agencies.

Table 13-1. Chemical and physical properties.

Physical Properties: These describe the characteristics of substances and mixtures. They may describe a physical state or changes between different physical states.

Examples: melting point, density, color, ability to dissolve in certain solvents, ability to conduct electric current

Chemical Properties: These describe whether a particular chemical substance reacts with other substances; they describe chemical changes.

Examples: flammability, tendency to decompose when exposed to light, being inert (non-reactive), good oxidizing agent

---

Exercise 13-2.

Classify the following properties of iron (Fe) as physical or chemical.

    a. Items made of iron tend to rust when they are damp.
    b. Iron conducts heat well enough to be used in pots and pans.
    c. Iron becomes soft when heated and can then be bent into useful shapes.
    d. Iron placed into a flask containing chlorine gas forms brown $FeCl_3$.

Because chemical properties are descriptions of chemical reactivity, we will have to learn about the different classes of chemical reactions in order to better understand the possible categories of chemical properties.

13-2. CHANGES OF MATTER

Matter can undergo physical changes (changes of state), chemical changes, or nuclear changes. How can we tell these apart and how do we notate these changes?

A. Physical Changes

In the context of biology and chemistry, physical changes are generally considered to be changes in phase.[54] Six of the most familiar of the phase changes are summarized in Figure 13-3. The "balls" in Figure 13-2 could be individual atoms, for a substance such as argon (Ar), or they

---

[54] Although grinding crystalline sugar with a mortar and pestle to create powdered sugar, for instance, is also a physical change.

could represent a molecule for a substance such as sugar. Using "reaction" equation notation for physical changes is often done. In typical reaction equation notation, the reactant(s) are shown on the left, an arrow represents the change, and the product(s) are shown on the right. When the change is a purely physical one, there can be no change in chemical formula: molecules stay intact during physical changes. There will be a change in the **phase tag**. The most common phase tags are:

$$(s) = \text{solid} \qquad (\ell) = \text{liquid} \qquad (g) = \text{gas} \qquad (aq) = \text{aqueous solution (dissolved in water).}$$

All of the following reaction equations indicate a physical change:

1. $H_2O(\ell) \longrightarrow H_2O(s)$ freezing
2. $I_2(g) \longrightarrow I_2(s)$ vapor deposition
3. $C_6H_6(g) \longrightarrow C_6H_6(\ell)$ condensation
4. $C_{12}H_{22}O_{11}(s) \longrightarrow C_{12}H_{22}O_{11}(aq)$ dissolving
5. $PbCl_2(s) \xrightarrow{\Delta} PbCl_2(aq)$ dissolving
6. $PbCl_2(s) \xrightarrow{\Delta} Pb^{2+}(aq) + 2\,Cl^-(aq)$ dissolving

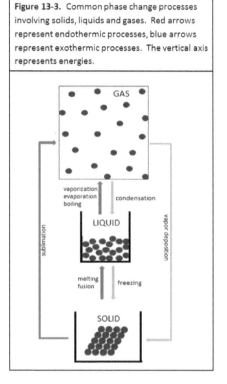

Figure 13-3. Common phase change processes involving solids, liquids and gases. Red arrows represent endothermic processes, blue arrows represent exothermic processes. The vertical axis represents energies.

Examples 1-3 (listed above) represent a subset of the processes shown in Figure 13-3. Sucrose (table sugar, $C_{12}H_{22}O_{11}$) is a molecular solid that dissolves as molecules, as we see in reaction equation 4, above. As we saw in Chapter 12, there are multiple ways to notate the dissolution of an ionic solid. Reaction equations 5 and 6 show two different ways to notate the dissolution of the salt, lead(II) chloride. Lead(II) chloride dissolves in hot water, but not in cool water. The triangle over the reaction arrow is one way to indicate the need for heat. The notation shown in number 5 utilizes only neutral formulas. The notation in number 6 is both more complicated and more helpful. It is called an **ionic reaction equation**. In an ionic reaction equation, we endeavor to show formulas of dissolved salts "as they actually exist." As a solid, lead(II) chloride exists as a neutral conglomeration of ions, as signified by the formula, $PbCl_2(s)$. However, when dissolved in water, the ions are no longer in close contact with one another. Instead, they are individually solubilized, as we discussed in Chapter 12. The notation in number 6 respects this difference and visualizes it for the reader. While it may appear that the chemical formula changed in number 6 (from "$PbCl_2$" to "$Pb^{2+} + 2\,Cl^-$"), it did not; all of the same ions exist on both sides of the reaction arrow. The ionic reaction equation merely helps the reader to "see" the true form of the reactants and products.

Any of the example reaction equations, 1-6, above, could be reversed to indicate the opposite phase change:

1. $H_2O(s) \longrightarrow H_2O(\ell)$ melting
2. $I_2(s) \longrightarrow I_2(g)$ sublimation
3. $C_6H_6(\ell) \longrightarrow C_6H_6(g)$ vaporization (evaporation)[55]
4. $C_{12}H_{22}O_{11}(aq) \longrightarrow C_{12}H_{22}O_{11}(s)$ **precipitation** or **crystallization**[56]

---

[55] "Vaporization" and "evaporation" describe the liquid-to-gas process when it occurs below the boiling temperature of the liquid. "Boiling" describes the liquid-to-gas process when it occurs at the boiling temperature of the liquid.

[56] **Crystallization** is the process wherein a solid comes out of solution in the form of a well-ordered crystal. **Precipitation** is essentially the same process, but the usual outcome is an amorphous (un-ordered) solid. Crystallization usually requires much more time and care than precipitation. We will use the term "precipitation" with the understanding that under appropriate conditions crystals may result.

5. $PbCl_2(aq) \longrightarrow PbCl_2(s)$ precipitation (neutral formula equation)

6. $Pb^{2+}(aq) + 2\ Cl^-(aq) \longrightarrow PbCl_2(s)$ precipitation (ionic reaction equation)

One interesting thing that we can add to reaction equations is a notation for energy flow. Any process either <u>requires</u> energy or <u>releases</u> energy. When energy is required, it is similar to a "reactant" for the process. When energy is released, it is similar to a "product" of the process. The phase changes shown in Figure 13-3 have well-understood energy relationships: melting, vaporization and sublimation require energy input. We could write:

a. $H_2O(s) + heat \longrightarrow H_2O(\ell)$ melting

b. $I_2(s) + heat \longrightarrow I_2(g)$ sublimation

c. $C_6H_6(\ell) + heat \longrightarrow C_6H_6(g)$ vaporization (evaporation)

These processes are called **endothermic**, where "endo-" means "into." Energy must flow <u>into</u> the system (the chemicals) in order for the process to occur. Sweating cools you down because as the sweat evaporates, it must take in some heat. The heat comes from you!

The reverse processes must also reverse the energy flow. Reversing examples a-c, above, give three **exothermic** processes (and the other 3 phase changes shown in Figure 13-3):

d. $H_2O(\ell) \longrightarrow H_2O(s) + heat$ freezing

e. $I_2(g) \longrightarrow I_2(s) + heat$ vapor deposition

f. $C_6H_6(g) \longrightarrow C_6H_6(\ell) + heat$ condensation

"Exo-" means "out of" or "exiting." During these processes, heat is released (<u>exits</u>) the chemical systems. The chemical systems move to lower energy states, and the extra energy flows out of the system and into the surroundings. Let's say we buy a raw steak and place it in our freezer at home (we'll call the steak our system; then the freezer environment is the surroundings). Once in the freezer, heat flows from the warmer steak into the surroundings. Your freezer "runs" to keep the atmosphere from warming up. The processes is exothermic for the steak; it continues to release heat until its temperature matches the temperature of the surroundings.

It is instructive to notice that a forward and reverse reaction equation pair, such as

$$H_2O(s) + heat \longrightarrow H_2O(\ell)$$
$$H_2O(\ell) \longrightarrow H_2O(s) + heat$$

both tell you the <u>same thing</u> about energetics. Either reaction equation shows that "heat" and "ice" are on the same side of the arrow. Either can be interpreted to mean that solid ice is in a lower energy state than liquid water. In other words, solid ice is less energetic than liquid water. The lower energy of the ice is manifest in molecules with less kinetic energy.

Dissolution and precipitation processes are not as easy to predict in terms of energy flow. Some solutes dissolve in an endothermic manner and others dissolve in an exothermic manner.[57] As we learned in Chapter 12, the distinction depends on the relative strengths and numbers of bonding interactions before and after the dissolution. What we can say, absolutely, however, is that if a dissolution process is exothermic, the reverse precipitation process will be endothermic, and vice versa. Urea, NH_2CONH_2, (structure at right) is a molecular solid at room temperature that dissolves in a noticeably endothermic process:

$$NH_2CONH_2(s) + heat \longrightarrow NH_2CONH_2(aq)$$

---

[57] Many solutes have small enough magnitudes of endo- or exo-thermicity that it is difficult to observe the heat flow without careful measurements.

Therefore, we know that the precipitation of urea from aqueous solution <u>must be</u> an exothermic process:

$$NH_2CONH_2(aq) \longrightarrow NH_2CONH_2(s) + heat$$

Exercise 13-3.

When urea dissolves in water in a glass beaker, will the water (and glass) get warm or cold? Explain.

Exercise 13-4.

One way to think about the difference between a compound and a mixture is to consider whether a physical method (tweezers, dissolving, boiling, etc.)[58] could be used to separate the components. Physical methods can often be used to separate mixed substances from one another, but cannot separate the elements involved in a compound. A chemical method (a chemical reaction) is necessary to obtain elements from a compound; formulas need to change!

a. Sugar ($C_{12}H_{22}O_{11}$) and sand (SiO_2) are mixed together. How could you use solubility differences (a physical method) to separate them? Would either formula change?

b. Sand (SiO_2) and iron filings (Fe) are mixed together. How could you use physical methods to separate them? Would either formula change?

c. Consider NaCl. What are the formulas of the ions in this salt? What are the formulas of the elements sodium and chlorine? What does this imply about the method needed to obtain the elements from NaCl?

B. Chemical Changes

Chemical reaction equations are recognizable by the fact that chemical formulas change, but the numbers and types of atoms must stay constant. This is because chemical reactions are characterized by *rearrangements of bonding electrons*; old bonds are lost and new bonds are made. Atom identities must stay constant; no changes happen to a nucleus and the nucleus defines the type of atom present. A chemical reaction equation may show different phase tags in the reactants and products, but, if a solid becomes a gas, for instance, the formulas of the solid and the gas are different. This is not a "physical change":

$$KClO_4(s) \longrightarrow KCl(s) + 2 O_2(g)$$

The reaction equation above must denote a chemical change because formulas change. It is a "balanced" chemical reaction equation because there are the same numbers of the same types of atoms on each side of the arrow: one K, one Cl, and four O atoms and the same overall charge (neutral). Note that in order to "count" the atoms, one has to pay attention both to the subscripts AND to the coefficients (numbers in front of the formulas). If no coefficient is present, it is understood to be "1," as in

$$1 KClO_4(s) \longrightarrow 1 KCl(s) + 2 O_2(g)$$

What do the coefficients in a chemical reaction equation mean? The coefficients can be interpreted in many ways. As pure numbers, they show us the relative numbers of "formula units" involved in a reaction. Consider the case of a reaction such as

$$3 O_2(g) \longrightarrow 2 O_3(g)$$

---

[58] A physical method does not change the chemical formula of components of the mixture.

The coefficients could mean that 3 oxygen molecules can be converted to 2 ozone molecules, or that 3 million oxygen molecules can be converted to 2 million ozone molecules, or that 3 moles oxygen molecules can be converted to 2 moles ozone molecules. For purposes of calculations, the most usual interpretation of the coefficients is "3 moles" oxygen and "2 moles" ozone.

As we saw with physical changes, chemical changes can be endothermic or exothermic. We could write a chemical reaction equation to explicitly show the energy flow:

$$KClO_4(s) + heat \longrightarrow KCl(s) + 2 O_2(g)$$

In words, we could say that "potassium perchlorate decomposes when heated to produce potassium chloride and oxygen." In chemistry, a *decomposition reaction* has ONE reactant and multiple products.[59] Because decomposition is a chemical change (formulas changed!), a substance's predisposition to decompose is a chemical property. Notice the heat flow indicted for the decomposition reaction, above. Is the reaction endothermic or exothermic? Is it more likely that you can help this reaction "go" by warming it up or cooling it down?[60]

Example 13-2.

Classify the following behaviors of iodine (I_2) as physical or chemical changes.

   a. It sublimes.

   Physical change. I_2 is simply going from the solid phase to the gas phase; the molecular formula I_2 is preserved.

   b. It reacts with F_2 to form IF_5 and IF_7.

   Chemical change. Chemical formulas are changing as I_2 reacts with F_2:

   $$I_2(s) + 5 F_2(g) \longrightarrow 2 IF_5(\ell)$$
   $$I_2(s) + 7 F_2(g) \longrightarrow 2 IF_7(g)$$

   c. It dissolves in alcohol to give a brown solution ("tincture of iodine").

   Physical change. I_2 is not undergoing a change in chemical formula; it is simply dissolving.

   d. When added to sodium, it forms NaI.

   Chemical change. Chemical formulas are changing:

   $$2 Na(s) + I_2 (s) \longrightarrow 2 NaI(s)$$

13-3. WRITING CHEMICAL REACTION EQUATIONS

A chemical reaction equation gives a summary of the chemical changes occurring (or believed to be occurring) in a reaction. It includes chemical formulas of elements, compounds, and ions involved in a reaction; and, if correctly balanced, accounts for each atom (including all of the electrons) of each element.

A. Writing Balanced Chemical Reaction Equations

An important objective is to be able to predict accurately just how much of a product can be formed in a given chemical reaction. Such a prediction is important in a variety of settings and particularly essential in the industrial production of chemicals, where products need to be produced as efficiently as possible, in the desired quantities and with a minimum of wasted material. In the laboratory we also need to be able to determine exactly what proportions of reactants to combine, and

---

[59] "Decomposition," in general, is the process by which a complicated system separates into simpler components.

[60] This reaction is endothermic, it requires an influx of heat. Warming it up is more likely to be helpful.

to make an accurate estimate of the amounts of products to be formed. To be able to make such predictions we must, first of all, be able to balance chemical equations in such a way as to account for each atom present (both the nuclei and the electrons). Simple chemical equations can be balanced by the following procedure:

1. Write the chemical formulas of all reactants and products, with an arrow separating the two.

$$\text{Example: } H_2 + Cl_2 \longrightarrow HCl$$

2. Change the coefficients as necessary until the total number of atoms of each element is the same on both sides. Two related hints:

    a. Start by considering the reactant or product having the most complicated chemical formula.
    b. If there is an elemental substance present (such as Fe, Cl_2, S_8), balance those atoms last.

    We add a "2" in front of "HCl" to obtain: $H_2 + Cl_2 \longrightarrow 2\,HCl$
    This results in a balanced reaction equation with 2 "H" and 2 "Cl" on each side. We also check to make sure that overall charge on both sides of the arrow is the same. In this case, both sides are neutral.[61]

3. Finally, we add appropriate phase tags. All of the substances in this example are gases under normal conditions. The final result is given here:

$$H_2(g) + Cl_2(g) \longrightarrow 2\,HCl(g)$$

(If you are unsure about the phase of a substance, there are a variety of sources of this information on the internet. One strategy is to locate a Safety Data Sheet (SDS) for substances about which you are uncertain.)

Emphases:

Never change a chemical formula during the balancing process![62]

If reactants and/or products are charged (ions), be sure that the total charge on the left side of the equation equals the total charge on the right side. If no species are ionic, this will take care of itself and both sides will be neutral!

Check to be sure that the equation is balanced, both in the number of atoms of each element on each side and in the total charge on each side. The number of atoms of each element and the total charge *must* be conserved!

The procedure for balancing chemical equations is best shown through examples; see Example 13-3.

---

[61] If all of the atoms are balanced there must be equal numbers of protons (in the atom nuclei) on both sides of the arrow. Then, if the overall charge is the same on both sides of the arrow, there must also be equal numbers of electrons. There cannot be an overall gain or loss of electrons as the reaction proceeds.

[62] Changing a formula changes the chemical reaction to a fundamentally different reaction. If you are to balance a particular chemical reaction, you cannot change the identity of the reaction! This means you may change coefficients, but NOT subscripts.

Example 13-3. Write balanced reaction equations for the following transformations based on the description given.

a. Iron reacts with chlorine gas to form brown iron(III) chloride.

The chemical formulas of the reactants and products are:[63]

Reactants: Fe and Cl_2 Product: $FeCl_3$

We can write an unbalanced description of the reaction as follows:

$$Fe \ + \ Cl_2 \ \longrightarrow \ FeCl_3$$

Although the number of atoms of iron is the same on both sides of the equation, the number of atoms of chlorine is not. Looking at the most complicated formula, $FeCl_3$, we see that there are 3 Cl atoms for every Fe atom. We look for a way to have the same 3 Cl : 1 Fe ratio on the reactant side. Placing a "2" in front of Fe and a 3 in front of Cl_2 achieves this goal.

$$2 \, Fe \ + \ 3 \, Cl_2 \ \longrightarrow \ FeCl_3$$

Now we can add a coefficient of "2" to the product side to equalize the numbers of atoms on each side (2 Fe atoms and 6 Cl atoms):

$$2 \, Fe \ + \ 3 \, Cl_2 \ \longrightarrow \ 2 \, FeCl_3$$

Finally, we consider phase tags. At normal temperatures and pressures almost all metals are solids, chlorine is a gas, and salts are solids.

$$\mathbf{2 \, Fe(s) \ + \ 3 \, Cl_2(g) \ \longrightarrow \ 2 \, FeCl_3(s)}$$

b. Methane, the principal component of natural gas, burns in air (reacts with O_2) to form carbon dioxide and water.

First, we generate formulas from the word description of the reaction:

$$CH_4 \ + \ O_2 \ \longrightarrow \ CO_2 \ + \ H_2O$$

The most complex formula is CH_4 (5 atoms); this requires that the number of carbon and hydrogen atoms must be in the ratio 1:4. This ratio can be achieved on the right side by multiplying the formula H_2O by 2:

$$CH_4 \ + \ O_2 \ \longrightarrow \ CO_2 \ + \ 2 \, H_2O$$

Carbon and hydrogen are now balanced, but oxygen is not: there are 2 oxygen atoms on the left but 4 on the right.[64] Balance O_2 by giving it a coefficient of "2."

$$CH_4 \ + \ 2 \, O_2 \ \longrightarrow \ CO_2 \ + \ 2 \, H_2O$$

Finally, we consider phase tags. At normal temperatures and pressures the first three substances are all gases. Water can exist as ice, liquid or water vapor. Because this water is being produced during combustion (hot!), it may be best to show it as water vapor.

$$\mathbf{CH_4(g) \ + \ 2 \, O_2(g) \ \longrightarrow \ CO_2(g) \ + \ 2 \, H_2O(g)}$$

---

[63]Recall that elemental chlorine is diatomic, Cl_2.

[64] It is a good strategy to balance O_2 last, because there are no other atoms impacted by changing its coefficient.

c. Pale yellow chlorine reacts with colorless bromide ions in aqueous solution to form chloride ions and bromine; formation of an orange color indicates the presence of bromine.

The formulas of reactants and products are:[65]

$$Cl_2 \;+\; Br^- \longrightarrow Cl^- \;+\; Br_2$$

In this case we must be careful to be sure that not only the atoms are balanced, but also that the total charges on both sides of the equation are the same. The atoms can be balanced by adding a coefficient of 2 to each ion:

$$Cl_2 \;+\; 2\,Br^- \longrightarrow 2\,Cl^- \;+\; Br_2$$

Do the charges balance? Yes. In this case the total charge on each side of the equation is –2. We started out with two more electrons than protons and we end up with two more electrons than protons.

Finally, we consider phase tags. At normal temperatures and pressures chlorine is a gas and bromine is a liquid. However, the description of this reaction says that it is occurring in aqueous solution. We use the (aq) tag on all species.

$$Cl_2(aq) \;+\; 2\,Br^-(aq) \longrightarrow 2\,Cl^-(aq) \;+\; Br_2(aq)$$

Exercise 13-5.

Balance the following:

a. $P_4 + H_2 \longrightarrow PH_3$

b. $Fe_2O_3 + C \longrightarrow Fe_3O_4 + CO$

c. In aqueous solution, the thiosulfate ion reacts with elemental iodine to form the tetrathionate ion, $S_4O_6^{2-}$, and the iodide ion.

d. Hydrogen chloride reacts with manganese(IV) oxide to yield water, manganese(II) chlorideand chlorine.

Exercise 13-6.

Balance the following:[66]

a. $CS_2 + O_2 \longrightarrow CO_2 + SO_2$

b. $Cr_2O_7^{2-} + H_2O \rightleftharpoons HCrO_4^-$

c. Iodine reacts reversibly with xenon difluoride to form iodine trifluoride and xenon.

d. Potassium nitrate, sulfur, and carbon react to form potassium sulfide, carbon dioxide, and elemental nitrogen.

---

[65]Remember that the -*ide* endings on chloride and bromide designate ions having a charge of 1-; the -*ine* endings of chlorine and bromine (and the other elements in this group) indicate the neutral elements, which are both diatomic in this case: Cl_2 and Br_2.

[66] When balancing reaction equations, use the type of reaction arrow, $\longrightarrow$ or $\rightleftharpoons$, shown in the problem. If the reaction is described in prose (such as parts c and d) use $\longrightarrow$ unless the problem makes it clear that the reaction is *reversible* in nature or that an *equilibrium state* is obtained.

B. Types of Chemical Reactions

The variety of chemical reactions is astonishing. Literally thousands of different types of reactions, with variations, have been reported. To attempt to classify even a modest fraction of these reaction types would be well beyond the scope of our needs here. Nevertheless, we will begin by considering briefly in this section some of the most common reactions that involve the types of chemical compounds discussed to this point. Even within this small set of categories, we will find that a given chemical reaction may fit in more than one category.

1. Reactions between metals and nonmetals

2. Combustion reactions
    a. Carbon-containing compounds
    b. Metals

3. Reactions between positive and negative ions
    a. Precipitation reactions
    b. Acid-base reactions (Bronsted-Lowry definitions)

4. Oxidation-reduction reactions

There are many other categories for types of chemical reactions. We saw, in Chapter 10, for example, reactions between Lewis acids and Lewis bases.

1. Reactions Between Metals and Nonmetals

In many cases, metals react with nonmetals to give products containing the characteristic ions formed by the metal and nonmetal. For example, sodium metal reacts (vigorously!) with the nonmetal iodine to form sodium iodide, NaI. Two processes happen simultaneously in this reaction:

Each Na atom <u>loses</u> an electron to form the characteristic Na^+ ion. The loss of electrons is called **oxidation**. This process results in an ion that is isoelectronic with the noble gas, neon, Ne.

oxidation **half reaction:**[67] $Na \longrightarrow Na^+ + e^-$ (e^- symbolizes an electron)

The electrons lost by the Na atoms are taken up by I_2. Each iodine atom of I_2 gains an electron to form the characteristic anion, I^-. Gaining electrons is called **reduction.** This ion is isoelectronic with the noble gas, xenon, Xe.

reduction **half reaction:** $I_2 + 2\,e^- \longrightarrow 2\,I^-$

The total number of electrons lost by Na must equal the total number of electrons gained by I_2. In any chemical reaction equation, all electrons must be accounted for! Thus every molecule of I_2 that reacts requires the reaction of two atoms of Na. We can multiply the oxidation half reaction by 2:

$2 \times (Na \longrightarrow Na^+ + e^-)$ yielding $2\,Na \longrightarrow 2\,Na^+ + 2\,e^-$

Now we add the two half reactions together; all reactants stay reactants and all products stay products. If something appears on both sides of the arrow, in exactly the same form, it may be cancelled out (such as the electrons, in this case):

---

[67] Half reactions show free electrons as either reactants (reductions) or products (oxidations). A complete, balanced reaction equation cannot show free electrons. Thus two half reactions must be summed in such a way that the electrons on each side cancel.

$$2 \, Na \longrightarrow 2 \, Na^+ + 2 \, e^-$$

$$I_2 + 2 \, e^- \longrightarrow 2 \, I^-$$

sum: $\quad\quad 2 \, Na + I_2 \longrightarrow 2 \, Na^+ + 2 \, I^-$

Then, we note that the sodium ions and iodide ions on the product side of the arrow will combine to make a neutral salt, and we add appropriate phase tags to obtain: $\quad$ **$2 \, Na(s) + I_2(s) \longrightarrow 2 \, NaI(s)$**

Both sides of this reaction equation have an overall charge of zero, the reactants because each atom is in a neutral form and the product because the charges on the cations are balanced by the charges on the anions.

Another example of this type of reaction occurs between calcium and chlorine to form calcium chloride:

$$Ca(s) + Cl_2(g) \longrightarrow CaCl_2(s)$$

The product is a salt composed of calcium ions (Ca^{2+}) and chloride ions (Cl^-) in a 3-dimensional array.

Exercise 13-7.

Write the two half reactions for the formation of calcium chloride. The overall reaction is given, above.

Exercise 13-8.

Predict the product, write half reactions and a balanced chemical equation:

    a. The reaction of magnesium with sulfur.
    b. The reaction of zinc with chlorine.

---

2. Combustion Reactions

a. Combustion of carbon-containing compounds

Figure 13-4. Combustion of the hydrocarbon, heptane.

©Photo by Rachel Miessler

Complete **combustion**[68] of a compound containing only carbon and hydrogen (a hydrocarbon) or only carbon, hydrogen, and oxygen yields carbon dioxide and water,[69] as well as a large amount of heat. In general we can write:

$$[\, C_xH_y \text{ or } C_xH_yO_z \,] \; + \; n \, O_2 \longrightarrow x \, CO_2 + \frac{y}{2} \, H_2O$$

A specific example is the combustion of heptane, C_7H_{16}.

$$C_7H_{16} \; + \; 11 \, O_2 \longrightarrow 7 \, CO_2 + 8 \, H_2O$$

Figure 13-4 shows this reaction. In practice, combustion of these compounds is usually incomplete; some carbon monoxide (CO) and elemental carbon (soot, small

---

[68] Combustion reactions are defined as reactions of molecular oxygen with another substance. These reactions must generally be started with the input of some "activation energy." The combustion reaction then emits a lot of heat and light, so that the net energy flow is highly exothermic.
[69] These are the most stable "oxides" of carbon and hydrogen.

particles of graphite) are usually formed, especially when the amount of available oxygen is limited, in which case all the carbon cannot be converted into CO_2. One circumstance that limits available oxygen for combustion is a clogged furnace filter. This has, too often, resulted in tragedy due to the poisonous effects of carbon monoxide.

Try writing some combustion reaction equations yourself. For compounds such as C_2H_2, C_4H_{10}, C_6H_6, C_6H_8, and C_8H_{10}, notice that x is always the subscript of C in the reactant *and* the coefficient of CO_2 in the product. Also, the coefficient of the product H_2O is always half of the subscript of H in the hydrocarbon (C_xH_y) formula. For oxygen-containing molecules, such as CH_3OH, the relationship is the same, but the y value must incorporate all of the H atoms: $CH_3OH = CH_4O$

$$CH_4O + \frac{3}{2}O_2 \longrightarrow CO_2 + 2\,H_2O$$

Example 13-4.

Write balanced equations for the following reactions.

a. Combustion of propane, C_3H_8, the major component of "liquid petroleum gas" (LPG) burned in many rural homes.

$$C_3H_8 + O_2 \longrightarrow CO_2 + H_2O$$

The most complicated formula is C_3H_8. This dictates a ratio of 3 C : 8 H. This ratio can be achieved on the right side by adding coefficients of 3 and 4:

$$C_3H_8 + O_2 \longrightarrow 3\,CO_2 + 4\,H_2O$$

There are now 10 oxygen atoms on the right side. Adding a coefficient of 5 for O_2, checking for overall charge balance, and providing appropriate phase tags produces the balanced equation:

$$C_3H_8(g) + 5\,O_2(g) \longrightarrow 3\,CO_2(g) + 4\,H_2O(g)$$

b. Ethanol, C_2H_5OH (also known as ethyl alcohol), is the major component of E85 automobile fuel. The products of ethanol combustion are the familiar oxides of carbon and hydrogen:

$$C_2H_5OH + O_2 \longrightarrow CO_2 + H_2O$$

The formula of ethanol dictates a 2:6 ratio of carbon to hydrogen. This can be met by adding coefficients to the right side:

$$C_2H_5OH + O_2 \longrightarrow 2\,CO_2 + 3\,H_2O$$

The oxygen atoms can now be balanced by adding a coefficient of 3 for O_2 and we finish by checking for charge balance and adding appropriate phase tags:

$$C_2H_5OH(\ell) + 3\,O_2(g) \longrightarrow 2\,CO_2(g) + 3\,H_2O(g)$$

b. Combustion of metals

Combustion reactions are also possible for elements and compounds that do not contain carbon. An example is the reaction that occurs when magnesium ribbon is ignited in air:

$$2 \, Mg(s) + O_2(g) \longrightarrow 2 \, MgO(s)$$

A very intense, white light is given off in this highly exothermic reaction (Figure 13-5). Note that this reaction equation would also "fit" in our first category of reactions between metals and non-metals!

Combustion reactions of metals usually yield metal oxides, as with magnesium, above. The classic exception occurs among the alkali metals, in which the product depends on the metal. Combustion of lithium occurs as expected to yield primarily lithium oxide. When sodium is burned,

Figure 13-5. Combustion of magnesium ribbon.

©Photo by Rachel Miessler

however, the principal product is sodium peroxide (peroxide = O_2^{2-}), and when the heavier alkali metals (K, Rb, Cs, and Fr) are burned, they form superoxide salts (superoxide ion = O_2^-).

Exercise 13-9.

Based on information, above, write balanced equations for the combustion of lithium, sodium, and potassium.

Exercise 13-10.

Write balanced equations for the following reactions.

a. Combustion of butane, C_4H_{10}, a liquid used in pocket lighters.

b. Combustion of acetone, $(CH_3)_2CO$, a common solvent.

c. Reaction of aluminum powder with oxygen.

---

3. Reactions between positive and negative ions, and the net ionic reaction equation

When two different salt solutions are poured together, the positive ion from one salt may combine with the negative ion from the other salt to form an (essentially) insoluble salt. This trading of partners is called a **double displacement** reaction, or **metathesis**. The insoluble salt precipitates from the solution, usually settling at the bottom of the container over time. Two examples are offered here:

a. When solutions of silver nitrate and potassium chloride are combined,[70] silver ions come into contact with chloride ions. Because silver chloride is an essentially insoluble salt, it precipitates from the solution. We can write a **neutral formula reaction equation**:

$$AgNO_3(aq) + KCl(aq) \longrightarrow AgCl(s) + KNO_3(aq)$$

Of the four ions present in the reactants (Ag^+, NO_3^-, K^+, and Cl^-) only two react. The neutral formula reaction equation makes it difficult to focus on the actual reactive species, silver(I) ion and chloride ion. Scientists often prefer a reaction equation that concentrates attention of

---

[70] Because solutions are being poured together, we know that the reactant salts must be soluble. You can check solubility rules to confirm. A table of solubility rules appears just 1-2 page turns ahead!

the reactive species. This is called the net ionic reaction equation. Let's explore how to write one of these, starting with the neutral formula reaction equation, above.

From the neutral formula reaction equation we can write an **ionic reaction equation**. This will be the precursor to the net ionic reaction equation. Remember that in an ionic reaction equation, we show dissolved salts and other strong electrolytes as separated ions. Solid salts, weak electrolytes and nonelectrolytes are not separated into ions! Everything is notated to best show how it exists.

The ionic reaction equation for our precipitation reaction is:

$$Ag^+(aq) + NO_3^-(aq) + K^+(aq) + Cl^-(aq) \longrightarrow AgCl(s) + NO_3^-(aq) + K^+(aq)$$

This may not have simplified things much, but it makes the next step pretty obvious: if any species is unchanged during the chemical reaction, it will appear in exactly the same form on each side of the arrow. We see that nitrate ion and potassium ion, in blue, are in this situation. We call ions such as these **spectator ions**; they "watch" the action, but take no part in the action. We can cancel them from the reaction equation, because they have not changed:

$$Ag^+(aq) + Cl^-(aq) \longrightarrow AgCl(s)$$

This final version of the reaction equation is called a **net ionic reaction equation**. The word "net" is used similarly to how it is used on a box of cereal, where the "NET WT 24 OZ" means that the important part of the whole package (the cereal) weighs 24 ounces. The box and liner (and secret decoder ring, if you are that lucky) make the whole package weigh more than 24 ounces; but nobody really cares how much more. In the same way, the net ionic reaction equation shows the important chemical change, ignoring other extraneous information.

Notice that a net ionic reaction equation cuts to the chase and lets you easily focus on the chemistry that is occurring. The net ionic reaction equation would be exactly the same if aqueous sodium chloride or aqueous lithium chloride had been the source of the chloride ion (instead of potassium chloride). Because any of these cations would have been non-reactive under these conditions, any of them could be the spectator ion. We see that the neutral formula equation tells us more details (which spectator ions were present) but the net ionic reaction equation lets us focus on the chemical change.

As we saw, above, one way to determine the net ionic reaction equation for a precipitation reaction is to start with the neutral formula reaction equation and progress through the ionic reaction equation and then the net ionic reaction equation. A shorter process for writing net ionic reaction equations for precipitation reactions is often used. This process starts with the identification of the formula of the precipitate; in our case this would be the solid silver chloride, AgCl. We write it in as the product

$$\longrightarrow AgCl(s)$$

Then we use the necessary ions, in the necessary amounts, to make that salt:

$$Ag^+(aq) + Cl^-(aq) \longrightarrow AgCl(s)$$

You can see this precipitate in Figure 13-6.

b. Here's another example: consider pouring together solutions of lead(II) nitrate and sodium chromate. Is there a precipitation? If so, what is the net ionic reaction equation?

What do we do? Start by identifying the ions involved in the reactants:

Lead(II) nitrate = Pb^{2+} and NO_3^- ions   sodium chromate = Na^+ and CrO_4^{2-} ions.

We check the possible recombinations of cations and anions: sodium nitrate and lead(II) chromate. Because all nitrate salts are soluble, we know that sodium nitrate will not precipitate. Looking up $PbCrO_4$ in a solubility table shows it to be an essentially insoluble salt. So it will precipitate!

You can write the net ionic reaction equation for this precipitation by writing the formula of the precipitate on the product side and the formulas of the necessary ions (thinking about appropriate coefficients) on the reactant side:

$$Pb^{2+}(aq) \ + \ CrO_4^{2-}(aq) \ \longrightarrow \ PbCrO_4(s)$$

Exercise 13-11.

Write balanced *net ionic* reaction equations for each precipitation in Figure 13-6.

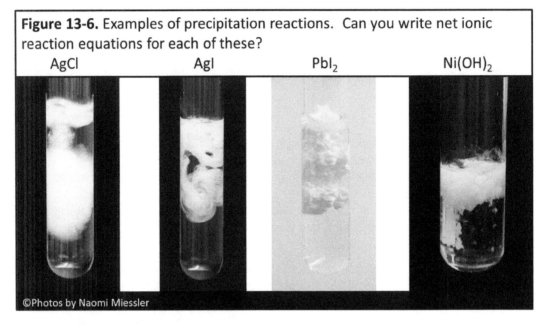

Figure 13-6. Examples of precipitation reactions. Can you write net ionic reaction equations for each of these?

AgCl   AgI PbI_2 $Ni(OH)_2$

©Photos by Naomi Miessler

c. In other cases, oppositely charged ions may combine, but no precipitate forms. In these cases, the product is generally a small, neutral molecule. The classic example is a **neutralization** reaction between a strong acid and a strong base in aqueous solution. Any strong acid solution, as we have seen in Chapter 12 (strong electrolytes), contains the hydronium ion (H_3O^+) and the anion of the strong acid: Cl^-, NO_3^-, Br^-, etc. The soluble strong bases dissociate to provide the hydroxide ion, OH^-, in solution along with a cation, most commonly Na^+ or K^+. A neutralization reaction is the reaction between the H_3O^+ and OH^- ions to produce water:

$$H_3O^+(aq) \ + \ OH^-(aq) \ \longrightarrow \ 2 \, H_2O(\ell)^{[71]}$$

This is the net ionic reaction equation; the anion of the acid and the cation of the base are spectator ions in this process.

---

[71] This reaction equation can also be written as $H^+(aq) + OH^-(aq) \longrightarrow H_2O(\ell)$ which utilizes H^+ instead of H_3O^+, and thus represents a (further) simplification. Your instructor may prefer that you use one or the other notation.

Summary of Rules for Net Ionic Reaction Equations

Three types of reaction equations can be used to describe reactions involving ions in solution. If a neutral formula equation is provided and a net ionic equation is requested, working through these in order, top-to-bottom, can be a successful strategy for getting the job done.

Neutral formula equation:
Contains complete formulas (and phase tags) of all reactants and products.

Complete ionic equation:
Shows strong electrolytes (soluble salts, strong acids/bases) in their dissociated or ionized forms.

Net ionic equation:
Meets criteria of complete ionic equation, but additionally includes only chemical species that undergo change, these could be ions or molecules.

Of these three types of equation, the most commonly used—and the one that is most important for a student of chemistry to understand—is the net ionic equation. We offer a summary about notations used in a net ionic reaction equation below.

1. Aqueous solutions of soluble salts and strong acids are considered to be completely **dissociated** (salts), or **ionized** (strong acids). For example:

   $NaCl(aq)$ is completely dissociated into $Na^+(aq) + Cl^-(aq)$

   $K_2SO_4(aq)$ is completely dissociated into $2 K^+(aq) + SO_4^{2-}(aq)$

   $HNO_3(aq)$ is completely ionized into $H_3O^+(aq)$[72] $+ NO_3^-(aq)$

   $KOH(aq)$ is completely dissociated into $K^+(aq) + OH^-(aq)$

   Aqueous solutions of these strong electrolytes are assumed, in general, to be fully dissociated or fully ionized.

2. Insoluble salts consist of closely combined positive and negative ions. These are represented by their full, neutral chemical formulas, including the phase tag, for example $AgCl(s)$.

3. Because weak electrolytes (weak acids, weak bases) are ionized only to a small extent, they are represented in a net ionic reaction equation with the un-ionized formula. For example, acetic acid is represented as CH_3CO_2H, not as $CH_3CO_2^- + H_3O^+$ and ammonia is represented as NH_3, not as $NH_4^+ + OH^-$.

4. Nonelectrolytes are represented by their intact formulas. NEVER ionize a nonelectrolyte! Remember, the goal of any ionic reaction equation is to show species as they primarily exist.

5. The following ions rarely appear in net ionic equations for precipitation reactions or acid-base reactions. Their compounds are highly soluble, so these ions do not often form precipitates. These ions are very common **spectator ions**, or **spectators**:[73]

Na^+, K^+, and other alkali metal ions (Group 1 ions)
NO_3^- (nitrate) ClO_4^- (perchlorate)

---

[72] Or, $H^+(aq)$. Your instructor may have a preference.

[73] These spectator ions are known to undergo changes in some oxidation-reduction reactions, but they do not form precipitates in these double displacement reactions.

In the examples used in this text, these ions may be assumed to be spectators; <u>they should not, therefore, appear in net ionic equations</u>. (In specific reactions there can be a much wider variety of spectator ions; these are just the ones that are essentially always spectators.)

Two examples of these circumstances are offered below. In both cases the boxed ions, above, disappear when the net ionic reaction equation is written.

$$3 \text{ AgNO}_3(aq) + \text{Na}_3\text{PO}_4(aq) \longrightarrow \text{Ag}_3\text{PO}_4(s) + 3 \text{ NaNO}_3(aq) \text{ becomes}$$
$$3 \text{ Ag}^+(aq) + \text{PO}_4{}^{3-}(aq) \longrightarrow \text{Ag}_3\text{PO}_4(s)$$

$$\text{HClO}_4(aq) + \text{KOH}(aq) \longrightarrow \text{H}_2\text{O}(\ell) + \text{KClO}_4(aq) \text{ becomes}$$
$$\text{H}_3\text{O}^+(aq) + \text{OH}^-(aq) \longrightarrow 2 \text{ H}_2\text{O}(\ell)$$

6. As in the preceding example, the net ionic equation for the reaction of a <u>strong acid</u> with a <u>strong base</u> in aqueous solution is *always*:

$$\text{H}_3\text{O}^+(aq) + \text{OH}^-(aq) \longrightarrow 2 \text{ H}_2\text{O}(\ell)^{[74]}$$

In the cases of strong acid + strong base the anion of the acid and the cation of the base will always be spectators.

7. The degree to which certain ions combine to form precipitates can be difficult to predict. You are not therefore asked to memorize lists of ions which form precipitates. The table of solubility rules from Chapter 12 is reposted here. Using the table will be expected, memorizing it will not! In this chapter, if a situation is not adequately addressed by this table, information on precipitates will be provided.[75]

Table 12-6. Solubility Rules for Salts.

Ions that promote <u>solubility</u>:

- All salts of the ammonium ion ($\text{NH}_4{}^+$), and of Group 1 cations, are *soluble*.
- All nitrates ($\text{NO}_3{}^-$), perchlorates ($\text{ClO}_4{}^-$), and acetates ($\text{C}_2\text{H}_3\text{O}_2{}^-$) are *soluble*.
- All chlorides (Cl^-), bromides (Br^-), and iodides (I^-), are *soluble* **EXCEPT** those of silver (Ag^+), lead(II), and mercury(I) (and also mercury(II) for bromides and iodides).
- All sulfates ($\text{SO}_4{}^{2-}$) are soluble **EXCEPT** Ag_2SO_4, Hg_2SO_4, BaSO_4, SrSO_4, and CaSO_4, PbSO_4. (*Ag_2SO_4 is the most soluble of these low-solubility sulfates.)

Ions that promote <u>insolubility</u>:

- All carbonates ($\text{CO}_3{}^{2-}$), sulfites ($\text{SO}_3{}^{2-}$), and phosphates ($\text{PO}_4{}^{3-}$) are *insoluble* **EXCEPT** those of ammonium ($\text{NH}_4{}^+$) and Group 1 cations (see first rule, above).
- All hydroxides (OH^-) are *insoluble* **EXCEPT** those of ammonium, Group 1 cations, barium and strontium. (Calcium hydroxide is slightly soluble.)
- All sulfides (S^{2-}) are *insoluble* **EXCEPT** those of ammonium, Group 1 cations and Group 2 cations.
- All oxides (O^{2-}) are *insoluble* **EXCEPT** those of Group 1 cations, calcium, and barium. *Note:* ammonium oxide does not exist! *Note:* the soluble oxides actually react with the solvent water to form hydroxides: $\text{O}_2{}^{2-} (aq) + \text{H}_2\text{O}(\ell) \rightarrow 2 \text{ OH}^- (aq)$

---

[74] Or, $\text{H}^+(aq) + \text{OH}^-(aq) \rightarrow \text{H}_2\text{O}(\ell)$. Your instructor may have a preference.

[75] Sometimes it is enough to know what the precipitate <u>cannot</u> be because this leaves only one choice for what it is.

8. Warning: if a reaction involves only nonelectrolytes or weak electrolytes in aqueous solution, a net ionic reaction equation cannot be written (or even a complete ionic equation). The **hydrolysis**[76] of methyl acetate in water to produce acetic acid (a weak acid, and thus a weak electrolyte) and methanol serves as an example:

$$CH_3CO_2CH_3(aq) + H_2O(\ell) \longrightarrow CH_3CO_2H(aq) + CH_3OH(aq)$$

This reaction equation involves no strong electrolytes.[77] It must be represented by neutral formulas because this is how the species exist!

Similarly, reactions taking place in the gas phase, even if a strong acid molecule is involved, cannot be represented with an ionic equation. Consider the reaction:

$$HCl(g) + NH_3(g) \longrightarrow NH_4Cl(s)$$

While HCl is a strong acid molecule and ammonium chloride is a water-soluble salt, no separately solubilized ions exist at any time during this gas phase reaction which is shown in Figure 13-7. The gaseous HCl and NH$_3$ molecules are generated at opposite ends of the tube and diffuse through the air until they meet and react to form solid NH$_4$Cl.[78]

Figure 13-7. Gas phase reaction between HCl and NH$_3$. **Left:** Formation of ring of solid NH$_4$Cl (yellow arrow) at point of contact between the two gases. **Right:** Looking into the tube shows the ring of solid NH$_4$Cl deposited.

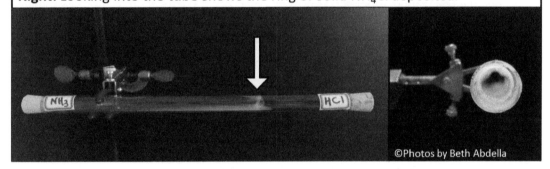

©Photos by Beth Abdella

Example 13-5.

Aqueous mercury(II) chloride reacts with aqueous potassium iodide to form a precipitate. Determine the identity of the precipitate, the net ionic equation for this reaction, and the identity any spectator ions.

Solution:

The reactants are: $HgCl_2$ (aq) + KI (aq)

We rearrange cations and anions to see the choices for the precipitate: HgI_2 or KCl

Solubility rules indicate that mercury(II) iodide must be the precipitate. One method for generating the net ionic reaction equation is to proceed through the three stages (neutral formula, complete ionic, net ionic):

---

[76] "Hydrolysis" literally means breaking with water.

[77] There are no strong acids and no salts (and therefore no soluble salts).

[78] The gases are released from small sponges soaked in aqueous solutions of HCl and NH$_3$ and placed just inside the corks at opposite ends of the tube. Note that the meeting point is closer to the HCl end of the tube due to the slower diffusion of the heavier HCl molecule.

We begin by writing all of the neutral formulas:

$$HgCl_2(aq) + KI(aq) \longrightarrow HgI_2(s) + KCl(aq)$$

Then we balance the neutral formula equation:

$$HgCl_2(aq) + 2\,KI(aq) \longrightarrow HgI_2(s) + 2\,KCl(aq)$$

Next, we dissociate the ions of soluble salts to arrive at the complete ionic reaction equation:

$$Hg^{2+}(aq) + 2\,Cl^-(aq) + 2\,K^+(aq) + 2\,I^-(aq) \longrightarrow HgI_2(s) + 2\,K^+(aq) + 2\,Cl^-(aq)$$

Finally, we cancel identical species on both sides to obtain the net ionic reaction equation:

$$Hg^{2+}(aq) + 2\,I^-(aq) \longrightarrow HgI_2(s)$$

The ions that were eliminated in the writing of the net ionic reaction equation are the spectators: K^+ and Cl^-.

Another method, once you've identified HgI_2 as the precipitate, is to write $HgI_2(s)$ as the product: $\longrightarrow HgI_2(s)$

and then use the appropriate aqueous ions to make it:

$$Hg^{2+}(aq) + 2\,I^-(aq) \longrightarrow HgI_2(s)$$

The spectator ions are the unused ions: K^+ and Cl^-.

Clearly, if you are just asked for a net ionic reaction equation for a precipitation reaction, the second method is more efficient. However, especially if the reaction is not a precipitation reaction, you may want to use the three-step process!

Example 13-6.

Aqueous perchloric acid reacts with aqueous sodium hydroxide. Determine the net ionic equation for this reaction, and identify any spectator ions.

The neutral formula reaction equation is:

$$HClO_4(aq) + NaOH(aq) \longrightarrow H_2O(\ell) + NaClO_4(aq)$$

(As in any reaction between a strong acid and a strong base in aqueous solution, one of the products is water.)

The strong acid is ionized and the strong base is dissociated into its ions. Therefore, the complete ionic reaction equation is:

$$H_3O^+(aq) + ClO_4^-(aq) + Na^+(aq) + OH^-(aq) \longrightarrow H_2O(\ell) + ClO_4^-(aq) + Na^+(aq)$$

The ClO_4^- and Na^+ ions appear on both sides of the equation and may be canceled to obtain the net ionic equation (ClO_4^- and Na^+ are spectator ions in this case):

$$H_3O^+(aq) + OH^-(aq) \longrightarrow 2\,H_2O(\ell)$$

$$\text{or: } H^+(aq) + OH^-(aq) \longrightarrow H_2O(\ell)$$

Note! If you immediately recognize the reactants as a strong acid and a strong base, you can write the net ionic reaction equation without working through the whole process!

Exercise 13-12.

In the following examples, write the net ionic reaction equations, and identify any spectator ions:

   a. The reaction of barium chloride with sodium sulfate in aqueous solution to form
      a precipitate.
   b. The reaction of nitric acid with potassium hydroxide in aqueous solution.
   c. The reaction of silver nitrate with potassium phosphate in aqueous solution to form
      a precipitate.

Example 13-7.

For each of the following processes, write a *balanced* net ionic reaction equation and identify any spectator ions. Parts a-d are precipitation processes for which you should be able to identify the precipitate without help from a table of solubility rules.

   a. $BaCl_2(aq) + Na_2CrO_4(aq) \longrightarrow$

   b. $Pb(NO_3)_2(aq) + HCl(aq) \longrightarrow$

   c. $AgNO_3(aq) + Na_3PO_4(aq) \longrightarrow$

   d. $NaOH(aq) + Fe(NO_3)_3(aq) \longrightarrow$

   e. $HCl(aq) + KOH(aq) \longrightarrow$

Solutions:

   a. $Ba^{2+}(aq) + CrO_4^{2-}(aq) \longrightarrow BaCrO_4(s)$ (Na^+, Cl^- are spectators)

   b. $Pb^{2+}(aq) + 2Cl^-(aq) \longrightarrow PbCl_2(s)$ (H_3O^+, NO_3^- are spectators)

   c. $3Ag^+(aq) + PO_4^{3-}(aq) \longrightarrow Ag_3PO_4(s)$ (Na^+, NO_3^- are spectators)

   d. $Fe^{3+}(aq) + 3OH^-(aq) \longrightarrow Fe(OH)_3(s)$ (Na^+, NO_3^- are spectators)

   e. $H_3O^+(aq) + OH^-(aq) \longrightarrow 2 H_2O(\ell)$ (acid-base neutralization; K^+, Cl^- are spectators)

In some cases, no reaction occurs when aqueous solutions of ionic compounds are mixed. The most easily recognizable of these situations is when the reactants are composed entirely of strong acids and/or the common spectator ions listed in a box on page 87. For example, when aqueous hydrochloric acid and sodium nitrate are mixed:

$$HCl(aq) + NaNO_3(aq) \longrightarrow \quad ?$$

The reactants are completely ionized (strong acid) or dissociated into ions (soluble salt):

$$H_3O^+(aq) + Cl^-(aq) + Na^+(aq) + NO_3^-(aq) \longrightarrow$$

Rearranging the cations and anions produces no stable molecules and no insoluble salts:

$H_3O^+(aq) + NO_3^-(aq)$ is simply ionized HNO_3, another strong acid
$Cl^-(aq) + Na^+(aq)$ is simply the soluble salt, NaCl

Under such circumstances no reaction occurs, and we may write:[79]

$$HCl(aq) + NaNO_3(aq) \longrightarrow \quad \text{No Reaction}$$

[79] A homogeneous mixture has been produced.

Exercise 13-13.

For each of the following, write a <u>net ionic reaction equation</u> (unless there is no reaction) and identify any spectator ions.

a. $FeCl_3(aq)$ + $Na_2S(aq)$ $\longrightarrow$ 　　　　**d.** $Pb(ClO_4)_2(aq)$ + $K_2CrO_4(aq)$ $\longrightarrow$

b. $NiSO_4(aq)$ + $KOH(aq)$ $\longrightarrow$ 　　　　**e.** $KNO_3(aq)$ + $NaClO_4(aq)$ $\longrightarrow$

c. $Hg_2(NO_3)_2(aq)$ + $HCl(aq)$ $\longrightarrow$

4. *Oxidation-reduction reactions*

a. Definitions

Oxidation-reduction reactions, commonly abbreviated **redox** reactions, involve the transfer of electrons between reactants. The following definitions apply:

> **Reduction** = gain of one or more electrons
> **Oxidation** = loss of one or more electrons

One way to remember these is to think of reduction as "reduction in charge," corresponding to a gain of (negative) electrons.[80]

Historically the term "oxidation" was associated with reactions involving oxygen, but this notion no longer applies; both oxidation and reduction are defined in terms of transfer of electrons, and many oxidations do not involve the element oxygen at all.

An example of an oxidation-reduction reaction occurs when a nearly colorless aqueous solution of Cl_2 gas is combined with a colorless aqueous solution of NaI. Figure 13-8 shows three photos of this reaction at different stages. In the first photo, a colorless layer of liquid heptane (C_7H_{16}, less dense than water) floats on top of an aqueous KI solution. When an aqueous solution of Cl_2 is dripped in, the more dense aqueous solution travels through the heptane layer and mixes with the KI solution. A yellow-brown color appears in the aqueous layer, as shown in the second photo. What is happening? It is useful to know that elemental iodine, I_2, is yellow-brown when dissolved in water, and pink when dissolved in nonpolar solvents[81] such as heptane, C_7H_{16}. If the yellow-brown solution is shaken with heptane, the heptane layer turns pink and re-separates (third photo), thus indicating the presence of I_2. When a solute moves from one solvent to another, the process is called an **extraction**. We say that I_2 was **extracted** from water into heptane. During extractions, solutes move into solvents that they prefer; iodine is non-polar and prefers heptane as a solvent. Let's write the net ionic reaction equation for the chemical reaction (not the extraction), which involves both strong electrolytes and non-electrolytes.

---

[80]Here are two other ways to remember these terms; by all means use them if they are helpful:

By using the sentence "LEO the lion says GER!" In this sentence, LEO represents "<u>L</u>oss of <u>E</u>lectrons = <u>O</u>xidation" and GER represents "<u>G</u>ain of <u>E</u>lectrons = <u>R</u>eduction."

"OIL RIG": "<u>O</u>xidation <u>I</u>s <u>L</u>oss" (of electrons), "<u>R</u>eduction <u>I</u>s <u>G</u>ain (of electrons)."

[81]Nonpolar solvents are liquids whose molecules are nonpolar. Hydrocarbons with only C and H in the formula are nonpolar by definition.

We begin by writing the neutral formula reaction equation and balancing it:

$$Cl_2(aq) + 2\ KI(aq) \longrightarrow 2\ KCl(aq) + I_2(aq)$$

Then we write the complete ionic reaction equation, being careful to note that the halogen molecules (Cl_2 and I_2) cannot be dissociated or ionized!

$$Cl_2(aq) + 2\ K^+(aq) + 2\ I^-(aq) \longrightarrow$$
$$2\ K^+(aq) + 2\ Cl^-(aq) + I_2(aq)$$

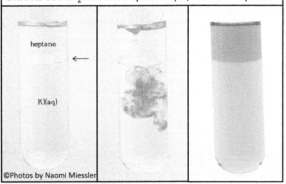

Figure 13-8. Reaction of I^- and Cl_2 produces I_2 (and Cl^-). **Left:** Heptane layer over aqueous KI solution. **Middle:** Adding aqueous Cl_2 (essentially colorless) produces yellow-brown I_2 in aqueous layer. **Right:** Vigorous shaking extracts some I_2 into the heptane layer, where it is pink.

©Photos by Naomi Miessler

Finally, we cancel the species that are unchanged as reactant becomes product (the K^+ ions):

$$Cl_2(aq) + 2\ I^-(aq) \longrightarrow 2\ Cl^-(aq) + I_2(aq)$$

Now that we have a simplified form of the reaction equation, we can see that two electrons are transferred from I^- ions (one from each I^-) to Cl_2. The transfer of electrons is a sign of an oxidation-reduction reaction. Chlorine, Cl_2 is reduced (the atoms of Cl_2 are neutral atoms; they become –1 ions in the product), and I^- is oxidized (its charge increases from –1 to 0). As we saw previously, these processes can be described by half reactions:

Reduction of Cl_2:	$Cl_2 + 2\ e^- \longrightarrow 2\ Cl^-$
Oxidation of I^-:	$2\ I^- \longrightarrow I_2 + 2\ e^-$
Net:	$Cl_2 + 2\ I^- \longrightarrow 2\ Cl^- + I_2$

In oxidation-reduction reactions <u>the number of electrons gained in the reduction process must be exactly balanced by the number lost in the oxidation process</u>. In the example above, 2 electrons are gained in the reduction of Cl_2, and 2 electrons are lost in the oxidation of I^-. The movement of electrons in a reaction such as this one is influenced by the relative electronegativities of the atoms involved. Because Cl atoms are more electronegative than I atoms, the extra electron density ends up on the Cl atoms, so that Cl^- ions are produced.

Oxidation-reduction reactions (quite simple ones, anyway) can be illustrated schematically to emphasize that both reduction and oxidation processes *must* occur simultaneously:

$$Cl_2 + 2\ I^- \longrightarrow 2\ Cl^- + I_2$$

2 e⁻ reduction

2 e⁻ oxidation

The procedure for balancing such equations will be described in another course. For now we will consider only how to identify the species being oxidized or reduced. This is best seen by example.

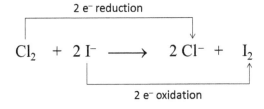

$$2\ Al \longrightarrow 2\ Al^{3+} + 6e^-$$
$$6e^- + 6\ H^+ \longrightarrow 3\ H_2$$
$$2\ Al + 6\ H^+ \longrightarrow 2\ Al^{3+} + 3H_2$$

Example 13-8.

Identify the chemical species being oxidized and reduced in the following reactions, and illustrate schematically as in the example, above.

a. $2\ I^-(aq)\ +\ Br_2(aq)\ \longrightarrow\ I_2(aq)\ +\ 2\ Br^-(aq)$

The charge on Br atoms starts at 0 and moves to –1 (becomes more negative). Bromine must be gaining electrons (one electron per Br) and is therefore being reduced. Iodine starts as a –1 ion and becomes neutral; charge is increasing (becoming more positive), so each I^- ion is losing an electron. This is an oxidation.

$$2\ I^-\ +\ Br_2\ \longrightarrow\ I_2 +\ 2\ Br^-$$

2 e⁻ reduction

2 e⁻ oxidation

b. $2\ H^+(aq)\ +\ Zn(s)\ \longrightarrow\ H_2(g) + Zn^{2+}(aq)$

Each H^+ ion is gaining one electron; H^+ is being reduced (its charge decreases). Zn is losing 2 electrons; it is being oxidized (its charge increases):

$$2\ H^+\ +\ Zn\ \longrightarrow\ H_2 + Zn^{2+}$$

2 e⁻ reduction

2 e⁻ oxidation

c. $2\ S_2O_3^{2-}(aq)\ +\ I_2(aq)\ \longrightarrow\ S_4O_6^{2-}(aq) + 2\ I^-(aq)$

It is easier to begin with the simpler I_2. I_2 is gaining electrons (one per I) and thus is reduced. Consequently, the other reactant, $S_2O_3^{2-}$, must be oxidized. (If one chemical species is being reduced, another <u>must</u> be oxidized. You can see that the overall charge on TWO $S_2O_3^{2-}$ ions is –4. On the product side, the same atoms have a total charge of –2. This is an oxidation because the charge on the same set of atoms became more positive.)

$$2\ S_2O_3^{2-}\ +\ I_2\ \longrightarrow\ S_4O_6^{2-} + 2\ I^-$$

2 e⁻ reduction

2 e⁻ oxidation

d. $2\ Fe(s) + 3\ Cl_2(g)\ \longrightarrow\ 2\ FeCl_3(s)$

Iron is being converted from iron(0) (neutral elements have oxidation states of zero) to iron(III); it is being oxidized. Chlorine is being reduced from a zero oxidation state (again, as a free, neutral element) to Cl^- as a part of a salt. It is being reduced.

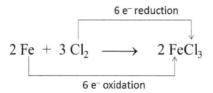

$$2\ Fe\ +\ 3\ Cl_2\ \longrightarrow\ 2\ FeCl_3$$

6 e⁻ reduction

6 e⁻ oxidation

Exercise 13-14.

Identify the chemical species being oxidized and reduced in the following reactions.

    a. $Fe^{3+} + Cu^+ \longrightarrow Fe^{2+} + Cu^{2+}$

    b. $2\,Fe^{3+} + 2\,I^- \longrightarrow 2\,Fe^{2+} + I_2$

    c. $Cu + Cl_2 \longrightarrow CuCl_2$

    d. $4\,Al + 3\,O_2 \longrightarrow 2\,Al_2O_3$

    e. $P_4 + 6\,Cl_2 \longrightarrow 4\,PCl_3$ (Note: PCl_3 is not ionic, but you can use *electronegativities* to determine which atoms gain electron density, and which lose electron density, as the product is formed.)

Remember that we also wrote half reactions when discussing reactions between metals and nonmetals (reaction category #1). Reactions of metals and nonmetals are also redox reactions. The combustion of metals (category #2b) represents a very particular reaction of a metal and a nonmetal (the nonmetal must be O_2). This is also a redox reaction equation that can be written with **half reactions**. Consider, again, the combustion of magnesium metal:

$$2\,Mg(s) + O_2(g) \longrightarrow 2\,MgO(s)$$

Magnesium starts out as a neutral metal and becomes the cation of a salt, so it is oxidized. A half reaction for the oxidation can be written:

$$2\,Mg \longrightarrow 2\,Mg^{2+} + 4\,e^-$$

Oxygen starts out as a neutral molecule and becomes the anion of a salt, so it is reduced. A half reaction for the reduction can be written:

$$O_2 + 4\,e^- \longrightarrow 2\,O^{2-}$$

Make sure to notice that each half reaction is balanced in both atoms and charge, and that the two half reactions can be summed to achieve the overall balanced reaction equation.

The combustion of a metal fits three out of our four categories of chemical reactions!

<u>b. Oxidizing agents, reducing agents</u>

It is common for reactants in redox reactions to be labeled as an **oxidizing agent** or a **reducing agent**. The word "agent" in these phrases is used similarly to a *travel agent*. A travel agent helps to make your travels possible. The travel agent isn't the traveler, you are. Likewise, an oxidizing agent does NOT get oxidized; rather, it is the agent of some other species' oxidation. The species that gets oxidized must lose electrons. The oxidizing agent helps out by accepting those electrons. Therefore, *an oxidizing agent is the species being reduced.*

By the same logic, a reducing agent is the agent of the reduction of some other species. Because that species must gain electrons, the reducing agent helps out by donating those electrons. Therefore, *a reducing agent is the species being oxidized.*

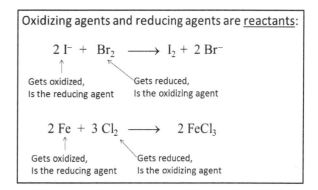

Two examples are given in the box at right. Remember that $FeCl_3$ is composed of Fe^{3+} and Cl^-.

13-4. NUCLEAR REACTION EQUATIONS

Chemical reactions involve the rearrangements of electrons. Nuclear reactions involve changes to the nuclei of atoms. Ancient alchemists, in attempting to turn lead into gold, were unwittingly trying to perform a nuclear reaction! In the area of nuclear chemistry, atoms are often called **nuclides** (note the emphasis on the nucleus!) and are characterized by both the number of protons and the number of neutrons found in the nucleus. Nuclides can have a variety of relationships with one another. Different nuclides of the same element are called **isotopes**: examples include $^{13}_{6}C$ and $^{12}_{6}C$, both of which are nuclides of carbon and isotopes of carbon. Two atoms having the same number of neutrons, such as $^{37}_{17}Cl$ and $^{39}_{19}K$ (both have 20 neutrons, 37–17 = 20 and 39–19 = 20) are called **isotones**. Isotones have the same number of neutrons, but different numbers of protons; they are always different elements.

Radioactivity, or **radioactive decay** is the spontaneous decay of an unstable nucleus via loss of ionizing radiation or nuclear particles. Figure 13-9 shows the periodic table colored to indicate the degree of instability of various elements. Blue indicates that the most stable isotope of the element is completely stable. Green indicates that the most stable isotope is radioactive, but with such a long half-life (millions of years) that the decay events do not occur on a timeframe that is noticeable. From there, instability increases from yellow to orange to red to purple. The elements colored purple are not naturally occurring elements. They are synthesized in laboratories and even the most stable of the isotopes produced have exceeding short half-lives. The longest half-life of a known meitnerium (Mt) isotope, for instance, is less than 8 seconds.

Figure 13-9. Elements colored based on the stability of the most stable isotope. Blue elements have at least one stable isotope. Green, yellow, orange, red and purple indicate increasing instability of the most stable isotope.

H																															He
Li	Be																										B	C	N	O	F	Ne
Na	Mg																										Al	Si	P	S	Cl	Ar
K	Ca	Sc																Ti	V	Cr	Mn	Fe	Co	Ni	Cu	Zn	Ga	Ge	As	Se	Br	Kr
Rb	Sr	Y																Zr	Nb	Mo	Tc	Ru	Rh	Pd	Ag	Cd	In	Sn	Sb	Te	I	Xe
Cs	Ba	La	Ce	Pr	Nd	Pm	Sm	Eu	Gd	Tb	Dy	Ho	Er	Tm	Yb	Lu	Hf	Ta	W	Re	Os	Ir	Pt	Au	Hg	Tl	Pb	Bi	Po	At	Rn
Fr	Ra	Ac	Th	Pa	U	Np	Pu	Am	Cm	Bk	Cf	Es	Fm	Md	No	Lr	Rf	Db	Sg	Bh	Hs	Mt	Ds	Rg	Cn	Nh	Fl	Mc	Lv	Ts	Og

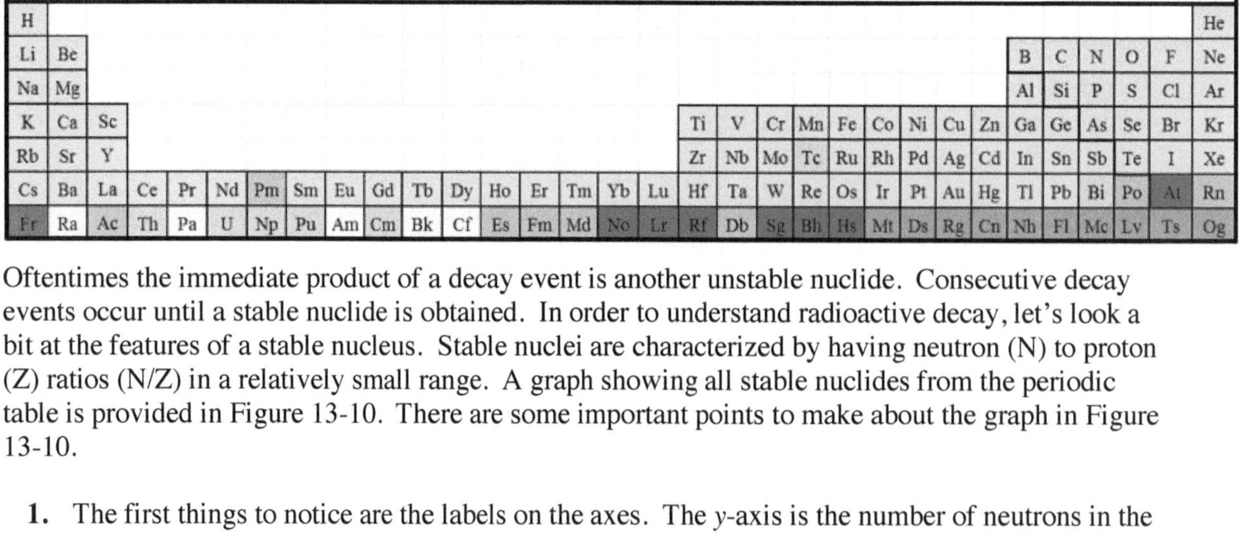

Oftentimes the immediate product of a decay event is another unstable nuclide. Consecutive decay events occur until a stable nuclide is obtained. In order to understand radioactive decay, let's look a bit at the features of a stable nucleus. Stable nuclei are characterized by having neutron (N) to proton (Z) ratios (N/Z) in a relatively small range. A graph showing all stable nuclides from the periodic table is provided in Figure 13-10. There are some important points to make about the graph in Figure 13-10.

1. The first things to notice are the labels on the axes. The y-axis is the number of neutrons in the nucleus and the x-axis is the number of protons. Therefore, blue marks on the same verticle line indicate **isotopes** of the same element (same number of protons, Z, different numbers of neutrons, N). For instance, on the Z =30 line verticle line, we see 5 markers. The lowest one is at 30 protons and 34 neutrons (^{64}Zn) and highest one is at 30 protons and 40 neutrons (^{70}Zn).

2. Markers on the same horizontal line represent **isotones.** These are nuclides with the same number of neutrons, but different numbers of protons. The markers on the same horizontal line must represent different elements, because the number of protons is different. For instance on the horizontal line of N = 60, there are four blue markers. The most left marker is at N = 60, Z = 44 (^{104}Ru) and the most right of these markers is at N = 60, Z = 48 (^{108}Cd).

In both cases, remember that this Figure 13-10 shows only STABLE isotopes.

3. You can find two gaps along the x-axis for elements that have no stable isotopes (Z = 43 and Z = 61). All isotopes of technetium and promethium are unstable toward radioactive decay.

4. This graph ends at a Z of 82 (element = lead). All elements beyond Pb on the periodic table exist only as radioactive nuclides. One bismuth nuclide, $^{209}_{83}Bi$, deserves special comment. It is radioactive, but its **half-life**[82] is 1.9×10^{19} years! Thus, it behaves as if stable. This is why the bismuth block in Figure 13-9 is green!

5. Looking carefully should convince you that having an even number of protons encourages stability; note the longer vertical rises at even values of Z.

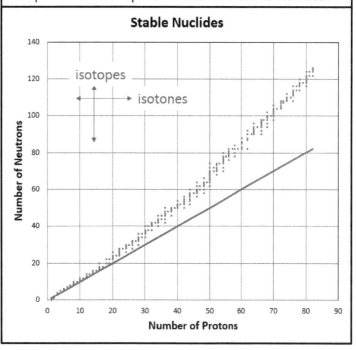

Figure 13-10. A graph of all stable nuclides of the elements (blue). For comparison, a line corresponding to equal numbers of protons and neutrons is included.

6. Stable nuclides with Z < 20 have approximately the same numbers of protons and neutrons. The red line and blue markers coincide quite well. The average value of N/Z = 1.06. As nuclides get heavier, the ratio of N/Z in stable nuclides grows:

when $20 \le Z < 50$, the average value of N/Z = 1.25; when $Z \ge 50$, the average value of N/Z = 1.44.

On average, the slope of the nuclide data increases as nuclides get heavier; the blue broken line moves further above the red (N/Z = 1) line.

Where on this plot do the unstable nuclides appear? There are many unstable nuclides and most of them occur in three regions outside of the boundary of the blue markers in Figure 13-10:

a. *Above and left of the blue "line."* Compared to stable nuclides, these could be described either as isotopes with too many neutrons or isotones with too few protons. Their N/Z ratios are <u>too large</u> for stability.

b. *Below and right of the blue "line."* Compared to stable nuclides, these could be described either as isotopes with too few neutrons or isotones with too many protons. Their N/Z ratios are <u>too small</u> for stability.

c. *Beyond the existing "line."* The elements beyond lead on the periodic table only exist as unstable nuclides, thus the blue broken line ends at Z = 82. Unstable nuclides with Z > 82, need to lose mass in order to achieve stability.

What should the strategy of radioactive decay be in these three cases?

---

[82] The amount of time it takes for half of the nuclides to undergo the decay event.

In case "**a**" the N/Z ratio must be decreased (it is too big). A nuclear process that converts neutrons into protons will help. A process called **beta emission** will be a preferred method of decay for these nuclides.

In case "**b**," the N/Z ratio must be increased. A nuclear process that converts protons into neutrons will be helpful. Both **positron emission** and **electron capture** have this effect.

Finally, in case "**c**," the unstable nuclide will often employ **alpha emission** in a general strategy to lose nuclear mass. If the nuclide has a mass greater than 90, **spontaneous fission** may also occur.

We'll take a look at each of these types of radioactive decay.

A. Beta (β^-) Emission

In nuclear chemistry, the beta-minus (β^-) particle is equivalent to an electron. However, the β^- particle is lost from the nucleus of an atom as a very high energy particle; it is not an inhabitant of the electron cloud. The symbol for a β^- particle is

$$_{-1}^{0}e$$ a notation analogous to carbon-12 being $_{6}^{12}C$. (Remember that the general form of this notation is $_{Z}^{A}X$, where A = mass number and Z = atomic number.)

That A = 0 for a β^- particle indicates that there are no protons or neutrons present. In the notation for carbon-12, the "6" indicates the presence of 6 protons in the nucleus, or a +6 charge (in the nucleus). The analogous "–1" in the β^- particle notation represents the charge of the β^- particle.

When a nucleus emits a β^- particle, the nucleus becomes more positively charged; loss of negative charge increases the remaining positive charge. In essence, we think about one of the neutrons in the nucleus losing the β^- particle. That neutron becomes a proton! We could write:

$$n^0 \longrightarrow p^+ + e^-$$

But in nuclear chemistry notation, we would write this instead:

$$_{0}^{1}n \longrightarrow _{1}^{1}p + _{-1}^{0}e$$

The balance of matter and charge in a nuclear reaction equation is manifest in that the total A values must be equal on both sides of the arrow and the total Z values must be equal on both sides of the arrow. In the representation above, A = 1 on each side and Z = 0.

Nuclear medicine is a field in which radioactive materials are used in the diagnosis and/or treatment of disease. Iodine-131 is a β^- emitter that is used in some cases of thyroid cancer therapy and in thyroid imaging. The reaction equation for the emission of the β^- particle is given here.

$$_{53}^{131}I \longrightarrow _{54}^{131}Xe + _{-1}^{0}e$$

In a reaction equation such as the one above, iodine-131 is known as the **parent nuclide** and xenon-131 is called the **daughter nuclide**. The ability to use iodine-131 for imaging is not a direct result of the β^- particle. Instead, imaging is a result of the release of gamma radiation during the decay event. This radiation can be visualized with a gamma camera.

The medical use of radioisotopes is dependent on three major considerations:

1.   The half-life of the radioisotope, which is related to the **dosage rate** (decay events per time). For medical applications short half-lives are generally necessary to avoid prolonged exposure for the patient and others. The half-life of iodine-131 is about 8 days. This means that every 8 days, half of the iodine-131 is converted to xenon-131.

2.   Targeting the diseased tissue. Because the thyroid gland naturally takes up iodine, the use of iodine-131 for thyroid therapy provides excellent targeting.

3. The energy of the emitted β^- particle. Different β^- emitters[83] release the particle at different energies. The energy of the emission controls the extent of penetration of the particle into surrounding tissues, and thus controls the extent of tissue damage expected.

B. Positron (β^+) Emission and Electron Capture

Unstable nuclides with an N/Z ratio that is too small tend to employ decay behaviors that result in protons becoming neutrons. Smaller Z and larger N increase the size of the N/Z ratio. **Positron emission** is one of these tactics. A **positron** is the positively charged equivalent to the electron. Positrons are often represented as β^+ and may be called beta-plus particles. In nuclear reaction equations they are represented as $_1^0 e$. The event of interest for increasing the N/Z ratio is the conversion of a proton into a neutron. We can write

$$_1^1 p \longrightarrow {}_0^1 n + {}_1^0 e$$

We see that the emission of a positron from a proton leaves the particle without charge; it is now a neutron.

Positron emission tomography (PET) is a nuclear medicine imaging technique that uses the fluorine-18 nuclide. This nuclide is a positron emitter with a half-life of only about 110 minutes. The fluorine-18 nuclide is delivered via a modified glucose molecule (see structure, right) where the fluorine atom replaces one of the hydroxyl (OH) groups of the sugar. Molecules of this sort are known as **radiotracers**. The fluorination of glucose makes the molecule inert to normal metabolic processing. However, after the positron emission event, the glucose molecule can enter normal metabolic routes. Here's why:

The balanced nuclear equation for the decay event is

$$_9^{18} F \longrightarrow {}_8^{18} O + {}_1^0 e$$

The oxygen-18 daughter nuclide is produced as an anion: $-\!\!\!-\!\!\!-\ddot{\underset{..}{F}}:$ becomes $-\!\!\!-\!\!\!-\ddot{\underset{..}{O}}:$

This F had formal charge = 0, but this O has formal charge = –1! Remember, the nucleus now has one less proton! In a biological setting, the oxygen anion is quickly protonated by any number of H^+ donors. Thus, after the decay event, the glucose molecule attains the normal –OH structure, except for the unusual oxygen isotope, which is not a problem in terms of enzyme recognition.

Fluorinated deoxyglucose → Positron emission → glucose

The decay event produces pairs of gamma rays (γ) when the emitted positron decelerates enough to interact with an electron in an **annihilation event**:

$$_1^0 e + {}_{-1}^0 e \longrightarrow 2\gamma$$

The detector disregards any radiation not occurring in pairs and thus is specific for radiation stemming from the radiotracer. Computerized visualization of three-dimensional images follows.

A second nuclear event with the *same essential outcome* is called **electron capture**. Unlike the other events we have discussed so far, this event features the addition of a particle to the nucleus,

---

[83] Any nuclide whose radioactive decay features beta-particle emission.

rather than the loss of a particle. The particle in question is a core electron of the atom. The core electron is captured by the nucleus and promotes the transformation of a proton into a neutron. We can write the nuclear reaction equation:

$$_1^1p \; + \; _{-1}^0e \longrightarrow \; _0^1n$$

So, a proton can become a neutron either by losing a positron or gaining an electron. Iodine-123 is medically useful as an imaging nuclide. In comparison to iodine-131, discussed above, iodine-123 has a much shorter half-life (13.2 hours), generates gamma radiation for the imaging process, but does not release β^- particles. The electron capture event can be summarized as follows:

$$_{53}^{123}I \; + \; _{-1}^0e \longrightarrow \; _{52}^{123}Te + \text{gamma radiation}$$

As you can see, this nuclide is useful for imaging, but not for therapies. Remember, the captured electron comes from the iodine-123 electronic core. The electron capture event impacts only the iodine atom; surrounding molecules and tissues are not affected in any way.

C. Alpha (α) Emission

An **alpha particle** is identical to a helium nucleus, containing 2 protons and 2 neutrons. It is a much more massive particle than the beta-minus (β^-) or beta-plus (β^+) particles discussed above. An alpha particle can be represented as $_2^4He^{2+}$. **Alpha decay** is a process by which an unstable nuclide (a radio-isotope) may stabilize itself by loss of an alpha particle from the nucleus. Because of the mass of an alpha particle, this decay event can help heavy atoms become lighter (and eventually stable). Additionally, unstable nuclides with N/Z ratios that are too small can benefit from the loss of an alpha particle. For example, when radon-210 emits an alpha particle, it becomes a polonium-206 nuclide.

$$_{86}^{210}Rn \longrightarrow \; _{84}^{206}Po + \; _2^4He$$

The N/Z ratio of the original radon is 124/86 = 1.44 whereas the N/Z ratio of the polonium daughter nuclide is 122/84 = 1.45.

Alpha-decay is used as an ionization strategy in some smoke detector units. The alpha particle has particularly low penetrative power, and thus alpha particles are much easier to confine than beta particles, β^- or β^+. The alpha particle ionizes air components by knocking away electrons from stable molecules such as nitrogen and oxygen. The negatively charged free electrons and positively charged ions can produce a current between two electrodes. If smoke particles enter the ionizing chamber, the ions tend to stick to the smoke particles and thus can no longer contribute to the current in the detector. A diminished current causes the alarm to sound. Americium-241 is the parent nuclide used:

$$_{95}^{241}Am \longrightarrow \; _{93}^{237}Np + \; _2^4He$$

Americium has a half-life of 432 years, so you don't have to worry about your smoke detector running out of it! Also, because the radiation dosage that might occur to occupants of the home is far smaller (essentially zero) than normal background radiation, having this material in the home is not a danger.

D. Spontaneous Fission

Some very large nuclides (> 90 amu) undergo **spontaneous fission** events, resulting in two much lighter daughter nuclides and (usually) some number of free neutrons. Spontaneous fission, being true to its name, does not require an induction event, as is necessary to begin fission processes in the types of nuclear chain reactions commonly employed by nuclear reactors and bombs. Californium-252 undergoes the following spontaneous fission event:

$$_{98}^{252}Cf \longrightarrow \; _{54}^{140}Xe + \; _{44}^{108}Ru + \; 4 \; _0^1n$$

Neither daughter nuclide is stable, so further decay will ensue; xenon-140, for example, has too many neutrons to be stable (N/Z is too large) and emits β⁻ particles. The half-life of californium-252 is just over 2.5 years. Californium is produced in the United States at Oak Ridge National Lab near Knoxville, Tennessee. The neutrons produced by this spontaneous fission event can be used to initiate fission reactions in nuclear reactors, or as neutron sources for neutron spectroscopy or neutron diffraction experiments.

E. Induced Fission

As mentioned in the previous section, not all fission reactions are spontaneous. **Chain reactions** (capable of self-propagation) in nuclear reactors can be initiated by exposing uranium-235 to a small number of energetic neutrons (such as californium-252 could provide, see above). The natural half-life of uranium-235 is 700 million years; clearly we need to help it along if its decay is to be useful. The fission event caused by a collision of a free neutron with the uranium-235 nucleus can be described as follows:

$$\ce{^{235}_{92}U} + \ce{^{1}_{0}n} \longrightarrow \ce{^{90}_{38}Sr} + \ce{^{143}_{54}Xe} + 3\,\ce{^{1}_{0}n}$$

If the product neutrons find additional uranium-235 nuclei with which to collide, a chain reaction ensues, as diagrammed in Figure 13-11. Each round generates 3 neutrons from 1, so the magnitude of the reaction continues to build if each neutron can "find" a uranium-235 nucleus.

The first fission step of a chain reaction almost invariably produces additional unstable nuclides (such as $\ce{^{90}_{38}Sr}$ and $\ce{^{143}_{54}Xe}$ in Figure 13-11). As these daughter nuclides continue to decay, one or more of them may spawn additional neutrons. Neutrons that become available in this manner are called **delayed neutrons**, because they come from subsequent events rather than

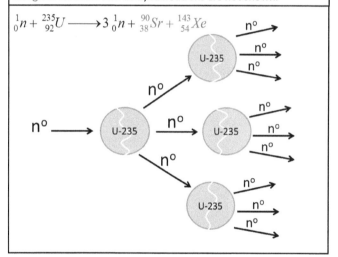

Figure 13-11. A schematic diagram of a self-sustaining nuclear chain reaction. The fission reaction was induced by an initial collision between a free neutron and a uranium-235 nuclide. Daughter nuclides and delayed neutrons are not shown.

the primary fission event. Figure 13-11 shows the minimal number of sustaining neutrons, none of these are delayed neutrons.

Surprisingly, perhaps, neutrons can be too high in energy to lead to the fission event. Such high energy neutrons can lead instead to **neutron capture**:

$$\ce{^{235}_{92}U} + \ce{^{1}_{0}n} \longrightarrow \ce{^{236}_{92}U}$$

The neutron capture process contributes toward the **termination** of the chain reaction by using a neutron without producing at least one replacement.

13-5. BIOCHEMICAL REACTION TYPES

The chemical reactions that take place in living cells control all of the systems necessary for life. Many of these reactions are parts of metabolic pathways. All of **metabolism** can be sub-classified as either **catabolism**, which is concerned with the breakdown of foodstuffs and conversion into biological energy forms such as ATP, and **anabolism**, which is concerned with the bio-synthesis of necessary structures and macromolecules (proteins, RNA, etc.) within the cell. In a sense, catabolism and anabolism are opposite pathways: catabolism generally starts with large molecules and processes them, eventually, into small stable molecules such as CO_2. Anabolism, on the other hand, tends to start with small molecules (the monomers, perhaps) and build up the polymeric structure of needed proteins and nucleic acids. Photosynthesis, for example, is a fundamental anabolic pathway in plants. It features simple reagents (CO_2 and H_2O) and builds up the more complex sugar molecules such as glucose and sucrose.

While there are thousands of reactions to study within the scope of metabolic pathways, these can be categorized into a subset of types of reactions, some of which are familiar to us. For example, within the ten step process called **glycolysis** (see Table 13-2 for help with bold words in this section), there are **isomerization** reactions, **phosphorylation** reactions, a **decomposition**-like reaction, and **oxidation-reduction** reactions. A particularly interesting type of redox reaction is an **internal redox reaction** wherein one carbon atom of the reactant is oxidized while another is reduced. Internal redox reactions are a type of **isomerization**, because the reactant and product have the same formulas. As we have seen with chemical reactions, one biochemical reaction may fit more than one category. Examples of these types of reactions are shown in Figure 13-12.

Table 13-2. Comments about the **bold** words in the paragraph, above.	
Glycolysis	Catabolic process achieving the initial stages of glucose breakdown.
Isomerization	One molecule (or ion) rearranges structurally to become an isomer.
Phosphorylation	A phosphate group, PO_4^{3-}, is added to a metabolite.
Decomposition	A metabolite is cleaved into two smaller metabolites
Oxidation-Reduction (Redox)	These are generally oxidations of fuel molecules (in catabolism) or reductions of small molecules in order to synthesize larger ones (in anabolism).
Internal Redox	A structural rearrangement of a molecule that results in electron density differences around two of the carbon atoms, so that one is oxidized and the other is reduced. This is a type of isomerization, the overall formulas of the reactant and product are identical.

The structures of the cyclic molecules (in Figure 13-12) are drawn in a style called **Haworth projections**. In Haworth projections, every corner that is not labeled in some other way is a carbon atom. Bond angles are not shown realistically, but rather these structures err on the side of trying to simplify the view of the molecule, similar to most Lewis dot structures showing 90° geometries when actual geometries are quite different. Remember that almost all carbon atoms in stable structures are involved in four bonds. For simplicity, if a bond is C-H, it is not shown in a Haworth projection; we just recognize that it must be there. The hexagon and

Figure 13-12. Examples of types of biochemical reactions, in the order that these particular reactions occur in glycolysis. From the top: *phosphorylation; isomerization; decomposition; oxidation-reduction.*

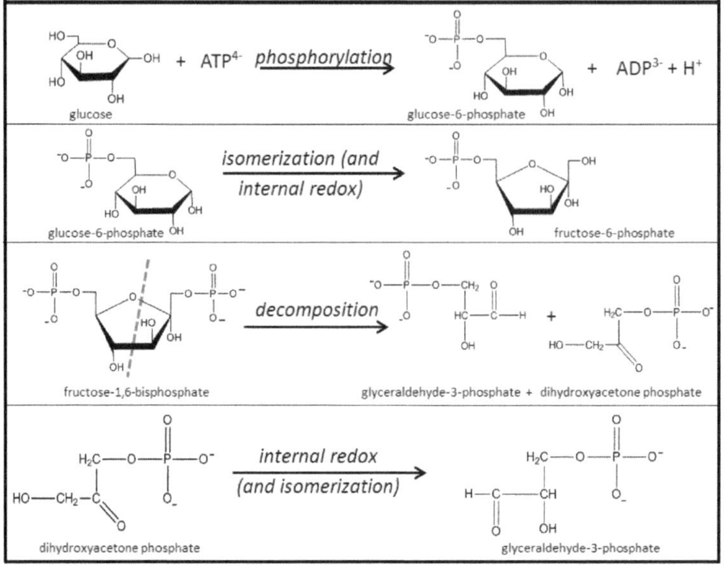

pentagon rings of these molecules are not actually planar and the bonds aimed "up" and "down" are not actually straight up and down because the carbon centers are tetrahedral!

We can learn a little bit about each of the reactions outlined in Figure 13-12. Before we begin, notice that all of the "molecules" shown in Figure 13-12 (except glucose) are actually ions. In the context of biochemistry, it is not unusual to call charged species "molecules." We will do that in the discussion, below. Note that each of the reactions shown in Figure 13-12 is balanced in atoms and in charge; this is definitely hard to see when a reactant is called "ATP⁴⁻." What are all the atoms? Having to think about "invisible" hydrogen atoms doesn't help, either. We'll help you out in the sections below.

Figure 13-13. Top: The structure of ATP with the terminal phosphate group in red. **Bottom:** An abbreviated structure.

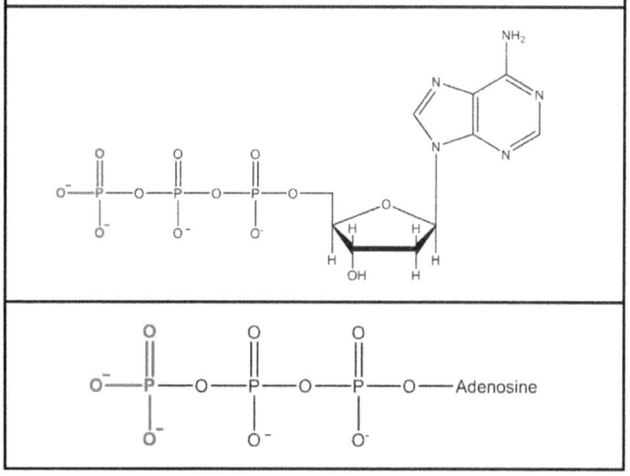

A. Phosphorylation

In the **phosphorylation** of glucose, the terminal phosphate group of an ATP molecule (see Figure 13-13) is "attacked" by a lone pair of electrons on the oxygen atom of carbon #6 (see Figure 13-14). This results in a new bond between glucose and the terminal phosphate group (and loss of the bond from the phosphate group to the remaining ADP portion of ATP). Comparison of this **reaction mechanism**[84] to the serine phosphorylation event associated with the Na⁺-K⁺ ATPase enzyme in Chapter 12 (Figure 12-42) should

Figure 13-14. The movements of electron pairs (the *mechanism*) of a phosphorylation reaction. This one features glucose as the substrate (using stylized structures for simplicity). The blue arrow represents the "attack" of a pair of electrons to form a new bond.

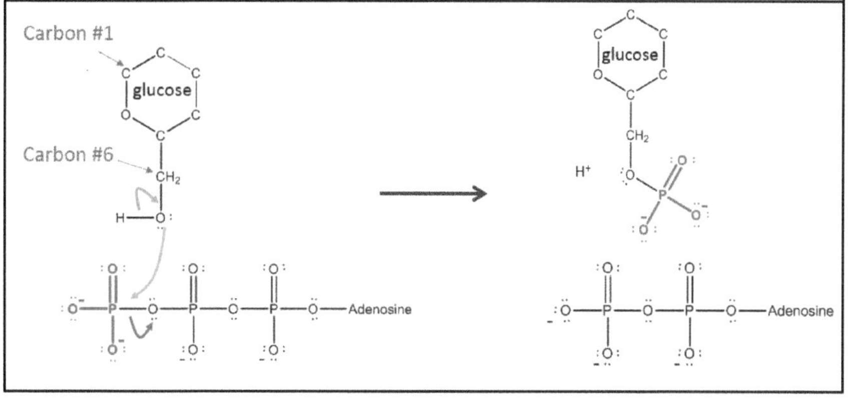

convince you that the processes are essentially identical, differing only in the identity of the molecule containing the attacking OH group to be phosphorylated.

When a cell takes in glucose from the blood stream, phosphorylation occurs very quickly. The goal is to change the glucose molecule in such a way that the same mechanism that brought it into the cell, will not recognize it and let it back out! A phosphate group carries a –2 charge that makes glucose-6-phosphate unrecognizable to a transport molecule looking to bind glucose. Additionally, because charged species cannot travel through the hydrophobic interior of a membrane, cells quickly add charge to molecules that they want to sequester for their own use. A charged species will definitely not be able to diffuse through a membrane.

---

[84] A "mechanism" is a step-by-step illustration of how a reaction proceeds. These illustrations often utilize curved arrows showing the movements of valence electrons as bonds are rearranged.

B. Isomerization

In the second reaction of Figure 13-12, glucose-6-phosphate is isomerized to fructose-6-phosphate. These two molecules are compared in Figure 13-15. Both have the same formula, so they are isomers. The carbon atoms in the two molecules are numbered in red to help you see the relationship of one molecule to the other. Notice that the OH group on carbon #4 is "down" and on carbon #3 is "up" and on carbon #2 is "down." These aspects of the structures are unchanged during the isomerization! In the glucose structure, the ring oxygen (blue) bonds carbons #5 and #1. In the fructose structure the ring oxygen bonds carbons #5 and #2.

Figure 13-15. Glucose-6-phosphate and fructose-6-phosphate are isomers with formula $C_6H_{11}O_9P$. There are 7 "understood" hydrogen atoms in each structure; for example, carbon #6 in both structures shows two bonds, there must be two more (to H atoms).

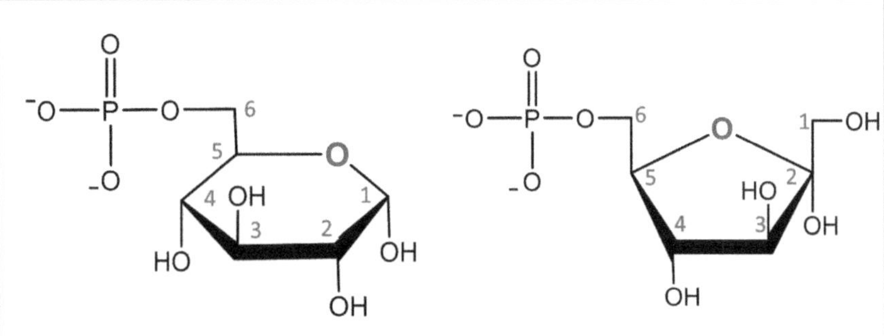

As noted in Figure 13-12, this reaction can also be categorized as an internal redox reaction. In glucose, carbon #1 is the most highly oxidized (having the 2 bonds to oxygen instead of 1 is a good way to see this.) In fructose, carbon #2 is the most highly oxidized. Because oxygen is more electronegative than carbon, carbon loses electron density when bonded to oxygen. The more bonds to oxygen, the more electron density is lost by carbon. Thus, in the transition from the left structure to the right structure, carbon #1 is reduced (fewer bonds to oxygen) and carbon #2 is oxidized (more bonds to oxygen).

C. Decomposition

Actually, the whole catabolic process is a decomposition pathway, but this particular reaction lets us see a 6-carbon molecule coming apart into two 3-carbon molecules.

We have carried the carbon numbering scheme of the reactant over to the products. The blue dotted line separates the original molecule into the two halves. Notice that the cell places a phosphate on each half of the reactant before cleaving it, thus assuring that both products will be trapped inside the cell membrane!

Figure 13-16. Decomposition of fructose-1,6-bisphosphate into two 3-carbon pieces. The blue dotted line shows the two halves of the substrate. Carbons are numbered identically in reactant and products. All H atoms are shown in the products. $C_6H_{10}O_{12}P_2^{4-} \rightarrow 2\ C_3H_5O_6P^{2-}$

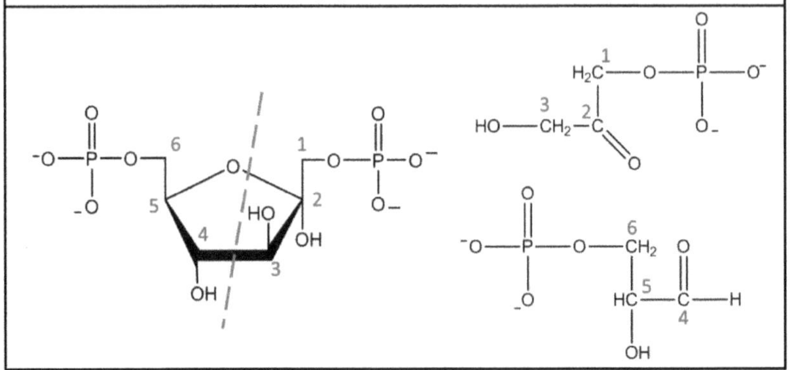

This reaction is also an oxidation reaction for one of the carbons. Can you find the one?[85]

D. Internal redox (a type of isomerization)

As seen in Figure 13-16 and 13-17, the 3-carbon products of the decomposition reaction are isomers of each other; they have identical formulas. Only one of them (glyceraldehyde-3-phosphate)

---

[85] Carbon #4 starts with one bond to oxygen and ends with two bonds to oxygen. Thus it was oxidized.

can continue in the glycolytic pathway, so the other one must be converted into that same form. The difference between the two has to do with the oxidation states of two of the carbon atoms. In the reactant (dihydroxyacetone phosphate, Fig. 13-17) the blue carbon is the most oxidized (has two bonds to oxygen) and in the product (glyceraldehyde-3-phosphate) the pink carbon is the most oxidized (has two bonds to oxygen).

Figure 13-17. Internal redox reaction (and isomerization). Dihydroxyacetone phosphate becomes a second glyceraldehyde-3-phosphate. The oxidation state of the red carbon is unchanged. The blue carbon goes from two bonds to oxygen to one bond to oxygen (it is reduced). The pink carbon goes from one bond to oxygen to two bonds to oxygen (it is oxidized).

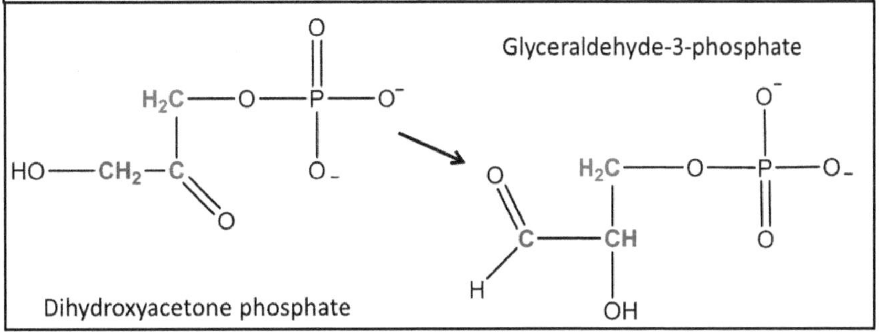

Thus, during this isomerization reaction, the blue carbon gets reduced; it has more electron density in the product than in the reactant because it loses a bond to oxygen. Its partial charge becomes less positive. The pink carbon gets oxidized; it loses electron density as it increases its number of bonds to oxygen. Its partial charge becomes more positive. These definitions of oxidation and reduction match our earlier treatment of the terms. It is more difficult to see here than in ionic examples because the overall charges on these ions do not change, instead, partial charges on substituent atoms change.

In your future study of organic chemistry and biochemistry, make sure to look for *patterns* in reactivity. If you learn a pattern (how a phosphorylation reaction proceeds, for example) it can be applied in many different instances without "memorizing" each separate occurrence.

CHAPTER 13 PROBLEMS

1. Name the phase change and indicate if it is endothermic or exothermic.

    a. $I_2(g) \longrightarrow I_2(s)$ **b.** $C_6H_6(\ell) \longrightarrow C_6H_6(g)$

    c. $CO_2(s) \longrightarrow CO_2(g)$

2. Indicate whether each process is endothermic or exothermic. Make a case for your answer.

    a. $Cu(s) \longrightarrow Cu(\ell)$ **b.** $H_2O(g) \longrightarrow H_2O(\ell)$

    c. concrete(unset) $\longrightarrow$ concrete(set)

3. Write reaction equations for each of the following physical processes.

    a. evaporation of acetone (CH_3COCH_3)   **b.** vapor deposition of carbon dioxide

    c. melting of iron   **d.** freezing of methanol (CH_3OH)

    e. sublimation of naphthalene ($C_{10}H_8$)   **f.** condensation of oxygen

    g. precipitation of menthol ($C_{10}H_{20}O$)

4. Water can be decomposed to its elements by electrolysis. Write a balanced reaction equation for the change that occurs. Is this a physical or chemical change?

5. Classify each of the following properties as physical or chemical.

    a. crystallization   **b.** excellent oxidizing agent

    c. explosive   **d.** non-reactive

    e. soluble in alcohol   **f.** high density

    g. unstable in the presence of moisture

6. Balance the following chemical equations:

    a. $C_{10}H_8 + O_2 \longrightarrow CO_2 + H_2O$ **b.** $Al + Br_2 \longrightarrow Al_2Br_6$

    c. $B_2O_3 + BrF_3 \longrightarrow BF_3 + Br_2 + O_2$ **d.** $XeF_6 + H_2O \longrightarrow XeO_3 + HF$

    e. $I_2O_5 + IF_5 \longrightarrow IOF_3$

7. Write balanced chemical equations for the following reactions:

    a. Ammonium dichromate decomposes when heated to give chromium(III) oxide, water, and nitrogen gas.

    b. Dinitrogen dioxide reacts with oxygen gas to form nitrogen dioxide.

    c. Silver oxide reacts with perchloric acid to give silver perchlorate plus water.

    d. Palladium(II) iodide reacts with fluorine gas to form palladium(II) fluoride plus iodine heptafluoride.

8. Write and balance the chemical equation for the complete combustion of propane, C_3H_8, the major component in many home heating fuels.

9. Sodium hydride reacts *vigorously* with hydrogen chloride gas. Write a balanced chemical equation for this reaction.

10.   Write net ionic equations for the following reactions:

   a. $Pb(NO_3)_2(aq) + 2\ KI(aq) \longrightarrow PbI_2(s) + 2\ KNO_3(aq)$

   b. $Pb(NO_3)_2(aq) + (NH_4)_2S(aq) \longrightarrow PbS(s) + 2\ NH_4NO_3(aq)$

   c. $Zn(s) + Cu(SO_4)(aq) \longrightarrow ZnSO_4(aq) + Cu(s)$

   d. $Cl_2(aq) + 2\ NaOH(aq) \longrightarrow NaCl(aq) + NaOCl(aq) + H_2O(\ell)$

11.   Complete and/or balance these neutral formula equations and then write a net ionic equation.

   a. $Mg(s) + HCl(aq) \longrightarrow MgCl_2(aq) + H_2(aq)$

   b. $Cl_2(aq) + KBr(aq) \longrightarrow Br_2(aq) + KCl(aq)$

   c. $Na_2CO_3(aq) + HNO_3(aq) \longrightarrow NaNO_3(aq) + H_2O(\ell) + CO_2(g)$

   d. $H_3PO_4(aq) + NaOH(aq) \longrightarrow Na_3PO_4(aq) + H_2O(\ell)$

   e. $CdSO_4(aq) + K_2S(aq) \longrightarrow$ precipitate

   f. $Al_2(SO_4)_3(aq) + BaCl_2(aq) \longrightarrow$ precipitate

12.   When aqueous solutions of lead(II) nitrate and rubidium chromate are mixed, a precipitate forms. Write a net ionic equation for this reaction.

13.   Aqueous lead(II) nitrate reacts with aqueous hydrochloric acid to yield a precipitate.

   a.   Write a net ionic equation for this reaction.

   b.   The product of this reaction dissolves in hot water (but not cold). Is the reaction as you have written it in part a exothermic or endothermic?

   c.   Addition of aqueous potassium chromate to the hot solution in part b gives a yellow precipitate. What is the formula of this precipitate?

14.   When an aqueous solution of bromine is mixed with an aqueous solution of potassium iodide, the resulting solution becomes brown. When this solution is subsequently stirred with heptane, the heptane layer becomes purple.

   a.   Write a <u>net ionic</u> equation for the reaction that occurs between aqueous bromine and aqueous potassium iodide.

   b.   What is the formula of the chemical species that is responsible for the purple color?

15.   Write balanced, <u>net ionic</u> equations for the following reactions in aqueous solution:

   a.   Iron(III) chloride reacts with sodium hydroxide to form a precipitate.

   b.   Mercury(I) nitrate reacts with ammonium chloride to form a precipitate.

   c.   Barium chloride reacts with sulfuric acid to form a precipitate.

   d.   Calcium chloride reacts with sodium carbonate to form a precipitate.

   e.   Mercury(I) nitrate reacts with lithium bromide to form a precipitate.

   f.   Hydroiodic acid reacts with barium hydroxide.

16. An overworked chemistry student accidentally spilled some iodine solution on her instructor's white lab coat, leaving a hideous brown stain. She thought rapidly: she prepared a solution of sodium thiosulfate, used the solution to rinse the spot, and the brown color went away. Write a balanced chemical equation (<u>net ionic</u> equation) for the chemical reaction that removed the iodine stain. [Hint: one product was the ion $S_4O_6^{2-}$.]

17. One way to remove carbon dioxide from air is to bubble the air through aqueous KOH; the carbon dioxide is converted to carbonate, and water is formed as a byproduct. Write a net ionic equation for this reaction.

18. Each of the reaction equations, below, is a redox reaction. Balance the reaction equation, and then write both half reaction equations.

    a. $Na + Cl_2 \longrightarrow NaCl$ **b.** $AlBr_3 \longrightarrow Al + Br_2$

    c. $Ag_2S \longrightarrow Ag + S_8$ **d.** $Fe + O_2 \longrightarrow Fe_2O_3$

    e. $Ni_2O_3 \longrightarrow Ni + O_2$ **f.** $Zn + P_4 \longrightarrow Zn_3P_2$

19. Problem #18, above, provided six unbalanced redox reaction equations.

    a. Which of the reaction equations in number 18 can also be categorized as combustion reaction equations?

    b. Which of the reactions equations in number 18 can also be categorized as reactions between a metal and a nonmetal?

20. Write balanced nuclear reaction equations for each of the following processes.

    a. β^- emission from carbon-14   **b.** electron capture by iodine-125

    c. β^+ emission from boron-8   **d.** alpha emission from plutonium-240

21. Uranium-236 can undergo very slow spontaneous fission events. Supply the missing notation in each of the following spontaneous fission reactions.

    a. $^{236}_{92}U \longrightarrow {}^{140}_{56}Ba + \text{\textit{daugher nuclide?}} + 3\,^{1}_{0}n$

    b. $^{236}_{92}U \longrightarrow {}^{144}_{54}Xe + {}^{90}_{38}Sr + ?\,^{1}_{0}n$ *How many neutrons?*

    c. $^{236}_{92}U \longrightarrow {}^{144}_{55}Cs + \text{\textit{daugher nuclide?}} + 2\,^{1}_{0}n$

22. Starting with the parent nuclide potassium-40, write balanced reaction equations for each of the following nuclear processes:

    a. positron emission   **b.** beta-minus emission   **c.** electron capture

23. Write alpha-decay reaction equations for uranium-238 and uranium-235.

24. A 12-step decay path for neptunium-237 ending with stable thallium-205 is shown.

    a. What type of decay event occurs at each step along the way?

$$^{237}_{93}\text{Np} \xrightarrow{\;①\;} {}^{233}_{91}\text{Pa} \xrightarrow{\;②\;} {}^{233}_{92}\text{U} \xrightarrow{\;③\;} {}^{229}_{90}\text{Th} \xrightarrow{\;④\;} {}^{225}_{88}\text{Ra} \xrightarrow{\;⑤\;} {}^{225}_{89}\text{Ac} \xrightarrow{\;⑥\;}$$

$$^{221}_{87}\text{Fr} \xrightarrow{\;⑦\;} {}^{217}_{85}\text{At} \xrightarrow{\;⑧\;} {}^{213}_{83}\text{Bi} \xrightarrow{\;⑨\;} {}^{213}_{84}\text{Po} \xrightarrow{\;⑩\;} {}^{209}_{82}\text{Pb} \xrightarrow{\;⑪\;} {}^{209}_{83}\text{Bi} \xrightarrow{\;⑫\;} {}^{205}_{81}\text{Tl}$$

    b. What is the N/Z ratio for Np-237? What are the primary stability issues (ratio too high? ratio too low? nucleus too heavy?) How did the decay event remedy this/these problem(s)?

25. Radioactive promethium-145 is the most stable isotope of promethium, Pm.

    a. Describe the position of this nuclide on the graph of stable nuclides (Figure 13-9). Is there an obvious reason for the instability of this nuclide? Explain.

    b. Promethium-145 decays via electron capture with a half-life of 17.7 years. Write the reaction equation for this nuclear process.

    c. Promethium-145 rarely decays by alpha emission. Write the reaction equation for this nuclear process, which has a probability of occurring of just 2.8×10^{-9}.

CHAPTER 14: CHEMICAL STOICHIOMETRY

14-1. INTRODUCTION

Much of the development of chemistry has been an effort to explain chemical phenomena in mathematical terms. In this chapter we will begin to treat chemical reactions mathematically. **Stoichiometry** is the study or use of quantitative relationships between the amount of one substance and the amount of another, which requires an understanding of chemical formulas and the coefficients of reaction equations. While it is likely that many of the problems you will encounter in this chapter are similar to problems that you have seen before, you should be prepared to deal with some new types of problems and some new ways of looking at familiar problems.

Before describing the specific approaches to take in solving various types of calculations involving masses and moles, this chapter will first provide some general suggestions on how to approach chemical calculations.

A. General Suggestions on Chemical Calculations

One way of viewing a chemical problem may be summarized schematically:

Given: Objective:

Data ◄——————— Connection between ——————► A numerical result

How do we make the connection between the information given in the problem and the numerical result? In other words, how do we develop a plan to <u>translate</u> or <u>convert</u> from information to the desired result?

To make the connection between the information given in the problem and the objective of the problem, several steps are often useful:

1. <u>Write down</u> the numeric information, <u>with appropriate units</u>.

2. <u>Write down</u> the type of answer required, <u>with the units it will have</u>.

   The physical act of writing down the information in these two steps will help you get started. Once this information is down on paper, you may realize that the problem is much simpler than it first appears!

3. Devise a method for translating from information to the answer.

   Often this will involve making use of a balanced chemical equation (to convert from moles of one compound to moles of another) or a molar mass[86] (to convert from grams to moles or moles to grams).

---

[86]This could be an atomic mass, molecular mass, or formula mass.

Here is an example of the use of this approach for a problem outside the realm of chemistry:

Example 14-1.

A quilting project requires 1.70 yards of a particular fabric. This fabric is on sale at a nearby store for 15% off its regular price of $2.99/yd. How much will the fabric cost (excluding taxes)?

Solution:

First, list the information given in the problem:

1.70 yd of fabric

Regular price is $2.99 per yd

Sale price is 85% of regular price (15% off):   0.85(2.99) = $2.5415 per yd
(this generates an equivalency: 1 yd = $2.54)

Second, write down the type of answer required:

Wanted: total cost of the fabric (units = $).

Finally, decide on a process for translating from the information to the objective. This will often require the use of one or more appropriate conversion factors. You can make a plan without using any of the numbers, see the boxed plan, below.

We need to get from yds to $, so we need a conversion factor with units of

$$\frac{\$}{yd}: \quad yd \times \frac{\$}{yd} = \$$$

From the equivalence, above, we can write the necessary conversion factor: $\frac{\$2.54}{1 \text{ yd}}$.

Now we can solve the problem: $1.70 \text{ yd} \times \frac{\$2.54}{1 \text{ yd}} = \mathbf{\$4.32}$

Practice should make the process of translating from information to objective much easier. Many examples and exercises involving chemical calculations are included in this chapter. You are strongly encouraged to work out these examples and exercises (on paper!) right away, as you go through the chapter the first time.

Exercise 14-1.

On the planet Smud, the atmosphere contains 4.5×10^3 molecules of H_2 per L. The total concentration of gas particles in Smud's atmosphere is 5.7×10^5 particles per L. The typical Smud-ite inhales 0.60 L in every breath, and the breathing rate is about 4 breaths per minute. How many molecules of H_2 will the typical Smudite inhale in 1.0 hour?

[Sounds complicated! Write down each value with its units. While there are multiple ways to solve a problem of this type, starting a string of dimensional analysis with a value whose units are not a ratio is usually safe!]

How did you do on Exercise 14-1? Were you able to sort through the information and write a continuous stream of conversions to arrive at a sensible answer? One of the tough parts of Exercise 14-1 is the presence of unnecessary data. Excellent problem-solvers understand that not all presented information will necessarily be useful. The problems that are solved in research labs are not generally presented with a short statement of appropriate data. Scientists must become adept at sorting through information to find the relevant facts.

A. Types of Chemical Calculations

In this chapter we will consider the following, some of which are among the most common of all chemical calculations:

1. **Calculation of Empirical Formula** from mass percent information. (Section C-1)

2. **Calculation of Molecular Formula** from mass percent information and molar mass. (Section C-3)

3. **Calculation of Moles of a Reactant Used or a Product Formed** from information on amounts of other reactants or products. (Section D)

4. **Calculation of Masses of a Reactant Used or a Product Formed** from information on amounts of other reactant or products. (Section E)

5. **Calculation to Determine Limiting Reagent and Theoretical Yield** from information on the amounts of all reagents present. (Section F)

6. **Calculation of Percent Yield** from knowledge of theoretical yield and actual yield. (Section G)

B. Definitions of Terms and Introduction to Concepts

Before presenting calculation strategies for each of the categories listed, it is important to define necessary terms and introduce helpful ideas.

Molecular formulas. This formula represents the actual number of atoms of each element in a molecule. Molecular formulas are only possible for substances that exist as discrete <u>molecules</u>; ionic compounds cannot have molecular formulas because there are no molecules. Molecular substances might be elements (H_2, N_2, P_4, S_8, C_{60}) or compounds (H_2O, C_2H_6, N_2H_4, ICl). For example, C_2H_6 would designate a molecule having two atoms of carbon and six of hydrogen.

Empirical formulas. The empirical formula expresses the *simplest* whole number mole ratio of atoms in a compound.

For molecular compounds, the empirical formula may or may not be the same as the molecular formula. For instance, for the molecular formula C_2H_6, the empirical formula would be CH_3, simply indicating there are three times as many hydrogen atoms as carbon atoms in the compound. For the water molecule, the molecular and empirical formulas are the same: H_2O. Formulas must be expressed in whole numbers, $H_3O_{1.5}$ will not do, even though it indicates twice as many hydrogen atoms as oxygen atoms.

For ionic compounds, formulas represent the ratios and identities of the cations and anions present. Most ionic compound formulas are empirical formulas. Remember to recognize ionic compounds by seeing that they are combinations of ions: metals and non-metals ($NaCl$), or polyatomic ions (NH_4NO_3), or a combination of any of these ion types: (KNO_3, NH_4Cl). Writing $NaCl$ for sodium chloride only tells us that there is one chloride ion for every sodium ion in the crystal. There are no discrete "molecules" of sodium chloride. Similarly, writing $(NH_4)_2SO_4$, indicates that the crystal structure of this ionic compound includes two ammonium ions for every sulfate ion. There is no discrete particle with the formula $(NH_4)_2SO_4$.

There are a few ionic compounds whose formulas are not empirical formulas: as examples consider Hg_2Cl_2, mercury(I) chloride, and $K_2C_2O_4$, potassium oxalate. Both of these formulas can be simplified to an empirical formula, $HgCl$ and KCO_2, respectively, but important information as to the identity of at least one of the ions is lost. In particular, mercury(I) does not exist as Hg^+ (but as the dimer, Hg_2^{2+}) and CO_2^- is not the oxalate ion, $C_2O_4^{2-}$.

Here are some examples of empirical and molecular formulas (of molecular substances):

Empirical Formula	Examples of Molecular Formulas (of Actual Compounds)
CH_2	$C_2H_4, C_3H_6, C_4H_8, C_5H_{10}$, etc.
CH	C_2H_2, C_4H_4, C_6H_6, etc.
HO	H_2O_2
BNH_2	$B_3N_3H_6$
CH_2O	$CH_2O, C_6H_{12}O_6$

Molecular formulas are integer multiples ($\times$ 1 or $\times$ 2, or $\times$ 3, etc.) of empirical formulas.

Exercise 14-2.

A molecular species has the empirical formula C_3H_6O. List three possible molecular formulas.

Formulas as Conversion Factors. Because formulas indicate the *mole ratios* of atoms (or ions) that are associated with one another for particular compounds, they can be used to produce conversion factors that allow us to translate from an amount of one atom to an amount of another. For instance, sucrose is $C_{12}H_{22}O_{11}$. In sucrose, then, 12 moles of carbon is associated with 22 moles of hydrogen and 11 moles of oxygen. Equivalencies for sucrose could be written:

> 12 moles C = 22 moles H
> 12 moles C = 11 moles O
> 11 moles O = 22 moles H

Conversion factors from these equivalencies include:

$$\frac{22\ mol\ H}{12\ mol\ C} \quad \text{or} \quad \frac{12\ mol\ C}{11\ mol\ O} \quad \text{or} \quad \frac{11\ mol\ O}{22\ mol\ H} \quad \text{(or the reciprocals of any of these.)}$$

Example 14-2.

Choose one of the conversion factors above to solve this problem: A sucrose sample contains 4.87 moles of carbon. How many moles of hydrogen does it contain?

Solution:

We need to convert from moles of carbon, to moles of hydrogen, so use the first conversion factor:

$$4.87 \text{ mol C} \times \frac{22\ mol\ H}{12\ mol\ C} = 8.93 \text{ mol H}$$

Note that the whole numbers found in formulas are <u>exact</u> numbers (counting items) for the purposes of significant digits.

Balanced Chemical Reaction Equations as Conversion Factors. The balanced chemical reaction equation is similar to a chemical formula in that it presents us with mole ratios of materials that are associated with each other in that particular chemical reaction. These ratios can be used to convert from moles of one reactant or product to moles of another. For instance, in the case of the reaction:

$$3 H_2 + N_2 \rightarrow 2 NH_3$$

one could say that for every mole of nitrogen that reacts, 3 moles of hydrogen react, or, for every 3 moles of hydrogen that reacts, 2 moles of ammonia (NH_3) are produced. These equivalencies can be turned into conversion factors such as:

$$\frac{1 \text{ mol N}_2}{3 \text{ mol H}_2} \quad \text{or} \quad \frac{3 \text{ mol H}_2}{1 \text{ mol N}_2} \quad \text{or} \quad \frac{3 \text{ mol H}_2}{2 \text{ mol NH}_3} \quad \text{or} \quad \frac{2 \text{ mol NH}_3}{3 \text{ mol N}_2}$$

Similar to conversion factors from chemical formulas, conversion factors from balanced equations are also exact numbers, with an infinite number of significant digits.

Molar Masses as Conversion Factors. One of the most common conversions used by chemists in the lab is to convert from masses to moles, or vice versa. Atomic masses, molecular masses, and formula masses (all of these are molar masses) serve as the conversion factors. Any value whose units are a ratio can be used as a conversion factor. The molecular mass of water is $18.015 \; \frac{g}{mol}$. This means, that for water, 1 mol = 18.015 g. Two conversion factors arise from this equivalency:

$$\frac{1 \; mol \; H_2O}{18.015 \; g \; H_2O} \quad \text{or} \quad \frac{18.015 \; g \; H_2O}{1 \; mol \; H_2O}$$

Here, the "1" mole is taken as exact, but 18.015 is a number with 5 significant digits. Conversion factors from molar masses are not exact numbers, except for 1 mole ^{12}C = exactly 12 g.[87]

Limiting reactants (also called **limiting reagents**). In many reactions set up in the laboratory, one reactant is present in insufficient quantity compared to the others (which are in surplus). This reactant *limits* the amount of product that can be formed. Consider an assembly line for dolls: each doll needs 1 head, 2 arms and 2 legs. If there are 30 heads, 70 arms and 46 legs in the factory, legs will limit the number of dolls produced, *even though there are more legs than heads available*. There will be heads and arms left over. A variety of strategies can be used to identify the limiting reagent. Here are two possibilities:

Method A. For any two reagents, compare the ratio needed (according to the balanced reaction equation) to the ratio present. We can write a balanced "reaction" equation for our assembly line:

$$1 \text{ head} + 2 \text{ legs} + 2 \text{ arms} \rightarrow 1 \text{ doll}$$

We can compare numbers of legs to numbers of heads:

$$Compare: \frac{\# \; legs}{\# \; heads} \qquad Need: \frac{2 \; legs}{1 \; head} = 2.0 \qquad Have: \frac{46 \; legs}{30 \; heads} = 1.53$$

Here, with legs in the numerator, the value 1.53 (being smaller than the needed 2.0) indicates that the numerator is too small. This means that legs limit the production of dolls in comparison to heads. We also check the arms against the legs:

$$Compare: \frac{\# \; legs}{\# \; arms} \qquad Need: \frac{2 \; legs}{2 \; arms} = 1.0 \qquad Have: \frac{46 \; legs}{70 \; arms} = 0.66$$

Here, with "legs" in the numerator, the value of 0.66 (being smaller than 1.0) indicates that we have fewer legs than needed for the number of arms available. Overall, then, compared to arms and heads, legs are the limiting "reagent."

Method B. Determine the amount of product that each reactant could produce. Whichever reactant can make the least product is the limiting reagent. We use the balanced reaction equation for our assembly line:

$$1 \text{ head} + 2 \text{ legs} + 2 \text{ arms} \rightarrow 1 \text{ doll}$$

---

[87] This is a definition, and is therefore exact.

A series of equivalencies is inherent in these relationships: 1 head = 2 legs = 2 arms = 1 doll. Conversion factors can be constructed from these equivalencies, such as:

$$\frac{2\ arms}{1\ head}\ \text{or}\ \frac{1\ doll}{2\ legs}\ , \text{etc.}$$

We convert each reactant to product using appropriate conversion factors:

$$30 \text{ heads} \times \frac{1\ doll}{1\ head} = 30 \text{ dolls}$$

$$70 \text{ arms} \times \frac{1\ doll}{2\ arms} = 35 \text{ dolls}$$

$$46 \text{ legs} \times \frac{1\ doll}{2\ legs} = 23 \text{ dolls}$$

Because the legs can make fewest dolls, the legs are the limiting reagent.

Important point: Notice that legs are the limiting reagent even though

1. there are more legs than heads (more legs are needed!), and

2. the legs may well weigh more than the heads (numbers are important, not masses!)

Limiting reagents in chemical reactions have similar issues:

1. If all of the reaction coefficients are not the same, it may be incorrect to assume that the substance present in fewer moles is the limiting reagent.

2. Masses of the items are not important; the number of items is important. One must always convert masses to moles in order to compare numbers of atoms, ions, or molecules.

The boxed information brings up an important point. In the lab, the obvious way to obtain a particular amount of a substance is to weigh it. But the important aspect as far as a balanced reaction equation is concerned is the number of formula units, or the number of molecules in the sample. This means that a really important part of our work will always be to translate between masses and moles, and vice versa.

Reaction yields. Once the limiting reagent has been identified (by any method), the amount of product expected (the **theoretical yield**) can be calculated using the balanced equation and molar masses. How many dolls can be made from the supplies on hand? The idea is very much the same.

Example 14-3.

What will be the yield of dolls if the supplies in a warehouse include 1529 heads, 3028 arms and 3675 legs?

Solution:

Our "balanced equation" is: 1 head + 2 legs + 2 arms → 1 doll

We can use either method to determine the identity of the limiting reagent, and determine the yield of dolls.

Method A:

$$Compare: \frac{\#\ legs}{\#\ heads} \qquad Need: \frac{2\ legs}{1\ head} = 2.0 \qquad Have: \frac{3675\ legs}{1529\ heads} = 2.40$$

Heads limit because the "have" ratio is too big, meaning that the either the numerator is too big or the denominator is too small. So far, heads limit, so now we compare heads to arms:

$$Compare: \frac{\# \text{ heads}}{\# \text{ arms}} \qquad Need: \frac{1 \text{ head}}{2 \text{ arms}} = 0.5 \qquad Have: \frac{1529 \text{ heads}}{3028 \text{ arms}} = 0.505$$

Because the "have" ratio is (slightly) too big, the numerator is too big and the denominator is too small.

Together this tells us that **arms are the limiting reagent** (we don't have to compare arms to legs directly!) and we can calculate the expected yield of dolls:

$$3028 \text{ arms} \times \frac{1 \text{ doll}}{2 \text{ arms}} = \textbf{1514 dolls}$$

Method B:

$$1529 \text{ heads} \times \frac{1 \text{ doll}}{1 \text{ head}} = 1529 \text{ dolls}$$

$$3028 \text{ arms} \times \frac{1 \text{ doll}}{2 \text{ arms}} = \textbf{1514 dolls}$$

$$3675 \text{ legs} \times \frac{1 \text{ doll}}{2 \text{ legs}} = 1837.5 \text{ dolls} \text{ (which means 1837 whole dolls)}$$

Method B calculations indicate that 1514 dolls can be made because that is the smallest of the possibilities. Becasue that result was based on the number of arms available, arms are the limiting reagent.

In chemistry problems, theoretical yields are usually expressed in mass units, such as grams, rather than in moles. Why? When you actually perform the reaction in the lab, you will determine your yield by weighing it. You can easily compare the mass of the your product to the mass theoretically expected!

C. Calculation of Empirical Formulas and Molecular Formulas

A common objective in chemistry research is to determine the chemical formula of a new compound. The next several pages will present a method by which the chemical formula can be determined via experimental data and calculation. One important piece of information is often the **percentage composition** of the compound: the percent, by mass, of each element making up the compound.[88]

The percentage composition can easily be found for a compound whose chemical formula is known. As an example, consider acetic acid, the compound responsible for the intense odor of vinegar. Acetic acid, has the chemical formula $HC_2H_3O_2$ which may be written as a condensed formula where each carbon is listed separately, followed by the atoms to which it is bonded: CH_3CO_2H. Condensed formulas aid the reader in understanding which atoms are bonded to which other atoms. The mass percent composition of acetic acid may be found as follows:

Bond structure of acetic acid

[88]This is often done by sending samples to companies specializing in chemical analyses.

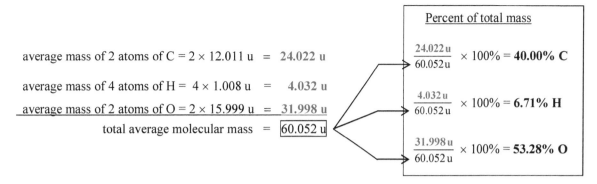

average mass of 2 atoms of C = 2 × 12.011 u = 24.022 u

average mass of 4 atoms of H = 4 × 1.008 u = 4.032 u

average mass of 2 atoms of O = 2 × 15.999 u = 31.998 u

total average molecular mass = 60.052 u

Percent of total mass

$\dfrac{24.022\,u}{60.052\,u} \times 100\% = \mathbf{40.00\%\ C}$

$\dfrac{4.032\,u}{60.052\,u} \times 100\% = \mathbf{6.71\%\ H}$

$\dfrac{31.998\,u}{60.052\,u} \times 100\% = \mathbf{53.28\%\ O}$

The result (40.00% carbon, 6.71% hydrogen, 53.28% oxygen by mass) is the percentage composition of acetic acid.[89]

We've seen that we can calculate the % composition from the formula, as shown above. Can we work the other direction and calculate a formula from % composition? Sometimes. For a chemical compound whose formula is *not* known (such as a new compound whose identity has not yet been established) the percentage composition can lead to a determination of the **empirical formula**. In this case, the % composition must be determined by experimentation. The following section explains how to obtain an empirical formula from % composition information.

1. Determination of empirical formulas

One way to determine the formula of a new compound is to first determine its empirical formula from information on percent composition. Additional information can then lead to a correct determination of the molecular formula. Section 2 (following this section) will explain the analysis that can lead to the % composition values. We begin by assuming that we already know the mass percent compositions of the substance. How can we find the chemical formula? To know the mass percent composition is to know mass ratios. We could write these in the form of a chemical formula, such as:

mass ratios: $C_{40.00}H_{6.71}O_{53.28}$

Actual chemical formulas, of course, indicate <u>numbers</u> of each particle rather than <u>masses</u>. We need to convert from mass information to mole information: atomic masses provide the conversion factors. The next example shows how this works.

Example 14-4.

Analysis of compound **A** shows that it contains 85.7% carbon and 14.3% hydrogen by mass. It contains no other elements. Determine its empirical formula.

<u>Solution</u>:

For convenience, assume a total mass of exactly 100 grams (we can choose any convenient total mass, because the percentage composition does not depend on the total mass). Such a sample would contain:

85.7 g of C   and   14.3 g of H

We want to determine the number of atoms (or moles of atoms) represented by each of these masses, and then reduce that to the simplest whole number ratio.
Using the atomic masses of carbon and hydrogen:

---

[89] The fact that these percentages add to 99.99% instead of 100.00% should not be a concern. This is merely a result of a small amount of rounding error, based on the number of digits reported.

$$85.7 \text{ g C} \times \frac{1 \text{ mol C}}{12.011 \text{ g C}} = 7.14 \text{ mol C}$$

$$14.3 \text{ g H} \times \frac{1 \text{ mol H}}{1.0079 \text{ g H}} = 14.2 \text{ mol H}$$

This implies a formula of $C_{7.14}H_{14.2}$, but, of course, we want a <u>whole number ratio</u> of the atoms for our finished empirical formula. One trick to try is to divide each number of moles by the smallest one: $C_{\frac{7.14}{7.14}} H_{\frac{14.2}{7.14}} = C_1H_{1.99}$, which is certainly within experimental error of **CH₂**.

In Example 14-4, why didn't the ratio of moles H to moles C in the calculation come out to *exactly* 2.0 : 1.0? In any chemical analysis there is some error associated with the percentage of each element—depending on the method of analysis used, the purity of the sample, and the care with which the analysis is performed. It is typical, therefore, to end up with results such as that above (ratio of 1.99 : 1.0) and to have to round (up or down) to the nearest ratio of whole numbers.

Finally, how did we know to present the empirical formula as CH_2 rather than H_2C? When writing formulas of carbon-based compounds (**organic**[90] compounds), the carbon is always listed first, followed next by the hydrogen atoms. For our purposes, if other atoms are present, we will place them in alphabetical order (by symbol), so Br's come before N's, which come before O's, which come before S's, etc.[91]

This method for the determination of empirical formulas can be described schematically as follows:

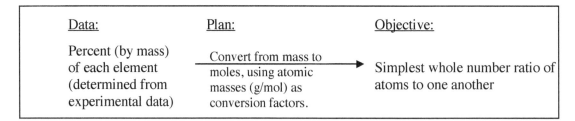

Data:

Percent (by mass) of each element (determined from experimental data)

Plan:

Convert from mass to moles, using atomic masses (g/mol) as conversion factors.

Objective:

Simplest whole number ratio of atoms to one another

Example 14-5.

Compound **B** contains only chlorine and oxygen. Chemical analysis gives the following percentage composition (by mass):

Cl   38.77%   O   61.23%

What is the empirical formula of this compound?

Solution:

For convenience, again assume a total sample mass of 100 grams. Such a sample would contain:

38.77 g of Cl   and   61.23 g of O

---

[90] Organic compounds have skeletons composed primarily of carbon atoms. Because carbon atoms can bond with each other in many different ways, there are an infinite number of possible organic compounds. Most biologically relevant molecules and ions are organic in nature, including proteins, nucleic acids, lipids and carbohydrates.

[91] Actual IUPAC guidelines are very complex, but alphabetical order is a good first step.

We want to determine the number of atoms represented by each of these masses, and then reduce that to the simplest whole number ratio. Using the atomic masses of chlorine and oxygen:

$$\text{Cl:} \quad 38.77 \text{ g Cl} \times \frac{1 \text{ mol Cl}}{35.453 \text{ g Cl}} = 1.094 \text{ mol Cl}$$

$$\text{O:} \quad 61.23 \text{ g O} \times \frac{1 \text{ mol O}}{15.999 \text{ g O}} = 3.827 \text{ mol O}$$

The chlorine and oxygen atoms occur in a mole ratio of $Cl_{1.094}O_{3.827}$ (the mole ratio of atoms is the same as the atom ratio). We try dividing each value by the smallest one:

$$Cl_{\frac{1.094}{1.094}} O_{\frac{3.827}{1.094}} = Cl_1 O_{3.5}$$

Rounding 3.5 either to 3 or to 4 is quite a stretch. The experiment likely provided better data than that! In a case such as this, look for a multiplier that will give you all whole numbers. In this case, multiplying both subscripts by "2" will give Cl_2O_7.

The empirical formula is therefore **Cl_2O_7**. Here we follow the practice of listing the atoms with the less electronegative one, Cl, first. This is NOT an organic (carbon-based) compound.

Example 14-6.

Compound **C** contains only potassium, chromium, and oxygen. Chemical analysis gives the following percentage composition (by mass):

$$K = 40.2\% \qquad Cr = 26.8\% \qquad O = 33.0\%$$

What is the empirical formula of this compound?

Solution:

For convenience, assume a total mass of 100 grams. Such a sample would contain:

$$40.2 \text{ g of K} \qquad 26.8 \text{ g of Cr} \qquad \text{and} \qquad 33.0 \text{ g of O}$$

We want to determine the number of atoms represented by each of these masses and then reduce that to the simplest whole number ratio. Using the appropriate atomic masses:

$$\text{K:} \quad 40.2 \text{ g K} \times \frac{1 \text{ mol K}}{39.098 \text{ g K}} = 1.03 \text{ mol K}$$

$$\text{Cr:} \quad 26.8 \text{ g Cr} \times \frac{1 \text{ mol Cr}}{51.996 \text{ g Cr}} = 0.515 \text{ mol Cr}$$

$$\text{O:} \quad 33.0 \text{ g O} \times \frac{1 \text{ mol O}}{15.999 \text{ g O}} = 2.06 \text{ mol O}$$

The potassium, chromium, and oxygen atoms therefore occur in a ratio of $K_{1.03}Cr_{0.515}O_{2.06}$. As in the preceding example, we divide by the smallest number of moles (0.515 mol):

$$K_{\frac{1.03}{0.515}} Cr_{\frac{0.515}{0.515}} O_{\frac{2.06}{0.515}} = K_2CrO_4$$

The empirical formula is therefore **K₂CrO₄**. Getting the atoms listed in the correct order can be a puzzle. Here, because there are metal atoms, we determine that we have a salt and attempt to identify cations and anions. If you recognize CrO_4^{2-} as the chromate anion, you will get the atoms in the correct order.

Exercise 14-3.

Glucose, an important metabolic sugar, has the percentage composition:

    6.71% H   40.00% C   53.29% O   (listed in order of mass %)

What is its empirical formula? In what order should the atoms appear in the formula?

Exercise 14-4.

Compound **C** contains only carbon, hydrogen, and sulfur. The compound is analyzed for carbon and hydrogen; it contains 25.5% carbon and 6.42% hydrogen by mass. What is its empirical formula? (HINT: what must be its mass % of sulfur?)

---

2. Experimental determination of percent composition

What kind of experiment can be used to determine the percent composition of an unknown compound? Historically, an experiment called **combustion analysis**[92] has served this purpose. Most labs are not equipped to perform this experiment so many researchers with this need send small (very pure[93]) samples of a new compound to fee-based analytical labs that specialize in this type of work.

Combustion analysis is greatly simplified if the new molecule contains only carbon, hydrogen and (at most) one other element. Combustion, as seen in Chapter 13, is the process of "burning" a material, which means to react it with molecular oxygen. These reactions usually do not occur spontaneously; you must begin the combustion process by providing a high temperature environment such as an oven.[94] During combustion, all atoms in the unknown react with molecular oxygen to form oxide products. For example, if only carbon and hydrogen are present, the balanced combustion reaction equation will be similar to the following reaction for the combustion of heptane (C_7H_{16}):

$$C_7H_{16}(\ell)+11O_2(g)\longrightarrow 7CO_2(g)+8H_2O(g)$$

Note that the water will be produced as water vapor, because of the high temperature of combustion. If an unknown hydrocarbon is combusted, we can write:

$$C_xH_y+nO_2(g)\longrightarrow xCO_2(g)+\frac{y}{2}H_2O(g)\qquad \text{where } n=x+\frac{y}{4}$$

Some things to notice:

1. The mass of C in the sample of unknown can be related to the mass of C in the carbon dioxide produced. There is no other source of C for the production of CO_2 and no other product containing C. This assumption provides one reason that the sample combusted must be as pure as possible. Impurities would be likely sources of other carbon atoms!

---

[92] Combustion analysis can also be called *elemental analysis*.
[93] Food for thought: what happens during the analysis if the sample is not pure? Keep alert for more information about this issue as you continue reading.
[94] Some substances are **pyrophoric,** meaning that they spontaneously ignite in air at temperatures below 55 °C (150 °F). Some of the more common pyrophoric substances are white phosphorus (a particular allotrope of phosphorus), the alkali metals, several finely divided metals, iron(II) sulfide, and some metal hydrides.

2. The mass of H in the sample of unknown can be related to the mass of H in the water produced. In the case of a pure sample and a clean gas stream (see Figure 14-1), there would be no other source of H atoms in the experiment.

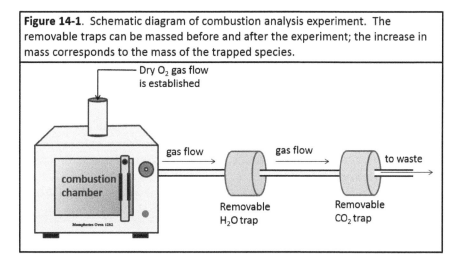

Figure 14-1. Schematic diagram of combustion analysis experiment. The removable traps can be massed before and after the experiment; the increase in mass corresponds to the mass of the trapped species.

3. The mass of C and the mass of H from the original sample can be determined by measuring the masses of CO_2 and H_2O produced. Those masses of C and H can then be compared to the total mass of the original sample to determine the mass percent of each element. For instance:

$$\text{mass}\,\%\,C = \frac{\text{mass}\,C}{\text{mass original sample}} \times 100\%$$

Here we see that if the original sample is impure we will have data that is the mass of C and the mass of H from a mixture (instead of from a compound). Additionally, what should be the mass of a compound will also be the mass of a mixture. The mass percentages of atoms in a mixture are not likely to be small whole numbers!

4. Molecular oxygen for the combustion must be present in large amounts (excess, more than "n" in the **blue** balanced reaction equation, above). One has to guard against incomplete combustion, which leads to the formation of CO instead of CO_2. Carbon monoxide only forms during combustion when a limited amount of oxygen is present (such as when a furnace filter is clogged and not enough air can get into the combustion chamber).

5. It is OK for there to be one other element (beyond C and H). If, for instance your data tell you that the unknown was 56.7% C and 8.2% H, you can determine the mass percent of the third element:

    $$100\% - 56.7\% - 8.2\% = 35.1\% \text{ element \#3}$$

How can the mass of the CO_2 and H_2O be determined? Look again at Figure 14-1, which shows a schematic diagram of the experimental set-up. A sample of unknown composition is placed in the combustion chamber and a flow of dry oxygen gas is established. The removable traps are pre-weighed, so that their mass increase during the combustion process can be determined by finding their mass when the combustion is complete.

A common trapping agent for H_2O (these are called *desiccants*) is an anhydrous salt, such as calcium sulfate, $CaSO_4$ (marketed as Drierite® a registered trademark of the W.A. Hammond Drierite Co., Ltd.). As moist gases flow through a container packed with Drierite® crystals, the water molecules in the gas become incorporated into the crystal structure of the anhydrous salt, resulting in the hydrated salt crystal, $CaSO_4 \cdot 2H_2O$. The salt gains mass according to the amount of water absorbed. Fully hydrated Drierite can be returned to its original anhydrous state by heating in an oven to drive the water molecules back out of the crystal structure.

Similarly, carbon dioxide can be trapped trapped from the gas stream by passing the gas through a column packed with pellets of NaOH. The reaction that occurs creates sodium bicarbonate, which stays in the trap:

$$CO_2(g) + NaOH(s) \longrightarrow NaHCO_3(s)$$

Thus, the mass of the trap is increased by the mass of the CO_2 produced during combustion. Because solid NaOH is highly hygroscopic (draws water into its crystal structure), it is imperative that the water trap comes before the CO_2 trap in this scenario.

Exercise 14-5.

What would go wrong if a trap containing sodium hydroxide came before a Drierite® trap?

Example 14-7 shows one way to determine the percent composition of an unknown sample using combustion analysis information.

Example 14-7.

An unknown sample with mass 0.4730 g containing only C, H, and N atoms undergoes combustion analysis. The water trap gains 0.6318 g and the CO_2 trap gains 1.2345 g. Determine the percent composition of the unknown.

<u>Solution:</u>

We want to know the mass of carbon and hydrogen in the sample. That will be identical (ideally) to the mass of carbon in CO_2 and the mass of hydrogen in H_2O. We can find these masses as follows:

$$1.2345\,g\,CO_2 \times \frac{1\,mol\,CO_2}{44.0098\,g\,CO_2} \times \frac{1\,mol\,C}{1\,mol\,CO_2} \times \frac{12.011\,g\,C}{1\,mol\,C} = 0.33692\,g\,C$$

$$0.6318\,g\,H_2O \times \frac{1\,mol\,H_2O}{18.015\,g\,H_2O} \times \frac{2\,mol\,H}{1\,mol\,H_2O} \times \frac{1.00794\,g\,H}{1\,mol\,H} = 0.07070\,g\,H$$

Make sure to carefully consider these strings of calculations. What quantity exists after each step? Why is it essential to use units of "moles X" or "grams Y" instead of just "moles" and "grams?" The percent compositions are obtained by dividing the mass of an element by the mass of the sample:

$$\frac{0.33692\,g\,C}{0.4730\,g\,sample} \times 100\% = 71.23\%\,C$$

$$\frac{0.07070\,g\,H}{0.4730\,g\,sample} \times 100\% = 14.95\%\,H$$

The percent composition of nitrogen (or any other third element) is found by difference:

$$100\% - 71.23\% - 14.95\% = 13.82\%\,N$$

Notice that if you are given combustion analysis information (such as the masses of CO_2 and H_2O in Example 14-7) you could be asked directly for the empirical formula rather than for the percent composition of the unknown. If this is the case, there is no point in finding the percent composition, as you would have to work to it and then back to masses again. Rather, finding the masses of C (0.33695 g) and H (0.07070 g) in Example 14-7 puts you well on the way to an empirical formula. You just have to get from mass ratios to mole ratios. And, you need a slightly different way to learn about the nitrogen. See Example 14-8.

Example 14-8.

An unknown sample with mass 0.4730 g containing only C, H, and N atoms undergoes combustion analysis. The water trap gains 0.6318 g and the CO_2 trap gains 1.2345 g. Determine the empirical formula of the unknown.

<u>Solution</u>:

We want to know the moles of C, H and N in the sample. We can get to these from the masses of C, H and N. We can find the masses of C and H exactly as we did previously:

$$1.2345 \text{ g } CO_2 \times \frac{1 \text{ mol } CO_2}{44.0098 \text{ g } CO_2} \times \frac{1 \text{ mol C}}{1 \text{ mol } CO_2} \times \frac{12.011 \text{ g C}}{1 \text{ mol C}} = 0.33692 \text{ g C}$$

$$0.6318 \text{ g } H_2O \times \frac{1 \text{ mol } H_2O}{18.015 \text{ g } H_2O} \times \frac{2 \text{ mol H}}{1 \text{ mol } H_2O} \times \frac{1.00794 \text{ g } H}{1 \text{ mol H}} = 0.07070 \text{ g H}$$

To find the mass of nitrogen, we subtract the C and H masses from the mass of the original sample (which contained only C, H, and N):

$$\begin{aligned} \text{mass of N} &= \text{mass of entire sample} - \text{mass C} - \text{mass H} \\ &= 0.4730\text{g} - 0.33692\text{g C} - 0.07070 \text{ g H} \\ &= 0.0654 \text{ g N} \end{aligned}$$

The moles of each element can be calculated from these masses:

$$\text{moles C:} \quad 0.33692 \text{ g C} \times \frac{1 \text{ mol C}}{12.011 \text{ g C}} = 2.805 \times 10^{-2} \text{ mol C}$$

$$\text{moles H:} \quad 0.07070 \text{ g H} \times \frac{1 \text{ mol H}}{1.00794 \text{ g H}} = 7.014 \times 10^{-2} \text{ mol H}$$

$$\text{moles N:} \quad 0.0654 \text{ g N} \times \frac{1 \text{ mol N}}{14.0067 \text{ g N}} = 4.669 \times 10^{-3} \text{ mol N}$$

As we've seen previously, dividing by the smallest number of moles is often a useful strategy for working toward a whole number ratio:

$$\text{moles C:} \quad \frac{2.805 \times 10^{-2} \text{ mol C}}{4.669 \times 10^{-3}} = 6.008 \text{ mol C} \sim 6 \text{ mol C}$$

$$\text{moles H:} \quad \frac{7.014 \times 10^{-2} \text{ mol H}}{4.669 \times 10^{-3}} = 15.022 \text{ mol H} \sim 15 \text{ mol H}$$

$$\text{moles N:} \quad \frac{4.669 \times 10^{-3} \text{ mol N}}{4.669 \times 10^{-3}} = 1.000 \text{ mol N} = 1 \text{ mol N}$$

The empirical formula is $C_6H_{15}N$.

3. Molecular formulas

Additional information, most commonly the molecular mass, is necessary to determine the molecular formula from the empirical formula, especially because a variety of molecules can share the same empirical formula. Using a small sample of the unknown in a gentle mass spectroscopy analysis may allow you to see molecular ion peaks,[95] thus letting you know the molar mass of the substance.

Once the molar mass has been determined, it can be compared to the molar mass of the empirical formula. Remember that the molecular formula must be an integer multiple of the empirical formula. If the molecular mass is 80 g/mol, but the atoms of the empirical formula only add to 40 g/mol, the molecular formula must be two times the empirical formula. Problems to determine molecular formulas may be described by the following scheme:

Data:	Plan:	Objective:
Empirical formula, molecular mass	Molecular mass must be an integer multiple of empirical formula mass. → Multiply the empirical formula by this integer.	Molecular formula

---

Example 14-9.

In Example 14-4 we found that compound **A** has an empirical formula of CH_2. If compound **A** has molar mass of 84.0 g/mol, what is its molecular formula?

Solution:

The empirical formula is CH_2. Because the molecule must contain an integer number of CH_2 units (the molecular formula must be $1 \times CH_2 = CH_2$, $2 \times CH_2 = C_2H_4$, etc.), the molecular mass must be an integer times the mass of the empirical formula:

molecular mass = integer × empirical formula mass

We need to find this integer. To do so, we can rearrange this equation:

$$\text{integer} = \frac{\text{molecular mass}}{\text{empirical formula mass}}$$

In this case: integer = 84.0 g/mol / 14.0 g/mol = 6

And the molecular formula must be $6 \times CH_2 = \mathbf{C_6H_{12}}$

Example 14-10.

In Example 14-5, we found that Compound **B** has an empirical formula of Cl_2O_7. Suppose we also determine that the molecular mass of Compound B is 181±2 g/mol. What is its molecular formula?

(The range of values ±2 g/mol represents a degree of uncertainty in mass related to experimental limitations in the method used to measure the molecular mass. This uncertainty is only slightly more than 1% and in this case should not be sufficient to cause a problem in determining the most likely molecular formula—but it should not be forgotten that each experimental measurement, including those of molecular masses, has its limitations in accuracy and precision.)

---

[95] Plural, because of the presence of a variety of isotopes.

Solution:

The empirical formula is Cl_2O_7. The molecular mass must be an integer times the empirical formula mass:

$$\text{integer} = \frac{\text{molecular mass}}{\text{empirical formula mass}} = \frac{181 \text{ g/mol}}{182.9 \text{ g/mol}} = 0.990 \sim 1$$

Clearly, in this case, the molecular formula is the same as the empirical formula, $\mathbf{Cl_2O_7}$.

Notice that determination of the molecular formula will not necessarily indicate the bonding that exists. Some formulas can indicate a set of molecules (isomers! Remember *cis* and *trans*?). So, determination of a molecular formula is often not enough information to draw a Lewis dot structure! We can come up with the structure shown here for our compound, but we won't know that we are correct without doing additional studies.

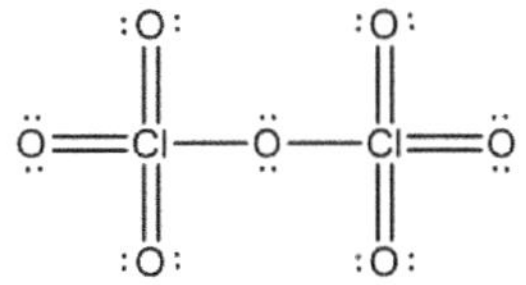

Exercise 14-6.

In Exercise 14-3, glucose was found to have an empirical formula of CH_2O. Glucose has a molecular mass of 180 g/mol. What is its molecular formula?

Exercise 14-7.

In Exercise 14-4, you found that Compound **C** has an empirical formula of CH_3S. Compound **C** has a molar mass of 94.2 g/mol. What is its molecular formula?

D. Calculation of Moles of a Reactant Used or a Product Formed

Using a balanced chemical reaction equation to determine the number of moles of one compound associated some number of moles of another can be described by the scheme:

Data:	Plan:	Objective:
Known moles of a reactant or product	Use coefficients in balanced chemical equation to determine appropriate conversion ratio ⟶	Moles of another reactant or product

---

Example 14-11.

Octane, C_8H_{18}, combusts in air to form carbon dioxide and water vapor:

$$2 \text{ C}_8\text{H}_{18} + 25 \text{ O}_2 \longrightarrow 16 \text{ CO}_2 + 18 \text{ H}_2\text{O}$$

How many moles of oxygen would be necessary for the complete combustion of 1.00 mol of octane, and how many moles of each of the products would be formed?

Solution:

We can use the coefficients[96] in the balanced equation to set up ratios as follows:

$$1.00 \text{ mol } C_8H_{18} \left(\frac{25 \text{ mol } O_2}{2 \text{ mol } C_8H_{18}} \right) = \textbf{12.5 mol } O_2 \text{ necessary for combustion}$$

$$1.00 \text{ mol } C_8H_{18} \left(\frac{16 \text{ mol } CO_2}{2 \text{ mol } C_8H_{18}} \right) = \textbf{8.00 mol } CO_2 \text{ formed}$$

$$1.00 \text{ mol } C_8H_{18} \left(\frac{18 \text{ mol } H_2O}{2 \text{ mol } C_8H_{18}} \right) = \textbf{9.00 mol } H_2O \text{ formed}$$

Example 14-12.

The thermal <u>decomposition</u> of ammonium dichromate, $(NH_4)_2Cr_2O_7$, is spectacular: a small pile of bright orange crystals gives off sparks as a small mountain of gray-green solid looking similar to green eraser shavings is formed (Want to see it? Look for "ammonium dichromate volcano" on YouTube!) The products of this reaction are chromium(III) oxide, nitrogen gas, and water vapor. If 0.0100 mol of $(NH_4)_2Cr_2O_7$ is used, how many moles of each of the products should be formed?

Solution:

First, we must write formulas for the chemical species involved in the reaction:
chromium(III) oxide: made from Cr^{3+} and O^{2-}. Must be $Cr_2O_3(s)$; salts are solids.
nitrogen gas: $N_2(g)$
water vapor: $H_2O(g)$
Then we must write *and balance* the chemical equation:

$$(NH_4)_2Cr_2O_7(s) \longrightarrow Cr_2O_3(s) + N_2(g) + 4 H_2O(g)$$

By inspection we see that, because the coefficients of Cr_2O_3 and N_2 are the same as the reactant (one), the number of moles of these products must also be 0.0100 mol. For practice, this can be set up in terms of ratios:

$$0.0100 \text{ mol } (NH_4)_2Cr_2O_7 \left(\frac{1 \text{ mol } Cr_2O_3}{1 \text{ mol } (NH_4)_2Cr_2O_7} \right) = 0.0100 \text{ mol } Cr_2O_3$$

$$0.0100 \text{ mol } (NH_4)_2Cr_2O_7 \left(\frac{1 \text{ mol } N_2}{1 \text{ mol } (NH_4)_2Cr_2O_7} \right) = 0.0100 \text{ mol } N_2$$

For H_2O the calculation is set up similarly:

$$0.0100 \text{ mol } ((NH_4)_2Cr_2O_7 \left(\frac{4 \text{ mol } H_2O}{1 \text{ mol } (NH_4)_2Cr_2O_7} \right) = 0.0400 \text{ mol } H_2O$$

---

[96]For the purposes of counting significant figures, the coefficients are considered exact numbers.

Exercise 14-8.

Nitrogen trifluoride decomposes to give the gases nitrogen and fluorine. How many moles of each product would be formed on complete decomposition of 0.50 moles of nitrogen trifluoride?

Exercise 14-9.

Diphosphorus pentasulfide reacts with phosphorus pentachloride as follows:

$$P_2S_5 + 3\ PCl_5 \longrightarrow 5\ PSCl_3$$

Determine the number of moles of P_2S_5 used up, and the number of moles of $PSCl_3$ formed from this reaction if 1.00 mole of PCl_5 is consumed.

E. Calculation of Masses of a Reactant Used or a Product Formed

As seen above, the number of moles of reactants and products can be determined using the coefficients of the balanced chemical equation. One additional step makes it possible to determine masses of reactants and products. This step uses the appropriate molar masses:

Data:	Plan:	Objective:
Mass of a reactant or product	Use coefficients of balanced chemical equation to determine mole ratio; then use molar mass(es) to convert from moles to grams. $\longrightarrow$	Mass of another reactant or product

The molar mass, with its units of g/mol, can be used as a convenient conversion factor. Although the schematic diagram above may seem to imply separate steps, the steps can be strung together into what is effectively a long conversion factor problem. This is best seen by example. First we will solve a problem the "long way," by a step-by-step approach; then we will see how these steps can be combined into a series of conversion factors to provide a more convenient way to determine the solution without encountering the problem of successive rounding errors.

Example 14-13.

One way to prepare the compound nitrogen trifluoride is by reacting ammonia with elemental fluorine, using a copper catalyst:

$$4\ NH_3 + 3\ F_2 \xrightarrow{Cu} NF_3 + 3\ NH_4F$$

What mass of NF_3 can be formed from 1.00 g of NH_3 in this reaction?

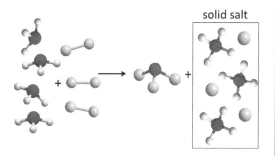

solid salt

Method 1 Solution:

This is probably the most common kind of chemical stoichiometry problem encountered. Chemists get data on amounts of material using balances, so data are obtained in units of grams. Balanced chemical reaction equations provide the conversion factors, but these are in units of moles. So the *mass A → mol A → mol B → mass B* series of conversions is very common. In the case of our particular problem, we need to determine the number of moles of NH_3 in the 1.00 g sample by using its molecular mass as a conversion factor. Then, we can convert from moles NH_3 to moles NF_3 using a conversion factor from the coefficients of the balanced equation. Finally, the moles of NF_3 produced can be converted into grams by using the molecular mass of NF_3.

Schematically: $g\ NH_3 \xrightarrow[\substack{molar \\ mass}]{} mol\ NH_3 \xrightarrow[\substack{balanced \\ reaction \\ equation}]{} mol\ NF_3 \xrightarrow[\substack{molar \\ mass}]{} g\ NF_3$

or as a series of steps:

(1) Conversion of 1.00 g of NH_3 to moles of NH_3 (use molecular mass of NH_3)

(2) Conversion of moles of NH_3 to moles of NF_3 (use balanced chemical equation)

(3) Conversion of moles of NF_3 to mass of NF_3 (use molecular mass of NF_3)

The work:

(1) $1.00\ g\ NH_3 \left(\dfrac{1\ mol\ NH_3}{17.0\ g\ NH_3} \right) = \boxed{0.058824\ mol\ NH_3}$

(2) $0.058824\ mol\ NH_3 \left(\dfrac{1\ mol\ NF_3}{4\ mol\ NH_3} \right) = \boxed{0.014706\ mol\ NF_3}$

(3) $0.014706\ mol\ NF_3 \left(\dfrac{71.0\ g\ NF_3}{1\ mol\ NF_3} \right) = \mathbf{1.04\ g}\ NF_3$

NOTE: Because the boxed values are used in the following steps, they should not be rounded to three significant digits. It is bests to use all the digits supplied by your calculator for the next step (but who wants to write them all down?). This problem of having to write down intermediate "answers" is avoided by Method 2.

Method 2 Solution:

The three steps of Method 1 do not need to be performed separately but can be combined into a single calculation:

$$(1.00\ g\ NH_3) \underbrace{\left(\frac{1\ mol\ NH_3}{17.0\ g\ NH_3} \right)}_{\text{(Step 1)}} \underbrace{\left(\frac{1\ mol\ NF_3}{4\ mol\ NH_3} \right)}_{\text{(Step 2)}} \underbrace{\left(\frac{71.0\ g\ NF_3}{1\ mol\ NF_3} \right)}_{\text{(Step 3)}} = \mathbf{1.04\ g}\ NF_3$$

Not only is this a quicker method but it also prevents rounding errors (and errors in copying digits from a calculator) that might occur in the intermediate steps of Method 1. For these reasons, Method 2 should be used whenever possible. Note that the order of the conversion factors is important to your solution; after every step the units should make sense. Don't mix up the conversions as shown below! Notice that the units that exist after each step do not make physical sense below, but do in the well executed work, above.

$$(1.00\ g\ NH_3) \left(\frac{1\ mol\ NF_3}{4\ mol\ NH_3} \right) \left(\frac{71.0\ g\ NH_3}{mol\ NF_3} \right) \left(\frac{1mol\ NH_3}{17.0\ g\ NH_3} \right) = 1.04\ g\ NF_3$$

Exercise 14-10.[97]

The tetrahedral coordination compound $Ni(PF_3)_4$ can be formed from the reaction between the metal and the ligand, trifluorophosphine:

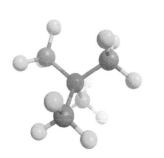

$$Ni + 4\,PF_3 \longrightarrow Ni(PF_3)_4$$

What mass of nickel is necessary to prepare 1.000 g of $Ni(PF_3)_4$ using this reaction if PF_3 is present in excess?

F. Determination of the Limiting Reactant and Theoretical Yield

Balanced chemical equations indicate the exact mole ratios of reagents that will react together. However, chemists often combine reactants in other ratios. For instance, they often add extra of the cheapest reagents; this helps to ensure that the more expensive reagent will react, and not be wasted. The **limiting reactant** (or **limiting reagent**), as we have mentioned, is the reactant that is in shortest supply. This does not necessarily mean that there are fewest grams of it, or fewest moles. It does mean that the reaction will run out of this particular reactant first. The determination of the limiting reagent and the **theoretical yield** (amount of product that can be made, usually expressed in grams) are closely related, because the limiting reagent controls the amount of product that can be made.

> The amount of limiting reagent determines the theoretical yield.

Limiting reactant problems can be recognized as those in which the amount of more than one reactant is given. For example, the compound IBr can be produced from its elements (I_2 and Br_2) at room temperature:

$$I_2(s) + Br_2(\ell) \longrightarrow 2\,IBr(s)$$

Suppose 1.0 mol of I_2 and 2.0 mol of Br_2 are mixed, and this reaction is allowed to occur. The limiting reactant is I_2; it limits how much product can be formed. The other reactant, Br_2, is in excess. Even after the reaction has gone to completion, 1.0 mol of Br_2 remains.

One point to emphasize is that <u>the limiting reactant is completely converted to product in the reaction.</u> In our example, above, we can easily tabulate the initial amounts, the changes during reaction, and the final amounts. In the stoichiometry table, below, the "initial moles" entries come from the premise of the problem. The "change in moles" entries (Δ moles) come from comparing the initial moles line to the stoichiometry in the headings of the table and applying the concept of limiting reagent (2 moles of Br_2 cannot react if there is only 1 mol of I_2). Columns are summed to obtain the bottom line.

	I_2 +	Br_2 →	2 IBr
Initial moles	1.0	2.0	0
Δ moles[98]	−1.0	−1.0	+2.0
Final moles	0.0	1.0	2.0

---

[97] Structure by Ben Mills (Own work) [Public domain], via Wikimedia Commons.

[98] The Greek letter Δ (delta) is used to express "change in." To fill in these values, consider that 2.0 moles Br_2 (top line) would require 2.0 moles of I_2, but we only have 1.0 mole I_2. Therefore, I_2 limits and the amount of reaction that occurs depends on the amount of I_2 available. Changes in moles will be negative for reactants and positive for products.

At the conclusion of the reaction, no I_2 (the limiting reactant) remains; 1.0 mol of the other reactant, Br_2, is left over. <u>The amount of product formed is based on the initial number of moles of the limiting reactant:</u>

$$1.0 \, \text{mol } I_2 \times \underbrace{\frac{2 \, \text{mol IBr}}{1 \, \text{mol } I_2}} = 2.0 \, \text{mol IBr}$$

from coefficients of balanced reaction equation

Because the limiting reactant governs how much product in a reaction can possibly be formed, a key step in limiting reactant problems is to identify the limiting reactant. In Method A (in the doll manufacturing example) we saw that the limiting reagent can be identified by comparing the mole ratio of reactant molecules available with the mole ratio needed according to the balanced chemical equation. The following problems are solved using this method:

Example 14-14.

Palladium(II) fluoride, PdF_2, can be synthesized according to the reaction

$$2 \, PdF_3 + SeF_4 \longrightarrow 2 \, PdF_2 + SeF_6$$

Identify the limiting reactant, and predict the number of moles of PdF_2 formed in the following three experiments.

    a. 3.0 mol PdF_3 and 1.0 mol SeF_4 are mixed.

    b. 1.0 mol PdF_3 and 1.0 mol SeF_4 are mixed.

    c. 1.5 mol PdF_3 and 1.0 mol SeF_4 are mixed.

<u>Solutions:</u>

    a. 3.0 mol PdF_3 + 1.0 mol SeF_4

We must first find, from the balanced chemical equation, the ratio of moles of reactants necessary for the reaction to go to completion (using up all of the reactants). We can then compare this ratio with the actual ratio of reactants available. If the actual ratio is different from the ratio provided in the equation, one reactant must be limiting.

According to the balanced chemical equation, for the reaction to go to completion there must be:

$$\frac{2 \, \text{mol } PdF_3}{1 \, \text{mol } SeF_4} \qquad \text{In other words, the ratio needed is} \qquad \frac{\text{mol } PdF_3}{\text{mol } SeF_4} = 2$$

In part a, the actual ratio is: $\dfrac{3.0 \, \text{mol } PdF_3}{1.0 \, \text{mol } SeF_4} = 3.0$. Because this ratio is greater than 2 (the ratio for the balanced equation), the compound in the numerator, PdF_3, is in excess, and **SeF_4** is the limiting reactant.

The number of moles of PdF_2 formed is based on the initial number of moles of SeF_4, the limiting reactant:

$$(1.0 \, \text{mol } SeF_4) \, \frac{2 \, \text{mol } PdF_2}{1 \, \text{mol } SeF_4} = \textbf{2.0 mol } PdF_2$$

Summarizing in a stoichiometry table:

	$2\,PdF_3$	$+\;\;1\,SeF_4$	$\longrightarrow\;\;2\,PdF_2$	$+\;\;1\,SeF_6$
Initial moles	3.0	1.0	0	0
Change	−2.0	−1.0	+2.0	+1.0
Final moles	1.0	0	2.0	1.0

↑ *limiting reactant completely used up*

b. 1.0 mol PdF$_3$ + 1.0 mol SeF$_4$

The "needed" ratio of $\dfrac{\text{mol PdF}_3}{\text{mol SeF}_4}$ is still 2.0. We calculate the ratio of moles of reactants we

have: $\dfrac{1.0\ \text{mol PdF}_3}{1.0\ \text{mol SeF}_4}=1.0$

Now our ratio is less than the mole ratio taken from the balanced equation. This means that there is now a shortage of compound in the numerator; this compound, **PdF$_3$**, must be the limiting reactant.

We can easily test this deduction by determining how many moles of SeF$_4$ will react if PdF$_3$ is used up (recall again that the limiting reactant must be used up):

$$(1.0\ \text{mol PdF}_3\ \text{reacting})\ \frac{1\ \text{mol SeF}_4}{2\ \text{mol PdF}_3}=0.5\ \text{mol SeF}_4\ \text{reacting}$$

The initial number of moles of SeF$_4$ is greater than 0.5, so SeF$_4$ is present beyond the amount needed to react with the PdF$_3$; we have more than enough SeF$_4$.

The number of moles of PdF$_2$ formed is based on the initial moles of PdF$_3$:

$$(1.0\ \text{mol PdF}_3)\ \frac{2\ \text{mol PdF}_2}{2\ \text{mol PdF}_3}=\textbf{1.0 mol}\ PdF_2$$

Summarizing with a stoichiometry table:

	$2\,PdF_3$	$+\;\;1\,SeF_4$	$\longrightarrow\;\;2\,PdF_2$	$+\;\;1\,SeF_6$
Initial moles	1.0	1.0	0	0
Change	−1.0	−0.50	+1.0	+0.50
Final moles	0	0.50	1.0	0.50

↑ *limiting reactant completely used up*

c. 1.5 mol PdF$_3$ + 1.0 mol SeF$_4$

The temptation might be to select SeF$_4$ as the limiting reactant, because fewer moles of it are present. However, we must test this by calculation as we have done in parts **a** and **b**.

The "needed" ratio of $\dfrac{\text{mol PdF}_3}{\text{mol SeF}_4}$ is still 2.0. Again we find the mole ratio of reactants we

have: $\dfrac{1.5\ \text{mol PdF}_3}{1.0\ \text{mol SeF}_4}=1.5$

This ratio is smaller than the mole ratio from the balanced equation, so there must be a deficiency of the compound in the numerator; **PdF_3** must be the limiting reactant (even though it is initially present in greater molar amount).

We now calculate the yield of product on the basis of PdF_3 as the limiting reactant:

$$(1.5 \text{ mol } PdF_3) \left(\frac{2 \text{ mol } PdF_2}{2 \text{ mol } PdF_3} \right) = \textbf{1.5 mol } PdF_2$$

Summarizing with a stoichiometry table:

	$2\,PdF_3$ +	$1\,SeF_4$	$\longrightarrow$ $2\,PdF_2$ +	$1\,SeF_6$
Initial moles	1.5	1.0	0	0
Change	−1.5	−0.75	+1.5	+0.75
Final moles	0	0.25	1.5	0.75

↑ *limiting reactant completely used up*

Earlier, we explored a second method (Method B) for solving limiting reagent problems. This method is illustrated, below, for the same set of problems, except that here we are asked to calculate the theoretical yield (in grams), rather than to predict the number of moles of product formed.

Example 14-15.

PdF_2 can be synthesized according to the reaction

$$2\,PdF_3 + SeF_4 \longrightarrow 2\,PdF_2 + SeF_6$$

Identify the limiting reactant, and calculate the theoretical yield of PdF_2 formed in the following three experiments.
  a. 3.0 mol PdF_3 and 1.0 mol SeF_4 are mixed.
  b. 1.0 mol PdF_3 and 1.0 mol SeF_4 are mixed.
  c. 1.5 mol PdF_3 and 1.0 mol SeF_4 are mixed.

<u>Solutions:</u>

  a. We can identify the limiting reagent by choosing one product and determining which of the reactants can make the smaller amount. Because this problem also asks us to determine the mass of PdF_2 synthesized, we will choose PdF_2 as the product for our other calculations.

$$3.0 \text{ mol } PdF_3 \times \frac{2 \text{ mol } PdF_2}{2 \text{ mol } PdF_3} = 3.0 \text{ mol } PdF_2$$

$$1.0 \text{ mol } SeF_4 \times \frac{2 \text{ mol } PdF_2}{1 \text{ mol } SeF_4} = 2.0 \text{ mol } PdF_2$$

Because SeF_4 can make less product than PdF_3, **SeF_4** is the limiting reagent. The amount of PdF_2 expected is 2.0 moles. The theoretical yield of PdF_2 requires conversion from moles to grams:

$$2.0 \text{ mol } PdF_2 \times \frac{144.42 \text{ g } PdF_2}{1 \text{ mol } PdF_2} = 288.84 \text{ g } PdF_2$$

Because the number of moles of reactant is known to only 2 significant figures, the answer must be rounded to **290 g PdF_2**.

b. We use the same method, but do the determination of limiting reagent by calculating all the way to masses of PdF_2, because this is the number we will need:

$$1.0 \text{ mol PdF}_3 \times \frac{2 \text{ mol PdF}_2}{2 \text{ mol PdF}_3} \times \frac{144.42 \text{ g PdF}_2}{1 \text{ mol PdF}_2} = 144.42 \text{ g PdF}_2$$

$$1.0 \text{ mol SeF}_4 \times \frac{2 \text{ mol PdF}_2}{1 \text{ mol SeF}_4} \times \frac{144.42 \text{ g PdF}_2}{1 \text{ mol PdF}_2} = 288.84 \text{ g PdF}_2$$

Because the PdF_3 can produce less product than the SeF_4, PdF_3 is the limiting reagent, and the theoretical yield of PdF_2, to 2 significant figures, is 140 g.

c. Using the same method:

$$1.5 \text{ mol PdF}_3 \times \frac{2 \text{ mol PdF}_2}{2 \text{ mol PdF}_3} \times \frac{144.42 \text{ g PdF}_2}{1 \text{ mol PdF}_2} = 216.63 \text{ g PdF}_2$$

$$1.0 \text{ mol SeF}_4 \times \frac{2 \text{ mol PdF}_2}{1 \text{ mol SeF}_4} \times \frac{144.42 \text{ g PdF}_2}{1 \text{ mol PdF}_2} = 288.84 \text{ g PdF}_2$$

Because PdF_3 can produce less product than SeF_4, **PdF_3** is the limiting reagent, and the theoretical yield of PdF_2, to 2 significant figures, is **220 g**.

To summarize, here are some useful points about **limiting reactant** problems:

1. Limiting reactant problems can be recognized as those in which the initial amount of more than one reactant is given.

2. The limiting reactant is completely converted to product as the reaction proceeds.

3. The amount of a particular product formed is based on the initial number of moles of the limiting reactant and the mole ratio of that product to the limiting reactant.

4. <u>The identity of the limiting reactant cannot necessarily be determined by simply comparing the number of moles of reactants, or masses of reactants.</u> Two approaches to identifying the limiting reagent have been introduced:

<u>Method A</u>

(1) Compare the ratio of reactants needed (based on the balanced chemical reaction equation) to the ratio available.

(2) If the ratio available is larger than the ratio from the balanced equation, the compound in the numerator is in excess, and the compound in the denominator is limiting.

(3) If the ratio available is smaller than the ratio from the balanced equation, the compound in the numerator is the limiting reactant.

(4) If the ratio available is identical to the ratio from the balanced equation, the reactants exactly balance and both (or all) reactants will be completely used up.

<u>Method B</u>

(1) Calculate the moles (or mass) of <u>one</u> product that can be produced by the available amount of each reactant. Use dimensional analysis.

(2) Whichever reactant produces the least of that product is the limiting reactant.

(3) If the reactants can all make the same amount of product, then they are exactly in stoichiometric balance with one another, and all reactants will be used up.

Exercise 14-11.

Phosphorus trichloride is made industrially by the reaction of elemental phosphorus with chlorine:

$$P_4 + 6\,Cl_2 \longrightarrow 4\,PCl_3$$

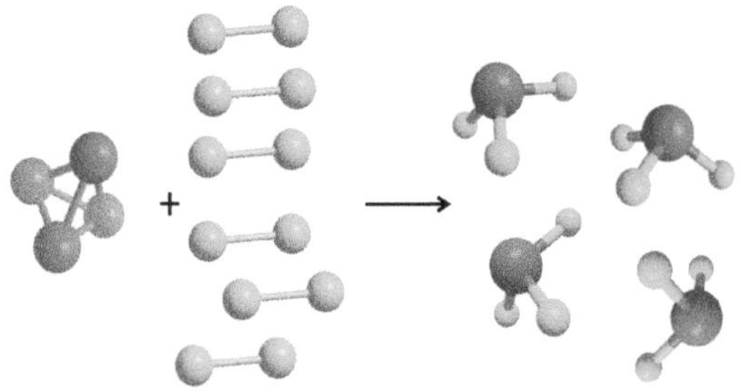

Identify the limiting reagent, and predict the number of moles of PCl_3 formed in the following three experiments:

a. 1.0 mol P_4 and 10.0 mol Cl_2 are mixed.

b. 2.0 mol P_4 and 8.0 mol Cl_2 are mixed.

c. 1.3 mol P_4 and 8.0 mol Cl_2 are mixed.

A situation commonly encountered in the laboratory is to identify the limiting reagent when quantities of reactants are presented as masses rather than moles. To identify the limiting reagent in this situation it is necessary to convert from masses to moles, as shown in Example 14-16.

Example 14-16.

Potassium chloride reacts with elemental fluorine to form potassium fluoride and chlorine pentafluoride.

a. Write a balanced chemical equation for this reaction.

b. Identify the limiting reactant if 10.00 g of potassium chloride and 10. g of fluorine are mixed.

c. What is the theoretical yield of potassium fluoride in this reaction?

d. Which reactant is in excess? What mass of this reactant is left over at the end of the reaction?

Solution:

a. $KCl + 3\,F_2 \longrightarrow KF + ClF_5$

b. To identify the limiting reactant we must first convert from grams to moles:

KCl: $10.00 \text{ g KCl} \left(\dfrac{1 \text{ mol KCl}}{74.551 \text{ g KCl}} \right) = 0.1341 \text{ mol KCl}$ (known to 4 sig figs)

F_2: $10. \text{ g } F_2 \left(\dfrac{1 \text{ mol } F_2}{38.00 \text{ g } F_2} \right) = 0.26 \text{ mol } F_2$ (known to only 2 sig figs)

According to the balanced equation, if the reaction were to occur to completely use up both reactants, the ratio of reactants needed would be: $\dfrac{3 \text{ mol } F_2}{1 \text{ mol KCl}}$

The actual ratio is: $\dfrac{0.26 \text{ mol } F_2}{0.1341 \text{ mol KCl}} = \dfrac{1.9 \text{ mol } F_2}{1 \text{ mol KCl}}$

Because this ratio is smaller than 3 (the ratio demanded by the balanced equation), there is not enough F_2 to completely react with the KCl; $\mathbf{F_2}$ is the limiting reactant.

c. The mass of KF that can be formed is based on the amount of the limiting reactant, F_2:

$$0.26 \text{ mol } F_2 \left(\frac{1 \text{ mol KF}}{3 \text{ mol } F_2} \right)\left(\frac{58.10 \text{ g KF}}{1 \text{ mol KF}} \right) = \mathbf{5.0 \text{ g KF}}$$

d. Because F_2 is the limiting reactant, **KCl** is in excess. The amount used must be the amount that reacts with 0.26 mol F_2:

$$0.26 \text{ mol } F_2 \left(\frac{1 \text{ mol KCl}}{3 \text{ mol } F_2} \right)\left(\frac{74.55 \text{ g KCl}}{1 \text{ mol KCl}} \right) = 6.5 \text{ g KCl}$$

The remaining mass of KCl is therefore: 10.00 g (known to 2 places to right of decimal)
                                          $- 6.5$ g (known to only 1 place to right of decimal)
                                          3.5 g

Exercise 14-12.

Sulfur reacts with phosphorus to form tetraphosphorus trisulfide. If 10.0 g of sulfur and 12.0 g of phosphorus are mixed, how many grams of tetraphosphorus trisulfide, at most, can be formed?

G. Calculation of Reaction Yields

In addition to the limit placed on the amount of product obtained by the limiting reagent, other complications that reduce the yield of product may occur in a chemical reaction. There may be side reactions, a product may decompose, or some product may be lost while it is being collected. We learned to calculate the **theoretical yield**, the maximum possible mass of product expected if the reaction occurs "perfectly" by starting with the limiting reagent. However, the **actual yield** (the product actually obtained in pure form) is likely to be less than the theoretical yield. The overall success of a reaction is sometimes measured by the **percent yield**:

$$\% \text{ Yield} = \left(\frac{\text{Actual yield}}{\text{Theoretical yield}} \right) \times 100\%$$

Notice that a % yield larger than 100% should not be possible because actual yields cannot be larger than theoretical yields. When % yield values are too large, the product is often found to be impure in some way, and thus has a mass that reflects more than just the product in question.

Suppose that the reaction described in Example 14-13 yielded 0.88 g of NF_3 rather than the 1.04 g predicted as the theoretical yield. The percent yield would be:

$$\% \text{ Yield} = \frac{0.88 \text{ g}}{1.04 \text{ g}} \times 100\% = 85\%$$

Example 14-17 provides an additional example of calculating theoretical and percent yields.

Example 14-17.

Metallic iron reacts with chlorine gas to form $FeCl_3$: $2\ Fe(s) + 3\ Cl_2(g) \longrightarrow 2\ FeCl_3(s)$

a. In a reaction, 25.0 g of Fe reacts with excess Cl_2. What is the theoretical yield (in grams) of $FeCl_3$?

b. If 64.2 g of $FeCl_3$ is actually obtained, what is the percent yield?

Solution:

The problem states that Cl_2 is in excess, so the limiting reagent is iron.

a. The theoretical yield can be found using the coefficients in the balanced equation and the molecular masses:

$$25.0\ \text{g Fe}\left(\frac{1\ \text{mol Fe}}{55.85\ \text{g Fe}}\right)\left(\frac{2\ \text{mol FeCl}_3}{2\ \text{mol Fe}}\right)\left(\frac{162.2\ \text{g FeCl}_3}{1\ \text{mol FeCl}_3}\right) = \textbf{72.6 g } FeCl_3$$

b. The percent yield is given by:

$$\%\ \text{yield} = \left(\frac{\text{actual yield}}{\text{theoretical yield}}\right) \times 100\ \% = \left(\frac{64.2\ \text{g}}{72.6\ \text{g}}\right) \times 100\ \% = \textbf{88.4\%}$$

Exercise 14-13.

Elemental bromine reacts with ethylene, C_2H_4, to form 1,2-dibromoethane, $C_2H_4Br_2$.

In a reaction, excess bromine is mixed with 20.00 g of ethylene.

a. What is the theoretical yield of $C_2H_4Br_2$?

b. Suppose 110.6 g of $C_2H_4Br_2$ is actually obtained. What is the percent yield?

Always be on the lookout for limiting reactants! These frequently appear in problems dealing with reaction yields (because the limiting reagent, by its definition, limits how much product can be formed). Example 14-18 is a case in point.

Example 14-18.

Iodine reacts with xenon difluoride to form iodine trifluoride and xenon:

$$I_2(s) + 3\ XeF_2(s) \longrightarrow 2\ IF_3(s) + 3\ Xe(g)$$

When 10.0 g of I_2 and 15.0 g of XeF_2 are mixed, and the above reaction occurs, 8.00 g of IF_3 forms. Calculate (**a**) the theoretical yield and (**b**) the percentage yield.

a. First, identify the limiting reactant. (Whenever amounts of more than one reagent are given in a problem we must consider which one is limiting!) To do this, we must first find the mole ratio of reactants needed for the balanced equation: $\dfrac{3 \text{ mol XeF}_2}{1 \text{ mol I}_2} = 3$

Next, we calculate the moles of each reactant from the information given and compare the actual mole ratio with the ratio from the balanced equation:

$$10.0 \text{ g I}_2 \left(\frac{1 \text{ mol I}_2}{253.8 \text{ g I}_2} \right) = 0.0394 \text{ mol I}_2 \text{ and } 15.0 \text{ g XeF}_2 \left(\frac{1 \text{ mol XeF}_2}{169.3 \text{ g XeF}_2} \right) = 0.0886 \text{ mol XeF}_2$$

The actual mole ratio is: $\dfrac{0.0886 \text{ mol XeF}_2}{0.0394 \text{ mol I}_2} = 2.25$.

This is smaller than the mole ratio from the balanced equation, meaning that there is a shortage of the compound in the numerator; XeF_2 is the limiting reagent.

<u>The theoretical yield must then be calculated using the amount of the limiting reagent</u>, XeF_2:

$$0.0886 \text{ mol XeF}_2 \left(\frac{2 \text{ mol IF}_3}{3 \text{ mol XeF}_2} \right)\left(\frac{183.9 \text{ g IF}_3}{1 \text{ mol IF}_3} \right) = \mathbf{10.9 \text{ g IF}_3}$$

b. % yield $= \dfrac{8.00 \text{ g IF}_3}{10.9 \text{ g IF}_3} \times 100\% = \mathbf{73.4\ \%}$

To close this section, Example 14-19 provides a review of some of the types of chemical calculations discussed in this chapter.

Example 14-19.

Cryolite, the coordination compound with formula $Na_3[AlF_6]$, is used in its *molten form* (melted! requires almost 1000 °C!) as a solvent in the purification of aluminum. Cryolite can be synthesized via the reaction:

$$6 \text{ HF} + Al(OH)_3 + 3 \text{ NaOH} \longrightarrow Na_3[AlF_6] + 6 \text{ H}_2O$$

a. How many moles of $Na_3[AlF_6]$ can be prepared from 1 mole of $Al(OH)_3$? How many moles of other reactants are required?

Solution:

These answers can be determined directly from the balanced equation, using the respective coefficients. From the equation we can see that:

1 mole of $Na_3[AlF_6]$ can be prepared from 1 mole of $Al(OH)_3$ (each of these compounds has a coefficient of 1).

To prepare 1 mole of $Na_3[AlF_6]$ we would require **6** moles of HF and **3** moles of NaOH; these are the coefficients of these compounds in the equation.

b. If only 0.50 mol of NaOH is available and the other reactants are present in excess, how many moles of $Na_3[AlF_6]$ can, at most, be formed?

Solution:

The balanced equation, as stated, expresses the mole ratios of reactants and products. We use one of these mole ratios to solve this problem. From the balanced equation, we see that 1 mole of Na_3AlF_6 can be formed from 3 moles of NaOH, if sufficient quantities of the other reactants are available. Hence the essential mole ratio is

$$\left(\frac{1 \text{ mol } Na_3[AlF_6]}{3 \text{ mol NaOH}} \right)$$

The calculation can be set up most simply as a conversion factor problem:

$$0.50 \text{ mol NaOH} \times \left(\frac{1 \text{ mol } Na_3[AlF_6]}{3 \text{ mol NaOH}} \right) = \textbf{0.17 mol } Na_3[AlF_6]$$

c. Suppose only 25.0 g of HF is available. How many grams of $Na_3[AlF_6]$, at most, can be formed?

Solution:

The coefficients can be used, in combination with molecular masses, to calculate masses of reactants and products. In this case we can set up the entire problem as a series of conversion factors; if we set this up correctly, the units will cancel appropriately (this is a mass-to-mole-to-mole-to-mass problem!)

$$25.0 \text{ g HF} \left(\frac{1 \text{ mol HF}}{20.0 \text{ g HF}} \right) \left(\frac{1 \text{ mol } Na_3[AlF_6]}{6 \text{ mol HF}} \right) \left(\frac{209.9 \text{ g } Na_3[AlF_6]}{1 \text{ mol } Na_3[AlF_6]} \right) = \textbf{43.7 g } Na_3[AlF_6]$$

d. Suppose 3.0 mol HF, 2.0 mol NaOH, and an excess of $Al(OH)_3$ are mixed. At most, how many moles of $Na_3[AlF_6]$ can be formed?

Solution:

Because the amount of product will be limited by HF or NaOH, we must first determine which is the limiting reactant. It is tempting to assume that the reactant present in least amount, NaOH, will limit the amount of product formed. But is this the case?

$Al(OH)_3$ cannot be the limiting reagent, because it is present in excess. From the balanced equation, we can determine the mole ratio of the other two reactants, HF and NaOH:

$$\left(\frac{6 \text{ mol HF}}{3 \text{ mol NaOH}} \right) = 2$$

The actual ratio in this problem is: $\dfrac{3.0 \text{ mol HF}}{2.0 \text{ mol NaOH}} = 1.5$

There is therefore a shortage of HF; it is the limiting reagent.

To determine the number of moles of $Na_3[AlF_6]$ formed, we must begin with the 3.0 mol HF available:

$$3.0 \text{ mol HF} \left(\frac{1 \text{ mol } Na_3[AlF_6]}{6 \text{ mol HF}} \right) = \textbf{0.50 mol } Na_3[AlF_6]$$

14-3. ECOLOGICAL AND BIOCHEMICAL STOICHIOMETRY

Stoichiometric considerations for living systems vary from a more chemical foundation to a more engineering foundation. Let's take a look at three levels of stoichiometric thinking in the biological sciences.

A. Ecological Stoichiometry

At a very basic level, stoichiometry is a quantitative relationship between materials available and materials needed. In this context, living systems must be in a stoichiometric relationship with their environment. Ecological stoichiometry is the study of the balance of chemical elements in ecological interactions. The substances required for life-processes (growth, maintenance, reproduction) must be secured from the environment. When nutritional requirements are not adequately met by the environment, growth and reproduction can be negatively impacted. Both the impact of the environment on the organism and the impact of the organism on the environment are important aspects of ecological stoichiometry.

A much studied area within ecological stoichiometry is the sometimes disparate elemental make-up of an organism compared to its food source. Grasshoppers' bodies, for instance, have a relatively constant carbon:nitrogen (C:N) atom ratio of about 5, while their major food source, grass, is relatively nitrogen poor with a C:N ratio of approximately 33. The grasshopper must eliminate a great deal of carbon (much through normal metabolic processing to CO_2) but must hold on to essentially all of the nitrogen taken in.

While grasses have a relatively constant C:N ratio, many food sources are much more variable. For example, a particular zooplankton may have a carbon:phosphorus (C:P) ratio of 80, while the various ponds in which it resides have suspended organic materials (food stuff for zooplankton) with a range of C:P ratios from 10 to 1000. Depending on its environment, a particular zooplankton may need to conserve dietary carbon and excrete dietary phosphorus (if the food stuff has C:P <80) or conserve the phosphorus and excrete much of the carbon (if the food stuff has C:P > 80). It is typical that nutritional sources have much larger ranges of elemental make-up than organisms. The interesting point is to determine how an organism adapts to differences in the elemental make up of its food source(s).

What is the reason that different life forms have different C:N:P ratios? This depends almost entirely on the elements needed to build the structures of that organism. DNA and proteins, for instance, demand certain amounts of carbon, nitrogen and phosphorus. Plants require cell walls, but animals have no such requirement. The presence of bony structures can greatly impact the need for phosphorus. A particularly bony and armored fish, for example, will sequester a lot of phosphorus for bones from its environment. This may impact other life forms, especially if phosphorus levels in the habitat are low. The balance and flow of the elements among competing systems in an ecological system is becoming a much-studied stoichiometric science.

B. Biochemical Stoichiometry

In Chapter 13, we looked quite closely at four reaction equations from the metabolic pathway called glycolysis. These reactions are listed here, without the structural information we focused on in Chapter 13.

$$C_6H_{12}O_6 + C_{10}H_{12}N_5O_{13}P_3^{4-} \xrightarrow{\text{phosphorylation}} C_6H_{11}O_9P^{2-} + C_{10}H_{12}N_5O_{10}P_2^{3-} + H^+$$

glucose ATP^{4-} glucose-6-phosphate ADP^{3-}

$$C_6H_{11}O_9P^{2-} \xrightarrow{\text{isomerization}} C_6H_{11}O_9P^{2-}$$

glucose-6-phosphate fructose-6-phosphate

$$C_6H_{10}O_{12}P_2^{4-} \xrightarrow{\text{decomposition}} C_3H_5O_6P^{2-} + C_3H_5O_6P^{2-}$$

fructose-1,6-bisphosphate glyceraldehyde-3-phosphate + dihydroxyacetone phosphate

$$C_3H_5O_6P^{2-} \xrightarrow{\text{internal redox}} C_3H_5O_6P^{2-}$$

dihydroxyacetone phosphate glyceraldehyde-3-phosphate

Each reaction has a set of reactants and products whose quantitative relationships are explicitly known. In metabolic pathways, the most common stoichiometric coefficients are definitely "1's." Individually, these reactions are similar to other chemical reaction equations, in that (for the most part) atoms and charges must balance as reactants become products. There is a striking exception to this rule on a practical level: in an actual cell, reactions that generate free protons (such as the phosphorylation reaction, above) don't seem to do so in a stoichiometric way. We would expect these protons to be taken up by water molecules to become H_3O^+ in the aqueous environment. If carefully measured, however, it is clear that many fewer H_3O^+ are present than expected. This result is due to the complex milieu of molecules in the system, many of which compete successfully with water molecules to bind free H^+ produced by the reaction. So, when a balanced biochemical reaction equation shows H^+ (as either reactant or product), you can expect not to be able to measure exactly where the H^+ comes from, or goes to. This is actually good! Because many of the H^+ ions do not bind to water molecules, the pH of the aqueous system is not changed as much as it would otherwise be. We will describe acid-base behaviors and pH much more in upcoming chapters.

While individual reactions within a metabolic pathway usually have relatively simple characteristics, overall reactions for a pathway (starting with the initial reagents and ending with the final products) often have some strange features. The overall reaction for the metabolism of glucose is often written as follows:

$$C_6H_{12}O_6 + 6\,O_2 \longrightarrow 6\,CO_2 + 6\,H_2O$$

By definition, this is a combustion reaction (a reaction with elemental oxygen). When performed by living cells, however, there is no fire! Nonetheless, it does make sense that we talk about "burning" calories. The really strange part from a beginning biochemist's perspective is that the glucose molecule and the oxygen molecules never interact directly:

molecule	processed by	results in
glucose	glycolysis, citric acid cycle	CO_2, NADH, FADH$_2$, a little ATP
oxygen, O_2	electron transport chain	H_2O

Glucose and oxygen are processed by different pathways. The connection between them is the NADH and FADH₂ molecules that are produced during the oxidation of glucose carbons to CO₂. See Figures 14-2, 14-3, and 14-4 for an overview of the metabolic scheme. Carbon dioxide (O=C=O) represents the ultimate oxidation of carbon atoms, all four bonds are to oxygen! Whenever oxidation occurs, reductions must also occur:

$$NAD^+ + 2e^- + H^+ \longrightarrow NADH$$

$$FAD + 2e^- + 2H^+ \longrightarrow FADH_2$$

As carbon atoms from glucose are oxidized, NAD⁺ and FAD are reduced. The connection between the glucose pathway and the oxygen pathway is the reduced products, NADH and FADH₂. These two species re-oxidize as they send their "extra" electrons into the electron transport chain (Figure 14-4). The final acceptor of those electrons is the O₂ molecule:

$$O_2 + 4e^- + 4H^+ \longrightarrow 2H_2O$$

The 4 electrons needed to reduce molecular oxygen come from the electron transport chain, which got the electrons, ultimately, from glucose molecules. So, while glucose is processed in glycolysis and the citric acid cycle, oxygen only makes an appearance at the end of the electron transport chain.

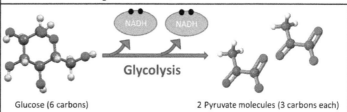

Figure 14-2. Glycolysis begins with glucose and ends with two molecules of pyruvate. In the process, two NADH molecules are produced; each one carries two electrons from the glucose molecule.

Glucose (6 carbons)   2 Pyruvate molecules (3 carbons each)

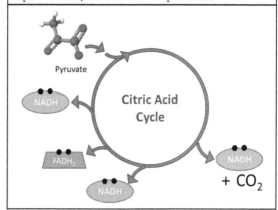

Figure 14-3. The carbons from pyruvate enter the citric acid cycle; products of the cycle include CO₂, NADH and FADH₂. The electrons lost by glucose carbon atoms during their oxidation to CO₂ are carried by the NADH and FADH₂ molecules.

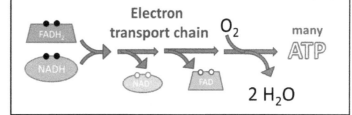

Figure 14-4. The electron transport chain utilizes the FADH₂ and NADH from glycolysis and the citric acid cycle to provide the energy necessary to synthesize ATP. NAD⁺ and FAD (without the extra electrons) are produced; they can return to glycolysis and citric acid cycle to obtain electrons again.

Exercise 14-14.

In the glucose molecule there are 7 C-O bonds for 6 carbon atoms. This means that there are 7/6 or ~1.2 C-O bonds per carbon atom. Determine the ratio of "C-O bonds per carbon atom" for pyruvate (see structure in Figure 14-2) and carbon dioxide. Use your results to argue that the carbons of glucose become oxidized via glycolysis and the citric acid cycle.

Here's another strange stoichiometric result: if you go on to study this metabolic process in detail, you will learn that in applying the overall balanced reaction equation:

$$C_6H_{12}O_6 + 6\,O_2 \longrightarrow 6\,CO_2 + 6\,H_2O$$

to a single molecule of glucose, one finds that the six carbon atoms on the left are not the exact same carbon atoms as the six on the right. Now that's odd! The short answer to this puzzle is that some carbon atoms spend a little time circling in the citric acid cycle before finally being converted to CO₂!

The overall reaction, above, leaves out the product that was actually desired: the ATP! If we include that, how can we write reaction equation?

$$C_6H_{12}O_6 + 6\ O_2 + \text{30-32 ADP} + \text{30-32 P}_i \longrightarrow 6\ CO_2 + 6\ H_2O + \text{30-32 ATP (usually)}[99]$$

Oh my! What's this about? Strange stoichiometry indeed! Biological systems are complicated. Actually, the maximum number of ATP that can theoretically be obtained from one glucose molecule is 38. However, one can expect some losses (across a leaky membrane, for example) and some ATP must be used in various processes along the way, so the maximum number is never actually obtained. One way that ATP is used along the way is to provide the energy necessary to move needed species across a membrane. In some instances there are multiple ways to accomplish a task, some requiring ATP and others relying on diffusion instead. Thus, the final count of ATP produced per glucose molecule will be variable, depending on the exact routes taken by a variety of molecules. Don't be surprised to see some stoichiometric hand-waving in biochemical pathways!

When chemists synthesize a large new molecule in a multi-step reaction, they gather the first set of reactants and prepare a product that is an intermediate along the path to the desired product. Then they usually isolate that intermediate, add any reagents needed for the second reaction and run that one. This step-by-step process repeats until the chemist arrives at the desired end product. Biochemical reactions also occur in steps, but these steps may all be happening at the same time! How does this work? Metabolic reactions take place in the active sites of different enzymes; there is a different enzyme for each step. The enzyme binds one or more reactants (or **substrates**), performs the reaction, and then releases the products. This **catalytic cycle** repeats itself over and over again in any particular active site. This means that biochemical pathways make progress by **flux**[100] through the pathway. The product of one enzymatic reaction is the substrate for the next. Individual **substrates** spend time in each successive active site. But as long as the initial reactants are available to enzyme #1, all of the enzymes are working on something! Metabolic flux is a continuum of activity rather than a sequestered, step-wise process. The first reaction of the pathway does not finish producing product before the second reaction begins. Rather, all of the reactions are taking place essentially simultaneously!

---

[99] "P$_i$" is an abbreviation for the phosphate ion in any of its various protonated forms: PO_4^{3-}, HPO_4^{2-}, $H_2PO_4^-$. Again, the presence, or not, of a proton here or there is not something that biochemists usually focus on. The distribution of protons to phosphate ions (and other weak bases) depends on the pH of the system.

[100] "Flux" is a continuous change or the process of flowing.

CHAPTER 14 PROBLEMS

1. Carbon disulfide burns in air to give carbon dioxide plus sulfur dioxide, a choking, poisonous gas.

    a. Write a balanced chemical equation for this reaction.

    b. How many molecules are in 50.0 grams of carbon disulfide?

    c. What mass of sulfur dioxide would be formed from combustion of 50.0 g of carbon disulfide?

2. Ammonium nitrate decomposes on heating to give *nitrous oxide* (dinitrogen monoxide) plus water.

    a. Write a balanced chemical equation for this reaction.

    b. How many molecules are in 25.0 grams of nitrous oxide?

    c. What mass of ammonium nitrate must be heated to give 25.0 g of nitrous oxide?

3. Butane, C_4H_{10}, burns in air to give carbon dioxide and water.

    a. Write a balanced equation for this reaction.

    b. How many molecules are in 75.0 g of butane?

    c. What mass of water is formed from combustion of 75.0 g of butane?

4. A solution contained an unknown amount of dissolved $Pb(NO_3)_2$. To this solution was added concentrated hydrochloric acid until no more precipitate was formed. A white solid was collected by filtration and dried; this solid had a mass of 1.43 g.

    a. What was the chemical formula of the solid?

    b. Write a net ionic equation to describe the formation of this solid.

    c. What was the mass of $Pb(NO_3)_2$ in the original solution?

5. Phosphines contain the elements phosphorus, carbon, and hydrogen. Determine the empirical formula of a phosphine having the following composition by mass:

    i.   P   40.7%
    ii. C   47.4%
    iii. H   11.9%

6. A compound consisting of I and Cl contains 45.6% Cl by mass. What is its empirical formula?

7. What is the empirical formula of a compound that contains 66.8% silver, 15.9% vanadium, and 17.3% oxygen by mass?

8. One of the principal components of Portland cement contains 52.7 % calcium, 12.3 % silicon, and 35.0 % oxygen by mass. What is its empirical formula?

9. "Fool's gold" is a compound of iron and sulfur called iron pyrite. When 0.6814 g of iron pyrite was roasted in air (reacted with the oxygen in air), the sulfur was converted completely to 0.7276 g of SO_2. What is the empirical formula of iron pyrite?

10. A compound containing only the elements iodine and oxygen was found to contain 79.86 percent iodine by mass.

      a. What was the empirical formula of this compound?

      b. The compound has a mass of approximately $318 \frac{g}{mol}$. What was its molecular formula?

11. Methyl salicylate is also known as "oil of wintergreen" and is used in a variety of products because of its characteristic smell. Methyl salicylate has the following mass percentage composition:

                63.14% C   5.31% H   31.55% O

      a. What is the empirical formula of methyl salicylate?

      b. Methyl salicylate has a mass of $152.1 \frac{g}{mol}$. What is the molecular formula of this compound?

12. Analysis of a compound containing only the elements chlorine and oxygen indicated that the compound contained 59.6 percent chlorine by mass.

      a. What was the empirical formula of the compound?

      b. The compound had a mass of $237.8 \frac{g}{mol}$. What was its molecular formula?

13. The percentages of C, H, and O in vitamin C are determined by burning a sample having a mass of 2.00 mg; the masses of CO_2 and H_2O formed are 3.00 mg and 0.816 mg respectively.

      a. Determine the empirical formula of vitamin C.

      b. Vitamin C has a mass of $176.1 \frac{g}{mol}$. What is the molecular formula of vitamin C?

14. A 0.537 g sample of an organic compound containing only carbon, hydrogen, and oxygen is burned in air to produce 1.030 g of CO_2 and 0.632 g of H_2O. What is the empirical formula of the compound?

15. Ammonia can be manufactured from the gas phase reaction of H_2 with N_2. If 50.0 g of N_2 and 25.0 g of H_2 are mixed and reacted as completely as possible, what is the maximum mass of ammonia that could be formed?

16. Phosphorus trichloride reacts with hydrogen fluoride to give phosphorus trifluoride plus hydrogen chloride. What mass of phosphorus trifluoride can be formed from 100.0 g of phosphorus trichloride and 50.0 g of hydrogen fluoride?

17. What mass of P_2I_4 can be prepared from P_4O_6 and I_2 according to the (unbalanced) equation $P_4O_6 + I_2 \longrightarrow P_2I_4 + P_4O_{10}$ from the following quantities of reactants:

      a. 5.00 mol of P_4O_6 and 6.00 mol of I_2

      b. 5.00 g of P_4O_6 and 6.00 g of I_2

18. Gaseous C_3H_8 (200.0 g) and O_2 (200.0 g) are reacted as completely as possible according to the reaction $C_3H_8 + 5\,O_2 \longrightarrow 3\,CO_2 + 4\,H_2O$. What mass of CO_2 is formed?

19. The reaction between iron(II) sulfide, oxygen, and water, forms iron(III) oxide and sulfuric acid:

$$FeS + O_2 + H_2O \longrightarrow Fe_2O_3 + H_2SO_4$$

    a.   Balance this equation.

    b.   If 50. grams of FeS and 45 grams of O_2 are reacted completely, how many grams of H_2O are required to give a maximum yield of Fe_2O_3?

20. How many grams of silver sulfide can be formed by the reaction

$$2Ag + S \longrightarrow Ag_2S$$

if we start with 5.00g of silver and 1.00g of sulfur? (Incidentally, silver sulfide is the main component of the dark tarnish that may form on silverware.)

21. Chemical analysis shows that hemoglobin contains 0.34% Fe by mass. The hemoglobin molecule contains four iron (II) ions. What is the molecular mass of hemoglobin?

22. An unknown metal M forms a cyanide compound of formula $M(CN)_4$. If this compound contains 19.67 percent carbon by mass, what is the atomic mass of M?

23. Antabuse® has nothing to do with mistreatment of insects. It is, rather, a compound used to treat alcoholism (it causes a violent physiological response when alcohol is consumed). Antabuse contains the elements S, C, N, and H; it contains 43.24% S and 9.46% N by mass. Combustion of 1.000 g of antabuse yields 1.486 g of CO_2 (assume that all the carbon in antabuse ends up in the CO_2 formed). What is the empirical formula of Antabuse?

CHAPTER 15: GASES

Introduction

Although we are surrounded by gases, we may rarely stop to consider just how essential and complex this resource is. The process of respiration, the use and production of gases by plants, and the functioning of the atmosphere and how it is affected by human activity are all subject to constant study, but they are not completely understood on the molecular level. The long range impact of the change in the atmosphere generated by human activity is a matter of controversy—not only within the sciences— and should be a matter of concern to everyone. More immediate effects on health and the environment have been evident for decades, for example in regard to the quality of air that we breathe and the impact on nature of acidic precipitation. Essential background to studying the nature of the atmosphere is an understanding of the fundamental nature of gases themselves.

The history of the development of an understanding of gases is a key aspect of the early development of chemistry as a science. It is important to appreciate how early scientists used their ingenuity in designing experiments to study a form of matter more or less invisible to them (although some gases are colored, most of the gases studied by early scientists were not).

15-1. HISTORICAL BACKGROUND

It is impossible to know when early humans first perceived wind, bubbles, waves on a body of water, ripples through a field of grass, or other phenomena that we now recognize as characteristics of the behavior of gases and the interaction of gases with other matter. While humans for many centuries observed the effects of gases and surmised explanations for these effects, not until careful measurements of gases and their properties (such as temperature, pressure, and volume) was it possible to develop an understanding of both how gases behave (quantitatively) and how this behavior can be understood on the basis of how gas particles behave. Some milestones in the study of gases are summarized in Table 15-1.

Table 15-1. Milestones in the study of gases

Scientist	Date	Discovery
Torricelli	1644	Invention of the mercury barometer
Boyle	1660	**Boyle's law**: for a sample of gas, the volume is inversely proportional to the pressure (if the temperature is held constant); $V \propto 1/P$ (if $V\uparrow$, $P\downarrow$)
Amonton	~1702	Amonton's Law: For gas at constant volume, pressure is proportional to temperature; $P \propto T$ (if $T\uparrow$, $P\uparrow$)
Scheele	1777	Air is a mixture of gases rather than a single gas
Charles, Gay-Lussac	1780-1800	Observed that all gases expand equally when heated; **Charles' law (Gay-Lussac's law)**: volume is proportional to temp (if the pressure is held constant); $V \propto T$ (if $T\uparrow$, $V\uparrow$)
Dalton	1802	**Dalton's law**: the total pressure of a mixture of gases is equal to the sum of the pressures of the individual gases $P_{total} = P_{gas\,1} + P_{gas\,2} + P_{gas\,3} + ...$
Avogadro	1813	**Avogadro's law**: Equal volumes of gases at the same temp and pressure contain the same number of particles (n); $V \propto n$ (if $n\uparrow$, $V\uparrow$)

The first step toward being able to make useful measurements of pressures of gases was taken by Evangelista Torricelli, who in 1644 described a mercury barometer similar in principle to those used today (Torricelli's diagram is shown in Figure 15-1). In this barometer, tubes such as the two shown in the figure were immersed in mercury, then inverted. Mercury spontaneously rose in the tubes (the tube on the left was permanently sealed, the tube on the right sealed with a round stopper that could be removed). Torricelli asserted that it was the force of the atmosphere (rather than the vacuum at the top of the tubes or something else inside the tubes) that caused mercury to rise to a height of "a cubit and a quarter and an inch over" [probably about 30 inches, or 75 cm].

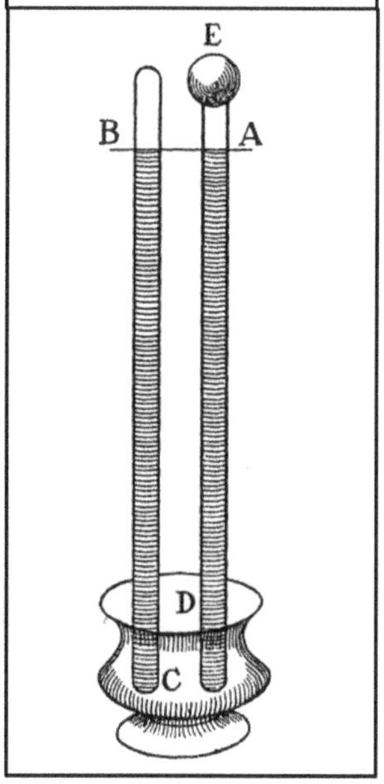

Robert Boyle subsequently studied the effects of pressure on volume. He used a U-shaped tube sealed at one end and open at the other (Figure 15-2). A sample of gas was trapped at the sealed end by mercury. Boyle measured the difference in heights of the two levels of mercury in the arms of the tube (a measure of the pressure on the trapped gas). He then added more mercury. The increased amount of mercury squeezed the gas to a smaller volume—a volume that he measured. Boyle continued adding mercury and measuring the heights of the mercury levels and the volume of the trapped gas.

From his data, Boyle was able to show that the volume of the gas was inversely proportional to the pressure (the difference in the two levels of mercury in his apparatus). This relationship is now known as **Boyle's law**; in equation form it can be expressed as

$$V \propto \frac{1}{P} \quad \text{or as } PV = \text{constant}$$

Near the end of the 18th century Jacques Alexandre César Charles and Joseph Gay-Lussac performed experiments on the effect of heat on samples of gases. They demonstrated that all gases seemed to expand by the same proportion on heating. The direct relationship between volume and temperature that resulted from this work, $V \propto T$, is known as **Charles' law** or **Gay-Lussac's law**.

Early in the 19th century Amadeo Avogadro argued that equal volumes of different gases contained the same number of particles (an idea that had previously been rejected by John Dalton). His ideas did not gain widespread acceptance for nearly half a century. Nevertheless, the idea that equal volumes of gases contain equal numbers of particles (pressure and temperature being kept the same) is sometimes known as **Avogadro's law** (or **Avogadro's hypothesis**).

The work of these and other early scientists provided the foundation for the modern concepts of gases.[101] We will examine these concepts and how to use them in the remainder of this chapter.

---

[101] It is interesting (and sometimes difficult!) to read the reports of early scientists. Many "classic" early scientific papers can be found at http://webserver.lemoyne.edu/faculty/giunta/papers.html

Figure 15-1. Torricelli's barometer

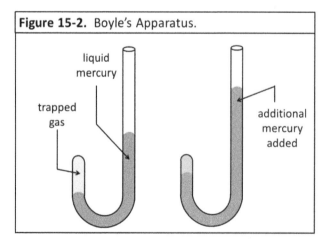

Figure 15-2. Boyle's Apparatus.

liquid mercury

trapped gas

additional mercury added

15-2. PROPERTIES OF GASES

A. Phases

Of the three common states of matter, only gases spontaneously adopt both the volume and shape of their container. A common way of distinguishing among the phases is:

Solids: Have definite volume and shape

Liquids: Have definite volume but not definite shape

Gases: Have neither definite volume nor shape

Gas particles mix spontaneously, and do not settle appreciably. For example, the composition of air is similar at both the top and bottom of a container; the most massive components (traces of xenon and krypton) do not settle to the bottom. In general, gas particles mix freely with each other.

In addition, it is instructive to consider the density of gases in comparison with other phases. For example, the density of liquid water and ice are similar and they change only slightly with changes in temperature (top entries):

	Density $\left(\dfrac{g}{mL}\right)$
Ice (0°C)	0.917
H_2O (liquid at 0°C)	0.99987
H_2O (liquid at 25°C)	0.99707
H_2O (gas at 0°C)	0.000803
H_2O (gas at 25° C)	0.000736

In contrast, at room temperature and a pressure of 1.00 atm, water in the gas phase (lower table entries, above) has less than one thousandth the density of the liquid or the solid!

Liquid water is more than a thousand times as dense as water in the gas phase! Why? The intermolecular forces (primarily hydrogen bonding in this case) are very successful in a "cold" system, but are easily broken when a little thermal energy is supplied. Gases (at ordinary pressures) are mostly "empty" space.

Proportionately, the density of the gas changes with temperature much more rapidly than the liquid; between 0°C and 25°C the density of water in the gas phase decreases by 8.3% but the corresponding change in density of liquid water over this temperature range is only 0.28%.

B. Air

The most familiar gas to us, of course, is air. A complex mixture of gases, together with traces of dust, soot, moisture droplets, and other non-gaseous components, air presents significant challenges to science and society in general as human activity affects the composition of this essential resource. It is useful to consider the composition of air, as summarized in Figure 15-3 and Table 15-2.

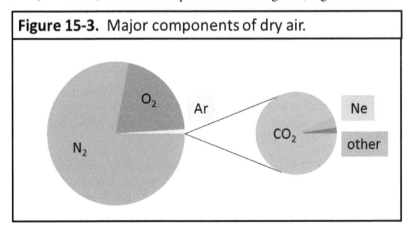

Figure 15-3. Major components of dry air.

Table 15-2. Gaseous components of dry air (as of 2016).

Rank	Gas	Abundance (% by mole)	Abundance (ppm)[102]
1	N_2	78.08	780,800
2	O_2	20.94	209,400
3	Ar	0.934	9340
4	CO_2	0.0409	409[103]
5	Ne	0.0018	18.2
6	He	0.0005	5.2
7	CH_4 (methane)	0.0002	2
8	Kr	0.00011	1.1
9	H_2	0.00005	0.5
10	N_2O	0.00005	0.5
11	Xe	0.0000087	0.087

Several items in Figure 15-3 and Table 15-2 are particularly worth noting. First, one major component of air is missing: water. The amount of water in air (the humidity) varies greatly with temperature and the availability of water, from very low amounts in dry, frigid climates (where it would rank fourth behind argon) to abundances of several percent in steamy jungles. The average abundance of water in the earth's atmosphere has been estimated as approximately 2 percent, making it third in abundance overall. The values in Table 15-2 have been calculated for air in the absence of any water. The proportions of components listed in this table are remarkably consistent worldwide with respect to each other. Some components, such as methane, fluctuate slightly from region to region depending on such factors as proximity to industrial areas that use fossil fuels, local topography, and the exchange of gas particles with the oceans.

Nitrogen and oxygen make up more than 99% of the particles in dry air (approximately 98% if water is included). It is perhaps surprising that the abundance of carbon dioxide is so low—about one molecule of every 2500 in air is CO_2. Yet this tiny fraction has grown significantly during the industrial revolution. Because of the ability of CO_2 to trap heat in the Earth's atmosphere (the greenhouse effect) there is considerable concern about the long term effects of rising CO_2 levels on the earth's climate. The CRC Handbook of Chemistry and Physics provides a historical record of CO_2 levels in the Earth's atmosphere since 1959, when the abundance of CO_2 was 316 ppm.

Exercise 15-1.

Based on the five most abundant components of dry air, what is the average molar mass of particles in air? Be sure to take into account the relative abundances of the components.

C. Physical Properties

Gases are most commonly described by three physical quantities: volume, temperature, and pressure. Volume is ordinarily recorded in metric units—liters, milliliters, etc. Calculations involving gases use temperature in degrees Kelvin. An absolute temperature scale is required; gas sample properties (such as volume or density) are proportional to the energy content of the system, so the temperature value used in calculations must be proportional to the energy content.

---

[102]ppm = parts per million. This is the number of particles of a particular gas for every million gas particles. ppm can be determined by multiplying the percent by 10^4.

[103] This is the carbon dioxide value as of March, 2019. This value needs relatively frequent updating because although there are regular seasonal highs and lows, on the whole this value is on the rise. See https://www.esrl.noaa.gov/gmd/ccgg/trends/ to view these trends for yourself!

Several units have been used to describe gas pressures. Traditionally, from the time of Torricelli, pressure measurements were based on the height of a column of mercury (measured in inches or millimeters) that could be supported by the atmosphere (unit of mmHg, or **torr**). This led to coining of the unit "atmosphere" (atm) to represent the typical air pressure in a laboratory, designated as the pressure necessary to support a column of mercury 760 mm in height.

Pressure can be related directly to the force of a gas exerted per unit area. In traditional units this was expressed in pounds per square inch (abbreviated psi; this unit is often used when measuring pressures of automobile or bicycle tires). The SI unit of pressure is the pascal (Pa), a derived unit:

$$Pressure = \frac{force}{area} = \frac{N}{m^2} = Pa \qquad\qquad N = \frac{kg \cdot m}{s^2} \quad so \quad Pa = \frac{\frac{kg \cdot m}{s^2}}{m^2} = \frac{kg}{m \cdot s^2}$$

Because 1 Pa is such a small pressure, the **bar** is a favored unit in the physical sciences and engineering, 1 bar = 100,000 Pa (or 100 kPa). Thus the bar is metric, but is not an SI unit.

For our purposes, the most important of these units are the bar, torr, pascal, and atmosphere. The atmosphere unit has historically seen popular use in the chemical sciences and is very similar to the bar (1 atm = 1.01325 bar). In 1982, however, the IUPAC[104] recommended that *standard pressures* be defined as exactly 1 bar (1 atm had been the previous standard). Therefore, in this book, when a gas sample is said to be at **standard temperature and pressure (STP)**, we use the IUPAC recommended temperature of 273.15 K (0 °C) and pressure of 1 bar.

It is important to learn the difference between STP and the **standard state** of a substance. Within the area of chemical thermodynamics (topics that chemistry students will study in another course), the **standard state** of a gaseous substance occurs when its pressure is exactly 1 bar and the standard state of an aqueous solute occurs when its concentration is exactly 1 M. Interestingly, the standard state <u>does not specify a temperature</u>, but standard state data are most often tallied at 25.00 °C (or 298.15 K). The idea of standard state is important in the study of chemical equilibrium, a topic that we will take up in Chapter 16. Because standard state of gases is defined in terms of "bar" units, it is important to get comfortable working with pressures in bar.

For reference, various pressure units are summarized in Table 15-3; inexact conversions are in red. Notice that there are many more exact conversions between atmospheres and other units than between bars and other units. *You can often utilize exact conversion factors when converting bar to other units if you first convert to atm using the exact conversion 1.01325 bar = 1 atm.*

Table 15-3. Units of pressure, inexact conversion are in red.

Unit	Definitions and Conversions
bar	1 bar = 100,000 Pa = 0.9869 atm = 750.06 torr
atmosphere (atm)	1 atm = 101,325 Pa = 1.01325 bar = 760 torr
torr	1 torr = 1 mmHg = 133.3 Pa
pascal (Pa)	$Pa = \dfrac{N}{m^2} = \dfrac{kg}{ms^2}$
pounds per square inch (psi)	1 psi = 6.895 Pa

<u>Equivalences to pressure = 1 bar:</u>

1 bar = 100,000 Pa = 0.986923 atm = 750.061 torr = 750.061 mmHg = 14.5036 psi

NOTE: red designates conversions that are not exact (rounded here to 6 significant figures).

---

[104] IUPAC = International Union of Pure and Applied Chemistry

15-3. THE IDEAL GAS LAW

A. What is an ideal gas?

One dictionary definition of *ideal* is "pertaining to perfection." Some gases have, in fact, been called "perfect." What does this mean? Ideal gases are ones that follow a predictable pattern of behavior—analogous, perhaps, to an "ideal" pet dog that never barks at the neighbors or stains the carpets—that can be described by a set of equations (unlike the pet) that apply equally well for all gases meeting the definition.

Behavior that is "ideal" for a gas can be described as follows:

(1)   The gas particles do not attract or repel each other.

As we have seen, particles in close proximity to each other interact in a variety of ways including dispersion forces (instantaneous dipole-induced dipole attractions), dipole-dipole attractions and hydrogen bonds.

For a gas to behave ideally, such interactions must be so small as to be insignificant. Because interactions between particles diminish as the distance between them increases, this condition applies when the particles are far apart—a condition that is satisfied at relatively low pressures. Because even at atmospheric pressure gas particles are far apart (note the low density of water in the gas phase compared with liquid water), this condition is typically satisfied for gas samples at ordinary laboratory pressures.

(2)   The volume of the gas particles is insignificant in comparison with the volume of the container.

Because gas particles are typically far apart from each other, the volumes of the particles are generally insignificant in comparison with the volume of the container—so this condition is also typically satisfied at ordinary pressures.

(3)   The gas particles are not undergoing chemical change or conversion to another phase.

For example, the gases NO_2 and N_2O_4 exist in dynamic equilibrium:

$$2NO_2(g) \rightleftharpoons N_2O_4(g)$$

Dynamic equilibrium means that the forward and reverse reactions are both happening at the same rate, so that there is no net change in the amounts of either gas over time. A change in the pressure and/or temperature of the system causes the equilibrium to shift positions, to either favor more reactant or more product than the previous position; see Figure 15-4. Because the proportions of reactant and product gases change, the gases do not behave ideally; conversion of one molecule into another (or in this case 2 NO_2 particles into 1 N_2O_4 molecule) is not "ideal" behavior.[105] Furthermore, if a gas condenses into a liquid (as can be achieved by high pressure), the "ideal" label no longer applies; this term refers only to the gas phase, not to a combination of phases.

Figure 15-4. The equilibrium between NO_2 gas (brown) and N_2O_4 gas (colorless) is temperature dependent; these photos show the same flask at different temperatures. There is more NO_2 present at higher temperatures (left) and more N_2O_4 present at lower temperatures (right).

Photos by Beth Abdella

---

[105] Equilibrium systems are discussed more fully in Chapters 16 and 17.

An ideal gas is one that is <u>behaving</u> ideally. No gas is technically ideal, for example:

- All gas particles are capable of attracting one another via dispersion forces, if not other intermolecular attractions. (The gas phase exists when the amount of energy in the system is capable of disrupting those attractions.)

- All gas particles take up volume in their containers.

However, under conditions that keep the gas particles far from one another (relatively low pressures and high temperatures[106]), many gas samples behave ideally. Making measurements on the sample shows that certain mathematical relationships exist between properties of the sample. In the next section, we explore these relationships.

B. The Ideal Gas Law: PV = nRT

The relationships between pressure, volume, and temperature described by Boyle's law, Charles' law, and the other historical gas laws can conveniently be summarized by the ideal gas law. The law is most commonly written:

$$PV = nRT \quad \text{where:}$$

		Common Units
P = pressure		bar
V = volume		L
n = number of moles of gas		mol
T = temperature		K
R = gas constant		$\frac{L \cdot bar}{mol \cdot K}$

This equation describes the behavior of gases that behave "ideally." In almost all circumstances, it works remarkably well for samples of gases at common temperatures and pressures.

The gas constant, R, has been determined to many significant figures. We will usually use it with units of $\frac{L \cdot bar}{mol \cdot K}$, although it can also be expressed in a large number of other sets of units, including $\frac{J}{mol \cdot K}$, which is especially useful in the field of chemical thermodynamics. The values of R in these units are related by a factor of 100: $\boxed{R = 8.31446} \frac{J}{mol \cdot K} \boxed{= 0.0831446} \frac{L \cdot bar}{mol \cdot K}$

There are 100 J in 1 L·bar.

You may be familiar with the gas constant as $0.082057 \frac{L \cdot atm}{mol \cdot K}$. Notice that because of the very similar magnitudes of atmospheres (atm) and bars, the two gas constant values with those units also have very similar magnitudes.

The gas constant (often called the "ideal gas constant" or "universal gas constant") is encountered in a variety of contexts in chemistry, some not involving gases at all. In general, R has units of $\frac{energy}{mol \cdot K}$. One type of energy that you will eventually encounter in science courses is "pressure-volume" energy; pressure × volume = energy, thus units such as the L·bar. Whenever R is

---

[106] In this context, room temperature is a high enough temperature to support the gas phase for species with weak intermolecular attractions, such as the noble gases, small diatomics (H_2, Cl_2, etc.), and small hydrocarbons (CH_4, CH_3CH_3). Many of these do not condense to liquid except at extremely cold temps.

used in calculations, it is highly advisable to include the units along with the numerical value of R, to make sure that you are using the correct version of the constant.

$$R = 0.0831446 \frac{L \cdot bar}{mol \cdot K} = 0.0820573 \frac{L \cdot atm}{mol \cdot K} = 62.3636 \frac{L \cdot torr}{mol \cdot K} = 8314.46 \frac{L \cdot Pa}{mol \cdot K}$$

Reminder:	When using the gas constant, be sure to use temperature in Kelvin! K = °C + 273.15, exactly.

Exercise 15-2.

Use conversion factors to determine the value of R in units of $\frac{\mu L \cdot kPa}{mmol \cdot K}$ and $\frac{mL \cdot torr}{mol \cdot K}$.

Obtain at least 5 significant digits.

Example 15-1.

A glass bulb having a volume of 207.6 mL contains 0.678 g of oxygen at a temperature of 302 K. What is the pressure inside the bulb?

Solution:

Beginning with PV = nRT, we want to solve for pressure:

$$P = \frac{nRT}{V} = \frac{\left(0.678\ g\ O_2\right)\left(\dfrac{1\ mol\ O_2}{32.00\ g\ O_2}\right)\left(0.083145 \dfrac{L \cdot bar}{mol \cdot K}\right)\left(302\ K\right)}{\left(0.2076\ L\right)} = 2.56\ bar$$

Exercise 15-3.

A rubber stopper will pop out of a flask if the pressure inside the flask exceeds 2.00 bar. If the flask contains 0.100 mol of carbon dioxide and has a volume of 2.500 L, what is the maximum temperature to which the gas could be heated before the stopper would pop out?

Exercise 15-4.

Using the ideal gas law, determine the volume of exactly 1 mole of an ideal gas at STP.

C. An Alternative Form of the Ideal Gas Law

An alternative form of PV = nRT that is handy for calculations involving molar masses of gases can easily be derived. First, let's divide both sides of this equation by nV:

$$\frac{PV}{nV} = \frac{nRT}{nV} \qquad \Rightarrow \qquad \frac{P}{n} = \frac{RT}{V}$$

Now multiply both sides by the mass of the gas sample, **m**: $\quad \dfrac{P\mathbf{m}}{n} = \dfrac{\mathbf{m}RT}{V} \quad$ or $\quad P\left(\dfrac{\mathbf{m}}{n}\right) = \left(\dfrac{\mathbf{m}}{V}\right)RT$

The ratio $\left(\dfrac{\mathbf{m}}{n}\right)$ is the mass per mole; or the molar mass, which we may abbreviate **M**. The ratio $\left(\dfrac{\mathbf{m}}{V}\right)$, the mass per unit volume, is the density of the gas, which we symbolize as "d."[107] Making these substitutions yields:

$$\boxed{PM = dRT}$$ where $\mathbf{M}$ = molar mass $\left(\dfrac{g}{mol}\right)$ and   d = density $\left(\dfrac{g}{L}\right)$

This form of the ideal gas law is useful for calculating the molar mass of gases from experimental data on gas densities.

Example 15-2.

The density of an ideal gas, measured in a 200.37 mL gas bulb at a pressure of 0.995 bar and a temperature of 298 K, was found to be 3.36 $\dfrac{g}{L}$. What was the molar mass of the gas?

Solution:

Using $PM = dRT$, rearranged to $\mathbf{M} = \dfrac{dRT}{P}$:

$$\mathbf{M} = \frac{dRT}{P} = \frac{\left(3.36\dfrac{g}{L}\right)\left(0.083145\dfrac{L\cdot bar}{mol\cdot K}\right)(298\ K)}{0.995\ bar} = 83.7\frac{g}{mol}$$

Exercise 15-5.

Particles of dry air have an average (weighted) mass of 28.96 $\dfrac{g}{mol}$. What is the density of air on a frigid winter's night at a temperature of –34.0 °F and a pressure of 742 torr?

Exercise 15-6.

A component of the atmosphere is selectively removed. It is found to have a density of 1.78 $\dfrac{g}{L}$ at a pressure of 1.00 bar and a temperature of 25°C. What is its molar mass? Suggest the identity of the gas.

D. Applications of the Ideal Gas Law

1.   The ideal gas law is consistent with Boyle's law

For a particular gas sample at constant temperature, n × R × T must be constant. (Why?) Thus, because PV = nRT, PV must also be constant. Because P × V must be constant, the bigger P gets, the smaller V must be. This means that pressure is inversely proportional to volume. In Figure 15-5, the piston on the left is not moving because the pressure of the blue gas sample equals the pressure of the atmosphere. When weights are added to the piston, the pressure downward is

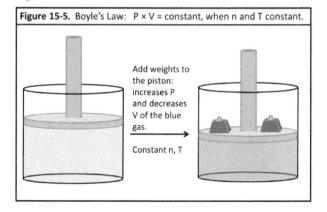

Figure 15-5. Boyle's Law: P × V = constant, when n and T constant.

Add weights to the piston: increases P and decreases V of the blue gas.

Constant n, T

---

[107]The density is sometimes indicated by the Greek letter rho, ρ.

increased and the piston settles at a new, lower position. Compression of the gas sample (by adding weights to the piston) results in a higher pressure and a smaller volume of the blue gas.

Example 15-3.

A sample of nitrogen gas occupies a volume of 157.2 mL at a pressure of 766 torr. What will be the final volume of the gas if the pressure is doubled while the temperature is held constant?

Solution:

Under this circumstance PV = constant. Therefore, we may write
$$P_1V_1 = P_2V_2 \; (= \text{constant}) \text{ where:}$$
$$\text{subscript 1 represents initial conditions}$$
$$\text{subscript 2 represents final conditions}$$

$$V_2 = \frac{P_1V_1}{P_2} = \left(\frac{P_1}{P_2}\right)V_1 = \left(\frac{766 \, torr}{2 \times 766 \, torr}\right)(157.2 \, mL) = \frac{1}{2}(157.2 \, mL) = 78.6 \, mL$$

Note that there is no need to convert to particular pressure units if the gas constant is not being used, or if the pressure units cancel!

---

2. The ideal gas law is consistent with Charles' Law

At constant pressure, the volume of a gas sample depends only on T:

$$V = \frac{nRT}{P}$$

(*n* is constant for a particular gas sample). This implies that volume must be proportional to temperature. In Figure 15-6, the pressure pushing down on the piston is supplied by the atmosphere while the pressure pushing up is supplied by the blue gas. On the left the gas is cold and the pressure of the blue gas is equal to the pressure of the atmosphere (so the piston is not moving). On

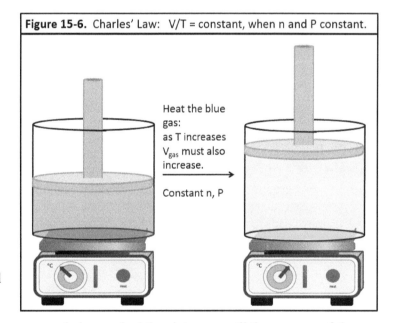

Figure 15-6. Charles' Law: V/T = constant, when n and P constant.

Heat the blue gas:
as T increases
V_{gas} must also increase.

Constant n, P

the right, with the hot plate on, a warmer sample has pushed the piston up until the pressure of the blue gas again equals the pressure of the atmosphere.

Example 15-4.

A sample of nitrogen gas occupies a volume of 157.2 mL at a pressure of 766 torr. The sample is heated while maintaining a constant pressure. What will be the final volume if the temperature is increased from 298.2 K to 373.2 K?

Solution:

Because, by Charles' law, V is proportional to T, we may write $\dfrac{V_1}{T_1} = \dfrac{V_2}{T_2} = \text{constant}$

thus, $V_2 = \dfrac{V_1 T_2}{T_1} = \left(\dfrac{T_2}{T_1}\right) V_1 = \left(\dfrac{373.2\ K}{298.2\ K}\right)(157.2\ mL) = 196.7\ mL$

Note that temperatures MUST be in kelvin, even when the units cancel. A ratio of non-

absolute temps will not be the same: $\left(\dfrac{373.2\ K}{298.2\ K}\right) \neq \left(\dfrac{100.0\ ^oC}{25.0\ ^oC}\right)$ This is due to the

$$1.25 \quad \neq \quad 4.00$$

different zero points of the two temperature scales!

3. Boyle's and Charles' Law together

For a given quantity of gas (constant *n*) the ideal gas law gives a convenient expression that combines Boyle's and Charles' laws. If we rearrange

$$PV = nRT \quad to \quad \frac{PV}{T} = nR$$

we recognize that because *n* and R are both constants, $\dfrac{PV}{T} = \text{constant}$ and we can write $\dfrac{P_1 V_1}{T_1} = \dfrac{P_2 V_2}{T_2}$.

Examination of this expression shows that, in accordance with Boyle's law, pressure and volume are inversely proportional if T is constant. Consider a "before" and "after" scenario for a gas sample, where the temperature doesn't change ($T_1 = T_2$). If the final pressure after is greater than the initial pressure ($P_2 > P_1$), it is necessary for the equivalency that the final volume be less than the initial volume. Thus, when the temperature is constant, pressure and volume are inversely proportional. Likewise, the expression above supports Charles' law; volume is proportional to temperature if P is constant. Make sure to reason that out!

Example 15-5.

At ground level, the helium in a balloon occupies a volume of 2350 L at a temperature of 25°C and a pressure of 0.988 bar. What volume will the helium occupy after the balloon ascends to a high elevation where the temperature is –42°C and the pressure is 0.166 bar?

Solution:

Using $\dfrac{P_1 V_1}{T_1} = \dfrac{P_2 V_2}{T_2}$:

$P_1 = 0.988$ bar	$P_2 = 0.166$ bar
$V_1 = 2.35 \times 10^3$ L	$V_2 = ?$
$T_1 = 25°C = 298$ K	$T_2 = –42°C = 231$ K

$$V_2 = \frac{P_1 V_1 T_2}{P_2 T_1} = \frac{(0.988\ bar)(2.35 \times 10^3\ L)(231\ K)}{(0.166\ bar)(298\ K)} = 10{,}800\ L = 1.08 \times 10^4\ L$$

Example 15-6.

A sample of gas occupies a glass container having a volume of 1.0×10^2 L at a temperature of 298 K and a pressure of 1.00 bar. If the gas behaves ideally, what will be the resulting pressure if the gas is heated to 373 K in this container?

Solution:

Initial	Final
P_1 = 1.00 atm	P_2 = ?
$V_1 = 1.0 \times 10^2$ L	$V_2 = 1.0 \times 10^2$ L
T_1 = 298 K	T_2 = 373 K

Beginning with $\dfrac{P_1 V_1}{T_1} = \dfrac{P_2 V_2}{T_2}$, we should recognize that the volume does not change (because the gas is remaining in its original container, which has a fixed volume). The equation then simplifies to:

$$\frac{P_1}{T_1} = \frac{P_2}{T_2} \quad \Rightarrow \quad \frac{1.00\ bar}{298\ K} = \frac{P_2}{373\ K} \quad \Rightarrow \quad P_2 = 1.25\ bar$$

Exercise 15-7.

The gas in a balloon has a volume of 4.25 L at a temperature of 23°C and a pressure of 0.983 bar. The balloon rises. At a high altitude the temperature has fallen to −18°C and the balloon has expanded to 4.00 times its original volume. What is the pressure?

4. The ideal gas law is consistent with Avogadro's law

Isolating n, the moles of gas in the sample, PV = nRT   becomes $n = \dfrac{PV}{RT} = \left(\dfrac{P}{RT} \right) \times V$

At constant pressure and temperature, all three terms in parentheses are constant, so we can write

$$n = \text{constant} \times V$$

This means that n is proportional to V and equal volumes of gas must contain equal numbers of moles—**Avogadro's law**.

5. Determination of the molar volume at STP

The **molar volume** of a gas is the volume of one mole. We can write

$$\text{molar volume} = \frac{volume}{mole} = \frac{V}{n}$$

Remember that STP is defined as conditions of exactly 1 bar and 0 °C. We can compute the molar volume:

$$PV = nRT, \quad \frac{V}{n} = \frac{RT}{P} \quad so \quad \frac{V}{n} = \frac{\left(0.083145 \dfrac{L \cdot bar}{mol \cdot K} \right)(273.15\ K)}{1\ bar} = 22.71\ L$$

NOTE: You may be more familiar with the molar volume of a gas being 22.41 L. This is true under the previous definition of STP using atmosphere units instead of bar.

6. The ideal gas law is consistent with Dalton's law

Because ideal gases show behaviors that are not dependent on the identity of the particles, the ideal gas law, $PV = nRT$, may be applied equally well to a mixture of gases, or separately to each gas in the mixture. For a mixture of gases A and B, the total moles is given by $n_A + n_B$ and we can write:

$$P_{mixture} = \frac{n_{total}RT}{V_{container}} = \frac{(n_A + n_B)RT}{V_{container}} \quad which \ means \quad P_{mixture} = \frac{n_A RT}{V_{container}} + \frac{n_B RT}{V_{container}}$$

The individual terms on the right side of the red equation describe what is called the **partial pressure** of gas A in the mixture (P_A) and the partial pressure of gas B in the mixture (P_B):

$$P_A = \frac{n_A RT}{V_{container}} \quad and \quad P_B = \frac{n_B RT}{V_{container}}$$

Remembering that every gas fills its container (so the volume of each individual gas is the volume of the container), these partial pressure relationships also arise from simply applying the ideal gas law to the individual gases. The **partial pressure** of one gas in a mixture is the pressure that only that gas would exert if it were alone in the container. **Dalton's law** asserts that the total pressure of a mixture is the sums of the partial pressures of the individual gases. We see this if we substitute the blue terms into the red equation:

$$P_{mixture} = P_A + P_B$$

More information about Dalton's law is discussed below.

7. The ideal gas law is consistent with the Kinetic-Molecular Theory of Gases

The ideal gas law can be derived directly from the kinetic-molecular theory of gases. This theory describes how gases behave at the molecular level. This theory will be used to derive the ideal gas law in Section 15-4 of this chapter.

E. Dalton's Law of Partial Pressures

The ideal gas law, $PV = nRT$, can be rearranged to $\quad P = \frac{nRT}{V} \quad or \quad P = n\left(\frac{RT}{V}\right)$

At a particular temperature and volume, the pressure is proportional to the number of moles of gas. One of the defining assumptions about ideal gases is that gas particles do not attract or repel each other. The pressure exerted by each gas molecule is, for an ideal gas, independent of the pressure exerted by every other gas molecule. Dalton's law states that in a mixture of gases each gas may be considered to exert its own pressure. These pressures, when added together, give the total pressure. For example, in a mixture of the gases oxygen, nitrogen, and argon:

$$P = P_{total} = P_{O_2} + P_{N_2} + P_{Ar}$$

Each gas contributes its **partial pressure** to the total pressure, P. Furthermore, the pressure exerted by each gas is proportional to its number of moles, as shown above.

Yet another possible unit of concentration, the **mole fraction**, (often symbolized by the Greek letter chi, χ) was introduced earlier (Chapter 12, 12-3C).

$$mole \ fraction \ (\chi) = \frac{moles \ of \ one \ component \ of \ mixture}{total \ moles \ of \ all \ components \ of \ mixture}$$

In a mixture of the three gases, therefore, the mole fractions can be written:

$$mole \ fraction \ of \ O_2 = \chi_{(O_2)} = \frac{n_{(O_2)}}{n_{(total)}} = \frac{n_{(O_2)}}{n_{(O_2)} + n_{(N_2)} + n_{(Ar)}}$$

$$\text{mole fraction of } N_2 = \chi_{(N_2)} = \frac{n_{(N_2)}}{n_{(total)}} = \frac{n_{(N_2)}}{n_{(O_2)} + n_{(N_2)} + n_{(Ar)}}$$

$$\text{mole fraction of Ar} = \chi_{(Ar)} = \frac{n_{(Ar)}}{n_{(total)}} = \frac{n_{(Ar)}}{n_{(O_2)} + n_{(N_2)} + n_{(Ar)}}$$

In a mixture of gases, if we know the mole fraction, χ, of each gas, we may determine their partial pressures by multiplying χ by the total pressure:

$$P_{O_2} = \chi_{(O_2)} \times P_{total}$$

$$P_{N_2} = \chi_{(N_2)} \times P_{total}$$

$$P_{Ar} = \chi_{(Ar)} \times P_{total}$$

Example 15-7.

The following gases are mixed: carbon dioxide (0.600 mol), helium (0.200 mol), and hydrogen (0.160 mol). The total pressure of the gas mixture is found to be 0.965 bar. What is the partial pressure of each gas in the mixture?

Solution:

The mole fractions (with an extra digit) are: $\chi_{(CO_2)} = \frac{n_{(CO_2)}}{n_{(total)}} = \frac{0.600 \; mol}{0.960 \; mol} = 0.6250$

$$\chi_{(He)} = \frac{n_{(He)}}{n_{(total)}} = \frac{0.200 \; mol}{0.960 \; mol} = 0.2083$$

$$\chi_{(H_2)} = \frac{n_{(H_2)}}{n_{(total)}} = \frac{0.160 \; mol}{0.960 \; mol} = 0.1667$$

From Dalton's law:

$$P_{CO_2} = \chi_{(CO_2)} \times P_{total} = 0.6250 \times (0.965 \; bar) = 0.603 \; bar$$

$$P_{He} = \chi_{(He)} \times P_{total} = 0.2083 \times (0.965 \; bar) = 0.201 \; bar$$

$$P_{H_2} = \chi_{(H_2)} \times P_{total} = 0.1667 \times (0.965 \; bar) = 0.161 \; bar$$

To check: The sum of the mole fractions is 1.00 and the sum of the partial pressures is the total pressure, 0.965 atm.

Exercise 15-8.

Neon is the sixth most abundant component of air. If air contains 0.0018% neon by mole, what is the partial pressure of neon if the total air pressure is 0.988 bar?

15-4. KINETIC-MOLECULAR THEORY OF GASES

The underlying theory of how gas particles behave is called the Kinetic-Molecular Theory. This theory makes the same assumptions about gases that we have made for an ideal gas: no attractions or repulsions, insignificant molecular volumes, no chemical reactions or changes of phase. In addition, other key assumptions are made about the motion of gas particles, their energies, and collisions of gas particles with each other and with surfaces. On the foundation of all these "postulates," the theory can then be used as the basis for deriving PV = nRT and other mathematical expressions that describe gas behavior.

A. Basic Assumptions

1. Gas particles (atoms such as Ar, molecules such as N_2) are in continuous, random motion.

    This means: Gas particles travel in all directions. They travel in straight lines until they collide with other gas particles or with surfaces.

2. Collisions between gas particles are *perfectly elastic* (kinetic energy is conserved).

    This means: When gas particles collide, the total kinetic energy of the particles after collision is the same as the total kinetic energy before collision. However, energy may be transferred from one particle to another.

    $$\text{kinetic energy} = \frac{1}{2}(\text{mass})(\text{speed})^2 = \frac{1}{2}mu^2$$

    If, upon collision, one particle speeds up, then the other must slow down.

3. The pressure exerted by gases is the result of collisions of gas particles with surfaces.

    (The surface may be anything in contact with the gas, for example the inside, or outside, of a balloon, the window of a car, or your skin.)

4. The average kinetic energy of gas particles is proportional to the absolute temperature.

    This means: The higher the temperature, the greater the average kinetic energy. Also, because kinetic energy is proportional to (speed)^2, the higher the temp, the faster the particles' speeds. (Not all particles have the same speed, but the average speed increases with temperature.)

5. The volume of gas particles is insignificant.

6. Intermolecular attractions and repulsions between gas particles are negligible.

Assumptions 5 and 6 are requirements for the "ideal" classification. Implied in 6 is that the theory will not take into account situations in which gas particles undergo chemical reactions or are converted to different phases (states of matter).

All of these assumptions provide the foundation for deriving many mathematical relationships that describe gases, such as the speeds at which gas particles travel, the distance they travel between collisions with other gas particles, and the relative rates at which gas particles pass through small openings. We will derive one such relationship—by far the most important one: the ideal gas law.

B. Derivation of the Ideal Gas Law

The following derivation is based on the assumptions about gases listed above. Figure 15-7 summarizes the steps of the deviation. Details of the work follow.

Figure 15-7. Outline of derivation of ideal gas law.

1. **Pressure exerted by gas particles is proportional to:**
   frequency of collisions and *force exerted per collision*

   which together are proportional to:

   u (average speed)   1/V   mu (momentum)
   N (number of particles)

2. Combine these proportionalities: $P \propto Nmu^2/V$ or $PV \propto Nmu^2$

3. Because $E_K \propto T$, and $E_K = \frac{1}{2}\,mu^2$, then $\frac{1}{2}\,mu^2 \propto T$ and: $mu^2 \propto T$

4. Substitution of T for mu^2 in top red equation yields: $PV \propto NT$

5. Because $N = nN_A$: $PV \propto nN_AT$

6. Creating an equivalency by adding a proportionality constant, k:
                    $PV = k\,(nN_AT)$
   Then combine constants $k(N_A)$ to yield the gas law constant, R:
                    $PV = nRT$

For convenience, we will consider a sample of an ideal gas enclosed in a sealed container. This sample and its container will be described by the following:

V = volume of container   n = number of moles of gas in container

P = pressure inside container   u = average speed of gas particles in container

T = absolute temperature   m = mass of one gas particle

N = number of particles in container

1. The pressure exerted by gases results from collisions of gas particles with surfaces.

It stands to reason that the more often gas particles collide with surfaces, and the more vigorous their collisions, the higher the pressure (force per unit area) that they will exert. Therefore:

P is proportional to   *frequency of collisions*
            and   *force exerted per collision*

a. The *frequency of collisions* is proportional to these three quantities:

u = average speed   (the faster the particles travel, the more frequently they collide with the walls of the container)

N = number of particles   (the more gas particles in a container, the more frequent the collisions of particles with the walls)

$\dfrac{1}{V} = \dfrac{1}{volume}$ (the greater the volume of the container, the less frequent the collisions with the walls—the particles have a greater distance to travel between collisions)

b. The *force exerted per collision* is proportional to:

(mass) × (speed) = **mu** = momentum   (The greater the mass and the speed, the more force the particles will exert when they collide.)

2. Setting up a proportionality expression by combining the terms in step 1:

$$P \propto (\textit{frequency of collisions}) \times (\textit{force exerted per collision})$$

$$P \propto \left(\frac{uN}{V}\right) \quad \times \quad (mu)$$

$$P \propto \cdot \left(\frac{mu^2N}{V}\right).$$

Multiplying both sides of this equation by V gives:

$$PV \propto Nmu^2$$

(This puts the term PV on the left, a milestone on our way to the expression PV = nRT.)

3. Relating a term in our proportionality to temperature:

The <u>average kinetic energy</u> of gas particles is proportional to the <u>absolute temperature</u>.

Using the definition of kinetic energy $\left(E_K\right)$ for a single particle we write:

$$E_K = \frac{1}{2}mu^2 \propto T \quad \text{and if} \quad \frac{1}{2}mu^2 \propto T \quad \text{then} \quad mu^2 \propto T$$

(a constant makes no difference)

4. Making the substitution to obtain a temperature term in our proportionality

So far, from step 2: $PV \propto Nmu^2$ and from step 3: $mu^2 \propto T$

substituting T for mu^2 yields: $PV \propto NT$

5. Converting number of particles to number of moles:

Because $N = nN_A$ $\left(\text{number of particles = number of moles} \times \dfrac{6.022 \times 10^{23}\, particles}{mol} \right)$

Substitute for N in our previous expression, $PV \propto NT$, and obtain $PV \propto nN_AT$

6. Creating an equality from the proportionality by including a proportionality constant, k:

$$PV = k\,(nN_AT)$$

Defining new constant, R, as $R = k\,N_A$ gives desired result $PV = nRT$

Notice that the gas law constant, R, is a "per mole" value due to the step 5 substitution. In the study of thermodynamics (CH/BI 126, Chem 126), we will see a version of this constant that is a "per particle" value called the Boltzmann constant and symbolized by k, or k_B. On a "per particle" basis we could write: $PV = N\,k_B\,T$, where N is the number of particles rather than the number of moles of particles. While the units of R are energy/(mol·K), the units of k_B are energy/(particle·K), which is usually just written as energy/K (with the "per particle" aspect understood when "mole" is not present in the units). Notice that because

$$n = \frac{N}{N_A} \quad \text{and} \quad R = k_B \times N_A; \quad \text{it must be true that}$$

$$n \times R = \frac{N}{N_A} \times k_B \times N_A \quad \text{and, thus:} \quad n \times R = N \times k_B$$

Thus, $PV = n\,R\,T$ and $PV = N\,k_B\,T$ are equivalent statements.

Exercise 15-9.

What is the value of k_B **a.** in units of $\dfrac{J}{K}$?   **b.** in units of $\dfrac{L \cdot bar}{K}$?

Exercise 15-10.

Determine the volume of a 3.68×10^{22} atom sample of Ne gas at 2.0 bar and 315 K utilizing $PV = Nk_BT$ and your result from Exercise 15-9b. Show that you can obtain the same answer using $PV = nRT$.

C. Speeds of Gas Particles

How fast do normal gas particles travel? Remarkably fast, as shown in Table 15-4.

Table 15-4. Average speeds of gas particles at 25°C

Gas	Mass $\left(\dfrac{g}{mol}\right)$	Speed $\left(\dfrac{m}{s}\right)$	Speed $\left(\dfrac{miles}{hr}\right)$
H_2	2.0	1770	3960
N_2	28.0	470	1060
O_2	32.0	440	990
HI	127.9	220	490
UF_6	352.0	130	290

At 25°C, the major components of air (N_2 and O_2 molecules) travel on the order of 1000 miles per hour! Even an extremely massive molecule such as UF_6 has a high speed. For comparison, the cruising speed of a commercial airliner is about 500-600 mph. Why, then, don't we feel buffeted by enormously strong winds? The particles do move as rapidly as indicated in Table 15-4, but in our atmosphere they travel only a short distance (about 70 nm) before being deflected by a collision with another particle. In addition, gas particles travel in all directions (in continuous, random motion, in accordance with our fundamental understanding of gases). Even when strong winds are felt, indicating an excess of flow of particles in a particular direction, the overall speed of the wind is far less than the speed at which the individual particles travel between collisions.

In Table 15-4, we also see a trend that we might have predicted: the more massive the gas molecule, the more slowly it moves. But even something as massive as a molecule of UF_6 travels more rapidly than all but the very speediest of race cars. Remember that (during our derivation of the ideal gas law) we learned that the kinetic energy of a gas particle is given by

$$E_K = \tfrac{1}{2}mu^2 \propto T$$

This means that a more massive particle and a less massive particle in the same sample must move at different speeds. Why? Because when the particles are at the same T, their kinetic energies must be identical. Thus when "m" is larger, "u" must be smaller so that E_K is unchanged.

An experiment is performed as shown in Figure 15-8. A hollow glass tube 1.00 meter long is clamped in a horizontal position. With tongs (and with good ventilation!) two balls of cotton are dipped into aqueous solutions, one containing hydrochloric acid, the other ammonia. Both of these solutes are quite **volatile** (easily move into the gas phase). These balls are then simultaneously applied to the two ends of the tube, and the ends are sealed with stoppers. At first, no change inside the tube is apparent. However, after a few minutes, a thin white ring of a solid salt appears slightly closer to one end. More and more solid is deposited inside the tube as time elapses. (Actual photos of this experiment are shown in Figure 13-6!)

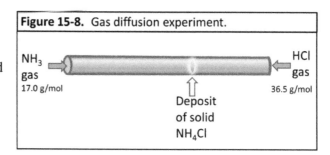

Figure 15-8. Gas diffusion experiment.

Example 15-8.

Why is the ring closer to the HCl side of the tube?

Solution:

We can surmise that the white ring appears as a result of interaction between the gas particles. The particles travel with different speeds because of their different masses. We have seen that more massive particles must travel more slowly in order that kinetic energy be the same. Therefore, we expect the more massive HCl particles ($36.5 \frac{g}{mol}$) to move more slowly than the NH_3 particles ($17.0 \frac{g}{mol}$) and the white ring to form closer to the end at which the HCl was introduced.

How can this experiment be explained? First, the white ring is a result of a chemical reaction between the gases HCl and NH_3. Hydrochloric acid, HCl, best known as a strong acid in aqueous solution, in this case acts as an acid in the gas phase, donating a proton to the base NH_3:

$$HCl(g) + NH_3(g) \longrightarrow NH_4Cl(s)$$

The salt, ammonium chloride, NH_4Cl, is a white solid.

The experiment supports our understanding about the relative speeds at which the gas particles travel. The NH_4Cl is formed closer to the end at which the HCl was introduced. This means that the more massive HCl molecule does not travel as far as the NH_3 before the two reach each other and react. This, we find, is a general phenomenon: the more massive the gas particles, the more slowly they travel.[108]

In a gas sample at a particular temperature, not all of the particles are traveling at the same speed. Some have more than their fair share of the available energy and others have less. We must consider the *average speed* of the particles in the sample. Equations describing the speeds of gas particles can be derived from the kinetic-molecular theory. Deriving such equations is beyond the scope of this text. However, it is useful to consider one of these expressions. The average speed of ideal gas particles is given by:

$$u = \text{average speed} = \sqrt{\frac{8RT}{\pi M}} \qquad \text{where } M = \text{molar mass} \left(\frac{g}{mol} \right)$$

Note that the average speed increase as the temperature increases and as the molar mass decreases!

---

[108]In this experiment the HCl and NH_3 particles carry "excess baggage" in the form of water molecules (from the original aqueous solutions). These water molecules are strongly attracted to both HCl and NH_3 and add to the mass of both HCl and NH_3. This slows the diffusion process down somewhat. Nevertheless, the HCl with its attached water molecules is still more massive than NH_3 with its water molecules; the "hydrated" HCl moves more slowly.

Exercise 15-11.

Show that the mathematics of $\sqrt{\dfrac{8RT}{\pi M}}$ results in units of speed. Hint: utilize joules, and its definition in terms of other SI units.

We have seen that the more massive the gas molecule, the more slowly it moves. Now we can be more specific: <u>the speeds of gas particles are inversely proportional to the square root of their molar (or molecular) masses</u>.

We can now compare the average speeds, u, of two different gases (gas 1 and gas 2) by determination of the ratio, $\dfrac{u_1}{u_2}$, for the two gases. Using the expression for average speed, we can write:

$$\frac{u_1}{u_2} = \frac{\sqrt{\dfrac{8RT}{\pi M_1}}}{\sqrt{\dfrac{8RT}{\pi M_2}}} = \sqrt{\frac{M_2}{M_1}} \quad \text{so} \quad \boxed{\frac{u_1}{u_2} = \sqrt{\frac{M_2}{M_1}}}$$

The boxed expression, above, is sometimes called **Graham's law.**

So, to find the relative speeds of two gas particles we simply take the square root of the inverse ratio of their molar masses. This applies to any calculation involving relative speeds of gas particles, including rates at which gas particles **effuse** (pass through small openings into a vacuum) or **diffuse** (mix with each other). See Figure 15-9.

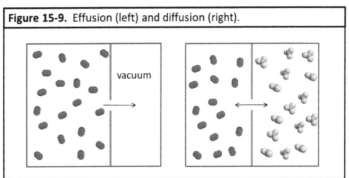
Figure 15-9. Effusion (left) and diffusion (right).

vacuum

Example 15-9.

Suppose a spacecraft has a pinhole leak that enables gas to escape into the near vacuum of outer space. The gas inside the spacecraft consists primarily of nitrogen and oxygen. Which gas effuses more rapidly through the leak? How much more rapidly does it effuse than the other gas?

Solution:

Like molecular speeds, the relative rates of effusion have an inverse relationship to the square root of the molar mass:

$$\frac{rate_1}{rate_2} = \sqrt{\frac{M_2}{M_1}}$$

Nitrogen, the lighter gas, effuses more rapidly. It doesn't matter which gas is assigned as "1" and which is assigned as "2." Both results are shown:

$$\frac{rate_{N_2}}{rate_{O_2}} = \sqrt{\frac{32.00 \, g/mol}{28.01 \, g/mol}} = 1.069 \qquad \frac{rate_{O_2}}{rate_{N_2}} = \sqrt{\frac{28.01 \, g/mol}{32.00 \, g/mol}} = \frac{1}{1.069} = 0.9355$$

Exercise 15-12.

Of the ten most abundant components of air, the heaviest is krypton and the lightest is hydrogen. How many times more rapidly do hydrogen molecules travel than krypton atoms? (Here's a case where you need to decide which gas to put in the numerator!)

One precaution to observe when using Graham's law to calculate relative speeds of gas particles or relative rates of effusion or diffusion: always check to be sure that the answer makes chemical sense; *more massive gas particles always move more slowly*.

Example 15-10.

Suppose in the spacecraft of Example 15-9 that 1.000 mmol of nitrogen gas escapes in 5.00 hours. How long would it take for the same amount of oxygen to escape?

Solution:

Graham's law, as stated on the preceding page, describes relative rates (speeds) of gas particles. To answer this question we need to recognize that *rate is inversely proportional to time*, or $rate \propto \dfrac{1}{time}$. Therefore, if we are comparing the relative times of two gas particles to travel a certain distance or to effuse from an opening, we can write:

$$\frac{rate_1}{rate_2} = \frac{u_1}{u_2} = \frac{t_2}{t_1} = \frac{time_2}{time_1}$$

Substituting $\dfrac{t_2}{t_1}$ in place of $\dfrac{u_1}{u_2}$ in Graham's law gives: $\dfrac{t_2}{t_1} = \sqrt{\dfrac{M_2}{M_1}}$.

This is an <u>alternate form of **Graham's law**</u>. Finally, if gas 1 = N_2 and gas 2 = O_2:

$$\frac{t_{O_2}}{t_{N_2}} = \sqrt{\frac{32.00\ g/mol}{28.01\ g/mol}} = 1.069 \quad \text{(meaning it takes } O_2 \text{ 1.069 times longer)}$$

The time for O_2 to escape is 1.069×5.00 hours = 5.34 hours. Again, the more massive gas, O_2, moves more slowly.

D. Deviations from Ideal Behavior

The ideal gas law works very well for most gases at common temperatures and pressures. However, at very high pressures the two main assumptions about ideality are brought into question:

(1)   The gas particles do not attract or repel each other.

(2)   The volume of the gas particles is insignificant in comparison with the total volume of the container.

First, as the particles are squeezed closer and closer together, at some point they begin to "notice" each other. They may begin to attract each other by virtue of dispersion forces, the polarity of bonds, or a tendency to form hydrogen bonds. Generally, attractive forces between gas particles outweigh repulsive forces, and the particles on the whole are closer together than would be predicted by PV = nRT.

If the pressure continues to increase, then a second factor becomes important: the volume of the gas particles themselves. This volume, neglected by the Kinetic-Molecular Theory, now becomes a factor that must be taken into account. For ideal gases, the V term in PV = nRT is the volume of the container—and is assumed to be the volume of "free space" available to the gas particles. At normal pressures and temperatures, the volume of the particles is so small compared to the volume of the container that this assumption works well. As the gas particles get pushed closer to one another (high P and/or low T), their volumes begin to be a significant portion of the volume of the container and must be taken into consideration. The volume available to any particular gas particle is the empty volume in the container, which is then obtained by subtracting the volume of the particles from the volume of the container.

Deviations from ideal behavior can be described graphically. For one mole of a gas, n = 1, we can write

$$PV = nRT, \text{ or } \frac{PV}{RT} = 1.$$

For one mole of an ideal gas, then, a plot of $\frac{PV}{RT}$ (y-axis) versus P (x-axis) is a straight horizontal line

at $\frac{PV}{RT} = 1$. However, real gases show deviations from linear behavior, as shown in Figure 15-10. For

real gases, the value of $\frac{PV}{RT}$ is somewhat pressure sensitive. Note the scale of the x-axis, a gas at 1.0 bar (or 1.0 atm) behaves quite ideally and it takes large pressures to alter the behavior significantly.

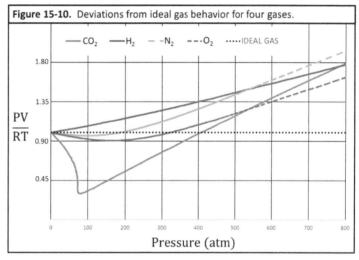

Figure 15-10. Deviations from ideal gas behavior for four gases.

As the pressure increases, the first thing that happens for many gases is that they begin to attract each other. This attraction causes them to be closer to each other than the Kinetic-Molecular Theory would predict, and V is smaller than expected. In general, this leads to a negative deviation, and PV/RT < 1. This effect can be seen for N_2, CH_4, and CO_2 in Figure 15-10. Note that attractive forces are very weak for H_2, so this gas does not show such behavior.

As the pressure becomes still greater, the volumes of the gas particles begin to come into play, and the volume predicted by the Kinetic-Molecular Theory is smaller than the actual volume required for the gas sample. In this case, the V in the actual $\frac{PV}{RT}$ ratio is larger than expected, so the value of the ratio is greater than 1.

Gases will be encountered frequently later this semester and upcoming courses. In particular, gases will provide useful examples in the study of chemical equilibria (Chapter 16) and the study of thermodynamics and kinetics in another course.

15-5. GASES AND BIOLOGICAL SYSTEMS: HEMOGLOBIN AND OXYGEN

Many life forms depend on oxygen as a reactant for the metabolism of foods. The overall metabolic process involved is called **catabolism**, the branch of metabolism in which large food molecules are broken down in energy-releasing oxidative reactions. The carbon atoms of the food molecules are eventually completely converted to carbon dioxide, as shown here for glucose:

$$C_6H_{12}O_6 + 6\,O_2 \longrightarrow 6\,CO_2 + 6\,H_2O$$

Humans, and many other animals, obtain oxygen directly from the air. Note that oxygen is a necessary reactant and carbon dioxide is a waste product of this process. Within the field of physiology, the process by which gas-phase oxygen is taken up and transported to the tissues (and CO_2 is transported back from tissues to lungs to be exhaled) is called **physiological respiration**; see Figure 15-11. For humans, and many other animals, the movement of oxygen molecules from the gas-phase to the aqueous phase occurs in the **alveolar** tissue of mammalian lungs. The biochemical use of oxygen in catabolic processes leading to the capture of energy is called **cellular respiration**; see Figure 15-11. All of the individual biochemical reactions that comprise the overall process

$$C_6H_{12}O_6 + 6\,O_2 \longrightarrow 6\,CO_2 + 6\,H_2O$$

are components of cellular respiration. Physiological respiration and cellular respiration are distinct, but intertwined processes. Physiological respiration delivers oxygen to the tissues. Cellular respiration then occurs and the oxygen atoms of the O_2 become oxygen atoms of H_2O. At the same time, carbon atoms of the fuel molecule become carbon atoms in CO_2 molecules. Finally, physiological respiration processes deliver the CO_2 back to the lungs for elimination.

Much of the chemistry of cellular respiration is **oxidation-reduction** chemistry. In the overall balanced reaction (above), carbon atoms from the food are **oxidized** to CO_2 (meaning that carbon atoms lose electrons). The electrons lost by carbon eventually are transferred to oxygen atoms of O_2, thus, oxygen atoms are **reduced** (gain electrons) and water molecules are formed.

Figure 15-11. Left: Physiological respiration involves breathing and the transport of oxygen throughout the body. **Right:** Cellular respiration involves the use of oxygen to process food in order to obtain energy for life.

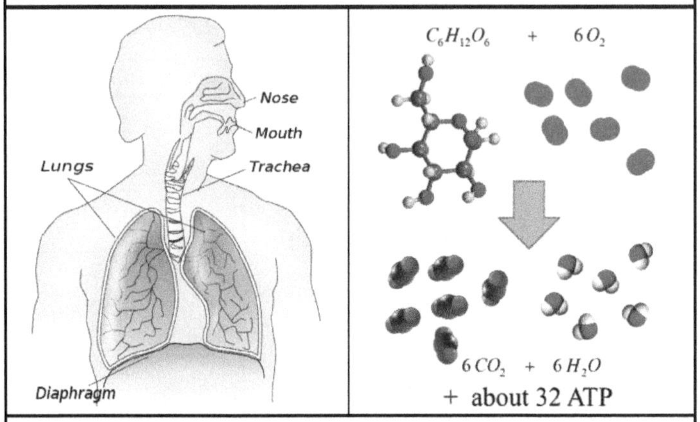

Left image obtained at wpclipart.com (Public Domain images)
wpclipart.com/medical/anatomy/lungs/respiratory_system.png.html

Before the final reduction of oxygen to water molecules, cellular respiration processes utilize the electrons obtained from carbon atoms to drive the production of ATP, a molecule that serves as an energy source for many **anabolic** processes. **Anabolism** is the branch of metabolism that is concerned with the building of structures necessary for life. Anabolism is characterized by processes that start with small molecules and build larger ones. Protein synthesis, for instance, is an anabolic process. Photosynthesis (the overall reverse of cellular respiration) is another anabolic process.

In the following sections, we concern ourselves with the process by which gaseous oxygen enters the bloodstream at the alveolar/capillary interfaces of the lung.

A. Solubility of Gases, Henry's Law

Consider a pure liquid (such as water) and a pure gas (such as O_2) that are placed together in a closed container at 25 °C. The water and oxygen are in physical contact with each other only at the liquid-gas interface. Let's assume that the oxygen pressure in the container is maintained at 1.00 bar. Oxygen molecules, moving in the gas phase, encounter the surface of the liquid water and some of them dissolve instead of "bouncing" off of the surface. Dissolved oxygen molecules diffuse away from the water surface into the bulk of the water, allowing more and more oxygen to dissolve. The solubility of oxygen under these conditions is 41.73 mg/L, or 1.304×10^{-3} M.

$$41.73\,\frac{\text{mg}}{\text{L}} \times \frac{1\,\text{g}}{1000\,\text{mg}} \times \frac{1\,\text{mol}\,O_2}{31.9988\,\text{g}\,O_2} = 1.304 \times 10^{-3}\,\frac{\text{mol}\,O_2}{\text{L}}$$

Once the water has attained a homogeneous 41.73 mg/L concentration of O_2, the forward process (dissolving) will be equally balanced by the reverse process:

$$O_2(g) \rightleftharpoons O_2(aq)$$

We say that the system has come to "equilibrium," a concept that we will explore in some depth in the next chapter. Essentially, an equilibrium is achieved when a forward and reverse process are occurring at the same rate. In our system, then, the total concentration of dissolved O_2 does not change while the system is at equilibrium; some oxygen molecules are dissolving, but a matching number are being released from the solution back into the gas phase.

Like solids, the solubilities of gases are temperature dependent. Unlike solids, gases tend to be more soluble at cool temperatures and less soluble at higher temperatures. Lakes sometimes experience "fish kills" in the heat of the summer; the warmed water does not hold enough dissolved oxygen to support all of the living creatures residing there. Thermal pollution of waterways can also be an issue. Some power plants and industrial manufacturers utilize water from natural sources for cooling. The water is not contaminated by any substances, but is returned to the waterway at a higher temperature. This "thermal pollution" can lead to the same types of fish kills that sometimes occur naturally in the heat of the summer.

Figure 15-12. Fountain-aided aeration.

Dissolving oxygen into surface waters can be a slow process because it depends on diffusion to move the newly dissolved oxygen from the surface into the lower depths of water. Diffusion can be greatly aided when water is moving; rivers generally stay more oxygenated than lakes and ponds due to the stirring that occurs as the water moves. Additionally, any situations that cause a larger gas-liquid surface area will aid in the dissolving process. Waves, river rapids and waterfalls all help to increase the surface area of the water that is exposed to the air. Artificial aeration of stagnant water is sometimes utilized to help keep a body of water healthy. The golf course pond in Figure 15-12 is aerated with a fountain. Small droplets of water generate much more surface area for dissolving gases and the fountain also aids in the redistribution of the aerated water into lower depths of the pond.

Returning to our oxygen-water system, consider what will happen if the pressure of the oxygen gas is decreased from 1.00 bar to 0.50 bar; half as much gas dissolves in the water, for a total concentration of about 20.86 mg/L, or 6.520×10^{-4} M. This relationship between the pressure of the gas and the amount dissolved is called **Henry's law**. Mathematically, it can take many forms; we will consider this form:

$$d[gas] = k_H \times P(gas)$$

where

　　　d[gas] is the concentration of dissolved gas (mol/L, mg/L, etc.),
　　　P(gas) is the *partial pressure* of the gas above the liquid, and
　　　k_H is the **Henry's law constant**, the value of which depends on the solute (what gas?), the solvent (what liquid?), the temperature, and the units used for pressure and concentration.

Did you notice that the pressure term in Henry's law is a partial pressure? Whether or not the gas is part of a gaseous mixture is unimportant. Because the partial pressure of oxygen in air is about 0.20 bar, we can determine the concentration of O_2 expected in room temperature water exposed to air. We first compute the Henry's law constant for O_2 from our data, above:

$$20.86 \text{ mg/L} = k_H \times 0.50 \text{ bar}$$

or

$$41.73 \text{ mg/L} = k_H \times 1.00 \text{ bar}$$

In either case, k_H = 41.7 mg/(L·bar). We can determine the solubility of oxygen in water exposed to air with a partial pressure of oxygen of 0.20 bar:

$$d[O_2] = \left(41.7 \frac{\text{mg } O_2}{\text{L} \times \text{bar}} \right) (0.20 \text{ bar}) = 8.3 \frac{\text{mg } O_2}{\text{L}}$$

Henry's Law is in the form of $y = mx + b$, where the dissolved concentration is y, the slope is the k_H value, and the partial pressure of the gas is x (and $b = 0$); see Figure 15-13.

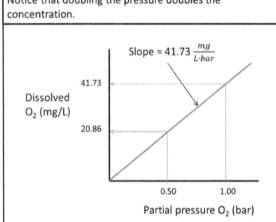

Figure 15-13. A plot of Henry's Law should be linear, with a slope equal to the value of the Henry's law constant. Notice that doubling the pressure doubles the concentration.

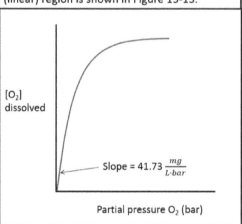

Figure 15-14. A plot of Henry's Law is only linear at relatively low pressures (and concentrations). Part of the low pressure (linear) region is shown in Figure 15-13.

Interestingly, the linearity of the Henry's Law plot is lost as the partial pressure of a gas increases. This is because gases at high pressures do not behave ideally. In the extreme, pressurizing a gas eventually causes it to condense to liquid form! A complete graph of dissolved oxygen vs. its partial pressure is offered in Figure 15-14. As long as a system exists at relatively low pressures and concentrations, Henry's law should hold.

Exercise 15-13.

Determine the value of the Henry's law constant for oxygen and water at 25 °C if
a. concentration is measured in mg/L, and pressure in pascals.
b. concentration is measured in molarity, and pressure in torr.

Exercise 15-14.

a. Under identical conditions, the solubility of gas A is 1.55 times the solubility of gas B. If gas A has a Henry's law constant of $1.9 \times 10^{-4} \dfrac{\text{mol}}{\text{L} \cdot \text{bar}}$, what would be the magnitude of the constant for gas B?

b. What partial pressure of gas B will establish a solution concentration of 0.0034 M?

B. Solubility of O₂ in Blood at Body Temperature, 37 °C

The general introduction to gas solubilities, above, allows us to consider the specific case of how much oxygen can be dissolved in blood, and whether or not this is enough to provide the oxygen requirements of a person.

The human body at rest requires about 0.012 moles of oxygen every minute. Cardiac output by a human heart is about 6 L of blood per minute. We use these values to determine the concentration of oxygen necessary in the blood in order to meet the minimum O₂ requirement:

$$\text{needed } d[O_2] = \left(0.012 \frac{\text{mol} O_2}{\text{min}} \right) \left(\frac{1 \text{min}}{6 \text{ L blood}} \right) = 2.0 \times 10^{-3} \frac{\text{mol} O_2}{\text{L blood}} = 2.0 \times 10^{-3} \text{M}$$

This is a minimum, because we are working from the oxygen requirement of a body at rest.

Now, how much oxygen can be dissolved in blood (simply dissolved, not utilizing any particular oxygen-transport mechanism)? The Henry's law constant for dissolving oxygen into blood at a body temperature of 37 °C is $1.04 \times 10^{-3} \dfrac{\text{mol}}{\text{L} \times \text{bar}}$. This value is lower than the constant for pure water, mostly because of the elevated temperature. A typical partial pressure of oxygen present in the lungs is 0.13 bar. This value is lower than the partial pressure of oxygen in air because of the *very high* humidity inside the lungs. As the partial pressure of gaseous water in air is increased, the partial pressures of other air components must decrease![109] We can use Henry's law to determine the expected concentration of dissolved oxygen, $d[O_2]$, in the blood:

$$d[O_2] = \left(1.04 \times 10^{-3} \frac{\text{mol} O_2}{\text{L blood} \times \text{bar}} \right) (0.13 \text{ bar}) = 1.4 \times 10^{-4} \frac{\text{mol} O_2}{\text{L blood}}$$

Comparing this value of available dissolved oxygen to the required oxygen (obtained earlier) shows that a simple dissolution process cannot deliver enough oxygen to the tissues to maintain life! The concentration of O₂ attainable in blood is less than one-tenth of the concentration necessary for even a resting body. Hence the biological need for a more efficient way to obtain oxygen from air.

C. Hemoglobin: Transporter of Oxygen

Hemoglobin is the protein component of blood with the ability to bind oxygen in the lung, and then let go of oxygen in the tissues, thus it plays a role in the physiological process of respiration. You may remember, from earlier chapters, that hemoglobin is a tetrameric protein; it is composed of 4 protein chains (called subunits) each of which is a distinct protein polymer. Each of the 4 associated subunits contains a heme group that is the site of O₂ binding; see Figure 15-15 (bound oxygen, red, is most apparent at the central position in the heme of the green subunit). Hemoglobin is a protein with 4 levels of structure: each subunit has primary, secondary, and tertiary structures and the association of the 4 subunits is known as quaternary structure.

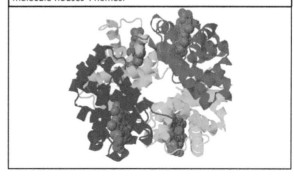

Figure 15-15. The quaternary structure of hemoglobin. Each colored polymer ribbon is a distinct protein chain. The heme groups (space-filling in figure) were introduced in Chapter 10, as the O₂-binding centers of myoglobin. Each working hemoglobin molecule houses 4 hemes.

Hemoglobin is essential for the success of many living species, including us! The presence of hemoglobin allows blood to carry about $9 \times 10^{-3} M$ oxygen, about 65 times more

---

[109] The air is at the same overall pressure and the partial pressures of all of the gases must add to that pressure. If one partial pressure increases, the others must decrease.

than simple dissolution. This oxygen is not simply dissolved in the blood, it is covalently bonded to the iron ions of the heme groups of hemoglobin. It is "as if" the blood has a much larger Henry's law constant (~65 times larger) due to the presence of hemoglobin. We could call the new constant "k_{Hb}" where Hb stands for hemoglobin.

$$\left(k_{Hb}\right)\left(0.13\,\text{bar}\right) = 9 \times 10^{-3}\,\frac{\text{mol O}_2}{\text{L blood}}$$

$$k_{Hb} = 7 \times 10^{-2}\,\frac{\text{mol}}{\text{L}\times\text{bar}}$$

However, inspection of the oxygen-binding curve for hemoglobin (Figure 15-16) makes it quite clear that hemoglobin does not behave in a way that is consistent with Henry's law; the plot is not linear at all! The ability of hemoglobin to carry oxygen is NOT directly proportional to the partial pressure of the gas (even at low pressures the graph is not linear). In other words, Henry's law does not apply. For hemoglobin, a plot of % oxygen binding vs. partial pressure of oxygen, is sigmoidal, rather than linear. The areas of the plot with smaller slopes are regions where hemoglobin has more trouble binding oxygen. For example, at very small partial pressures of oxygen, the tangent to the curve is quite flat and it takes a large increase in partial pressure to cause much change in percent binding. However, in the steeper regions of the plot, small changes in partial pressure of oxygen have large effects on % oxygen binding. Note that the plot is reasonably linear and steep between the active muscle and normal tissue landmarks. This means that small changes in the tissue environment will be able to cause maximum responsiveness by the hemoglobin molecule.

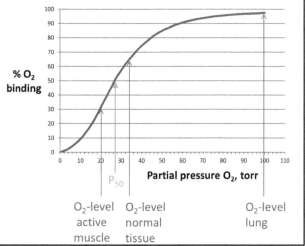

Figure 15-16. The oxygen-binding curve of hemoglobin. The green arrow shows that P_{50} =26.6 torr. The red arrows show three approximate physiological landmarks.

The **P_{50}** value marked in Figure 15-16 (green, 26.6 torr) is the O_2 pressure at which 50% of the binding sites are filled. Compared to myoglobin (Figure 15-17), whose P_{50} value is tiny (about 3 torr), hemoglobin is not as strong of an oxygen-binder. Importantly, even though the binding curve for hemoglobin is flattening at higher pressures, hemoglobin can pick up enough oxygen in the lungs to be nearly 100% filled, or **saturated**.[110] In the comparison of P_{50} values between myoglobin and hemoglobin, it appears that the tetrameric structure of hemoglobin must <u>help it to let go of oxygen</u>. Even so, consultation of the binding curve shows that under typical, unstressed conditions, hemoglobin delivers only about 30-35% of the oxygen it carries. In muscles under heavy metabolic stress, hemoglobin can deliver around 70% of the bound oxygen.

Figure 15-17. Myoglobin (Mb) is a single subunit, oxygen-binding protein with a much larger affinity for oxygen than hemoglobin, (Hb). Each subunit of Hb is very similar to Mb, yet Hb's affinity for O_2 is much lower.

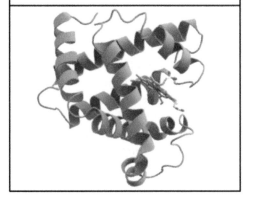

---

[110] In this context, *saturated* means that the binding sites have been completely filled. When a hemoglobin sample is *saturated*, each molecule will have 4 tightly bonded oxygen molecules.

How does hemoglobin's affinity for oxygen change under different conditions? As we suspect from our consideration of myoglobin, part of the answer lies in hemoglobin's tetrameric structure, which allows four potential binding sites to "communicate" with each other through small changes in tertiary structures; after a hemoglobin molecule binds one O_2 molecule it actually increases its affinity to bind the additional 3 O_2 molecules! This is a phenomenon called **cooperative binding**. Binding oxygen causes a small shift in tertiary and quaternary structures that result in a higher affinity for oxygen for the remaining sites. Each additional oxygen bond causes a higher affinity for the next one (within a particular molecule of hemoglobin). This phenomenon explains why the slope of the hemoglobin curve is so flat at the very left edge of the plot. It is much easier to bind the second, third and fourth oxygen molecules, thus the steeper curve in the middle of the plot. Cooperative behavior is eventually lost when all of the hemoglobin molecules have 3 or 4 bound oxygen molecules because adding the fourth O_2 to one molecule of hemoglobin cannot help the fourth O_2 bind to a different hemoglobin molecule!

Exercise 15-15.

Search online for an oxygen binding curve that includes data for both myoglobin and hemoglobin. Sketch the graph and show the P_{50} points for myoglobin and hemoglobin. Explain, based on the graph, whether myoglobin should be able to bind oxygen delivered to the tissues by hemoglobin, or not.

The tetrameric structure of hemoglobin not only allows cooperative binding, it also allows the hemoglobin molecule to interact with a variety of other molecules and ions in ways that tend to discourage oxygen-binding (because letting go of oxygen is the process that needs help). These strategies, which are often covered in some depth in beginning biochemistry courses, exist in order to allow hemoglobin to fulfill its difficult role of transporter.

Why is a transport role difficult? Think of it this way: if blood needs to carry large concentrations of oxygen, hemoglobin needs to have a high bonding affinity for oxygen. There needs to be very favorable bonding (in the lungs) in order to move lots of oxygen into the blood stream in a relatively short time. However, when the blood has been pumped out to tissues, the hemoglobin must be able to let go of the bound oxygen. This means that physical and chemical differences between the lung environment and the tissue environment must be exploited in such a way that the bond between hemoglobin and oxygen becomes much less stable in the tissues, thus leading to the delivery of oxygen. Look again at the binding curve to myoglobin that you found while answering Exercise 15-15. Notice that the high-affinity myoglobin molecule finds it very difficult to deliver reasonable amounts of oxygen until the partial pressure is very, very low. Myoglobin would not be a good transport molecule, but it is a good storage molecule!

What types of environmental differences are there between the lungs and the tissues? The most obvious one (and the only one we will consider in this chapter) is the presence, or not, of excess, unbound oxygen. The partial pressure of oxygen in the lungs is about 100 torr. In working muscle tissue, the free oxygen level is much lower (due to its rapid use during cellular respiration). Hemoglobin's percent binding in normal tissue is at the same level as it would be if in contact with a partial pressure of oxygen of only 20 torr. There is not a partial pressure of oxygen (gas) of 20 torr in active muscle tissues; there is no gas at all! Rather, hemoglobin's percent binding in active muscle tissue is the same *as if* the hemoglobin were in contact with 20 torr pressure of oxygen gas. Biochemists are fond of using partial pressure language, even in parts of the body with no access to gaseous oxygen (see the *x*-axis units of Figure 15-15)! Just remember that this language is simply an indirect way of indicating the level of oxygenation of the hemoglobin, *as if* it were in contact with oxygen gas at a particular partial pressure.

We have learned that the binding of oxygen to hemoglobin does not obey Henry's law. Hemoglobin is good at bonding to oxygen; even at the relatively low partial pressure of 100 torr, it becomes almost **saturated** with oxygen. However, it's not nearly as good at binding oxygen as the monomeric myoglobin molecule! Unlike myoglobin, once hemoglobin has moved out to the tissues where oxygen is scarce, it is able to unload from 30-70% of the carried oxygen, thus delivering a needed reactant for cellular respiration. We will think more about this in Chapter 17.

Exercise 15-16.

Extra oxygen in living tissues is a chemical hazard. Oxygen is an excellent oxidizing agent, which means that it is easy to reduce. Reduced forms of oxygen include the superoxide **radical**, O_2^-, and hydrogen peroxide, H_2O_2, both of which are highly reactive and can do great damage to membranes and other tissues. While living organisms have a number of ways to defend against these reactive oxygen species, how might myoglobin contribute to the defensive effort?

CHAPTER 15 PROBLEMS

1. Do you expect humid air to be more or less dense than dry air? Explain.

2. A glass bulb having a volume of 532.6 mL contains hydrogen gas at a pressure of 1.000 bar and a temperature of 30.0 °C. How many moles of gas are in the bulb?

3. A sealed glass bulb contains 1.40 mol of gas at a pressure of 1.00 bar and a temperature of 27 °C.

   a. What is the volume of the bulb?

   b. Suppose the temperature of the gas in the bulb is raised to 57 °C. What will be the final pressure of the gas?

4. At 32 °C a sample of gas in a sealed glass bulb of volume 189.6 mL exerts a pressure of 1.22 bar. What will be the final pressure if the gas is heated to 64 °C?

5. A sample of helium in a balloon had a volume of 1.37 L at a pressure of 0.95 bar. In a pressure chamber the balloon was compressed to exactly one half its original volume while maintaining a constant temperature. What was the final pressure of the gas?

6. A flexible balloon of volume 2.50 L at 1.2 bar and 25.0 °C is allowed to rise to the stratosphere, where the temperature is −73.0 °C and the pressure is 3.04×10^{-3} atm. What is the final volume of the balloon?

7. A mixture of gases contains 10.00 g H_2, 5.00 g Cl_2 and 5.00 g F_2. What are the mole fractions of each gas in the mixture?

8. A tank of compressed, dry air is used to fill a glass bulb to a final pressure of 2.00 bar. Using data presented in this chapter, determine the partial pressures of N_2, Ne, and CO_2.

9. Hemoglobin's ability to bind oxygen in the lungs depends on the partial pressure of oxygen present. The "P_{50}" for hemoglobin is the partial pressure of oxygen in the lungs that is necessary for half of hemoglobin's binding sites to be occupied with oxygen. Normal P_{50} for hemoglobin is about 26.7 torr. What is the normal partial pressure of oxygen in (dry) air? Will this populate more than 50% of the hemoglobin sites, or fewer?

10. What is the density of krypton gas at a pressure of 1.02 bar and a temperature of 31.5 °C?

11. Calculate the molecular mass of a gas if a 226 mL sample of the gas at 100 °C and 745 torr has a mass of 0.573 g.

12. At STP an unknown gas has a density of $1.504 \frac{g}{L}$. What is the molecular mass of the gas?

13. A hydrocarbon has 17.3% hydrogen by mass. A sample of this hydrocarbon contained in a 202.5 mL glass bulb at 80.0 °C and a pressure of 1.034 bar has a mass of 0.4143 g. Find:

   a. The empirical formula

   b. The molecular formula

14. Uranium can be separated into individual isotopes by a process that involves the formation of a gaseous compound containing only uranium and fluorine. If 250.0 mL of the gas has a mass of 2.7565 g at 77.0 °C and 684 torr:

    a. What is the molecular weight of the gas?

    b. What is the likely molecular formula?

15. A mysterious, somewhat explosive compound contains only C, H, and O. Analysis indicates that the compound contains 53.3% C and 11.1 % H by mass.

    a. What is the empirical formula of the compound?

    b. The vapor of the mystery compound has density 3.65 g/L at 27 °C and 1.01 bar. What is the molecular mass of the compound?

    c. What is the molecular formula of the compound?

16. The ammonium dichromate "volcano" reaction involves decomposition of ammonium dichromate to form the gray-green solid Cr_2O_3, plus gaseous H_2O and N_2.

    a. What is the chemical name of Cr_2O_3?

    b. Write a balanced chemical equation for this reaction.

    c. What volume of gas is given off by 10.0 g of ammonium dichromate at 23 °C and 750.0 torr?

17. A gas bulb containing a solid copper compound is filled with O_2. The volume of gas in the bulb is 1.06 liters, the pressure of O_2 is 1.005 bar, and its temperature is 37 °C. The copper compound slowly reacts with the O_2, forming a solid oxide. After two hours the pressure has dropped to 0.7924 bar. What mass of O_2 has reacted with the copper compound? (Assume that the total volume of gas in the bulb remains constant and that the temperature remains constant.)

18. Consider the molecule O_2.

    a. At what temperature will its average kinetic energy be exactly double that at 25 °C?

    b. A compound of formula UF_x effuses only 0.3015 times as rapidly as O_2. What is the molecular mass of UF_x? What is the value of x?

19. A sample of an unknown gas effuses through a porous barrier in 15.0 min. Under the same conditions of temperature and pressure it takes the same number of moles of nitrogen 12.0 min to effuse through the barrier. What is the molecular mass of the unknown gas?

20. 1.00 mol of carbon <u>mon</u>oxide effuses through a small opening in 684 seconds. Under the same conditions of temperature and pressure, how long would it take for 1.00 mol of carbon <u>di</u>oxide to effuse through the same opening?

21. A certain organic compound containing only carbon, hydrogen, and oxygen was found to have a gas phase density of 1.894 g L^{-1} at 1.00 atm and 100.0 °C.

    a. What was the molecular weight of the gas?

    b. Combustion of 1.000 g of the compound gave 2.276 g of CO_2. What was the molecular formula of the compound?

    c. Suggest a possible molecular structure of this compound.

22.   Over the years the label on an old tank of gas had carelessly been allowed to deteriorate and finally could no longer be read. It was found that 0.0100 mol of the gas effused through a small opening in 141.3 s. Under similar conditions of temperature and pressure 0.0100 mol of oxygen effused through the same opening in 100.0 s. What was the molecular weight of the gas in the old tank?

23.   Professor Chemfield had her impoverished laboratory assistant perform a demonstration for her class. For the demonstration the assistant had a 1.000 m hollow glass tube, two balls of glass wool, a bottle of concentrated ammonia, and a bottle of concentrated HBr. The student poured ammonia solution on one ball of glass wool, the acid on the other. He then simultaneously applied the balls to opposite ends of the tube. After a period of time, something interesting happened.

What was the interesting thing that happened? You should determine:

a. The chemical reaction that occurred (a balanced equation).

b. Where it occurred. Predict the approximate location, and explain.

24.   Why is the ideal gas law generally more valid at low pressures than at high pressures?

25.   Although the ratio $\dfrac{PV}{RT}$ is constant for an ideal gas, this ratio may vary for a non-ideal gas. Explain.

26.   Would you expect a sample of air to act in a more ideal fashion at 100 K or 100 °F? Explain.

27.   a. Determine the Henry's law constant (using units of torr and molarity) if a sample of gas A at 40 °C and 255 torr creates a 6.8 mM solution of A in water.

b. Do you expect the constant to have a larger, smaller, or same value at a temperature of 65 °C? Explain.

28.   Explain why natural fish kills in Minnesota lakes are more likely during humid weather than in drier, but equally warm, weather.

29.   Hemoglobin can bind with protons (H^+) in its environment. The binding of protons either helps hemoglobin to bind more oxygen, or helps it to let go of oxygen. Based on our discussion of hemoglobin, which do you think is more likely? Explain.

30.   a. Gas B at 1.0 bar and 25 °C produces aqueous solutions of 0.00024 M. If the gas pressure is increased to 1.0 kbar what concentration of B could be achieved in an aqueous solution at 25 °C?

b. Why is it unlikely your answer from part a would actually occur?

31.   Figure 15-12 shows the aeration of a golf course pond. A different strategy is used to maintain aeration of household aquariums. Compare and contrast these strategies.

32.   It might seem that hemoglobin with the ability to unload all of its carried oxygen would be an evolutionary improvement. Do a bit of research about the reactions of O_2 in the body and explain why evolutionary pressure might favor hemoglobin with the current capabilities.

CHAPTER 16: EQUILIBRIUM I
REACTION QUOTIENTS AND EQUILIBRIUM CONSTANTS

16-1. INTRODUCTION: REACTIONS THAT NEVER "FINISH"

Consider the reaction of iron(III) ion with thiocyanate ion to produce the iron thiocyanate complex ion:

$$Fe^{3+}(aq) + SCN^-(aq) \longrightarrow FeSCN^{2+}(aq)$$

yellow   colorless   red

The reactants are relatively colorless and the product is a deep blood-red color (if plentiful in solution) or rather orange (if dilute). We can tell if one sample has more or less product than another by the color. Study the photos of the reactant solutions and of the product formed after they are poured together; see Figure 16-1. You might be surprised to know that this reaction never "finishes," at least in the way we have previously used this idea. The solution does reach a certain color and then stops changing, but neither iron(III) ion nor thiocyanate ion is used up. How can we prove this?

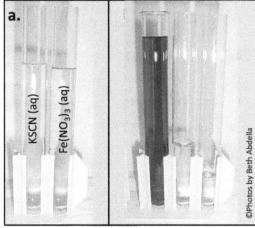

Figure 16-1. a. Aqueous solutions of potassium thiocyanate (colorless) and iron(III) nitrate (slightly yellow). **b.** After pouring some of each reagent into a third test tube. The product ion, $FeSCN^{2+}$ is red.

We can separate a dilute solution of this reaction system into three samples (Figure 16-2A). One sample (in the center) is kept as a color control; we compare other solutions to this one to determine if more or less product is present. To the sample on the left we add a little extra thiocyanate ion by pouring in a little solid KSCN. This solution gets <u>more red</u>; so more product has been made (Figure 16-2B). This means there <u>must have been unreacted iron(III) ion in the original solution</u>, because the added SCN⁻ must have reacted with some Fe^{3+}. Now, to the sample on the right, we add a little extra iron(III) ion by pouring in a little solid $Fe(NO_3)_3$. This solution also gets <u>more red</u> (Figure 16-2C). <u>There must have been unreacted thiocyanate ion in the original solution</u> with which the added iron(III) ion reacted.

Figure 16-2. A. Three samples of the same $FeSCN^{2+}$ system. These particular samples were all poured from one solution, so they are identical in color. The color is indicative of how much $FeSCN^{2+}$ has been produced (not much, based on the orange rather than red color!) Vials of solid KSCN and $Fe(NO_3)_3$ stand ready for experimentation. **B.** Adding solid KSCN to the left hand test tube. Notice the darkening of the color, more of the red $FeSCN^{2+}$ ion was made. **C.** Adding solid $Fe(NO_3)_3$ to the right hand test tube. Notice the darkening of the color, more of the red $FeSCN^{2+}$ ion was made.

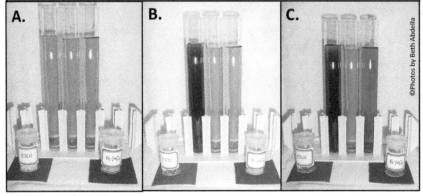

Together, these two experiments show that the original reaction solution contained unreacted thiocyanate ion *and* unreacted iron(III) ion; neither was used up in the original reaction.

Why did this reaction stop before it had used up either of the reactants? How can we predict the amount of product a reaction of this nature will produce? There must be properties of chemical reactions that we have not yet considered.

16-2. IRREVERSIBLE AND REVERSIBLE REACTIONS

A. Irreversible Reactions

Up until this point we have studied only reactions that "go to completion" or so close to completion that the assumption that they go to completion works mathematically to predict that amount of product that will be made. These are reactions that are **irreversible**, or that we can mathematically treat as irreversible. The product(s) formed are so stable that they do not noticeably revert to reactants. In truly irreversible situations, this is because the product **dissipates**[111] and is unavailable for the reverse process. In other cases, the product is just *much* more probable than the reactants.[112] The amount of product made by an irreversible reaction (or essentially irreversible reaction) is controlled by the limiting reagent. In other words, these reactions make product(s) until at least one reactant is (essentially) used up. All of the stoichiometric calculations we have made thus far have been based on the idea of irreversibility. Irreversible reactions (and essentially irreversible reactions) are generally depicted with a single forward arrow, such as

$$A + B \longrightarrow C$$

Example 16-1.

The following problems are based on the idea of irreversible reactions. Use these to refresh your mind about the types of logic we use for these reactions.

a. If 3.2 moles of Zn and 5.6 moles of HCl are reacted according to
$$Zn(s) + 2HCl(aq) \longrightarrow ZnCl_2(aq) + H_2(g)$$
how many moles of hydrogen gas can be produced?

b. Determine the number of grams of zinc necessary to produce 6.4 moles of hydrogen gas using the following chemical reaction:
$$Zn(s) + 2HCl(aq) \longrightarrow ZnCl_2(aq) + H_2(g)$$

c. Determine the mass (in kg) of phosphorus necessary to completely react with 2.1 kg of sodium according to the reaction:
$$3Na(s) + P(s) \longrightarrow Na_3P(s)$$

Solutions:

a. First, determine which of the two reagents is the limiting reagent. One way to do this compares the actual mole ratio of the two reactants with their mole ratio in the balanced chemical reaction. Here, the actual mole ratio of Zn to HCl is:
$$\frac{actual\ moles\ Zn}{actual\ moles\ HCl} = \frac{3.2}{5.6} = 0.57$$

The ratio of Zn to HCl in the balanced reaction equation is:

$$\frac{moles\ Zn\ in\ balanced\ equation}{moles\ HCl\ in\ balanced\ equation} = \frac{1}{2} = 0.50$$

---

[111] Disperses or scatters.

[112] This idea will be more fully explored in later courses.

Because 0.57 > 0.50 and zinc is in the numerator, we actually have more zinc than is necessary. This makes HCl the limiting reactant.

Next, determine how many moles of hydrogen gas can be formed by the limiting reagent:

$$5.6 \ mol \ HCl \times \frac{1 \ mol \ H_2}{2 \ mol \ HCl} = 2.8 \ mol \ H_2$$

Alternatively, we could determine how much hydrogen gas can be made from each of the reactants. Whichever one can make less H_2 is the limiting reagent:

$$3.2 \ mol \ Zn \times \frac{1 \ mol \ H_2}{1 \ mol \ Zn} = 3.2 \ mol \ H_2$$

$$5.6 \ mol \ HCl \times \frac{1 \ mol \ H_2}{2 \ mol \ HCl} = 2.8 \ mol \ H_2$$

Here because the HCl can produce less hydrogen gas, HCl must, again, be the limiting reagent. Therefore the specified amounts of the two reagents could produce 2.8 moles of hydrogen gas. (Some zinc would be left over. Can you determine how much?)

b. $6.4 \ mol \ H_2 \times \dfrac{1 \ mol \ Zn}{1 \ mol \ H_2} \times \dfrac{65.39 \ g \ Zn}{1 \ mol \ Zn} = 4.2 \times 10^2 \ g \ Zn$

c. $2.1 \ kg \ Na \times \dfrac{1000 \ g \ Na}{1 \ kg \ Na} \times \dfrac{1 \ mol \ Na}{22.99 \ g \ Na} \times \dfrac{1 \ mol \ P}{3 \ mol \ Na} \times \dfrac{30.97 \ g \ P}{1 \ mol \ P} \times \dfrac{1 \ kg \ P}{1000 \ g \ P} = 0.94 \ kg \ P$

B. Reversible Reactions

There is another "class" of reactions that we call **reversible**. *Reversible reactions* are aptly named: when some product has been made, the reverse reaction begins to occur. We use a different type of arrow in a reaction equation to show that a reaction is reversible:

$$A + B \rightleftharpoons C + D$$

Consider a reversible reaction occurring in a flask for some period of time: both the forward and the reverse processes are occurring simultaneously. In our case we would say that A+B——→C+D is the "forward" reaction and that C+D——→A+B is the "reverse" reaction. We would say that A and B are the reactants; C and D are the products. The labels, "forward," "reverse," "reactant," and "product," depend on how the reaction is written. The very same reaction system is equally well described by this equation:

$$C + D \rightleftharpoons A + B$$

Writing the equation this way makes C+D——→A+B the forward reaction and A+B——→C+D the reverse reaction. Now C and D are the "reactants," A and B are the "products." Because both reactions (forward and reverse) are occurring in the sample there is no preference for describing the system; either $A + B \rightleftharpoons C + D$ or $C + D \rightleftharpoons A + B$ will do.

C. Rates of Forward and Reverse Reactions

We will focus on the reaction: $Fe^{3+}(aq) + SCN^-(aq) \rightleftharpoons FeSCN^{2+}(aq)$

which we have now written with the correct, reversible arrow. Whether or not there is a net increase in the amount of the red $FeSCN^{2+}$ in a sample depends on the relative *rates* of the forward and reverse processes. If the forward reaction is faster, then $FeSCN^{2+}$ is building up and the red color increases. If the reverse reaction is faster, then the amount of $FeSCN^{2+}$ is decreasing and the red color fades.

It will help us to understand reversible reactions if we can develop just a little intuition about the rates of chemical reactions (rates of reactions will be studied in more depth in a later course). Reaction rates have units of concentration/time. We could measure the rates of the forward and reverse reactions by measuring the change in $[FeSCN^{2+}]$ per min.[113] Reactions, in general, go faster when there are higher concentrations of reactants. Reactions slow down as they progress *because their reactants become depleted*. If we start with a solution of Fe^{3+} and SCN^-, the only reaction that can occur is the "forward" reaction:

$$Fe^{3+}(aq) + SCN^-(aq) \longrightarrow FeSCN^{2+}(aq)$$

The solution gets darker red over time. Because the <u>product of the forward reaction is the reactant for the reverse reaction</u>, the reverse reaction

$$FeSCN^{2+}(aq) \longrightarrow Fe^{3+}(aq) + SCN^-(aq)$$

starts slowly and then goes faster and faster as more of its reactant is made by the forward reaction. The rates of the forward and reverse reactions continually adjust as the concentrations of the ions in solution change. The forward reaction continues to slow down (as its reactants are consumed) and the reverse reaction continues to speed up (as its reactant becomes more available).[114]

Exercise 16-1.

Take a few minutes <u>before continuing with your reading</u> to consider the last sentence before this box. At what point will the forward reaction stop slowing down and the reverse reaction stop speeding up?

Did you get it? The rates of the forward and reverse reactions will stop changing when they are equal to each other! Let's make up some data to help think about this, see the box below:

Forward reaction:

$$Fe^{3+}(aq) + SCN^-(aq) \longrightarrow FeSCN^{2+}(aq)$$

At time 0 min: $[FeSCN^{2+}]$ is made at a rate of 0.50 M per minute.
At time 5 min: $[FeSCN^{2+}]$ is made at a rate of 0.25 M per minute.

Reverse reaction:

$$FeSCN^{2+}(aq) \longrightarrow Fe^{3+}(aq) + SCN^-(aq)$$

At time 0: $[FeSCN^{2+}]$ is lost at a rate of 0 M per minute (there isn't any to lose).
At time 5 min: $[FeSCN^{2+}]$ is lost at a rate of 0.25 M per minute.

---

[113]Actually, this reaction is much too fast to use minute time periods. We are "slowing it down" to make it more understandable!

[114] Many reactions are too fast for us to see this change in rates as the reaction approaches equilibrium. Many reactions look instantaneous to us because they are so fast!

If we plot the rates of the forward and reverse reactions at different reaction times from zero to 5 minutes, the plot would resemble the graph shown in Figure 16-3.[115] *The rates stop changing when they are equal* because concentrations stop changing; rates were changing only because the concentrations were changing.

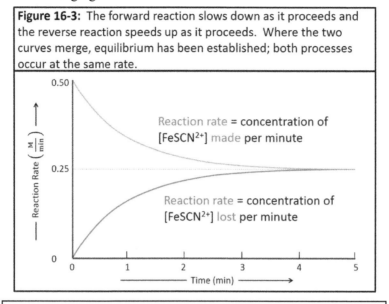

Figure 16-3: The forward reaction slows down as it proceeds and the reverse reaction speeds up as it proceeds. Where the two curves merge, equilibrium has been established; both processes occur at the same rate.

If you start with just reactants, as we did here, the reverse reaction cannot go faster than the forward reaction.

D. Dynamic Equilibrium

The equilibrium state achieved in our previous discussion is called **dynamic equilibrium**. The word "equilibrium" implies that no <u>net</u> changes are taking place in the reaction solution (the color stays the same, for instance). Once equilibrium has been achieved, the concentrations of all species remain constant with time. The word "dynamic" reminds us that even though concentrations of species are no longer changing, much is still happening in the system! Both the forward and reverse reactions are chugging away. The product ion, $FeSCN^{2+}$, is being made and also degraded, but the two processes are balancing one another.

One can see that reversible reactions require new methods for description. The concept of limiting reagent does not apply. There is no longer a straightforward arithmetic method for calculating the amounts of various species in the reaction when it is "finished." Much of the rest of this chapter will be devoted to understanding the reversible reaction and how to describe it both qualitatively and quantitatively.

16-3. THE REACTION QUOTIENT

A. Reaction Position and Reaction Quotient

Any aqueous reaction mixture (whether the reaction is "finished"[116] or not) can be described by <u>listing the concentrations</u> of each species at a particular time. Consider the general reaction:

$$aA(aq) + bB(aq) \rightleftharpoons cC(aq) + dD(aq)$$

---

[115] Again, we have taken liberties with this reaction; these data are not real.
[116] By "finished," we mean has either consumed the limiting reagent (irreversible reaction) or has reached equilibrium.

where A, B, C and D are the chemical species, and a, b, c and d are the coefficients in the balanced reaction. If, at some point in time, the concentrations of species in the flask are

$$[A] = 0.043\ M \qquad [B] = 0.122\ M \qquad [C] = 0.655\ M \qquad [D] = 0.323\ M$$

we might say that the reaction has, at that point in time, more product than reactant.

We call this list of concentrations the **reaction position.** If a reaction happens to be at equilibrium, the reaction position is called the **equilibrium position,** or **equilibrium composition**.

Chemists have developed another way to mathematically describe any reaction mixture. This method uses the reaction position (list of concentrations) to determine the value of a single entity called the **reaction quotient (Q).** Let's consider reactions with a variety of solutes and/or gases:

1. $aA(aq) + bB(aq) \rightleftharpoons cC(aq) + dD(aq)$

2. $aA(g) + bB(g) \rightleftharpoons cC(g) + dD(g)$

3. $aA(aq) + bB(aq) \rightleftharpoons cC(g) + dD(aq)$

The reaction quotient is a way to describe the relative amounts of reactants and products using one number, instead of listing an entire reaction position. Definitions of the reaction quotient for each of the three numbered reaction equations are given below.

Reaction 1: All species are solutes in an aqueous solution $\quad aA(aq) + bB(aq) \rightleftharpoons cC(aq) + dD(aq)$

The **reaction quotient** is defined as $\quad Q = \dfrac{[C]^c [D]^d}{[A]^a [B]^b}$

The convention is to use units of *molarity* for any solute. The exponents are the coefficients of each species in the balanced reaction equation. The square brackets indicate concentrations in molarities. The symbol [C] may be read "the molarity of solute C."

Reaction 2: All species are gases in the same container $\quad aA(g) + bB(g) \rightleftharpoons cC(g) + dD(g)$

The **reaction quotient** is defined as $\quad Q = \dfrac{\left(P_C\right)^c \left(P_D\right)^d}{\left(P_A\right)^a \left(P_B\right)^b}$

The convention is to use units of *bar* for any gas. The exponents are, again, the coefficients of each species in the balanced reaction equation. The symbol P_X may be read "the partial pressure of gas X."

Reaction 3: Some species are solutes in an aqueous solution, others are gases in the atmosphere above the solution. $\quad aA(aq) + bB(aq) \rightleftharpoons cC(g) + dD(aq)$

The **reaction quotient** is defined as $\quad Q = \dfrac{\left(P_C\right)^c [D]^d}{[A]^a [B]^b}$

The convention is to use units of *molarity* for any solute and *bar* for any gas. It is OK to mix and match the units, as we will discuss shortly.

The size of Q tells us about relative amounts of products and reactants in the system, also taking into account the stoichiometry of the reaction system (because reaction coefficients become exponents in the Q expression). Notice that product species are always found in the numerator while reactant species are found in the denominator. Sometimes, when the exact form of the Q expression is not needed, Q is simply represented as:

$$Q = \frac{[\text{products}]}{[\text{reactants}]}$$

The reaction quotient is larger when there is more product, and smaller when there is more reactant. In fact a Q value of 1 is a sort of middle ground, indicating a balance in the amounts of reactant and product. At the beginning of a reaction, when only reactant is present, Q is zero because there are zero products. In a reaction system where only product is present, Q is infinite because the denominator becomes zero. At any other reaction position Q has a non-zero, positive value.

Exercise 16-2.

Why can Q not be a negative number?

A classic example of a reversible chemical system is the reaction of NO_2 gas to produce N_2O_4 gas:

$$2NO_2(g) \rightleftharpoons N_2O_4(g) \qquad Q = \frac{P_{N_2O_4}}{\left(P_{NO_2}\right)^2}$$

Figure 16-4 shows this reaction at three different Q values. We can tell, because NO_2 gas is a red-brown color and N_2O_4 gas is colorless. Therefore, the darker colored gas samples have more <u>reactant</u> present. Which of the gas samples shown has the largest Q value?

Figure 16-4. The 2 NO_2(g) ⇌ N_2O_4(g) reaction at a variety of Q values. NO_2 is red-brown and N_2O_4 is colorless. Which sample has the largest Q value?

©Photos by Beth Abdella

The value of Q for any reaction (reversible or irreversible) changes as the reaction proceeds, until the reaction either uses up the limiting reagent or equilibrium is achieved. For a truly irreversible reaction, the final value of Q is infinity because at least one reactant is completely used up (the limiting reactant), so the denominator in the Q expression is zero. A truly **irreversible reaction** involving gases is one in which one or more products escape

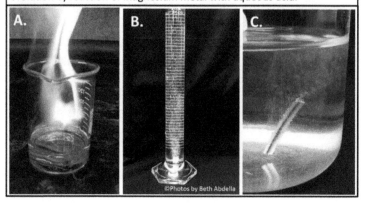

Figure 16-5. Irreversible reactions. **A.** Combustion of liquid acetone. **B.** Vinegar and baking soda produce CO_2 gas bubbles. **C.** Hydrogen gas evolution by reaction of magnesium metal with aqueous acid.

©Photos by Beth Abdella

into the atmosphere, and so are no longer available to react in the reverse reaction. The combustion of a fuel, such as methane in a natural gas furnace, is an example of this type of irreversibility:

$$CH_4(g) + 2O_2(g) \longrightarrow CO_2(g) + 2H_2O(g)$$

The waste gases escape to the atmosphere and are not available for the reverse reaction. Other gas-producing reactions are also irreversible. See Figure 16-5.

Reactions that stop proceeding when equilibrium is reached also achieve a final, equilibrium value of Q, because concentrations are no longer changing. Many reactions that are *treated mathematically as irreversible* are really reversible systems that simply have very large final values of Q. These reactions have reverse reactions that are often ignored due to the tiny extent to which they occur. An example of this type of reaction is the precipitation of PbI₂ when solutions of KI and Pb(NO₃)₂ are poured together. Lead(II) iodide is an *essentially* insoluble salt. The net ionic reaction equation is:

$$Pb^{2+}(aq)+2I^-(aq)\rightleftharpoons PbI_2(s)$$

When *stoichiometric* quantities of lead(II) ion and iodide ion are added together, we may assume, mathematically, that all of the ions precipitate. In fact, if we isolate, dry and weigh the precipitate, we will find that we obtained the expected amount.[117] However, tiny quantities of the dissolved ions do remain in solution. The masses of these ions are too small to be noticed by a laboratory balance, so we wouldn't know (by weighing the precipitate) that it wasn't quite all there. The final Q value is not infinite in cases such as this, although it is very large. Values of the final Q for these kinds of reactions can be on the order of 10^8 or even larger.

Here's an important concept:

> Many reactions are treated sometimes as if they are irreversible and other times as if they are reversible. Read on to see how this makes sense!

If a chemist is interested in how much lead(II) iodide precipitate can be made, it will make good sense to treat this system as irreversible and determine the expected yield based on simple stoichiometry and limiting reagents. If, however, the chemist is interested in the amounts of unreacted ions that remain in solution, the system's reversibility must be acknowledged. It is often crucial to pay attention to the tiny extent to which these reverse reactions occur. For instance, it would be dangerous to our health to assume that all lead(II) ions could be removed from a water source by adding a stoichiometric amount of iodide ions (thus assuming a reaction that is irreversible). Enough lead(II) ions would persist in the water to cause lead poisoning in anyone drinking the water over a period of time. The importance of studying the less favorable, reverse reaction is very important in a case such as this.

Example 16-2.

Write the reaction quotient, Q, for each of the following reactions

a. $2SO_3(g)\rightleftharpoons 2SO_2(g)+O_2(g)$

b. $Ag^+(aq)+2CN^-(aq)\rightleftharpoons Ag(CN)_2^-(aq)$ see note 118

Solutions: We remember that, in general, the reaction quotient is the concentration or partial pressure of products (taken to the appropriate powers) divided by the concentrations or partial pressures of reactants (taken to the appropriate powers), and we write:

a. $Q=\dfrac{\left(P_{SO_2}\right)^2\left(P_{O_2}\right)}{\left(P_{SO_3}\right)^2}$

b. $Q=\dfrac{\left[Ag(CN)_2^-\right]}{\left[Ag^+\right]\left[CN^-\right]^2}$

---

[117] This means that if 0.5 mole Pb²⁺ and 1 mole I⁻ are added together, we would obtain the expected 0.5 moles of PbI₂.

[118] While the proper notation for a complex ion (such as this product ion) would be [Ag(CN)₂]⁻, we have chosen to eliminate the square brackets for the sake of overall simplicity, especially in light of the fact that we will want to put this formula into square brackets to indicate its molarity in the Q expression! We will continue this notation for complex ions in this chapter.

B. Reaction Quotient Guidelines

1. The Units of the Reaction Quotient

Consideration of the Q expressions in Example 16-2 shows that the units of Q in part **a** appear to be (bar^2), while the units of Q in part b appear to be (M^{-2}). Actually, Q values should not be reported with units; <u>reaction quotient values are unitless</u>. An explanation of this circumstance will come later in your study of chemistry. If you are curious, make sure to study more chemistry! For now, simply know that all reaction quotient values should be reported without any units.

2. Pure Liquids and Pure Solids

Surprisingly, when a reaction equation includes pure liquids (ℓ) or pure solids (s), these substances *do not appear* in the reaction quotient expression. The reason for this depends on the original derivation of the Q expression and will be explained later in a physical chemistry course, or a physical chemistry unit in a general chemistry course.[119] Consider the examples shown here:

$$Mg_3\left(PO_4\right)_2(s) \rightleftharpoons 3\,Mg^{2+}(aq)+2\,PO_4^{3-}(aq) \qquad Q=\left[Mg^{2+}\right]^3\left[PO_4^{3-}\right]^2$$

$$Pb^{2+}(aq)+2\,Cl^-(aq) \rightleftharpoons PbCl_2(s) \qquad Q=\frac{1}{\left[Pb^{2+}\right]\left[Cl^-\right]^2}$$

$$Zn(s)+2\,H_3O^+(aq) \rightleftharpoons Zn^{2+}(aq)+H_2(g)+2\,H_2O(\ell) \qquad Q=\frac{\left[Zn^{2+}\right]\left(P_{H_2}\right)}{\left[H_3O^+\right]^2}$$

Notice (above) that it is possible for a reaction quotient expression to have a numerator or denominator equal to "1" if either <u>all</u> of the reactants or <u>all</u> of the products are pure solids and/or pure liquids.

Example 16-3.

Write the correct expressions for Q for each of the following reactions.

a. $CO\,(g)+2\,H_2(g) \rightleftharpoons CH_3OH(\ell)$ **b.** $Al^{3+}(aq)+6\,F^-(aq) \rightleftharpoons AlF_6^{3-}(aq)$

c. $Hg_2Cl_2(s) \rightleftharpoons Hg_2^{2+}(aq)+2\,Cl^-(aq)$ **d.** $2\,NO_2(g) \rightleftharpoons N_2O_4(g)$

Solutions:

a. $Q=\dfrac{1}{\left(P_{CO}\right)\left(P_{H_2}\right)^2}$ **b.** $Q=\dfrac{\left[AlF_6^{3-}\right]}{\left[Al^{3+}\right]\left[F^-\right]^6}$

c. $Q=\left[Hg_2^{2+}\right]\left[Cl^-\right]^2$ **d.** $Q=\dfrac{\left(P_{N_2O_4}\right)}{\left(P_{NO_2}\right)^2}$

---

[119] The reason, in a nutshell, is that pure solids and pure liquids do not have pressure-sensitive or concentration-sensitive entropies. We are not prepared to discuss that in this course!

3. Standard States

Recall that in Chapter 15 we introduced the idea that gases are said to be in their **standard state** when they are at a pressure of exactly 1 bar. This means that for a gas phase *reaction*, the reaction is said to be at standard state when each gas (reactant and product) is present at one bar of pressure. Similarly, the **standard state** of a dissolved substance is defined to exist when the dissolved substance has a concentration of exactly 1 M. Thus, an <u>aqueous</u> reaction system is in its standard state when all concentrations of dissolved species are exactly 1.0 *M.* Note well: the standard state is seldom the equilibrium state! A standard state system generates an interesting Q value. What would each Q value be in Example 16-3 (above) if each of the reactions were in the standard state?

Take time to answer the question posed above!

Do you agree that any system in its standard state has Q = 1? Because Q is the ratio of [products]/[reactants], a value of 1 implies some kind of a *balance* to the relative presence of products and reactants. The reaction quotient does not automatically equal 1 just because all species are at the same concentration or partial pressure unless that concentration/partial pressure is 1.0! For example, if all species in Example 16-3 were 0.5 M or 0.5 bar, the Q values would be 8, 64, 0.125, and 2.0, respectively.

All reactions at standard state generate Q values of exactly 1.0.

Remember: The **standard state** is different than the idea of **standard temperature and pressure (STP***)* as introduced in Chapter 15. The *standard state* for an aqueous or gas phase reaction does not indicate a temperature at all!

Exercise 16-3.

Calculate the value of Q for the following reaction under each set of conditions.

$$Cd(CN)_4^{2-}(aq) + 4H_2O(\ell) \rightleftharpoons Cd^{2+}(aq) + 4HCN(aq) + 4OH^-(aq)$$

a. All concentrations of dissolved species = 2.0 M; temp = 298 K.

b. All concentrations of dissolved species = 0.143 M; temp = 350 K.

c. The reaction under standard state conditions at a temp of 310 K.

C. Summary of Reaction Quotient Information

1. Q is a single number that gives information about how far a reaction has progressed.

2. Products in numerator, reactants in denominator:
   larger Q = more product present, smaller Q = more reactant present.

3. Use reaction coefficients as exponents.

4. Do not include pure liquids or pure solids.

5. Use molarities for solutes and bars for gases, but don't report any units for Q.

6. Reactions in their standard states (all dissolved species at 1.0 M, all gases at 1.0 bar) have Q values of 1.0.

7. For reactions starting with all reactant, Q starts at zero and increases as the reaction proceeds. For reactions starting with all product, Q starts at infinity and decreases as the reaction proceeds. Q stops changing when a reaction has reached equilibrium.

16-4. THE EQUILIBRIUM CONSTANT

Reaction quotients give us a method for describing any reaction's position at any time. Any in-progress reaction has a reaction quotient that is changing with time. Consider an aqueous reaction such as

$$A(aq) + B(aq) \rightleftharpoons C(aq)$$

that has reached equilibrium at a position that is close to completion in about ten minutes. We begin with A and B, the reactants, in separate solutions. At the instant that we pour them together no product will yet be made, so

$$Q = \frac{[C]}{[A][B]} = 0$$

After ten minutes the reaction has progressed as far as it will get. Because we defined this reaction as one that "goes nearly to completion," we can say that the concentrations of A and B have become very small, while [C] has become large; therefore Q at equilibrium is very large. At all times between the zero point and the ten minute point, the value of Q is changing and is somewhere between zero and the large final value. Once equilibrium has been established, the value of Q stops changing with time because concentrations are no longer changing.

Chemists and biochemists are interested in how far a reaction is able to get; they are interested in the final value of the reaction quotient. Final values of the reaction quotient tell us about the ability of a particular reaction to make product. If the reaction is very good at making product, the final value of Q will be very large. If the reaction is very poor at making product, the final value of Q will be close to zero.

A. Definitions

1. K_{eq} is the final value of Q

Cato Guldberg and Peter Waage, two Norwegian chemists, were the first to recognize that the *final value of the reaction quotient for a given reaction at a given temperature always has the same value*. The final value of Q does not depend on the amounts of reactants used. This statement is known as the **law of chemical equilibrium.** Because of the constant nature of this particular value of Q, it is given a new name and symbol, the **equilibrium constant, K_{eq}.** The *equilibrium constant* is the final value of Q attained by a reaction. *The value of the equilibrium constant is always the same for a given reaction at a given temperature;* if the temperature changes, the value of K_{eq} will also change. We say that the value of K_{eq} is temperature dependent.[120]

For the reaction: aA(g) + bB(aq) $\rightleftharpoons$ cC(aq) + dD(g) we can write the

equilibrium constant expression: $K_{eq} = \dfrac{[C]_{eq}^c (P_D)_{eq}^d}{(P_A)_{eq}^a [B]_{eq}^b}$

---

where the "eq" subscripts remind us that we mean the *equilibrium amounts*, not just any set of concentrations and partial pressures. A reaction in its **equilibrium position** has attained a set of equilibrium concentrations and/or partial pressures. Equilibrium constants (K_{eq}) are a special case of a reaction quotient, so the values of equilibrium constants are also unitless.

---

[120] Some reactions have larger K_{eq} values at higher temperatures, others have smaller K_{eq} values at higher temperatures. In other words, raising the temperature helps some reactions and hinders others.

2. *Different varieties of K_{eq}*

Other forms of the equilibrium constant are often introduced in high school and level one college chemistry courses. We introduce them here, for completeness.

Two slightly different versions of the equilibrium constant are symbolized as K_c and K_p. Let's explore these alternative forms of the equilibrium constant.

a. Introducing K_c

The "c" in K_c stands for *concentration*; by convention, the units of concentration that should be used are molarities. The concentrations of both solutes and gases can be given in terms of molarity. The **reaction quotient, Q_c**, is defined analogously, so that K_c is the final, equilibrium value of Q_c. We write the K_c *expression* for three reactions as follows:

$$Mg_3(PO_4)_2(s) \rightleftharpoons 3\,Mg^{2+}(aq) + 2\,PO_4^{3-}(aq) \qquad K_c = \left[Mg^{2+}\right]_{eq}^3 \left[PO_4^{3-}\right]_{eq}^2$$

$$2\,NO_2(g) \rightleftharpoons N_2O_4(g) \qquad K_c = \frac{\left[N_2O_4\right]_{eq}}{\left[NO_2\right]_{eq}^2}$$

$$Zn(s) + 2\,H_3O^+(aq) \rightleftharpoons Zn^{2+}(aq) + H_2(g) + 2\,H_2O(\ell) \qquad K_c = \frac{\left[Zn^{2+}\right]_{eq}\left[H_2\right]_{eq}}{\left[H_3O^+\right]_{eq}^2}$$

The first example, above, has a K_c expression that is identical to our original K_{eq} expression. In the other examples, which involve at least one gaseous substance, there is an important difference between K_c and K_{eq}; the gases are represented by concentration instead of partial pressure! This means that the value of K_c for this reaction will likely be different than the K_{eq} value. How can we convert a partial pressure into a molarity? Use the ideal gas law, noting that "n/V" is a molarity!

Example 16-4.

A mixture of gases is in a closed flask with a volume of 5.00 L at room temperature (298 K). One of the gases, Ne, is in its standard state.

a. What is the partial pressure of the neon gas?
b. What is concentration of the neon gas in molarity?

Solution:

a. If the neon gas is in its standard state, its partial pressure must be exactly 1 bar.

b. The ideal gas law, PV = nRT can be used to convert between pressures and concentrations. Notice that molarity equals $\frac{n}{V}$. Rearranging the ideal gas law and substituting known values gives:

$$\frac{n}{V} = \frac{P}{RT} = \frac{(1.0\ bar)}{\left(0.0831446\frac{L \cdot bar}{mol \cdot K}\right)(298K)} = 0.0404\ M$$

So the neon gas has a partial pressure of 1 bar, but a concentration of 0.0404 mol/L. Clearly, a standard state gas will not have a concentration of exactly 1 M. (Pressure and concentration will only be numerically the same if RT = 1.0; you could determine what Kelvin temperature this would entail!)

As shown in the example, above, to convert a pressure to molarity, we divide by RT. Conversely, to convert from a molarity to a pressure, we multiply by RT. It is important when working with the ideal gas law to make sure the units cancel properly. The gas law constant, R, can be depicted in a wide variety of units making conversions from pressures to molarity as simple as shown in Example 16-4 no matter what unit of pressure is offered. For instance:

$$R = 0.0831446 \frac{L \cdot bar}{mol \cdot K} = 0.0820573 \frac{L \cdot atm}{mol \cdot K} = 62.3636 \frac{L \cdot torr}{mol \cdot K} = 8314.46 \frac{L \cdot Pa}{mol \cdot K}$$

Exercise 16-4.

Show the conversion from $R = 0.082057 \dfrac{L \cdot atm}{mol \cdot K}$ to units of $\dfrac{L \cdot Pa}{mol \cdot K}$ where Pa is the abbreviation for the pressure unit "Pascal." Give your answer to 4 significant digits.

Exercise 16-5.

Convert the following gas partial pressures into molarities, and vice versa. All data were measured at room temperature (298 K).

a. 0.00454 atm (convert to molarity)   **c.** 0.044 bar (convert to molarity)

b. 804 mmHg (convert to molarity)   **d.** 0.65 M (convert to bar *and* to mmHg)

Exercise 16-6.

A flask at room temperature (298 K) is charged with a sample of NO_2 gas. The reaction to produce N_2O_4 gas is allowed to proceed for a short time and then the partial pressures of the two gases are measured: $P_{NO_2} = 0.980 \, bar$ and $P_{N_2O_4} = 0.122 \, bar$ The chemical reaction occurring is:

$$2NO_2(g) \rightleftharpoons N_2O_4(g)$$

Calculate the value of the reaction quotient, $Q_c = \dfrac{\left[N_2O_4 \right]}{\left[NO_2 \right]^2}$.

Hint: You must convert the partial pressures to concentrations!

---

b. Introducing K_p

The "p" in K_p stands for *pressure*. For a K_p equilibrium constant, only partial pressures in units of bar are allowed, so no solutes may be present, because they cannot be described in terms of pressures. The **reaction quotient, Q_p,** is defined analogously, so that K_p is the final, equilibrium value of Q_p. What happens when we try to write the **K_p expression** for our three example reaction equations?

$$Mg_3(PO_4)_2(s) \rightleftharpoons 3\,Mg^{2+}(aq) + 2\,PO_4^{3-}(aq) \qquad K_p = undefined$$

$$2\,NO_2(g) \rightleftharpoons N_2O_4(g) \qquad K_p = \frac{\left(P_{N_2O_4}\right)_{eq}}{\left(P_{NO_2}\right)_{eq}^2}$$

$$Zn(s) + 2\,H_3O^+(aq) \rightleftharpoons Zn^{2+}(aq) + H_2(g) + 2\,H_2O(\ell) \qquad K_p = undefined$$

K_p expressions can only be written for reactions that are either entirely in the gas phase, or involve only gases, pure solids or pure liquids. A dissolved species cannot be represented by a partial pressure! The presence of one or more solutes makes a K_p expression impossible.

c. Mathematical Relationship Between K_c and K_p

For reactions that can be represented by a K_p expression (such as the second example, above), the K_p expression is identical to the K_{eq} expression. But what is the relationship between a K_p value and a K_c value? That depends; what we do know is that we can use the ideal gas law to convert any pressure into a concentration, or vice versa. Check out the examples of conversions from K_p to K_c in the box, below. All of the pressures and concentrations are equilibrium position values, but we have omitted the "eq" subscripts in order to simplify the notations a bit.

FIRST CASE: $2NO_2(g) \rightleftharpoons N_2O_4(g)$

$$K_p = \frac{\left(P_{N_2O_4}\right)}{\left(P_{NO_2}\right)^2} = \frac{\left(P_{N_2O_4}\right)}{\left(P_{NO_2}\right)\left(P_{NO_2}\right)} = \frac{\left([N_2O_4] \times RT\right)}{\left([NO_2] \times RT\right)\left([NO_2] \times RT\right)} = \frac{[N_2O_4]}{[NO_2]^2} \times \frac{1}{RT} = \frac{K_c}{RT}$$

Result: $\qquad K_p = \dfrac{K_c}{RT}$

SECOND CASE: $H_2(g) + Cl_2(g) \rightleftharpoons 2HCl(g)$

$$K_p = \frac{\left(P_{HCl}\right)^2}{\left(P_{H_2}\right)\left(P_{Cl_2}\right)} = \frac{\left(P_{HCl}\right)\left(P_{HCl}\right)}{\left(P_{H_2}\right)\left(P_{Cl_2}\right)} = \frac{\left([HCl] \times RT\right)\left([HCl] \times RT\right)}{\left([H_2] \times RT\right)\left([Cl_2] \times RT\right)} = \frac{[HCl]^2}{[H_2][Cl_2]} \times \frac{(RT)^2}{(RT)^2} = K_c$$

Result: $\qquad K_p = K_c$

THIRD CASE: $2NH_3(g) \rightleftharpoons 3H_2(g) + N_2(g)$

$$K_p = \frac{\left(P_{H_2}\right)^3\left(P_{N_2}\right)}{\left(P_{NH_3}\right)^2} = \frac{\left(P_{H_2}\right)\left(P_{H_2}\right)\left(P_{H_2}\right)\left(P_{N_2}\right)}{\left(P_{NH_3}\right)\left(P_{NH_3}\right)} =$$

$$\frac{\left([H_2] \times RT\right)\left([H_2] \times RT\right)\left([H_2] \times RT\right)\left([N_2] \times RT\right)}{\left([NH_3] \times RT\right)\left([NH_3] \times RT\right)} = \frac{[H_2]^3[N_2]}{[NH_3]^2} \times \frac{(RT)^2}{1} = K_c \times (RT)^2$$

Result: $\qquad K_p = K_c \times (RT)^2$

In these three examples, K_p and K_c are only equivalent for the second case. The necessary circumstance for K_p to equal K_c is that the RT factors in numerator and denominator must cancel.

What must be true of the balanced chemical reaction for the RT factors to cancel?
*The __number of moles__ **of gas** on each side of the reaction arrow must be identical.*

Example 16-5.

Determine which of the following reactions can be described by K_c (only), K_p (only), or both K_c and K_p.

a. $CaCO_3(s) + H_2O(\ell) + CO_2(g) \rightleftharpoons Ca^{2+}(aq) + 2HCO_3^-(aq)$

b. $Fe_2O_3(s) + 3H_2(g) \rightleftharpoons 2Fe(s) + 3H_2O(g)$

c. $2CH_4(g) + 2NH_3(g) + 3O_2(g) \rightleftharpoons 2HCN(g) + 6H_2O(g)$

d. $2\,H_2O_2(aq) \xrightleftharpoons{\text{catalase enzyme}} 2\,H_2O(\ell) + O_2(aq)$

Solutions:

a. This reaction has pure solids and pure liquids which do not enter in to the K expressions. This reaction has both gases and aqueous substances. Because the aqueous substance can only be described by a concentration, only K_c can be used.

b. All species are either gases or pure solids. The solids do not enter in to the K expressions. The gases can be described by concentration or pressure. Either K_c or K_p could be used.

c. All species are in the gas phase. Gases can be described by concentration or pressure. Either K_c or K_p could be used.

d. This reaction is the principle method by which living systems protect against the highly reactive hydrogen peroxide molecule. Only K_c can be used; K_p is undefined.

Exercise 16-7.

Which of the reactions from Example 16-5 (above) have a K_c value equal to the mixed unit K_{eq} value? Which have a K_p value equal to the mixed unit K_{eq} value?

In this book, Q_c, K_c, Q_p and K_p will always be notated with the "c" or "p" subscript. If you see "K_{eq}" or "Q", use our original, mixed unit definition of the ratio.

Example 16-6.

The **equilibrium position** (concentrations or partial pressures) for particular reactions at particular temperatures are given. In each case determine the value of the equilibrium constant, K_{eq}.

a. $H_2(g) + I_2(g) \rightleftharpoons 2HI(g)$ at $699\,K$

$$\left(P_{H_2}\right)_{eq} = 0.12 \text{ bar} \quad \left(P_{I_2}\right)_{eq} = 0.13 \text{ bar} \quad \left(P_{HI}\right)_{eq} = 0.94 \text{ bar}$$

b. $2\,SO_2(g) + O_2(g) \rightleftharpoons 2\,SO_3(g)$ at $1000\,K$

$$\left[SO_2\right]_{eq} = 0.0799 \text{ M} \quad \left[O_2\right]_{eq} = 0.0265 \text{ M} \quad \left[SO_3\right]_{eq} = 0.204 \text{ M}$$

c. $\left(NH_4\right)_2 S(aq) + 2HCl(aq) \rightleftharpoons H_2S(g) + 2NH_4Cl(aq)$ at 305 K

$\left[\left(NH_4\right)_2 S\right]_{eq} = 0.040\ M$ $\left[HCl\right]_{eq} = 0.0044\ M$ $\left[NH_4Cl\right]_{eq} = 0.31\ M$ $\left(P_{H_2S}\right)_{eq} = 0.50\ bar$

Solutions:

a. $K_{eq} = \dfrac{\left(P_{HI}\right)_{eq}^2}{\left(P_{H_2}\right)_{eq}\left(P_{I_2}\right)_{eq}} = \dfrac{(0.94)^2}{(0.12)(0.13)} = 57$

(This is also the value for K_p for this reaction at 699 K, and $K_p = K_c$ because there are 2 moles of gas on each side of the reaction equation.)

b. We must convert these concentrations into partial pressures

$$P_{SO_3} = \left(0.204\,\frac{mol}{L}\right) \times \left(0.08314\,\frac{L \cdot bar}{mol \cdot K}\right) \times \left(1000\ K\right) = 19.96\ bar$$

$$P_{SO_2} = \left(0.0799\,\frac{mol}{L}\right) \times \left(0.08314\,\frac{L \cdot bar}{mol \cdot K}\right) \times \left(1000\ K\right) = 6.643\ bar$$

$$P_{O_2} = \left(0.0265\,\frac{mol}{L}\right) \times \left(0.08314\,\frac{L \cdot bar}{mol \cdot K}\right) \times \left(1000\ K\right) = 2.203\ bar$$

$$K_{eq} = \frac{\left(P_{SO_3}\right)_{eq}^2}{\left(P_{SO_2}\right)_{eq}^2\left(P_{O_2}\right)_{eq}} = \frac{(19.96)^2}{(6.643)^2(2.203)} = 410.$$

c. $K_{eq} = \dfrac{\left(P_{H_2S}\right)_{eq}\left[NH_4Cl\right]_{eq}^2}{\left[\left(NH_4\right)_2 S\right]_{eq}\left[HCl\right]_{eq}^2} = \dfrac{(0.50)(0.31)^2}{(0.040)(0.0044)^2} = 6.2 \times 10^4$

Example 16-7.

$$2NO_2(g) \rightleftharpoons N_2O_4(g)$$

The reaction of NO_2 to produce N_2O_4 was followed by measuring the partial pressures of each species present at various regularly spaced times at 303 K. The data are presented here:

time point	P_{NO_2} (bar)	$P_{N_2O_4}$ (bar)
0	1.000	0.000
1	0.613	0.194
2	0.472	0.264
3	0.300	0.350
4	0.276	0.362
5	0.276	0.362
6	0.276	0.362

Determine the value of Q for each data point. Do these data let you determine the value of K_{eq}? If so, what is the value of K_{eq}? If not, why not?

<u>Solution</u>:

Each value of Q can be determined by substituting the measured concentrations into the

Q expression: $Q = \dfrac{P_{N_2O_4}}{\left(P_{NO_2}\right)^2}$. These values are entered into the table, below, right. We expect

that the last three measurements represent the attainment of equilibrium because the concentrations of species are no longer changing with time. The value of K_{eq}, then, is 4.75. Check out the results, graphically, below.

time point	P_{NO_2} (bar)	$P_{N_2O_4}$ (bar)	Q_P value
0	1.000	0.000	0.00
1	0.613	0.194	0.52
2	0.472	0.264	1.19
3	0.300	0.350	3.89
4	0.276	0.362	4.75
5	0.276	0.362	4.75
6	0.276	0.362	4.75

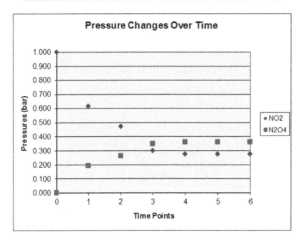

B. Temperature Dependence of K_{eq}

The value of K_{eq} depends on the temperature of the reaction system. Some reactions have large ranges of possible K_{eq} values and others have more modest ranges. Graphs of K_{eq} vs. temperature for particular reactions have one of two general shapes; see Figure 16-6. We might call these two shapes the downward swoosh (purple) and the upward swoosh (green). Either one can be a steeper or shallower swoosh. The unifying characteristic is that all of these curves flatten as the the temperature goes up. The purple curve starts with a negative slope while the green curve starts with a positive slope.

If you look back at the photos of the

$2NO_2(g) \rightleftharpoons N_2O_4(g)$ system in Figure 16-4 you see

three different "Q" values. Actually these are three different K_{eq} values, because this reaction is much too fast

Figure 16-6. The general shapes possible for K_{eq} vs. temperature plots for chemical reactions. In these examples, the purple reaction has a wider range of K_{eq} possibilities.

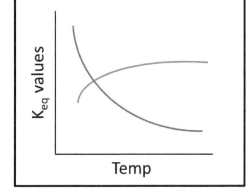

to catch it in the process of attaining equilibrium. From left to right in Figure 16-4, the temperatures of the flask are 320 K, 295 K, and 273 K.

Exercise 16-8.

Consider the $2NO_2(g) \rightleftharpoons N_2O_4(g)$ system shown in Figure 16-4 and having the temperature profile indicated above. Does this reaction's K_{eq} vs. T "swoosh" display a positive or negative slope?

C. Comparing Q Values to K_{eq} Values

Once we know the K_{eq} value for a particular reaction at a particular temperature, we can use this information to determine whether or not any specific mixture of the reactants and products has achieved equilibrium (as long as it is at the same temperature as the known K_{eq} value). Knowing a Q value is not terribly enlightening unless you also know the K_{eq} value, so that they can be compared. If the reaction quotient for the mixture has the same value as the equilibrium constant (if Q = K), then the mixture is at equilibrium. We must remember to compare Q_c's to K_c's and Q_p's to K_p's, and Q's to K_{eq}. If we determine that Q and K_{eq} are not equivalent, then we know that the reaction has not reached an equilibrium position. More reaction will occur.

If a reaction is not at equilibrium, we can determine which reaction (forward or reverse) must occur in order to reach equilibrium. Remember that in general terms, $Q = \dfrac{[\text{products}]}{[\text{reactants}]}$. We can logically conclude that if Q is less than K_{eq}, too few products exist (and too much reactant) and the forward reaction must occur. If Q is larger than K_{eq}, too many products exist and the reverse reaction must occur in order to achieve equilibrium.

Comparing Q and K_{eq}	
$Q < K_{eq}$	forward reaction will occur
$Q > K_{eq}$	reverse reaction will occur
$Q = K_{eq}$	system is at equilibrium

A reversible reaction that begins with the presence of only reactants cannot achieve a *Q* larger than K_{eq}. The reaction will not "go too far" and then have to back up. Instead, it will stop progressing when Q = K_{eq} (notice the data in Example 16-7). However, one might wish to consider a reaction from many different starting points. For instance, the reaction system

$$2NO_2(g) \rightleftharpoons N_2O_4(g) \qquad \text{with } K_{eq} = 4.75 \text{ at } 303 \text{ K}$$

might be studied by starting with a flask charged only with N_2O_4. In this case, the Q for the starting position of the reaction would be infinite. The Q's for this reaction would decrease with time until equilibrium was achieved. In this case, at any time before equilibrium is established *Q will be larger than K_{eq}* and the reaction occurring in the flask will be the *reverse reaction*, as written.

Example 16-8.

In Example 16-7 we determined that $K_{eq} = 4.75$ for $2NO_2(g) \rightleftharpoons N_2O_4(g)$ at 303 K.

Determine whether or not the mixture of gases described below has reached equilibrium. If it has not reached equilibrium, which reaction needs to occur, the forward reaction, or the reverse reaction?

$$P_{NO_2} = 0.19\,bar \text{ and } P_{N_2O_4} = 1.95\,bar \text{ at 303 K.}$$

Solution:

First we calculate the Q value for the mixture of gases: $Q = \dfrac{P_{N_2O_4}}{\left(P_{NO_2}\right)^2} = \dfrac{1.95}{\left(0.19\right)^2} = 54$.

Second, we compare the values of Q and K_{eq}. Here Q (54) > K_{eq} (4.75). The reaction is not at equilibrium. If Q > K_{eq}, then the numerator of the Q expression is too large and the denominator is too small. We can logically determine that the reaction would need to proceed in the <u>reverse direction,</u> producing more NO_2 (in the denominator) and using up some N_2O_4 (from the numerator).

A method to visualize a reaction approaching equilibrium is to place all possible Q values for a particular reaction *at a particular temperature* on a horizontal number line, as shown below. We will call the number line that shows these Q values the **Q axis**. Because Q is essentially a ratio of [products] / [reactants], we label the standard state (Q = 1) and then show Q values that represent more reactant than product on the left, Q < 1, and those that represent the more product than reactant on the right, Q > 1.

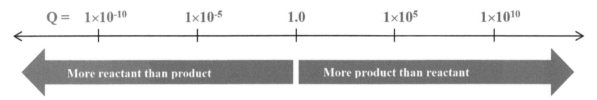

A word of caution: Because of the huge range of possible Q values, the scale of the Q values on this number line is *logarithmic* in nature, with equal divisions for each power of ten. If it were a linear scale, Q = 0 would be very, very close to Q = 1. Where is Q = 0 on this number line? It is to the left, but will never be reached! Consider the distance between Q = 1 and Q = 2, compared to Q = 0 and Q = 1! Values are much more spread out on the left and much more condensed on the right.

There is ONE point on the Q axis that is the K_{eq} value for a reaction being studied *at a particular temperature*. Consider the reaction

$$ClNO_2(g) + NO(g) \rightleftharpoons NO_2(g) + ClNO(g)$$

with $K_{eq} = 1.3 \times 10^4$ at 298 K. Let's label the Q axis with the reaction being studied and the temperature of that study. We'll add the K_{eq} value to the plot (we won't worry about being exactly "to scale"):

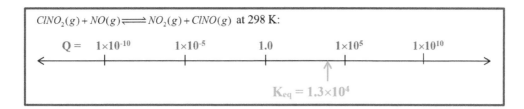

The marked K_{eq} value is the "goal" of the reaction, no matter what the initial Q value might be. If Q begins at 1×10^{-2}, the forward reaction will occur. Q will increase, move past the standard state, and come to rest at 1.3×10^4, see purple arrow on number line:

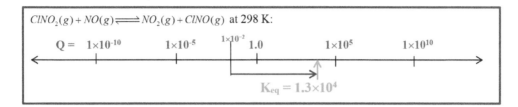

If Q begins at 1×10^9, the reverse reaction will occur until Q decreases to 1.3×10^4.

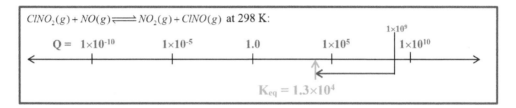

In this case, the reaction will never exist in its standard state; reactions do not move past the equilibrium point and then have to turn back around to reach equilibrium. Reactions only proceed in one direction, and that direction is dictated by the initial Q value.

Exercise 16-9.

    a. Draw the Q axis graph with an arrow that shows the reaction that occurs for $ClNO_2(g) + NO(g) \rightleftharpoons NO_2(g) + ClNO(g)$ at 298 K if the reaction starts in its standard state.

    b. Repeat part a for the same reaction at the same temperature but the following initial reaction position: 1.50 bar $ClNO_2$, 1.62 bar NO, 0.010 bar NO_2, and 0.025 bar ClNO. Always include the landmark of Q = 1 on your Q axis. Why? Because Q = 1 is the changeover point from more reactants present to more products present.

We might be tempted to think that the length of the purple arrow shows us "how much" reaction is needed to achieve equilibrium, but this idea is complicated by the logarithmic layout of the Q-axis values. Any arrow on the left side of the plot is much longer on a mole basis than any arrow on the right side of the plot (see the answer to Exercise 16-8). We use the arrows to see directionality from an initial point to an end point; for now we just want to know if the forward reaction or reverse reaction will occur.

Exercise 16-10.

For each of the following cases, determine whether the forward or reverse reaction must occur in order to achieve equilibrium. Sketch a Q axis for each problem below and place Q = 1 in the center. Show the Q and K_{eq} value for the scenario and draw the arrow that shows the reaction that must occur.

a. $2NO_2(g) \rightleftharpoons N_2O_4(g)$ with K_{eq} (at 298 K) = 6.8; $P_{NO_2} = 0.45 \, bar$, $P_{N_2O_4} = 0.13 \, bar$.

b. $N_2(g) + 3H_2(g) \rightleftharpoons 2NH_3(g)$ with K_c (at 500 °C) = 0.060
$[N_2] = 0.221 \, M$, $[H_2] = 0.342 \, M$ and $[NH_3] = 0.129 \, M$.

Exercise 16-11.

What happens on a Q axis if the initial reaction position turns out to be the equilibrium reaction position?

D. Equilibrium Constants and Equilibrium Positions

An **equilibrium constant** and an **equilibrium position** are two different (but related) bits of information. It is important to be able to distinguish what is constant and what is not.

Consider the data presented in Table 16-1 for the reaction: $2\,NO_2(g) \rightleftharpoons N_2(g) + 2\,O_2(g)$.

Each experiment starts with a particular mixture of gases that may include reactants and/or products, the reaction's "initial position." The reaction is run at a temperature at which the value of K_{eq} is 43. Enough time is allowed to ensure that equilibrium has been reached and the resulting equilibrium concentrations are determined.

Table 16-1 includes some expected results and some surprises. Let's start with things that probably don't seem surprising. The value of the equilibrium constant for each experiment is identical. Each of these experiments considers the same reaction at the same temperature, so we expect the K_{eq}'s to be equal. That is the essence of the **law of chemical equilibrium**. You should do the math for each and see that some rounding does occur. We only know equilibrium constant value to a few significant figures, usually.

Table 16-1	$2\,NO_2(g) \rightleftharpoons N_2(g) + 2\,O_2(g)$		
Experiment Number	Initial Position (bar)	Equilibrium Position (bar)	$K_{eq} = \dfrac{(P_{N_2})_{eq}(P_{O_2})_{eq}^2}{(P_{NO_2})_{eq}^2}$
1	$(P_{NO_2})_o = 2.00$ $(P_{N_2})_o = 0.00$ $(P_{O_2})_o = 0.00$	$(P_{NO_2})_{eq} = 0.250$ $(P_{N_2})_{eq} = 0.875$ $(P_{O_2})_{eq} = 1.75$	$K_{eq} = 43$
2	$(P_{NO_2})_o = 4.00$ $(P_{N_2})_o = 0.00$ $(P_{O_2})_o = 0.00$	$(P_{NO_2})_{eq} = 0.659$ $(P_{N_2})_{eq} = 1.671$ $(P_{O_2})_{eq} = 3.341$	$K_{eq} = 43$
3	$(P_{NO_2})_o = 1.00$ $(P_{N_2})_o = 0.00$ $(P_{O_2})_o = 0.00$	$(P_{NO_2})_{eq} = 0.0931$ $(P_{N_2})_{eq} = 0.453$ $(P_{O_2})_{eq} = 0.907$	$K_{eq} = 43$
4	$(P_{NO_2})_o = 0.00$ $(P_{N_2})_o = 0.50$ $(P_{O_2})_o = 1.00$	$(P_{NO_2})_{eq} = 0.0931$ $(P_{N_2})_{eq} = 0.453$ $(P_{O_2})_{eq} = 0.907$	$K_{eq} = 43$

Now, on to some more surprising results. First, the equilibrium positions of these reactions are not always the same. Only experiments 3 and 4 have identical equilibrium positions. This may seem odd. Second, and even more surprising, although the initial concentrations in experiment 2 are exactly double the initial concentrations in experiment 1, the equilibrium concentrations for Exp. 2 are not double those of Exp. 1. It seems that finding the equilibrium position of a reaction is less straightforward than we might have anticipated.

1. Systems with Identical Equilibrium Positions

Let's take the surprises one at a time. First, why do experiments 3 and 4 have identical equilibrium positions? We compare the initial positions in a way that disregards the bonding. We think in terms of the partial pressures of each gas that would be present *if there were no bonds at all.* Consider having a 1.00 bar pressure of NO_2 in a particular container. If the bonds were broken, every particle of NO_2 would yield one particle of N and two particles of O. In the same container at the same temperature, we would have 1.00 bar of N (gas) and 2.00 bar of O (gas). The total pressure goes from 1.00 bar to 3.00 bar because the number of gas particles triples. This is the type of reasoning used in Table 16-2.

Only in Experiments 3 and 4 do the reaction systems contain identical amounts of N and O atoms. With the same distribution of atoms, one obtains

	Table 16-2 $2NO_2(g) \rightleftharpoons N_2(g) + 2O_2(g)$	
Experiment Number	Initial Position Molecules (bar)	Initial Position Atoms (bar)
1	$(P_{NO_2})_o = 2.00$ $(P_{N_2})_o = 0.00$ $(P_{O_2})_o = 0.00$	$(P_N)_o = 2.00$ $(P_O)_o = 4.00$
2	$(P_{NO_2})_o = 4.00$ $(P_{N_2})_o = 0.00$ $(P_{O_2})_o = 0.00$	$(P_N)_o = 4.00$ $(P_O)_o = 8.00$
3	$(P_{NO_2})_o = 1.00$ $(P_{N_2})_o = 0.00$ $(P_{O_2})_o = 0.00$	$(P_N)_o = 1.00$ $(P_O)_o = 2.00$
4	$(P_{NO_2})_o = 0.00$ $(P_{N_2})_o = 0.50$ $(P_{O_2})_o = 1.00$	$(P_N)_o = 1.00$ $(P_O)_o = 2.00$

identical equilibrium positions; there is <u>one</u> most probable bonding pattern for those atoms. Experiments 1 and 2 start out with different amounts of material, on an atom by atom basis, and so cannot achieve the same equilibrium position as Experiments 3 and 4.

Example 16-9.

For Experiment 1 (Table 16-1), rationalize that the *equilibrium position* contains the same atom partial pressures as the initial position.

Solution:

Exp 1 equilibrium position: $P_{NO_2} = 0.250\ bar, P_{N_2} = 0.875\ bar, P_{O_2} = 1.75\ bar$

$P_{NO_2} = 0.250\ bar$ contributes 0.250 bar N atoms and 0.500 bar O atoms

$P_{N_2} = 0.875\ bar$ contributes 1.75 bar N atoms

$P_{O_2} = 1.75\ bar$ contributes 3.50 bar O atoms

Partial pressures are additive, so a total of 0.250 + 1.75 = 2.00 bar N atoms
And a total of 0.500 + 3.50 = 4.00 bar O atoms.

These values agree with the initial position for Experiment 1 shown in Table 16-2.

Exercise 16-12.

Rationalize that the following *initial* partial pressures are actually the same starting position on an atom by atom basis as in Experiment 1 of Table 16-1.

P_{NO_2} = 1.00 bar P_{N_2} = 0.50 bar P_{O_2} = 1.00 bar

Example 16-10.

Consider the reaction $2\,NO(g)+O_2(g)\rightleftharpoons 2\,NO_2(g)$

a. If the initial position is:

$(P_{NO})_0$ = 0.300 *bar*
$(P_{O_2})_0$ = 0.100 *bar*
$(P_{NO_2})_0$ = 0.100 *bar*

What would be the partial pressures of N atoms and O atoms in the absence of any bonds?

b. Do you expect the following initial position to give the same or different equilibrium position from that in part **a**? $(P_{NO})_0$ = 0.400 *M*; $(P_{O_2})_0$ = 0.150 *M*; $(P_{NO_2})_0$ = 0 *M*

Solutions:

a. 0.300 *bar* NO contributes 0.300 *bar* N atoms and 0.300 *bar* O atoms
0.100 *bar* O_2 contributes 0.200 *bar* O atoms
0.100 *bar* NO_2 contributes 0.100 *bar* N atoms and 0.200 *bar* O atoms

Summing all N pressures: 0.300 + 0.100 = 0.400 *bar* N atoms
Summing all O pressures: 0.300 + 0.200 + 0.200 = 0.700 *bar* O atoms

b. 0.400 *bar* NO contributes 0.400 *bar* N atoms and 0.400 *bar* O atoms
0.150 *bar* O_2 contributes 0.300 *bar* O atoms

Summing all N pressures: 0.400 *bar* N atoms
Summing all O pressures: 0.400 + 0.300 = 0.700 *bar* O atoms

This reaction starts with the same numbers of atoms, so it will achieve the same equilibrium position.

---

2. Effect on Equilibrium Position when the System is Doubled in Size

The second surprise (the fact that although the initial concentrations in experiment 2 are exactly double the initial concentrations in experiment 1, the equilibrium concentrations are not a factor of 2 different from one another) is more difficult to explain. Our gut reaction tells us that a system that starts with doubled concentrations ought to end up with doubled concentrations. But this is not always the case.

Consider a very simple reaction of the form $A(g)\rightleftharpoons B(g)$ with K_{eq} = 3. We construct Table 16-3 for this reaction. Note the similarity to the Table 16-1.

Table 16-3	$A(g) \rightleftharpoons B(g)$		
Experiment Number	Initial Position (bar)	Equilibrium Position (bar)	$K_{eq} = \dfrac{(P_B)_{eq}}{(P_A)_{eq}}$
1	$(P_A)_o = 1.000$ $(P_B)_o = 0$	$(P_A)_{eq} = 0.250$ $(P_B)_{eq} = 0.750$	$\dfrac{(P_B)_{eq}}{(P_A)_{eq}} = \dfrac{0.750}{0.250} = 3$
2	$(P_A)_o = 2.000$ $(P_B)_o = 0$	$(P_A)_{eq} = 0.500$ $(P_B)_{eq} = 1.500$	$\dfrac{(P_B)_{eq}}{(P_A)_{eq}} = \dfrac{1.500}{0.500} = 3$

Here, Experiment 2 begins with twice the starting material as Experiment 1, and the equilibrium partial pressures for Experiment 2 are also double those for Experiment 1. This reaction behaves differently than the reaction in Table 16-1. Our initial expectation is upheld: doubling the starting amount, doubles the equilibrium amounts.

Now we move to a slightly more complex reaction: $A(g) \rightleftharpoons 2B(g)$ with $K_c = 9$. Table 16-4 considers two experiments involving this reaction.

Table 16-4	$A(g) \rightleftharpoons 2B(g)$		
Experiment Number	Initial Position (bar)	Equilibrium Position (bar)	$K_{eq} = \dfrac{(P_B)_{eq}^2}{(P_A)_{eq}}$
1	$(P_A)_o = 1.000$ $(P_B)_o = 0$	$(P_A)_{eq} = 0.250$ $(P_B)_{eq} = 0.750$	$\dfrac{(P_B)_{eq}^2}{(P_A)_{eq}} = \dfrac{(1.500)^2}{0.250} = 9.0$
2	$(P_A)_o = 2.000$ $(P_B)_o = 0$	$(P_A)_{eq} = 0.724$ $(P_B)_{eq} = 2.552$	$\dfrac{(P_B)_{eq}^2}{(P_A)_{eq}} = \dfrac{(2.552)^2}{0.724} = 9.0$

Here is a circumstance similar to the reaction in Table 16-1, where doubling the initial concentrations does not lead to doubling of the equilibrium concentrations.

> We could do many more examples and in the end we would see that *the difference is whether or not the reaction equation contains the same number of gas particles on each side of the arrow.*

In other words, if the sum of exponents in the numerator of any K_{eq} expression is equal to the sum of the exponents in the denominator, then doubling the initial concentrations will result in doubling of the equilibrium concentrations. Different numbers of particles in reactant and product cause the mathematics of the associated exponents to complicate the result. With this in mind we can now predict that a reaction such as

$$2\,NO(g) + O_2(g) \rightleftharpoons 2\,NO_2(g)$$

should not behave in a simplistic way with respect to doubling reactant amounts because there are three particles on the reactant side and only two on the product side. It is no surprise, now, that the equilibrium concentrations of Experiment 2 are not double those of Experiment 1 in Table 16-1! Note that particles of pure liquids and pure solids do not influence this analysis because they do not appear in the equilibrium constant expression.

Exercise 16-13.

Which of the following reaction types results in a circumstance where doubling the initial partial pressures doubles the equilibrium partial pressures?

a. $A(g) + 2B(g) \rightleftharpoons 3C(g)$

b. $3A(g) \rightleftharpoons 2B(g)$

c. $A(s) + 2B(g) \rightleftharpoons 3C(g)$

d. $A(g) + 2B(g) \rightleftharpoons 2C(g) + D(g)$

e. $A(g) + 2B(s) \rightleftharpoons C(g)$

Exercise 16-14.

We can generalize the results found above to reactions that are aqueous rather than gaseous. Which of the following reactions are of a type that results in a circumstance where doubling the initial concentrations doubles the equilibrium concentrations?

a. $A(s) + 2B(aq) \rightleftharpoons 3C(aq)$

b. $3A(aq) \rightleftharpoons 2B(aq) + C(aq)$

c. $A(aq) + B(aq) \rightleftharpoons 2C(aq)$

d. $A(aq) + 2B(aq) \rightleftharpoons 2C(aq) + D(s)$

e. $A(aq) + 2B(s) \rightleftharpoons C(aq)$

E. K$_{eq}$ Values for Related Reactions

Reactions that are related to one another have equilibrium constants that are also related to one another. We explore three examples of related reactions and their equilibrium constants.

1. Forward and Reverse Reactions

Any reversible reaction system can be described by either of two reaction equations. In the case of the nitrogen/hydrogen/ammonia system, we could describe the system either as the synthesis of ammonia:

$$N_2(g) + 3H_2(g) \rightleftharpoons 2NH_3(g)$$

or as the breakdown of ammonia:

$$2NH_3(g) \rightleftharpoons N_2(g) + 3H_2(g)$$

The K$_{eq}$ values for these two representations of the same system are not equivalent, but they are related. Remember that the mathematical expression is based on "products" and "reactants" and these are defined based on the left-hand and right-hand sides of the reaction arrow. We could write:

$$N_2(g) + 3H_2(g) \rightleftharpoons 2NH_3(g) \qquad K_{eq} = \frac{\left(P_{NH_3}\right)_{eq}^2}{\left(P_{N_2}\right)_{eq}\left(P_{H_2}\right)_{eq}^3}$$

$$2NH_3(g) \rightleftharpoons N_2(g) + 3H_2(g) \qquad K_{eq} = \frac{\left(P_{N_2}\right)_{eq}\left(P_{H_2}\right)_{eq}^3}{\left(P_{NH_3}\right)_{eq}^2}$$

The values of these two equilibrium constants are reciprocals. *This means that if you know the value of the equilibrium constant for __any__ reaction, you will automatically also know the value of the equilibrium constant for the reverse reaction.* The ammonia-producing reaction at 700 K has the equilibrium constant value of 3.1×10^{-4}; the equilibrium constant for the breakdown of ammonia to its elements *at the same temperature* can be determined:

$$N_2(g) + 3H_2(g) \rightleftharpoons 2NH_3(g) \qquad K_{eq} = 3.1 \times 10^{-4}$$

$$2NH_3(g) \rightleftharpoons N_2(g) + 3H_2(g) \qquad K_{eq} = \frac{1}{3.1 \times 10^{-4}} = 3200$$

It is important to recognize that either of these K_{eq} values gives the chemist the same information about the reaction system:

- the K_{eq} value of 3.1×10^{-4} for ammonia production tells us that the reactants (N_2 and H_2) are favored; it is difficult to produce ammonia from its elements; and
- the K_{eq} value of 3200 for the breakdown of ammonia tells us that the products (N_2 and H_2) are favored; again, it is difficult to produce ammonia from its elements.

Because lead(II) carbonate is essentially insoluble, the reaction below goes essentially to completion and has a large value of K_{eq}:

$$Pb^{2+}(aq) + CO_3^{2-}(aq) \rightleftharpoons PbCO_3(s) \qquad K_{eq} = 8.3 \times 10^{12}$$

What does this tell you about the nature of the reverse reaction? The reverse reaction will have a K_{eq} value that is the reciprocal of this large number

$$PbCO_3(s) \rightleftharpoons Pb^{2+}(aq) + CO_3^{2-}(aq) \quad K_{eq} = \frac{1}{8.3 \times 10^{12}} = 1.2 \times 10^{-13}$$

This is a reaction that is almost unable to proceed at all. Notice that this K_{eq} value tells you that lead(II) carbonate is essentially insoluble!

It is impossible for both a forward reaction and reverse reaction to proceed well;[121]
if Pb^{2+} (aq) and CO_3^{2-} (aq) are good at producing the precipitate $PbCO_3$,
then solid $PbCO_3$ cannot be good at dissolving!

2. Systems Incorporating Multiple Interacting Equilibria

Some complex reaction systems can be viewed as multiple reactions happening in the same container. We call them **interacting equilibria** when they involve at least one of the same chemical species, for instance, if Ag^+ were a reactant for one reaction and a product for the other. As an illustration of this type of system, we will study how the addition of ammonia, NH_3, causes an increase in the solubility of silver chloride. Silver chloride, AgCl, is often said to be "insoluble;" meaning "essentially insoluble!" All salts dissolve to at least some tiny extent. For silver chloride we can write:

$$AgCl(s) \rightleftharpoons Ag^+(aq) + Cl^-(aq) \qquad K_{eq} = [Ag^+][Cl^-] = 1.8 \times 10^{-10}$$

Note the very small value of K_{eq} for the process of dissolving silver chloride. The concentration of each ion in a saturated solution must be very small (about 1.3×10^{-5} M).[122]

Adding ammonia to the water increases the solubility of AgCl. The silver ion that is a product, above, reacts with the ammonia molecule to form a complex ion as follows:

$$Ag^+(aq) + 2NH_3(aq) \rightleftharpoons Ag(NH_3)_2^+(aq)$$

---

[121] At some particular temperature.
[122] If each ion were present at $1.34 \times 10^{-5} M$, Q = K_{eq} = $[Ag^+][Cl^-]$ = $(1.34 \times 10^{-5})(1.34 \times 10^{-5})$ = 1.8×10^{-10} .

If we try to dissolve silver chloride in an ammonia-containing solution we will establish both of these *interacting equilibria*:

$$AgCl(s) \rightleftharpoons Ag^+(aq) + Cl^-(aq)$$

$$Ag^+(aq) + 2NH_3(aq) \rightleftharpoons Ag(NH_3)_2^+(aq)$$

We can consider the entire system by adding the individual reactions together to achieve an overall view of the chemical system (see box below). When adding reactions together, be sure that all reactants stay on the reactant side of the arrow and all products stay on the product side of the arrow. The summed reaction equation can be simplified by removing any species that appears as both a reactant and a product, such as the $Ag^+(aq)$, below.

---

1. $\quad AgCl(s) \rightleftharpoons Ag^+(aq) + Cl^-(aq) \qquad\qquad K_{(1)} = \left[Ag^+\right]_{eq}\left[Cl^-\right]_{eq}$

2. $\quad Ag^+(aq) + 2NH_3(aq) \rightleftharpoons Ag(NH_3)_2^+(aq) \qquad K_{(2)} = \dfrac{\left[Ag(NH_3)_2^+\right]_{eq}}{\left[Ag^+\right]_{eq}\left[NH_3\right]_{eq}^2}$

$$AgCl(s) + \cancel{Ag^+(aq)} + 2NH_3(aq) \rightleftharpoons \cancel{Ag^+(aq)} + Cl^-(aq) + Ag(NH_3)_2^+(aq)$$

$sum: AgCl(s) + 2NH_3(aq) \rightleftharpoons Ag(NH_3)_2^+(aq) + Cl^-(aq) \qquad K_{(sum)} = \dfrac{\left[Ag(NH_3)_2^+\right]_{eq}\left[Cl^-\right]_{eq}}{\left[NH_3\right]_{eq}^2}$

The summed reaction represents the process of dissolving silver chloride in aqueous ammonia. For us, the important result is that:

$K_{(sum)}$, is equal to the <u>product</u> of the equilibrium constant expressions for the two reaction steps:

$$K_{(1)} \quad\times\quad K_{(2)} \quad=\quad K_{(sum)}$$

$$\cancel{\left[Ag^+\right]_{eq}}\left[Cl^-\right]_{eq} \times \frac{\left[Ag(NH_3)_2^+\right]_{eq}}{\cancel{\left[Ag^+\right]_{eq}}\left[NH_3\right]_{eq}^2} = \frac{\left[Ag(NH_3)_2^+\right]_{eq}\left[Cl^-\right]_{eq}}{\left[NH_3\right]_{eq}^2}$$

Whenever two or more reactions can be added to give an overall reaction, the equilibrium constants of the individual reactions can be multiplied to give the equilibrium constant of the overall reaction.

This is a direct result of the definition of the equilibrium constant expression. Mathematically, any species occurring on both sides of the reaction arrow (and hence canceling from the overall reaction) will also be found in both the numerator and the denominator of equilibrium constant expressions and so will cancel there as well.

Now, while $K_{(1)}$ has a very small value (1.8×10^{-10}, in keeping with the negligible solubility of silver chloride in water), $K_{(2)}$ has a large equilibrium constant (1.5×10^7); the formation of $Ag(NH_3)_2^+$ is a very favorable reaction. The equilibrium constant of the summed reaction depends on both of these values:

---

1. $AgCl(s) \rightleftharpoons Ag^+(aq) + Cl^-(aq)$ $K_{(1)} = 1.8 \times 10^{-10}$

2. $Ag^+(aq) + 2NH_3(aq) \rightleftharpoons Ag(NH_3)_2^+(aq)$ $K_{(2)} = 1.5 \times 10^7$

$AgCl(s) + 2NH_3(aq) \rightleftharpoons Ag(NH_3)_2^+(aq) + Cl^-(aq)$ $K_{(sum)} = K_{(1)} \times K_{(2)} = 2.7 \times 10^{-3}$

The contribution of the large equilibrium constant for the second reaction promotes the more extensive dissolution of the original silver chloride salt. Considerably more silver chloride dissolves (compare $K_{(1)}$ to $K_{(sum)}$: $2.7 \times 10^{-3} > 1.8 \times 10^{-10}$) when ammonia is present to convert the silver ion to the $Ag(NH_3)_2^+$ ion.

3. Reactions Differing Only by the Magnitude of the Coefficients

Balanced reaction equations usually use whole number coefficients rather than fractional coefficients. For instance, we usually write:

$$N_2O_4(g) \rightleftharpoons 2NO_2(g) \quad \text{instead of} \quad \tfrac{1}{2} N_2O_4(g) \rightleftharpoons NO_2(g)$$

However, there is certainly nothing wrong with using fractions as coefficients in chemical reactions and sometimes there are very good reasons to use them. This leads to the possibility of different balanced reactions being used to describe the same reaction system. And, because the coefficients show up in the K_{eq} expressions, *the value of K_{eq} is different depending on which reaction equation is used.*

$$\tfrac{1}{2} N_2O_4(g) \rightleftharpoons NO_2(g) \qquad K_{eq} = \frac{\left(P_{NO_2}\right)_{eq}}{\left(P_{N_2O_4}\right)_{eq}^{0.5}}$$

$$N_2O_4(g) \rightleftharpoons 2NO_2(g) \qquad K_{eq} = \frac{\left(P_{NO_2}\right)_{eq}^2}{\left(P_{N_2O_4}\right)_{eq}}$$

Consider a system at equilibrium at room temperature, with $P_{NO_2} = 0.12$ bar and $P_{N_2O_4} = 0.097$ bar. We can determine the value of the equilibrium constant based on each of the reaction equations:

$$\tfrac{1}{2} N_2O_4(g) \rightleftharpoons NO_2(g) \qquad K_{eq} = \frac{\left(P_{NO_2}\right)_{eq}}{\left(P_{N_2O_4}\right)_{eq}^{0.5}} = \frac{0.12}{\left(0.097\right)^{0.5}} = 0.39$$

$$N_2O_4(g) \rightleftharpoons 2NO_2(g) \qquad K_{eq} = \frac{\left(P_{NO_2}\right)_{eq}^2}{\left(P_{N_2O_4}\right)_{eq}} = \frac{\left(0.12\right)^2}{0.097} = 0.15$$

Notice that the same equilibrium position (same concentrations of reactants and products at equilibrium) produce different values of the equilibrium constant when the reaction is written with a different set of coefficients.

What is the relationship between these two values of K_{eq}? Because the second reaction can be obtained by adding the first reaction to itself, we can use the same approach we used for the interacting equilibria in the previous section:

$$1. \quad \tfrac{1}{2}\,N_2O_4(g) \rightleftharpoons NO_2(g) \qquad K_{(1)} = \frac{\left(P_{NO_2}\right)_{eq}}{\left(P_{N_2O_4}\right)_{eq}^{0.5}} = \frac{0.12}{\left(0.097\right)^{0.5}} = 0.39$$

$$2. \quad \tfrac{1}{2}\,N_2O_4(g) \rightleftharpoons NO_2(g) \qquad K_{(2)} = \frac{\left(P_{NO_2}\right)_{eq}}{\left(P_{N_2O_4}\right)_{eq}^{0.5}} = \frac{0.12}{\left(0.097\right)^{0.5}} = 0.39$$

$$sum: \quad N_2O_4(g) \rightleftharpoons 2NO_2(g) \qquad K_{(sum)} = \left(0.39\right) \times \left(0.39\right) = 0.15$$

So, again, when reactions are added together to achieve a summed reaction, the K_{eq} values of the added reactions are multiplied to calculate the K_{eq} value of the summed reaction.

Another way to look at this is to see the second reaction as a multiple of the first:

$$2 \times \left(\tfrac{1}{2}\,N_2O_4(g) \rightleftharpoons NO_2(g) \right) \quad \text{gives} \quad N_2O_4(g) \rightleftharpoons 2NO_2(g)$$

The K_{eq} value of the first reaction: $\dfrac{\left(P_{NO_2}\right)_{eq}}{\left(P_{N_2O_4}\right)_{eq}^{0.5}} = 0.39$ must be squared to achieve the K_{eq} value of the

second equation:

$$\left(\frac{\left(P_{NO_2}\right)_{eq}}{\left(P_{N_2O_4}\right)_{eq}^{0.5}} \right)^2 = \frac{\left(P_{NO_2}\right)_{eq}^2}{\left(P_{N_2O_4}\right)_{eq}} = \left(0.39\right)^2 = 0.15$$

When a reaction equation is multiplied by some factor, the K_{eq} value of the original reaction can be raised to that power in order to calculate the equilibrium constant of the new reaction. In the case, above, where the original reaction is multiplied by 2, its K_{eq} value is squared. We summarize at right.

Reaction multiplier	Calculation of new K value
× 2	$\left(K_{original}\right)^2$
× 3	$\left(K_{original}\right)^3$
× 0.5	$\left(K_{original}\right)^{0.5} = \sqrt{K_{original}}$

Equilibrium constant values <u>are sensitive</u> to the particular reaction coefficients chosen to represent the process, but the equilibrium position of the reaction is not!

Exercise 16-15.

How are the K_{eq} values of the following reactions related? Use the symbols for the K's that are written over the reaction arrows in order to show the relationships.

a. $H_2(g) + \frac{1}{2}O_2(g) \xrightleftharpoons{K_1} H_2O(g)$ b. $I_2(g) \xrightleftharpoons{K_3} 2I(g)$

       $2H_2(g) + O_2(g) \xrightleftharpoons{K_2} 2H_2O(g)$ $2I(g) \xrightleftharpoons{K_4} I_2(g)$

c. $\frac{1}{3}S_3O_9(g) \xrightleftharpoons{K_5} SO_3(g)$

       $S_3O_9(g) \xrightleftharpoons{K_6} 3SO_3(g)$

Example 16-11.

Determine the value of K_{eq} for the reaction

$H_2C_2O_4(aq) + 2H_2O(\ell) \rightleftharpoons C_2O_4^{2-}(aq) + 2H_3O^+(aq)$ given the following data:

1. $H_2C_2O_4(aq) + H_2O(\ell) \rightleftharpoons HC_2O_4^-(aq) + H_3O^+(aq)$ $K_1 = 5.9 \times 10^{-2}$
2. $C_2O_4^{2-}(aq) + H_3O^+(aq) \rightleftharpoons HC_2O_4^-(aq) + H_2O(\ell)$ $K_2 = 1.6 \times 10^4$

Solution:

We need to find a way to combine the given reactions in order to achieve the desired overall reaction. Reaction 1 can be used as it is; it has reactant species that we need as reactants, and product species that we need as products. Reaction 2 is more helpful if we use its reverse; the overall reaction needs $C_2O_4^{2-}$ and H_3O^+ as products, not reactants. We'll call that reverse reaction: 2R, for "reverse." The equilibrium constant value for the reverse is the reciprocal of the given equilibrium constant.

1. $H_2C_2O_4(aq) + H_2O(\ell) \rightleftharpoons HC_2O_4^-(aq) + H_3O^+(aq)$ $K_1 = 5.9 \times 10^{-2}$

2R. $HC_2O_4^-(aq) + H_2O(\ell) \rightleftharpoons C_2O_4^{2-}(aq) + H_3O^+(aq)$ $K_{2R} = \dfrac{1}{K_2} = 6.3 \times 10^{-5}$

$H_2C_2O_4(aq) + 2H_2O(\ell) \rightleftharpoons C_2O_4^{2-}(aq) + 2H_3O^+(aq)$ $K_{(sum)} = K_1 \times \dfrac{1}{K_2} = 3.7 \times 10^{-6}$

Example 16-12.

Determine the value of K_{eq} for the reaction $NO_2(g) + CO(g) \rightleftharpoons NO(g) + CO_2(g)$ given the following data:

1. $N_2(g) + O_2(g) \rightleftharpoons 2NO(g)$ $K_1 = 4.3 \times 10^{-31}$
2. $N_2(g) + 2O_2(g) \rightleftharpoons 2NO_2(g)$ $K_2 = 9.1 \times 10^{-19}$
3. $2C(s) + O_2(g) \rightleftharpoons 2CO(g)$ $K_3 = 1.3 \times 10^{48}$
4. $C(s) + O_2(g) \rightleftharpoons CO_2(g)$ $K_4 = 1.5 \times 10^{69}$

<u>Solution</u>:

We need to find a way to combine the given reactions in order to achieve the desired overall reaction. Taking them one at the time:

1. the product of this reaction is a product of the overall reaction, keep it as written.
2. the product of this reaction is a reactant in the overall reaction, reverse the direction.
3. the product of this reaction is a reactant in the overall reaction, reverse the direction.
4. the product of this reaction is a product of the overall reaction, keep it as written.

This leads us to write:

1. $N_2(g) + O_2(g) \rightleftharpoons 2NO(g)$ $K_1 = 4.3 \times 10^{-31}$

2R. $2NO_2(g) \rightleftharpoons N_2(g) + 2O_2(g)$ $K_{2R} = \dfrac{1}{9.1 \times 10^{-19}} = 1.1 \times 10^{18}$

3R. $2CO(g) \rightleftharpoons 2C(s) + O_2(g)$ $K_{3R} = \dfrac{1}{1.3 \times 10^{48}} = 7.7 \times 10^{-49}$

4. $C(s) + O_2(g) \rightleftharpoons CO_2(g)$ $K_4 = 1.5 \times 10^{69}$

Now, if we think about adding these up, we can see that not everything is going to cancel out correctly. In particular, the 2C(s) product of reaction 3 is not going to be cancelled by the C(s) reactant of reaction 4. Try doubling reaction 4 (and squaring its K value):

1. $N_2(g) + O_2(g) \rightleftharpoons 2NO(g)$ $K_1 = 4.3 \times 10^{-31}$

2R. $2NO_2(g) \rightleftharpoons N_2(g) + 2O_2(g)$ $K_{2R} = \dfrac{1}{9.1 \times 10^{-19}} = 1.1 \times 10^{18}$

3R. $2CO(g) \rightleftharpoons 2C(s) + O_2(g)$ $K_{3R} = \dfrac{1}{1.3 \times 10^{48}} = 7.7 \times 10^{-49}$

4(2x). $2C(s) + 2O_2(g) \rightleftharpoons 2CO_2(g)$ $\left(K_4\right)^2 = \left(1.5 \times 10^{69}\right)^2 = 2.3 \times 10^{138}$

Now, add the four reactions, canceling any substances that show in equal amounts on both sides of the reaction arrow:

sum: $2NO_2(g) + 2CO(g) \rightleftharpoons 2NO(g) + 2CO_2(g)$

$$K = \left(4.3 \times 10^{-31}\right)\left(1.1 \times 10^{18}\right)\left(7.7 \times 10^{-49}\right)\left(2.3 \times 10^{138}\right)$$

$$K = 8.4 \times 10^{77}$$

The summed reaction, above, has doubled coefficients compared to our goal reaction. We can adjust. We need to multiply the reaction coefficients by 0.5, so we need to take the square root of the associated K value:

$$0.5 \times \left[2NO_2(g) + 2CO(g) \rightleftharpoons 2NO(g) + 2CO_2(g) \right]$$

$$NO_2(g) + CO(g) \rightleftharpoons NO(g) + CO_2(g) \quad\quad K = \left(8.4 \times 10^{77}\right)^{0.5} = \sqrt{8.4 \times 10^{77}} = 9.2 \times 10^{38}$$

Exercise 16-16.

Determine the value of the equilibrium constant in each case based on the data provided.

a. $2BrCl(g)+I_2(g)\rightleftharpoons 2IBr(g)+Cl_2(g)$ $\qquad K=?$
Data:

1. $Cl_2(g)+Br_2(g)\xrightarrow{K_1}2BrCl(g)$ $\qquad K_1=2.2$
2. $Br_2(g)+I_2(g)\xrightarrow{K_2}2IBr(g)$ $\qquad K_2=0.051$

b. $2NO(g)+Br_2(g)\rightleftharpoons 2NOBr(g)$ $\qquad K=?$
Data:

1. $Br_2(g)+N_2(g)+O_2(g)\xrightarrow{K_1}2NOBr(g)$ $\qquad K_1=1.3\times10^{-29}$
2. $N_2(g)+O_2(g)\xrightarrow{K_2}2NO(g)$ $\qquad K_2=4.3\times10^{-31}$

Make sure to notice the huge variations in values of equilibrium constants in the reactions in the previous Examples and Exercises. Some are very tiny (10^{-31}, 10^{-29}) and some are absolutely huge (10^{48}, 10^{69}). The extreme values of many equilibrium constants indicate the usefulness of treating many reactions as irreversible systems. In other words, when a K_{eq} value is tiny we can often treat the reaction as one that does not go at all. When a K_{eq} value is huge we can often threat the reaction as if it goes to completion. In the case of a huge K_{eq}, we can utilize the idea of limiting reagents to determine the amount of a product we expect. Of course, even when a K_{eq} value is huge, the tiny amount of unreacted material that remains may be important to us for any number of reasons and when the K_{eq} value is tiny, we might really need to know how much of the product was actually produced! In the next chapter, we will learn how to determine equilibrium concentrations of reactants and products based on starting amounts and knowledge of the value of K_{eq}.

16-5. SPECIALTY EQUILIBRIA: NAMED K'S

All chemical reactions and phase change processes have equilibrium constant expressions and values to go with those expressions. There are several *families of reactions* where essentially the same process is occurring to different species. Some families of related reactions have equilibrium constants that have been given their own names and symbols, so that they can be easily differentiated from other equilibrium processes. We will introduce five of these families.

A. When the K_{eq} is called K_{sp}

There are many minimally soluble salts. All of the dissolution processes for these salts are of a related form; the solid salt is the reactant and the dissolved ions are the products:

$$PbSO_4(s)\rightleftharpoons Pb^{2+}(aq)+SO_4^{2-}(aq)$$
$$Ni(OH)_2(s)\rightleftharpoons Ni^{2+}(aq)+2OH^-(aq)$$
$$Mg_3(PO_4)_2(s)\rightleftharpoons 3Mg^{2+}(aq)+2PO_4^{3-}(aq)$$

The coefficients are not necessarily the same, but the reaction equations all describe the dissolution process. The K_{eq} expressions for these reactions also take similar forms. None of them, for instance, have a denominator because the only reactant is a pure solid. These equilibrium constants are called **solubility product constants, K_{sp}**, because the reaction is about *solubility* and the K_{eq} value is the *product* of ion concentrations, with no denominator.

$$AgCl(s) \rightleftharpoons Ag^+(aq) + Cl^-(aq) \qquad K_{eq} = K_{sp} = \left[Ag^+\right]_{eq}\left[Cl^-\right]_{eq}$$

$$PbSO_4(s) \rightleftharpoons Pb^{2+}(aq) + SO_4^{2-}(aq) \qquad K_{eq} = K_{sp} = \left[Pb^{2+}\right]_{eq}\left[SO_4^{2-}\right]_{eq}$$

$$Ni(OH)_2(s) \rightleftharpoons Ni^{2+}(aq) + 2OH^-(aq) \qquad K_{eq} = K_{sp} = \left[Ni^{2+}\right]_{eq}\left[OH^-\right]_{eq}^2$$

$$Mg_3(PO_4)_2(s) \rightleftharpoons 3Mg^{2+}(aq) + 2PO_4^{3-}(aq) \qquad K_{eq} = K_{sp} = \left[Mg^{2+}\right]_{eq}^3\left[PO_4^{3-}\right]_{eq}^2$$

Notice that a larger value of K_{sp} means that the salt is more soluble.

B. When the K_{eq} is called K_f

A second family of reactions involves the *formation* of *complex ions* from a metal ion and a set of ligands. The equilibrium constants for reactions such as these are called **formation constants, K_f** :

$$Ag^+(aq) + 2NH_3(aq) \rightleftharpoons Ag(NH_3)_2^+(aq) \qquad K_{eq} = K_f = \frac{\left[Ag(NH_3)_2^+\right]_{eq}}{\left[Ag^+\right]_{eq}\left[NH_3\right]_{eq}^2}$$

$$Ni^{2+}(aq) + 6H_2O(\ell) \rightleftharpoons Ni(OH_2)_6^{2+}(aq) \qquad K_{eq} = K_f = \frac{\left[Ni(OH_2)_6^{2+}\right]_{eq}}{\left[Ni^{2+}\right]_{eq}}$$

Larger values of K_f represent complex ions that are easier to form.

C. When the K_{eq} is called K_s

A third family of reactions involves a complex ion decomposing to its separate metal ion and ligands. These are the reverse reactions to the ones discussed above. Here, the *stability* of the complex ion is being studied; hence, the equilibrium constants for these processes are called **stability constants**, and are symbolized, K_s:

$$Ag(NH_3)_2^+(aq) \rightleftharpoons Ag^+(aq) + 2NH_3(aq) \qquad K_{eq} = K_s = \frac{\left[Ag^+\right]_{eq}\left[NH_3\right]_{eq}^2}{\left[Ag(NH_3)_2^+\right]_{eq}}$$

$$Ni(OH_2)_6^{2+}(aq) \rightleftharpoons Ni^{2+}(aq) + 6H_2O(\ell) \qquad K_{eq} = K_s = \frac{\left[Ni^{2+}\right]_{eq}}{\left[Ni(OH_2)_6^{2+}\right]_{eq}}$$

The value of K_s is larger for complex ions that are *less stable*. Note that because complex ion stability reactions are the reverse reactions to complex ion formation reactions, K_s expressions are reciprocals of K_f expressions. Any complex ion that is easy to make (large K_f) will be stable (small K_s).

D. When the K_{eq} is called K_a

A fourth family of reactions involves a weak acid transferring a proton to water, *forming ions*. Here, the similar feature of these reactions is the formation of the hydronium ion, H_3O^+, from a water molecule by taking an H^+ from the other reactant. The equilibrium constants for reactions such as these are called **acid ionization**[123] **constants**, and are symbolized, K_a:

---

[123] Remember that "ionization" means the formation of new ions; in the reactions in sections D and E at least one new ion is produced.

$$HF(aq)+H_2O(\ell)\rightleftharpoons F^-(aq)+H_3O^+(aq) \qquad K_{eq}=K_a=\frac{[H_3O^+]_{eq}[F^-]_{eq}}{[HF]_{eq}}$$

$$HCN(aq)+H_2O(\ell)\rightleftharpoons CN^-(aq)+H_3O^+(aq) \qquad K_{eq}=K_a=\frac{[H_3O^+]_{eq}[CN^-]_{eq}}{[HCN]_{eq}}$$

$$NH_4^+(aq)+H_2O(\ell)\rightleftharpoons NH_3(aq)+H_3O^+(aq) \qquad K_{eq}=K_a=\frac{[H_3O^+]_{eq}[NH_3]_{eq}}{[NH_4^+]_{eq}}$$

Weak acids whose ionization reactions have larger equilibrium constants (larger K_a) values, are better at transferring a proton to water. Some weak acids are better acids than others!

E. When the K_{eq} is called K_b

A fifth family of reactions involves a weak base taking a proton away from water, forming the hydroxide ion. The equilibrium constants for these processes are called **base ionization constants**, and are symbolized, K_b. These reactions can be recognized by looking for a water molecule reactant forming a hydroxide ion, OH^-, by giving an H^+ to the other reactant.

$$CH_3NH_2(aq)+H_2O(\ell)\rightleftharpoons CH_3NH_3^+(aq)+OH^-(aq) \qquad K_{eq}=K_b=\frac{[OH^-]_{eq}[CH_3NH_3^+]_{eq}}{[CH_3NH_2]_{eq}}$$

$$HCO_3^-(aq)+H_2O(\ell)\rightleftharpoons H_2CO_3(aq)+OH^-(aq) \qquad K_{eq}=K_b=\frac{[OH^-]_{eq}[H_2CO_3]_{eq}}{[HCO_3^-]_{eq}}$$

$$F^-(aq)+H_2O(\ell)\rightleftharpoons HF(aq)+OH^-(aq) \qquad K_{eq}=K_b=\frac{[OH^-]_{eq}[HF]_{eq}}{[F^-]_{eq}}$$

Weak bases whose ionization reactions have larger equilibrium constant (larger K_b) values, are better at taking a proton away from water. Some weak bases are better bases than others!

F. Some Named Equilibrium Constants Prevalent in Biology

Of all of the activities taking place in a living cell, a great many of them can be described as the association and dissociation of binding partners such as an enzyme and a substrate, or a transport protein and its ligand, or a hormone and its target receptor. These associations are not all equally strong and these strengths can be described by a **dissociation constant, K_D**.

Myoglobin is an example of a ligand-binding protein, where the ligand is oxygen. The **dissociation** of oxygen from myoglobin can be represented as

$$Mb(O_2)\rightleftharpoons Mb+O_2$$

The dissociation constant expression can be written in the normal fashion of products over reactants:

$$K_D=\frac{[Mb][O_2]}{[Mb(O_2)]}$$

We learned in Chapter 15 that myoglobin has a large affinity for oxygen and binds it tightly under normal cellular conditions. The size of K_D is a measure of the strength of the bonding between myoglobin and oxygen; a large value of K_D indicates weak bonding (a large numerator), while a small value of K_D indicates strong bonding (a large denominator). We expect, then, that myglobin's K_D value is small (less than 1!) with the numerator of the ratio smaller than the denominator.

Conversely, the same system may be studied from the opposite perspective. The reverse reaction to a dissociation reaction is called an **association** reaction. For the myoglobin-oxygen system we write

$$Mb + O_2 \rightleftharpoons Mb(O_2) \qquad\qquad K_A = \frac{\left[Mb(O_2)\right]}{\left[Mb\right]\left[O_2\right]}$$

The equilibrium constant is the reciprocal of the dissociation constant, above, and is called the **association constant, K_A.** We use a capital "A" in K_A to distinguish this constant from the acid ionization constant introduced earlier as K_a. The association constant is the reciprocal of the dissociation constant; a strongly associated system has a large association constant and a small dissociation constant.

In practice, *most biological binding constants are described via the dissociation constant rather than the association constant.* Most biochemistry textbooks, for example, indicate that the myoglobin-oxygen dissociation constant is $K_D \sim 3$ torr. What? Why is this value bigger than 1? We were sure it should be less than 1. Also, why are there units on this K_{eq} value; aren't all K_{eq} values supposed to be unitless? It turns out that these two issues are closely related! Let's see how.

Let's focus first on the unit. In this case, the unit is necessary to inform us that the convention of utilizing units of bar for gas-phase substances has not been followed. But, why is there a gas involved in the association of oxygen with myoglobin? Surely the myoglobin is never in the lungs! Let's see everything that is involved in the simple statement that $K_D \sim 3$ torr for myoglobin and oxygen.

Consider the whole process (shown in the box, below) by which myoglobin ends up with oxygen bound: oxygen gas must move from the lung into the blood plasma before it is taken up by hemoglobin. Myoglobin (in muscles) only obtains its oxygen after hemoglobin has delivered it to the tissues. So the pathway for the binding of oxygen to myoglobin occurs in four steps, which can be summed to give an overall representation of the event. Species that cancel each other are indicated by the color of the strike-out line.

We can see that the gas phase oxygen from the first step of the process is still present in the overall reaction process. So, the overall equilibrium constant (for the bottom line, above) depends on the partial pressure of O_2 gas.

(dissolving O_2)	$4\,O_2(g) \rightleftharpoons 4\,O_2(aq)$
(uptake by Hb)	$Hb(aq) + 4\,O_2(aq) \rightleftharpoons Hb(O_2)_4(aq)$
(release to tissue by Hb)	$Hb(O_2)_4(aq) \rightleftharpoons Hb(aq) + 4\,O_2(aq)$
(uptake from tissue by Mb)	$4\,Mb + 4\,O_2(aq) \rightleftharpoons 4\,Mb(O_2)$
overall	$4\,Mb + 4\,O_2(g) \rightleftharpoons 4\,Mb(O_2)$
or, more simply	$Mb + O_2(g) \rightleftharpoons Mb(O_2)$

We reverse the final reaction, above, to obtain the *dissociation* reaction equation and we write the dissociation constant expression (molarities and partial pressures):

$$Mb(O_2) \rightleftharpoons Mb + O_2(g) \qquad\qquad K_D = \frac{[Mb](P_{O_2})}{[Mb(O_2)]}$$

The first thing we notice is that if we put units on all three terms, the units of molarity would cancel in numerator and denominator, so presenting just a pressure unit makes sense in that regard. Now, if we were to follow chemical convention, we would need to use units of bar for the gaseous oxygen. In that case, the value of K_D would be 4×10^{-3}! There's that "less-than-1" value that we were expecting:

$$3\,torr \times \frac{1\,bar}{750\,torr} = 4 \times 10^{-3}\,bar$$

Why not use the conventional unit? Whether or not one thinks it is a good idea, looking at side-by-side binding curves (Figure 16-7) does indicate a practical reason explaining why scientists studying oxygen-binding proteins might choose to use torr instead of bar. Who wouldn't rather deal in values between 0 and 100 rather than between 0 and 0.14?

In the end, at least this unconventional K_D value was labeled with its unconventional unit! Imagine if the biochemistry textbook just said that $K_D = 3$ for myoglobin. This would be very confusing given its binding curve shows such strong binding!

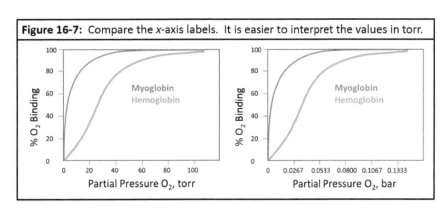

Figure 16-7: Compare the x-axis labels. It is easier to interpret the values in torr.

Moving on, let's consider the situation in which the concentration of free myoglobin, [Mb], is identical to that of oxygen-bound myoglobin, [Mb(O₂)]. When these two concentrations are identical, it <u>must be true</u> that half of the possible binding sites for O₂ are filled and half are empty. This means that on the binding curve we are at the 50% mark on the y-axis. We start with the knowledge about the value of K_D:

$$K_D = \frac{[Mb]P_{O_2}}{[Mb(O_2)]} = 3\,torr$$

When [Mb] = [Mb(O₂)], we can write:

$$K_D = \frac{[\cancel{Mb}]P_{O_2}}{[\cancel{Mb(O_2)}]} = P_{O_2} = 3\,torr$$

Taking a look at the binding curve for myoglobin in Figure 16-7, you will see that it is believable that when the partial pressure of oxygen is 3 torr, the % binding is indeed equal to 50%! This value of K_D is given a special name: **P₅₀**, where the "P" stands for "partial pressure" and the "50" stands for "50% binding". All-in-all, P₅₀ is just a special case K_D!

G. Why Give Some Equilibrium Constants a Name?

Naming certain families of equilibrium constants may seem pointless. The form of the equilibrium constant expression stays exactly the same, it just has a new name and symbol. The goal in grouping similar reactions together in these categories is to make communication about these processes more efficient.

Consider these two ways to say the same thing:

"The K_{sp} of $PbSO_4$ is 1.8×10^{-8}."

"The K_{eq} value for the reaction $PbSO_4(s) \rightleftharpoons Pb^{2+}(aq) + SO_4^{2-}(aq)$ is 1.8×10^{-8}."

In the absence of a special name and symbol the balanced reaction must be provided. Because chemists understand that the "K_{sp}" is the equilibrium constant for a specific balanced reaction, the reaction equation does not need to be provided. Aspiring chemists must learn to write the correct balanced reactions for these named K_{eq}'s.

Table 16-5 summarizes the named K_{eq}'s for which students should become familiar. Weak acid and weak base equilibria will be studied in much greater detail in Chapter 19, so don't worry about them too much right now.

Exercise 16-17.

Look for trends in Table 16-5 and answer each of the following:

a. What phase are the products of a solubility equilibrium? The reactants?

b. Which equilibrium constant is used for a reaction that produces a complex ion?

c. Which two of these equilibrium constants are reciprocals of each other? Be careful, there is only one pair of reciprocals!

d. What product is always made by the ionization of a weak acid?

e. What product is always made by the ionization of a weak base?

f. Is there a reciprocal relationship between the K_a of the weak acid HF and the K_b of the weak base F^-?

Table 16-5.

Reaction Type	Named K_c	Example Reactions	K_c Expressions
Solubility	**Solubility product constant, K_{sp}**	$PbSO_4(s) \rightleftharpoons Pb^{2+}(aq) + SO_4^{2-}(aq)$ $Mg_3(PO_4)_2(s) \rightleftharpoons 3Mg^{2+}(aq) + 2PO_4^{3-}(aq)$	$K_{sp} = \left[Pb^{2+}\right]_{eq}\left[SO_4^{2-}\right]_{eq}$ $K_{sp} = \left[Mg^{2+}\right]_{eq}^3\left[PO_4^{3-}\right]_{eq}^2$
Complex Ion Formation	**Formation constant, K_f**	$Fe^{3+}(aq) + SCN^-(aq) \rightleftharpoons FeSCN^{2+}(aq)$ $Ag^+(aq) + 2NH_3(aq) \rightleftharpoons Ag(NH_3)_2^+(aq)$	$K_f = \dfrac{\left[FeSCN^{2+}\right]_{eq}}{\left[Fe^{3+}\right]_{eq}\left[SCN^-\right]_{eq}}$ $K_f = \dfrac{\left[Ag(NH_3)_2^+\right]_{eq}}{\left[Ag^+\right]_{eq}\left[NH_3\right]_{eq}^2}$
Complex Ion Stability	**Stability constant, K_s**	$FeSCN^{2+}(aq) \rightleftharpoons Fe^{3+}(aq) + SCN^-(aq)$ $CdCN^+(aq) \rightleftharpoons Cd^{2+}(aq) + CN^-(aq)$	$K_s = \dfrac{\left[Fe^{3+}\right]_{eq}\left[SCN^-\right]_{eq}}{\left[FeSCN^{2+}\right]_{eq}}$ $K_s = \dfrac{\left[Cd^{2+}\right]_{eq}\left[CN^-\right]_{eq}}{\left[CdCN^+\right]_{eq}}$
Weak Acid Ionization	**Acid ionization constant, K_a**	$HF(aq) + H_2O(\ell) \rightleftharpoons H_3O^+(aq) + F^-(aq)$ $H_2CO_3(aq) + H_2O(\ell) \rightleftharpoons H_3O^+(aq) + HCO_3^-$	$K_a = \dfrac{\left[H_3O^+\right]_{eq}\left[F^-\right]_{eq}}{\left[HF\right]_{eq}}$ $K_a = \dfrac{\left[H_3O^+\right]_{eq}\left[HCO_3^-\right]_{eq}}{\left[H_2CO_3\right]_{eq}}$
Weak Base Ionization	**Base ionization constant, K_b**	$F^-(aq) + H_2O(\ell) \rightleftharpoons OH^-(aq) + HF(aq)$ $NH_3(aq) + H_2O(\ell) \rightleftharpoons OH^-(aq) + NH_4^+(aq)$	$K_b = \dfrac{\left[OH^-\right]_{eq}\left[HF\right]_{eq}}{\left[F^-\right]_{eq}}$ $K_b = \dfrac{\left[OH^-\right]_{eq}\left[NH_4^+\right]_{eq}}{\left[NH_3\right]_{eq}}$
Biological Systems	**Dissociation constant, K_D**	$Mb(O_2) \rightleftharpoons Mb + O_2(g)$ $estradiol \cdot ER \rightleftharpoons estradiol + ER$ [note 124]	$K_D = \dfrac{\left[Mb\right]_{eq}\left(P_{O_2}\right)_{eq}}{\left[Mb(O_2)\right]_{eq}}$

Exercise 16-18.

If the K_D for a hormone and its receptor is 3.4×10^{-6}, is there a strong association or weak association between the two entities?

---

[124] Where ER represents an estradiol receptor

Example 16-13.

    a. Write the reaction equation for the base ionization of cyanide ion (CN^-).

    b. Write the reaction equation for the acid ionization of ammonium ion $\left(NH_4^+\right)$.

    c. Write the reaction equation for the formation of the complex ion $CdCN^+$.

    d. Write the reaction equation for the dissolution of the slightly soluble $CaCO_3$.

    e. Write the reaction equation for the dissociation of estrogen (Es) from estrogen receptor-beta (ERβ). (ERβ is a soluble protein found in the cell cytoplasm. ERβ is activated by the estrogen-binding event, causing it to move into the nucleus of the cell where it regulates the activation of various genes.)

Solutions:

    a. All base ionizations involve the reaction of the basic species with water molecules. The products are hydroxide ion and the basic species with the addition of one hydrogen ion. So for cyanide ion we can write:

$$CN^-(aq) + H_2O(\ell) \rightleftharpoons OH^-(aq) + HCN(aq)$$

    b. All acid ionizations involve the reaction of the acidic species with water molecules. The products are the hydronium ion (H_3O^+) and the acidic species minus one hydrogen ion (H^+).

$$NH_4^+(aq) + H_2O(\ell) \rightleftharpoons H_3O^+(aq) + NH_3(aq)$$

    c. Complex ions are made by the reaction between a metal ion and a ligand. If the complex retains some charge, it stays in solution.

    d. Calcium carbonate is a minimally soluble salt:

$$CaCO_3(s) \rightleftharpoons Ca^{2+}(aq) + CO_3^{2-}(aq)$$

    e. We must write this as a dissociation event: $\left(Es\right)ER\beta \rightleftharpoons ER\beta + Es$

16-6. CHAPTER SUMMARY

A. The Nature of Dynamic Equilibrium

    Forward and reverse reaction rates are equivalent once equilibrium is established.

B. Summary of Reaction Quotient/Equilibrium Constant Information

1. Q and K_{eq} are single values that give information about how far a reaction has progressed.

2. Products in numerator, reactants in denominator:
   larger Q = more product present, smaller Q = less product present.
   larger K_{eq} = more product present at equilibrium, smaller K_{eq} = less product present at equilibrium.

3. Use reaction coefficients as exponents.

4. Do not include pure liquids or pure solids.

5. Q or K_{eq}:   use molarities for solutes and bars for gases, but report no units.
    Q_c or K_c: use molarities for both solutes and gases, but report no units.
    Q_p or K_p: use bars, but report no units (Q_p and K_p are "not defined" if there are aqueous species!)

6. Reactions in their standard states (all dissolved species at 1.0 M, all gases at 1.0 bar) have $Q = 1$. If all species are gases,[125] $Q_p = 1$ when in the standard state.
    If all species are aqueous,[125] $Q_c = 1$ when in the standard state; if gases are present, $Q_c \neq 1$ in the standard state because a standard state gas is at 1 bar of pressure, which is not equivalent to a 1 M concentration.

7. For reactions starting with all reactant, Q starts at zero and increases as the reaction proceeds. For reactions starting with all product, Q starts at infinity and decreases as the reaction proceeds. Reaction stops progressing when $Q = K_{eq}$.

8. $Q_c = Q_p$ and $K_c = K_p$ for gas phase reactions having the same number of moles of gas on each side of the reaction arrow. Otherwise, $Q_c \neq Q_p$ and $K_c \neq K_p$.

C. Comparing Q and K_{eq}

$Q < K_{eq}$	forward reaction will occur
$Q > K_{eq}$	reverse reaction will occur
$Q = K_{eq}$	system is at equilibrium

D. Related K_{eq} values

1. The K_{eq} values of reverse reactions are reciprocals.
2. When reaction equations can be added to give an overall reaction, their K_{eq} values can be multiplied to give the K_{eq} value of the overall process.
3. When one reaction equation is a multiple of another, the original K_{eq} value is raised to that power:
    double the reaction equation, square the K_{eq} value
    triple the reaction equation, cube the K_{eq} value
    halve the reaction equation, take the square root of the K_{eq} value.

E. Named K_{eq} values

Some reactions have K_{eq} values that are given a special name having to do with the type of chemical reaction it is. These K_{eq} values are exactly the same as generic ones. The names and special symbols just help in communication.

Solubility product constant, K_{sp} (any dissolution of a poorly soluble ionic compound)
Formation constant, K_f (any formation of a complex ion from the metal ion and ligands)
Stability constant, K_s (any decomposition of a complex ion into the metal ion and ligands)
Acid ionization constant, K_a (any H^+ transfer from a weak acid molecule to a water molecule)
Base ionization constant, K_b (any H^+ transfer from a water molecule to a weak base molecule)
Dissociation constant, K_D (the loss of any association between biological molecules)
Association constant, K_A (the association of biological molecules)

---

[125] Or pure solids or pure liquids.

CHAPTER 16: PROBLEMS

1. Write the expression for the reaction quotient, Q, for the following reactions:

   a. HCO_2^- (aq) $+ H_2O$ (ℓ) $\rightleftharpoons HCO_2H$ (aq) $+ OH^-$ (aq)

   b. Fe^{3+} (aq) $+ 4Cl^-$ (aq) $\rightleftharpoons FeCl_4^-$ (aq)

   c. $PbCrO_4$ (s) $\rightleftharpoons Pb^{2+}$ (aq) $+ CrO_4^{2-}$ (aq)

   d. HF (aq) $+ H_2O$ (ℓ) $\rightleftharpoons H_3O^+$ (aq) $+ F^-$ (aq)

   e. U (s) $+ 3 F_2$ (g) $\rightleftharpoons UF_6$ (g)

   f. $Ni(NH_3)_6^{2+}$ (aq) $+ 3en$ (aq) $\rightleftharpoons Ni(en)_3^{2+}$ (aq) $+ 6NH_3$ (aq)

2. Write the expression for the reaction quotient, Q, for the following reactions. If either Q_c or Q_p is appropriate, write that ratio as well.

   a. $3 Ca^{2+}$ (aq) $+ 2 PO_4^{3-}$ (aq) $\rightleftharpoons Ca_3(PO_4)_2$ (s)

   b. I_2 (s) $\rightleftharpoons I_2$ (g)

   c. Ag^+ (aq) $+ Cl^-$ (aq) $\rightleftharpoons AgCl$ (s)

   d. $2 NO_2$ (g) $\rightleftharpoons N_2O_4$ (g)

   e. N_2O_4 (g) $\rightleftharpoons 2 NO_2$ (g)

   f. HF (aq) $+ NH_3$ (aq) $\rightleftharpoons NH_4^+$ (aq) $+ F^-$ (aq)

   g. BF_3 (g) $+ NH_3$ (g) $\rightleftharpoons F_3BNH_3$ (s)

3. Write the Q expression for each of the following reactions.

   a. Mg (s) $+ 2 H_3O^+$ (aq) $\rightleftharpoons Mg^{2+}$ (aq) $+ H_2$ (g) $+ 2 H_2O$ (ℓ)

   b. HF (aq) $+ NH_3$ (aq) $\rightleftharpoons NH_4^+$ (aq) $+ F^-$ (aq)

   c. U (s) $+ 3 F_2$ (g) $\rightleftharpoons UF_6$ (g)

   d. $2 Na$ (s) $+ 2 H_2O$ (ℓ) $\rightleftharpoons 2 Na^+$ (aq) $+ 2 OH^-$ (aq) $+ H_2$ (g)

   e. CuO (s) $+ H_2$ (g) $\rightleftharpoons Cu$ (s) $+ H_2O$ (ℓ)

   f. Cl_2 (g) $+ 2 H_2O$ (ℓ) $\rightleftharpoons 2 Cl^-$ (aq) $+ O_2$ (g) $+ 4 H^+$ (aq)

4. a. Which of the reaction equations in problem number 1 can be described by a Q_p expression?

   b. For each of the reactions identified in part a, write the Q_p expression and indicate whether $Q_p = Q_c$ or $Q_p \neq Q_c$ for that reaction.

5. Perform the following conversions: (use T = 298 K where necessary)

   a. 0.984 bar into molarity   b. 7.81×10^3 torr into molarity

   c. 1.23×10^{-3} M into bar   d. 0.988 mM into bar

6. Consider the mythical reaction, $2A \rightleftharpoons B$, with a final achievable value of $Q = 60$.
a. If you start with only B in a container at time $t = 0$, what is the value of Q at $t = 0$?
b. Will Q be larger or smaller than your answer in part a when $t = 10$ min?
c. When, if ever, will $Q = 50$?

7. Consider the mythical reaction $D + E \rightleftharpoons G$, with a final achievable value of $Q = 0.45$.
a. If you start with only D and E in a container at time $t = 0$, what is the value of Q at $t = 0$?
b. Which of the following progressions of Q values might occur sequentially as equilibrium is achieved? Justify your choice.
    i) $0, 10, 5, 2, 0.13, 0.45, 0.45, 0.45$
    ii) $\infty, 1000, 100, 10, 0.45, 0.45, 0.45$
    iii) $0, 0.00003, 0.00091, 0.0048, 0.073, 0.12, 0.45, 0.45$

8. **a.** What criteria must be met for $K_{eq} = K_c$ for a particular reaction?
b. What criteria must be met for $K_{eq} = K_p$ for a particular reaction?
c. What criteria must be met for $K_c = K_p$ for a particular reaction?

9. Try this without looking back in the chapter:

a. Write the Q expression for the reaction $A(aq) \rightleftharpoons B(aq)$.

b. From your expression in part a, indicate which reaction (fwd or rev) would have to occur if a particular sample of this reaction had $Q > K_{eq}$. Briefly, explain your logic.

c. From your expression in part a, indicate which reaction (fwd or rev) would have to occur if a particular sample of this reaction had $Q < K_{eq}$. Briefly, explain your logic.

10. An equilibrium position for each of the following reactions is given. In each case determine the value of the equilibrium constant. One of these is a K_{sp}, one is a K_f, one is a K_a, one is a K_D. Label these appropriately, otherwise label as K_{eq}.

    a. $2 NO_2 (g) \rightleftharpoons N_2O_4 (g)$ $P_{NO_2} = 0.634$ bar; $P_{N_2O_4} = 0.311$ bar

    b. $HF (aq) + H_2O (\ell) \rightleftharpoons H_3O^+ (aq) + F^- (aq)$
                   $[HF] = 0.100\ M; [H_3O^+] = [F^-] = 5.9 \times 10^{-2}\ M$

    c. $AgCl (s) \rightleftharpoons Ag^+ (aq) + Cl^- (aq)$
                   $[Ag^+] = 1.12 \times 10^{-3}\ M; [Cl^-] = 2.02 \times 10^{-7}\ M$

    d. $Ca^{2+}\text{–calmodulin (aq)} \rightleftharpoons Ca^{2+} (aq) + \text{calmodulin (aq)}$
    $[Ca^{2+}\text{–calmodulin}] = 2.3 \times 10^{-4}\ M; [Ca^{2+}] = 1.0 \times 10^{-4}\ M; [\text{calmodulin}] = 1.2 \times 10^{-5}\ M$

    e. $PCl_5 (g) \rightleftharpoons PCl_3 (g) + Cl_2 (g)$
                   $P_{PCl_5} = 0.200$ bar; $P_{PCl_3} = 0.100$ bar; $P_{Cl_2} = 0.0200$ bar

    f. $Ag^+ (aq) + 2 NH_3 (aq) \rightleftharpoons Ag(NH_3)_2^+ (aq)$

                   $[Ag^+] = 3.12 \times 10^{-4}\ M; [NH_3] = 0.400\ M; \left[Ag(NH_3)_2^+\right] = 0.100\ M$

11. How is K_{eq} related to Q?

12. Consider the reaction $\qquad S_3O_9(g) \rightleftharpoons 3SO_3(g)$

A flask is charged with gaseous S_3O_9 1.000 *M*. The concentrations of the two gases are measured each minute for five minutes. The data are given here.

Time (min)	Conc. S_3O_9	Conc. SO_3
0.0	1.000 *M*	0 *M*
1.0	0.932	0.204
2.0	0.864	0.408
3.0	0.796	0.612
4.0	0.728	0.816
5.0	0.660	1.020

a. Determine the value of Q for every time point.

b. Do these data let you determine the value of K_{eq}? If so, what is the value of K_{eq}? If not, why not?

13. Consider the following reaction: $H_2(g) + I_2(g) \rightleftharpoons 2HI(g)$ with $K_{eq} = 52$ at some temperature. If a flask contains the following pressures of gases, is the system at equilibrium? If not, which reaction (forward or reverse) would need to occur to reach equilibrium? Draw a Q axis plot for each situation.

a. $P_{H_2} = 0.32\ bar \qquad P_{I_2} = 0.65\ bar \qquad P_{HI} = 0.18\ bar$

b. $P_{H_2} = 0.016\ bar \qquad P_{I_2} = 0.33\ bar \qquad P_{HI} = 1.1\ bar$

c. $P_{H_2} = 0.14\ bar \qquad P_{I_2} = 0.19\ bar \qquad P_{HI} = 1.18\ bar$

d. $P_{H_2} = 0.064\ bar \qquad P_{I_2} = 0.012\ bar \qquad P_{HI} = 0.87\ bar$

14. Consider the reaction: $N_2(g) + 3H_2(g) \rightleftharpoons 2NH_3(g)$ with $K_c = 0.059$ at 770 K. If a flask contains the following concentrations of gases, is the system at equilibrium? If not, which reaction (forward or reverse) would occur in order to attain equilibrium?

a. $[N_2] = 0.32\ M \qquad [H_2] = 0.65\ M \qquad [NH_3] = 0.18\ M$

b. $[N_2] = 0.91\ M \qquad [H_2] = 0.78\ M \qquad [NH_3] = 0.16\ M$

c. $[N_2] = 0.0034\ M \qquad [H_2] = 0.73\ M \qquad [NH_3] = 0.054\ M$

d. $[N_2] = 0.063\ M \qquad [H_2] = 0.80\ M \qquad [NH_3] = 0.022\ M$

15. The number of shoppers in a particular store is measured every 30 minutes. For a three hour period, the number of shoppers stays constant. How might the idea of *dynamic equilibrium* apply to this scenario?

16. Consider the following reaction in its standard state at 500.0 K.

$$N_2(g) + 3H_2(g) \rightleftharpoons 2NH_3(g)$$

   a. What the value of Q?
   b. What is the value of Q_p?
   c. What is the value of Q_c?

17. Write the equilibrium constant expression (K_{eq}) for each of the following reaction equations. Don't forget to include (eq) subscripts to distinguish these expressions from Q expressions. Do any of these reactions have a special named K_{eq}? If so, label appropriately.

   a. NH_4^+ (aq) + H_2O (ℓ) $\rightleftharpoons$ H_3O^+ (aq) + NH_3 (aq)

   b. Hg_2^{2+} (aq) + 2 Cl^- (aq) $\rightleftharpoons$ Hg_2Cl_2 (s)

   c. HF (aq) + H_2O (ℓ) $\rightleftharpoons$ H_3O^+ (aq) + F^- (aq)

   d. I_2 (s) $\rightleftharpoons$ I_2 (g)

18. Which of the following reactions are of the type where if the initial concentrations are doubled, the equilibrium concentrations will also be doubled?

   a. PCl_3 (g) + Cl_2 (g) $\rightleftharpoons$ PCl_5 (g)   b. $PbCrO_4$ (s) $\rightleftharpoons$ Pb^{2+} (aq) + CrO_4^{2-} (aq)

   c. 2 BrCl (g) $\rightleftharpoons$ Br_2 (g) + Cl_2 (g)   d. I_2 (s) $\rightleftharpoons$ I_2 (g)

   e. H_2 (g) + Cl_2 (g) $\rightleftharpoons$ 2HCl (g)   f. BF_3 (g) + NH_3 (g) $\rightleftharpoons$ F_3BNH_3 (s)

   g. HF (aq) + NH_3 (aq) $\rightleftharpoons$ NH_4^+ (aq) + F^- (aq)

19. Write the reaction equations for which the following K_{eq} values apply. It's OK to look up the patterns for K_a and K_b, for now, but the others you should be able to do on your own. (See Example 16-13).

   a. K_{sp} of $Co(OH)_3$ is 2×10^{-16} b. K_{sp} of AgBr is 5.0×10^{-13}
   c. K_{sp} of $PbCrO_4$ is 2×10^{-16} d. K_a of HSO_4^- is 1.2×10^{-2}
   e. K_a of C_6H_5OH is 1.3×10^{-10} (a product is $C_6H_5O^-$)
   f. K_a of $C_6H_5CO_2H$ is 6.5×10^{-5} (a product is $C_6H_5CO_2^-$)
   g. K_b of NO_2^- is 2.2×10^{-11} h. K_b of OCl^- is 3.1×10^{-7}
   i. K_f for $[AgBr_2]^-$ is 5.0×10^7 j. K_f of $[Cd(NH_3)_4]^{2+}$ is 3.1×10^{-7}
   k. K_f of $[AlF_6]^{3-}$ is 6.3×10^{19} l. K_s of $[Ag(CN)_2]^-$ is 3.3×10^{-21}
   m. K_s of $[Zn(OH)_4]^{2-}$ is 1.6×10^{-15}

20. Given that K_{eq} = 1.073 for the reaction: $2NO_2(g) \rightleftharpoons N_2O_4(g)$ at 45 °C,

   a. Determine K_{eq} for $NO_2(g) \rightleftharpoons$ ½ $N_2O_4(g)$ at 45 °C.

   b. Determine K_{eq} for $N_2O_4(g) \rightleftharpoons 2NO_2(g)$ at 45 °C.

21. Given that $K_a = 6.2 \times 10^{-10}$ for: $HCN(aq) + H_2O(\ell) \rightleftharpoons CN^-(aq) + H_3O^+(aq)$ at 25 °C,

determine the value of K_{eq} for: $CN^-(aq) + H_3O^+(aq) \rightleftharpoons HCN(aq) + H_2O(\ell)$ at 25 °C.

22. Given that $K_a = 0.16$ for: $HIO_3(aq) + H_2O(\ell) \rightleftharpoons IO_3^-(aq) + H_3O^+(aq)$ at 25 °C

and $K_b = 6.3 \times 10^{-14}$ for: $IO_3^-(aq) + H_2O(\ell) \rightleftharpoons HIO_3(aq) + OH^-(aq)$ at 25 °C,

determine the value of K_{eq} for: $H_3O^+(aq) + OH^-(aq) \rightleftharpoons 2H_2O(\ell)$ at 25 °C.

23. The value of the formation constant (K_f) for FeSCN^{2+} is 1000 at a particular temperature.

a. Write the reaction equation that this formation constant describes.

b. Determine the value of the stability constant (K_s) for FeSCN^{2+} at the same temperature.

24. The formation constant for $Fe(CN)_6^{3-}$ is 4.0×10^{43} and for FeSCN^{2+} is 1000 at a particular temperature.

a. Which of these complex ions is more stable?

b. Write the reaction equation for which the stability constant of $Fe(CN)_6^{3-}$ is the equilibrium constant.

c. Calculate the value of K_{eq} for the following reaction using the data in this problem:

$$FeSCN^{2+}(aq) + 6CN^-(aq) \rightleftharpoons Fe(CN)_6^{3-}(aq) + SCN^-(aq)$$

25. Data: $\quad K_{sp}(MnS) = 2.3 \times 10^{-13}$ $\qquad K_{sp}(CdS) = 1.0 \times 10^{-28}$

a. Determine the value of K_{eq} for the reaction: $Cd^{2+}(aq) + MnS(s) \rightleftharpoons Mn^{2+}(aq) + CdS(s)$

(Start by writing the reaction equations for the K_{eq} values given.)

b. Do you expect the reaction in part a to be a good source of product? Explain.

26. Data: $\quad K_f(AgI_2^-) = 1.1 \times 10^9$ $\quad K_{sp}(CuI) = 5 \times 10^{-13}$

a. Determine the value of K_{eq} for the reaction:

$$Ag^+(aq) + 2CuI(s) \rightleftharpoons 2Cu^+(aq) + AgI_2^-(aq)$$

(Start by writing the reaction equations for the K_{eq} values given.)

b. Do you expect the reaction in part a to be a good source of product? Explain.

27. The value of K_b for CO_3^{2-} is 1.8×10^{-4}. The K_{sp} value for CaCO$_3$ is 5.0×10^{-9}.

a. Write the reaction equations for each of the equilibrium constants listed above.

b. Use these data to calculate the value of K_{eq} for the reaction:

$$CaCO_3(s) + H_2O(\ell) \rightleftharpoons Ca^{2+}(aq) + HCO_3^-(aq) + OH^-(aq)$$

28. The value of K_s for Cd(CN)$_4^{2-}$ is 1.2×10^{-18}. The K_b value for CN$^-$ is 1.6×10^{-5}.

a. Write the reaction equations for each of the equilibrium constants listed above.

b. Use these data to calculate the value of K_{eq} for the reaction:

$$Cd(CN)_4^{2-}(aq) + 4H_2O(\ell) \rightleftharpoons Cd^{2+}(aq) + 4HCN(aq) + 4OH^-(aq)$$

c. Do you expect the reverse of the reaction in part b to be an efficient way to produce $Cd(CN)_4^{2-}$?

29.   In the paper, *High Affinity Insulin Binding: Insulin Interacts with Two Receptor Ligand Binding Sites* (published in Biochemistry. 2008 Dec 2; 47(48): 12900) the authors report that insulin binds to insulin receptor in a cooperative way. Thus the K_D values for the two insulin molecules that bind are not the same. This is analogous to hemoglobin's cooperativity, except that there are two binding events instead of four. The two reported K_D values for the interaction of insulin and insulin receptor are 520 pM and 42 pM.

   a. Write the balanced reaction equations for which each of these K_D values applies. (Write two different reaction equations, one for each K_D value.) Use "Ins" as a free insulin molecule and "IR" as a free insulin receptor; use "InsIR" and "Ins$_2$IR" as the receptor with 1 or 2 insulin molecules bound.

   b. What does the inclusion of units on the K_D values mean? If these values were reported according to chemical convention, what would be the values of these two K_D ratios?

   c. If the binding is cooperative (such as the binding of oxygen to hemoglobin) which of the two K_D values is for dissociation of the first insulin molecule (from Ins$_2$IR) and which is for the second dissociation (from InsIR)? Explain.

   d. In general, does this seem to be relatively strong or weak binding?

30.   One of the isomerization reactions of glycolysis and its equilibrium constant are given here:

   Glucose-6-phosphate $\rightleftharpoons$ fructose-6-phosphate $K_{eq} \sim 0.5$

   a. Which species is favored at equilibrium, reactant or product?

   b. If, at equilibrium, the concentration of fructose-6-phosphate was 0.026 µM, what would be the concentration of glucose-6-phosphate?

   c. If the reaction was in its standard state, would the proportion of product be more or less than the equilibrium state?

CHAPTER 17: EQUILIBRIUM II
EQUILIBRIUM STRESSES AND EQUILIBRIUM CALCULATIONS

In Chapter 16 we looked for ways to describe reversible changes. In the process, we learned that all reversible chemical systems can be treated as systems either approaching equilibrium, or at equilibrium. Chapter 17 further explores equilibrium systems. We look closely at systems that are at equilibrium, but then experience a stress that places them out of equilibrium. We consider the types of phenomena that can stress an equilibrium system and determine how the system responds to the stress. Finally, we explore the mathematical strategies necessary to determine the equilibrium partial pressures or concentrations of species in any system. As we pointed out in the previous chapter, reversible systems cannot be described by the arithmetic of limiting reagents; we need another strategy.

17-1. STRESSING A SYSTEM AT EQUILIBRIUM

We begin with the analysis of the behavior of reversible systems whose equilibrium status is disrupted by some outside influence.

In the next pages we will consider the following five scenarios:

A. A flask containing the $2NO_2(g) \rightleftharpoons N_2O_4(g)$ system at equilibrium, at room temperature, has additional NO₂ gas added.

B. A flask containing the $2NO_2(g) \rightleftharpoons N_2O_4(g)$ system at equilibrium, at room temperature, undergoes a change in temperature.

C. A balloon containing the $2NO_2(g) \rightleftharpoons N_2O_4(g)$ system at equilibrium, at room temperature, undergoes a change in volume.

D. A solution of silver chloride (dilute, but saturated, contains some solid silver chloride) experiences the addition of more water.

E. A solution of silver chloride (dilute, but saturated, contains some solid silver chloride) experiences the addition of ammonia.

In each scenario we begin with a system at equilibrium—either the NO₂/N₂O₄ gas system or a saturated (but dilute) solution of silver chloride.

> Silver chloride (AgCl) solutions can be both
> **saturated** and **dilute** because its solubility is very low.

In each case a **stress** to the equilibrium system is applied. By "stress" we mean that an event occurs that renders the system no longer at equilibrium.

If we consider the attributes of the equilibrium constant, we can guess at the types of circumstances that will stress an equilibrium system. First, because equilibrium constants are **temperature dependent**, we expect that changing the temperature will force a system at equilibrium to lose its equilibrium status. Changing the <u>temperature</u> will cause a new value for the equilibrium constant to come into play, and the reaction system will need to adjust its concentrations to achieve this new equilibrium constant value.

Second, because equilibrium constant values depend on the *concentrations (or partial pressures)* of species in the system, any activity that adds species or removes species, or in any way changes the <u>amounts</u> of the species, will likely cause the system to lose its equilibrium status. The system will need to react in such a way as to reestablish the necessary value of the equilibrium constant. When a system needs to react in one direction or another in order to regain equilibrium, we call this bit of reacting a **shift**. If the forward reaction occurs, we say that the system shifts to the right. If the reverse reaction occurs, we say that the system shifts to the left.

$$Reactant \underset{shift\ left}{\overset{shift\ right}{\rightleftharpoons}} Product$$

Our five scenarios (A-E) all fit one or the other of the two types of stresses. As we discuss each scenario, we will come across situations where a particular system is not stressed by a change that we think should stress it. Look carefully for the surprises that follow. Remember, *there are really only two ways to stress a system:*

Two ways to stress an equilibrium system:	Result of the stress:
Alter concentrations (or partial pressures) of system components.	The original value of K_{eq} must be regained.
Change the temperature of the system.	A new value for K_{eq} must be achieved.

There is a helpful principle called **LeChatelier's Principle** that describes qualitatively how a system will respond to a stress that sends it out of equilibrium.

LeChatelier's Principle states that an equilibrium system will adjust to a **stress** *by shifting so as to minimize the stressor, or alleviate the stress.*

We will apply LeChatelier's Principle to each of the stresses we study. Then, we will also provide a more mathematical approach to understanding why the reaction behaves as it does. Both methods are useful for a complete understanding of chemical equilibria, but your instructor may prefer one method over the other.

A. Stress: Adding (or Removing) Some Reactant (or Product)

The stress present in the first scenario is central to the understanding of equilibrium and the equilibrium constant. Consider the gas phase system

$$2NO_2(g) \rightleftharpoons N_2O_4(g)$$

at equilibrium at room temperature. We can use either K_{eq} or K_c to describe this system. The partial pressures present, when placed into the reaction quotient expression, produce the value that is the equilibrium constant for the reaction at room temperature:

$$K_{eq} = \frac{\left(P_{N_2O_4}\right)_{eq}}{\left(P_{NO_2}\right)^2_{eq}} \quad or \quad K_c = \frac{\left[N_2O_4\right]_{eq}}{\left[NO_2\right]^2_{eq}}$$

What happens, and why, when more NO_2 gas is added?

1. LeChatelier's Principle Applied to Shifts Caused by a Concentration/Partial Pressure Change

When additional NO_2 is added, the stress is: *too much NO_2*. According to LeChatelier's Principle the system will shift to try to alleviate that stress; it will try to eliminate some of that extra NO_2, which is a reactant. We say it shifts to the right, or toward product:

$$2NO_2(g) \xrightarrow{shift\ right} N_2O_4(g)$$

The shift to use up NO₂ will result in making additional N₂O₄. The shift will not use up all of the added NO₂. If it did, the system would still not be at equilibrium, because the [NO₂] would be back to where it began, but there would now be too much N₂O₄.

When a system shifts to use up additional reactant, not all of the additional reactant is used up. Only enough is used so that, along with the additional product created by the shift, the proper value of K_{eq} is restored.

NOTE: In a reaction with more than one reactant, only the concentration/partial pressure of one reactant must be changed in order for equilibrium to be lost. Changes in multiple concentrations will also (usually) cause a loss of equilibrium status.

Although we framed this stress as an addition of reactant, a change in the amount of any system component has a similar effect. We summarize the possibilities in the table below. Make sure to think about each entry.

$$\text{Reactant} \underset{\text{left}}{\overset{\text{right}}{\rightleftharpoons}} \text{Product}$$

System Component Stress	Direction of shift	Rationale
Addition of more reactant	Shift right	Uses up some of the added reactant
Addition of more product	Shift left	Uses up some of the added product
Removal of some reactant	Shift left	Replaces some of the missing reactant
Removal of some product	Shift right	Replaces some of the missing product

Don't let "partial pressure" language confuse you. In the example, above, adding NO₂ gas to a system "increases the partial pressure of NO₂" because more of it is found in the same volume (same container). The partial pressure of N₂O₄ did not change when NO₂ was added; there was still the same number of moles in the same size container at the same temperature! Adding more NO₂ gas increased the total pressure of the mixture of gases, but increased the partial pressure of only NO₂ (until the shift occurred)! The only way to increase the partial pressure of <u>one component</u> of a gas phase system, without increasing the partial pressures of other components, is to add more of the one component.

2. Mathematical Approach to the Analysis of Shifts Caused by a Concentration (or Partial Pressure) Change

In order to use the language of concentration instead of partial pressure in much of the remaining sections of this discussion, let's think in terms of K_c instead of K_{eq}; K_c can apply to either aqueous phase or gas phase reactions and allows us think in terms of molarity.

If the concentration of reactant, NO₂, is suddenly increased, the reaction quotient ratio will no longer be equal to the equilibrium constant. Instead, it will have some *smaller* value. The original [N₂O₄] divided by the new (larger) [NO₂] will give a value smaller than K_c:

$$\frac{\left[N_2O_4\right]_{original}}{\left[NO_2\right]^2_{original}} = K_c > Q_c = \frac{\left[N_2O_4\right]_{original}}{\left[NO_2\right]^2_{new,\,larger}}$$

The system will have to shift in order to regain equilibrium. In this case it will need to react in the direction that will decrease [NO₂] and increase [N₂O₄] in order to increase the value of the ratio back to the K_c value. It will shift right:

$$2NO_2(g) \xrightarrow{\text{shift right}} N_2O_4(g)$$

B. Stress: Changing the Temperature of a System

In the second scenario, the same gas system at equilibrium undergoes a change in temperature. Because the values of equilibrium constants are temperature dependent, there is a new value for K_c at the new temperature. The system will have to shift in order to obtain concentrations of reactants and products that produce the new value of the equilibrium constant. Will this be a shift to the right or left?

1. LeChatelier's Principle Applied to Shifts Caused by a Change in Temperature

LeChatelier's Principle can be a lot of help in deciding which direction a shift will occur upon a change in temperature. However, one must first know whether a reaction is endothermic or exothermic. Then, the strategy is to write in "heat" as either a reactant (in an endothermic, heat-requiring process), or as a product (in an exothermic, heat-releasing process). For the exothermic reaction forming N_2O_4, we would write:

$$2NO_2(g) \rightleftharpoons N_2O_4(g) + heat$$

Notice that whenever the forward reaction is exothermic, the reverse reaction will be endothermic (because heat will be a reactant in the reverse direction). LeChatelier's Principle maintains that a system will react to a stress by attempting to minimize the stressor.

> *Raising the temperature of a system at equilibrium will always stimulate the direction of the reaction that <u>uses up some of the excess heat</u>: the endothermic direction of the reaction. Conversely, lowering the temperature of a system at equilibrium will always stimulate the exothermic process; this can be seen as an attempt to <u>generate some heat to replace the heat that was removed</u> by cooling.*

All systems have both an exothermic process and an endothermic process at their disposal because forward and reverse reactions must be opposite in thermal character.

We expect that for the system

$$2NO_2(g) \rightleftharpoons N_2O_4(g) + heat$$

an increase in temperature will cause a shift to the left, because it is the reverse reaction that uses up heat. Conversely, a decrease in temperature would cause a shift to the right, because the forward reaction generates heat.

Classification of a reaction as endothermic or exothermic can be challenging. In some cases, we will simply have to rely on known thermodynamic information and indicate to you whether the forward reaction is endothermic or exothermic. In other cases, however, the knowledge of energy changes associated with bonding (review energy changes associated with bond formation in Chapter 6) allows prediction of the direction of heat flow. Remember that <u>energy is released when bonds are formed</u>. This means that in any case where it is clear that there is more bonding, or stronger bonding, in the products than in the reactants, the reaction will be exothermic. For instance, in the case

$$2NO_2(g) \rightleftharpoons N_2O_4(g)$$

two particles become one when an additional nitrogen-to-nitrogen bond forms:

The forward reaction is therefore exothermic. Prediction of the thermal characteristics of phase change processes is also possible. Melting and boiling require a heat input; so processes such as:

$$H_2O(s) \xrightleftharpoons{melt} H_2O(\ell) \qquad \text{and} \qquad Br_2(\ell) \xrightleftharpoons{boil} Br_2(g)$$

are endothermic in the forward direction. We can show this by including "heat" as a reactant:

$$H_2O(s) + heat \xrightleftharpoons{melt} H_2O(\ell) \qquad \text{and} \qquad Br_2(\ell) + heat \xrightleftharpoons{boil} Br_2(g)$$

Phase changes can also be considered from the standpoint of which side of the reaction arrow has more bonding interactions. In the melting of water, the actual water molecules do not gain or lose bonds, but the hydrogen bonding between separate water molecules is more extensive in ice than in liquid water. So, hydrogen bonds must be disrupted in order to melt water, thus the melting of water is endothermic.

Phase change language	State change	Bonding change	Thermal Character
melting	s → ℓ	more bonds → fewer bonds	Endothermic
freezing	ℓ → s	fewer bonds → more bonds	Exothermic
boiling, evaporation	ℓ → g	more bonds → fewer bonds	Endothermic
condensation	g → ℓ	fewer bonds → more bonds	Exothermic
sublimation	s → g	more bonds → fewer bonds	Endothermic
vapor deposition	g → s	fewer bonds → more bonds	Exothermic

2. Mathematical Approach to the Analysis of Shifts Caused by a Change in Temperature

The key to analyzing shifts associated with temperature changes is to remember that the value of the equilibrium constant changes when the temperature changes. In Chapter 16 we introduced the two general shapes of K_{eq} vs. temperature plots. Figure 17-1 shows the two possibilities. The difference is whether the forward reaction is endothermic or exothermic.

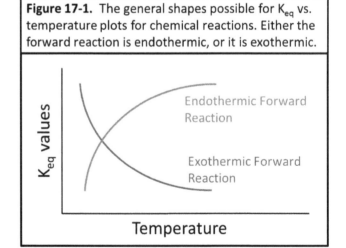

Figure 17-1. The general shapes possible for K_{eq} vs. temperature plots for chemical reactions. Either the forward reaction is endothermic, or it is exothermic.

Endothermic curve (green): As temperature increases, K_{eq} increases (more product forms). As temperature decreases, K_{eq} decreases (more reactant forms). This is in line with our analysis via LeChatelier's Principle, above.

Exothermic curve (purple): As temperature increases, K_{eq} decreases (more reactant forms). As temperature decreases, K_{eq} increases (more product forms). This is in line with our analysis via LeChatelier's Principle, above.

Alternatively, because reverse reactions must display opposite heat flow, we can state the situation this way: **adding heat** helps the endothermic process and **cooling** helps the exothermic process!

Two general reaction equations:	As temp increases:	As temp decreases:
$reactants \xrightleftharpoons[endothermic]{exothermic} products + heat$	Endothermic forward reaction is favored, more product is made, K_{eq} value increases, system shifts right to reach new K_{eq}.	Exothermic reverse reaction is favored, more reactants form, K_{eq} value decreases, system shifts left to reach new K_{eq}.
$reactants + heat \xrightleftharpoons[exothermic]{endothermic} products$	Endothermic reverse reaction is favored, more reactants form, K_{eq} value decreases, system shifts left to reach new K_{eq}.	Exothermic forward reaction is favored, more product is made, K_{eq} value increases, system shifts right to reach new K_{eq}.

We can set this up mathematically by writing the equilibrium constant expression at both the original and the new temperatures for our gas phase system:

$$2NO_2(g) \rightleftharpoons N_2O_4(g) + heat$$

At the original temperature (T_1):
$$K_{(T_1)} = \frac{[N_2O_4]_{(T_1)}}{[NO_2]^2_{(T_1)}}$$

At a higher temperature (T_2) the ratio must equal a new, <u>smaller</u> value (due to exothermicity):

$$K_{(T_2)} = \frac{[N_2O_4]_{(T_2)}}{[NO_2]^2_{(T_2)}}$$

Because $K_{(T_2)} < K_{(T_1)}$ we know that the value of the numerator must decrease and the value of the denominator must increase; therefore, the reaction must shift left. Product is lost and reactant is gained as the temperature increases.

Exercise 17-1.

Which of the following reactions has a K_{eq} value that will increase as temperature increases? Hint: for reactions where the heat flow is not shown, remember to look for a net gain or loss in bonds.

a. $2Cl(g) \rightleftharpoons Cl_2(g)$

c. $3NO(g) \rightleftharpoons N_2O(g) + NO_2(g) + heat$

b. $H_2O(\ell) \rightleftharpoons H_2O(g)$

d. $H_2S(g) + I_2(g) + heat \rightleftharpoons 2HI(g) + S(s)$

Exercise 17-2.

Consider the endothermic reaction $3Al_2Cl_6(g) \rightleftharpoons 2Al_3Cl_9(g)$.
(this means the forward reaction is endothermic.)

a. Which way will this reaction shift if an equilibrium mixture is cooled?

b. Do the K_{eq} values for this reaction rise or fall as the temperature is increased?

C. Stress: Changes in Volume of a Gaseous System

A balloon containing the $2NO_2(g) \rightleftharpoons N_2O_4(g)$ system at equilibrium at room temperature undergoes a change in volume. Can changing the volume of a system stress the system? Yes, each of the gases in the system suffers a *concentration change* when the volume changes. Concentration, after all, is moles per volume, or $\frac{n}{V}$. Because the volume change is the same for all gases in the system (they are all in the same container), the concentrations of all gases (reactants and products) change <u>in the same direction</u>. If the volume increases, all concentrations decrease, and vice versa. For our system

$$2NO_2(g) \rightleftharpoons N_2O_4(g) \quad \text{with } K_c = \frac{\left[N_2O_4\right]_{eq}}{\left[NO_2\right]_{eq}^2}$$

we can analyze the impact of a volume change by representing the concentrations as $\frac{n}{V}$ terms, equivalent to molarity. So, instead of writing: $K_c = \frac{\left[N_2O_4\right]_{eq}}{\left[NO_2\right]_{eq}^2}$

we write:

$$K_c = \frac{\left(\dfrac{n_{(N_2O_4)}}{V}\right)_{eq}}{\left(\dfrac{n_{(NO_2)}}{V}\right)_{eq}^2} = \frac{\left(\dfrac{n_{(N_2O_4)}}{V}\right)_{eq}}{\left(\dfrac{n_{(NO_2)}}{V}\right)_{eq}\left(\dfrac{n_{(NO_2)}}{V}\right)_{eq}} = \frac{\left(n_{(N_2O_4)}\right)_{eq}}{\left(n_{(NO_2)}\right)_{eq}^2} \times V$$

where $n_{(x)eq}$ is the *equilibrium* number of moles of substance x and V is the volume of the container. We see that the *volume of the container is a hidden factor in the value of this equilibrium constant.* If the volume of the container is changed, the equilibrium numbers of moles ($n_{(x)eq}$) will no longer be the correct ones to allow K_c to have the proper value. Numbers of moles will need to adjust so that the correct value of the equilibrium constant is reestablished. Because this stress involves *concentration changes*, like the first scenario (Section A), the shift is to re-establish the original K_c value rather than to establish a new K_c value (as was the case in the temperature change scenario, Section B).

There are three main ways to increase the volume of a gas system:

- rigid walled containers (glassware, tanks): open a stopcock, or valve, that allows the gas system to expand into additional space,

- flexible containers (pistons, balloons): decrease the pressure acting on the container (piston will push up, balloon will expand). Could travel up a mountain to lower atmospheric pressure, or just force a piston upward.

- flexible containers (pistons, balloons): add an **inert**[126] gas to the container, thus causing it to expand.

---

[126]**Inert** means unreactive. An inert gas is one that does not react in any way with the system components. The noble gases could almost always serve this purpose, because they rarely react with anything.

There is one main way to decrease the volume of a gas system:

- increase the pressure on the system in a flexible container (push down on a piston, travel down a mountain to increase atmospheric pressure).

1. LeChatelier's Principle Applied to Shifts Caused by Changes in Volume of the Container for Gas Phase Systems

A chemical reaction cannot control the volume of its container. If a system is stressed by a volume *increase*, the system has no means to decrease the volume. What the system can do is alleviate the stress by providing gas particles to fill up the newly created volume. Which direction of the reaction would have to occur in order to provide more gas particles? In the case of our system,

$$2NO_2(g) \rightleftharpoons N_2O_4(g)$$

the reverse reaction makes two particles from one particle, so the reverse reaction can alleviate the stress of too few particles for the volume. Conversely, a *decrease* in available volume would result in an over-crowded system. For our system, the forward reaction turns two particles into only one, so the forward reaction will alleviate the stress of a decreased volume.

2. Mathematical Approach to Understanding Shifts Caused by Changes in Volume of Container for Gas Phase Systems

We can determine the direction of the required shift (forward reaction or reverse reaction) by paying attention to the equation derived previously. We will use labels of "original" for our system beginning at equilibrium:

$$K_c = \frac{\left(n_{(N_2O_4)}\right)_{original}}{\left(n_{(NO_2)}\right)^2_{original}} \times V_{original}$$

If the volume of this system is *increased* (to some V_{larger}), the system will no longer be at equilibrium:

$$Q_c = \frac{\left(n_{(N_2O_4)}\right)_{original}}{\left(n_{(NO_2)}\right)^2_{original}} \times V_{larger} > K_c$$

Q_c is larger than K_c. In order to regain equilibrium the reverse reaction will need to occur so that the number of moles of product is decreased and the number of moles of reactant is increased. The value of the $\frac{\left(n_{(N_2O_4)}\right)}{\left(n_{(NO_2)}\right)^2}$ term must decrease enough to balance the increase in V and reestablish the proper value of K_c. The system will shift to the left. Make sure to also think through the issues surrounding a *decrease* in volume.

3. Volume Change is Not Always a Stress for Gas Phase Systems

We pause here to reflect on how the identity of the system we have just studied has influenced our result. For contrast, consider the following gas phase reaction system:

$$N_2(g) + O_2(g) \rightleftharpoons 2NO(g) \text{ with } K_c = \frac{[NO]^2_{eq}}{[N_2]_{eq}[O_2]_{eq}}$$

Let's proceed with the substitution of $\frac{n}{V}$ terms for the concentration terms as we did previously.

$$K_c = \frac{[NO]_{eq}^2}{[N_2]_{eq}[O_2]_{eq}} = \frac{\left(\dfrac{n_{NO}}{V}\right)_{eq}^2}{\left(\dfrac{n_{N_2}}{V}\right)_{eq}\left(\dfrac{n_{O_2}}{V}\right)_{eq}} = \frac{\left(n_{NO}\right)_{eq}^2}{\left(n_{N_2}\right)_{eq}\left(n_{O_2}\right)_{eq}} \times \frac{\left(V\right)^2}{\left(V\right)^2} = \frac{\left(n_{NO}\right)_{eq}^2}{\left(n_{N_2}\right)_{eq}\left(n_{O_2}\right)_{eq}}$$

In this case, all volume terms cancel; this is an important result. For this reaction, the value of K_c has no hidden dependence on volume (V). This gas phase reaction will not experience a volume change as a stressor. What is special about the reaction? Here both the reactants and the products contain two moles of gas. There is no shift that can create more gas particles or fewer gas particles. This is a case for which a change in volume of a gas phase reaction is not a stress. Even though concentrations of all system components change, the value of this equilibrium constant is equivalent to both a concentration ratio (in green, above) and to a <u>mole ratio</u> (in pink, above) of the products over the reactants; volume does not come into play. An illustration of this unchanged K_c value follows:

Consider the system

$$N_2(g) + O_2(g) \rightleftharpoons 2NO(g)$$

at equilibrium at some temperature where $K_c = 1.7 \times 10^{-3}$. At equilibrium, a one liter container holds the following equilibrium concentrations:

$$[N_2]_{eq} = 0.492\,M \qquad [O_2]_{eq} = 0.292\,M \qquad [NO]_{eq} = 0.0156\,M$$

These concentrations produce the known equilibrium constant when substituted into the equilibrium constant expression:

$$K_c = \frac{[NO]_{eq}^2}{[N_2]_{eq}[O_2]_{eq}} = \frac{(0.0156)^2}{(0.492)(0.292)} = 1.7 \times 10^{-3}$$

If the volume of the container is increased to two liters, the gases would all be half as concentrated. The new concentrations would be:

$$[N_2]_{eq} = 0.246\,M \qquad [O_2]_{eq} = 0.146\,M \qquad [NO]_{eq} = 0.00780\,M$$

Substitution of these concentrations into the reaction quotient expression yields

$$Q_c = \frac{[NO]^2}{[N_2][O_2]} = \frac{(0.00780)^2}{(0.246)(0.146)} = 1.7 \times 10^{-3} = K_c$$

The change in volume did not upset the equilibrium status of this particular reaction. Because all of the gases were decreased in concentration by the same factor, and there are the same numbers of gas particles in the numerator and the denominator, the system is still at equilibrium and no shift is necessary.

4. Volume Changes in Relation to Pressure Changes

We have been considering container volume changes for gas phase systems. Because gases completely fill their containers, the container's volume is equal to the system's volume. When the volume of a gas phase system is changed at constant temperature, the system's pressure will also change. We can calculate the pressure change associated with a given volume change using the ideal gas law:

$$PV = nRT$$

If a given sample of gas at a specific temperature (meaning that n and T are constant) undergoes changes in pressure and volume, we can write:

$$P_1V_1 = nRT$$

and

$$P_2V_2 = nRT$$

Because nRT is the same in each case we can write

$$P_1V_1 = P_2V_2$$

Substitution of the beginning and ending volumes, along with the original pressure will allow the calculation of the final pressure of the system. You have worked this type of problem in Chapter 15.

<u>a. These Stresses can be Described Either as a Volume Change or as a Pressure Change</u>

A gas phase system undergoing a volume change at constant temperature will also undergo a pressure change. The system might be described in terms of an original and final volume; but it could equally well be described by an initial and final pressure.[127] The two go hand-in-hand. Either can describe the stress to the system. A gas phase system suffering a stress due to a total pressure increase will shift to form fewer gas particles, thus reducing the pressure. Similarly, if the total pressure decreases, the gas phase system will shift to provide more gas particles. If there are the same numbers of gas particles on each side of the reaction equation, a change in pressure will not stress the equilibrium. Remember, *pressure changes that are associated with volume changes can stress a gas phase system because concentrations are changed.*

Exercise 17-3.

The gas phase system $2NO_2(g) \rightleftharpoons N_2O_4(g)$ is at equilibrium at room temperature in a piston cylinder. The piston is pulled outward, making the gas chamber larger. The temperature is held constant. Describe the shift, if any, that occurs for the system.

Exercise 17-4.

The gas phase system $2NO_2(g) \rightleftharpoons N_2O_4(g)$ is at equilibrium at room temperature in a piston cylinder. The piston is pulled outward, decreasing the pressure of the contained system. The temperature is held constant. Describe the shift, if any, that occurs for the system.

<u>b. Adding an Inert Gas to a System in a Rigid Container</u>

Earlier, we pointed out that one way to increase the volume of a gas phase system was to add an inert gas[128] to the system in a flexible container. The exterior pressure of the container stays constant, so the additional gas forces the volume of the container to increase. What happens if an inert gas is added to a system <u>in a rigid container</u>? In this case, the total pressure of the system will be increased by adding the additional gas; but the volume is not increased. This type of pressure change <u>does not affect the partial pressures or concentrations of the gases of the reacting system</u>: they are still present in the same number of moles in a container that is the same size. Therefore, this type of pressure change <u>will not stress the system</u>.

---

[127] Be sure to differentiate between the pressure of a system (the total pressure of all gas components), and the pressure of one system component (the partial pressure of that component). Here, we are considering the former. We considered the latter in Section A, the first scenario.

[128] Here, "inert gas" means more than just the noble gases. It means any gas that is unreactive with other system components. Nitrogen gas is another commonly "inert" gas. Its bond is so strong that it cannot be broken in most situations.

Exercise 17-5.

Imagine that each of the following gas phase systems is at equilibrium in a balloon. The exterior pressure on the balloon is constant. One mole of helium gas is added to each balloon, increasing the size of the balloon. In each case indicate if the equilibrium will shift to the right, the left, or not shift at all.

    a. $2NO_2(g) \rightleftharpoons N_2O_4(g)$

    b. $H_2(g) + I_2(g) \rightleftharpoons 2HI(g)$

    c. $N_2O(g) + NO_2(g) \rightleftharpoons 3NO(g)$

Example 17-1.

Which direction, if any, will each of these systems shift when treated as described?

    a. $2I(g) \rightleftharpoons I_2(g)$ if the volume of the container is increased.

    b. $H_2S(g) + I_2(g) \rightleftharpoons 2HI(g) + S(s)$ if the volume of the container is decreased.

    c. $3NO(g) \rightleftharpoons N_2O(g) + NO_2(g)$ in a rigid container, if a sample of inert neon gas is added.

    d. $H_2S(g) + I_2(g) \rightleftharpoons 2HI(g) + S(s)$ if the partial pressure of H_2S is increased.

    e. $H_2S(g) + I_2(g) \rightleftharpoons 2HI(g) + S(s)$ if the partial pressure of I_2 is decreased.

Solutions:

    a. There are more particles of gas in the reactants than in the products. Making more reactants can fill up the added volume. Shift left.

    b. This system will not experience stress from a volume change. There are two moles of gas on each side of the reaction equation. No shift.

    c. Adding an inert gas will not stress the system because it is in a rigid container. The volume available to each gas is the entire volume of the container. Adding an unreactive gas to a rigid container does not change the concentrations of the gases already in the system. No shift.

    d. The only way to increase the partial pressure of just one component is by adding more of that component. Adding a reactant will cause a shift toward products to use up some of the added reactant. Shift right.

    e. The only way to decrease the partial pressure of just one component is by selectively removing it from the system. Selective removal of a reactant will cause a shift toward reactants to replace the removed material. Shift left.

D. Stress: Dilution of an Aqueous System

    Consider a flask containing a very dilute, but saturated solution of silver chloride, along with some undissolved silver chloride.[129] The solution can be both dilute *and* saturated because silver

---

[129] The undissolved solid is crucial to the equilibrium situation, both the forward and reverse processes must be occurring. This necessitates the presence of solid.

chloride has an extremely low solubility. What happens if there is an addition of more water to this flask? The original system is described by the reaction equation:

$$AgCl(s) \rightleftharpoons Ag^+(aq) + Cl^-(aq)$$

with the equilibrium constant expression

$$K_{sp} = \left[Ag^+ \right]_{eq} \left[Cl^- \right]_{eq}$$

Adding water to this system will lower the concentrations of both of the dissolved ions. The system will no longer be at equilibrium. It will have to shift to reestablish equilibrium. *The process of dilution of an aqueous system is completely analogous to increasing the container size for a gas phase system; both result in increasing the volume of the system.*

1. LeChatelier's Principle Applied to Shifts Caused by a Dilution

We can approach this problem exactly how we approached the problem of increasing the volume of the container for a gas phase reaction. In both cases, system components find themselves in a larger volume, so all concentrations are lowered. The system will shift to try to provide particles to fill up the additional volume. More of the solid salt will dissolve. In the case of an aqueous reaction system with the same number of dissolved ions in the reactants as in the products, no shift will occur upon a change in volume because the system will not be stressed. An example of a system fitting this description is

$$Zn(s) + Cu^{2+}(aq) \rightleftharpoons Zn^{2+}(aq) + Cu(s)$$

Here we see that there are the same number of dissolved ions in the reactants and the products. Diluting a system such as this will not create a stress on the equilibrium position.

2. Mathematical Approach to Understanding Shifts Caused by a Dilution

Upon the addition of solvent, all ions become more dilute. When both $\left[Ag^+ \right]$ and $\left[Cl^- \right]$ become smaller, the value of $Q_{sp} = \left[Ag^+ \right]\left[Cl^- \right]$ becomes smaller than K_{sp}.[130] The system is no longer at equilibrium. A shift to the right occurs in order to re-establish equilibrium concentrations of the ions. More silver chloride will dissolve.

Exercise 17-6.

Which direction, if any, will each of these systems shift when additional water is added to the system at equilibrium?

    a. $Pb^{2+}(aq) + 2I^-(aq) \rightleftharpoons PbI_2(s)$ **b.** $Pb^{2+}(aq) + 2Cr^{2+}(aq) \rightleftharpoons Pb(s) + 2Cr^{3+}(aq)$

E. Stress: Chemical Removal of a Particular System Component

We have already considered the events that occur upon the simple addition or removal of reactants or products from a system at equilibrium (Section A). The following table serves as a review:

---

[130] Q_{sp} is the reaction quotient for a solubility product reaction.

$$\text{Reactants} \rightleftharpoons \text{Products}$$

System Component Stress	Direction of shift	Rationale
Addition of more reactant	Shift right	Uses up some of the added reactant
Addition of more product	Shift left	Uses up some of the added product
Removal of some reactant	Shift left	Replaces some of the missing reactant
Removal of some product	Shift right	Replaces some of the missing product

There are chemical ways to accomplish changes in concentration of species involved in an equilibrium system. In particular, a species can be removed from an equilibrium system by reacting it with something else. Here we look specifically at this type of stress.

Consider a flask containing a very dilute, but saturated solution of silver chloride, and some undissolved silver chloride. What occurs if ammonia is added to this system? As we saw in Chapter 16, Section E2, silver ion reacts with ammonia to produce the complex ion, $Ag(NH_3)_2^+$. The tiny bit of dissolved Ag^+ in a solution of AgCl can react with added ammonia to produce the complex ion. Two equilibria are occurring in the same solution. In essence, silver ion from the silver chloride system is removed from that system by reaction with ammonia. In Chapter 16, we treated this system as two interacting equilibria:

1.	$AgCl(s) \rightleftharpoons Ag^+(aq) + Cl^-(aq)$	$K_1 = 1.8 \times 10^{-10}$
2.	$Ag^+(aq) + 2NH_3(aq) \rightleftharpoons Ag(NH_3)_2^+(aq)$	$K_2 = 1.5 \times 10^7$
sum:	$AgCl(s) + 2NH_3(aq) \rightleftharpoons Ag(NH_3)_2^+(aq) + Cl^-(aq)$	$K_{sum} = K_1 \times K_2 = 2.7 \times 10^{-3}$

Now, however, instead of treating this system as two interacting equilibria, we look at it from the perspective of how the second reaction affects an equilibrium established by the first reaction.

1. LeChatelier's Principle Applied to a Shift Caused by a System Component being Chemically Removed from the System

We define our system as the silver chloride system at equilibrium (reaction 1 in the box, above). If this equilibrium is established, and then ammonia is added, the stress to the original system will be the removal of the product Ag^+ from the system (by reacting it with ammonia according to reaction 2). The system (reaction 1) shifts to add more Ag^+ to the solution (shifts right). As our previous treatment also concluded, more AgCl will dissolve when ammonia is added to the system.

2. Mathematical Approach to Understanding Shifts Caused by the Chemical Removal of a System Component

When ammonia is introduced to an equilibrium system of dissolved silver chloride, it reacts with silver ion from solution. Thus, free silver ion is removed from the solution; $[Ag^+]$ in solution drops upon the addition of the ammonia.

Because

$$K_{eq} = \left[Ag^+ \right]_{eq} \left[Cl^- \right]_{eq}$$

the sudden drop in $[Ag^+]$ sends the system out of equilibrium with

$$Q = \left[Ag^+ \right]_{smaller} \left[Cl^- \right]_{original}$$

In order to restore equilibrium, more of the silver chloride must dissolve; the system shifts to the right. This shift increases both [Ag⁺] and [Cl⁻]; the system has no means at its disposal of increasing only the [Ag⁺]. More silver chloride dissolves until the product $\left[Ag^+\right]\left[Cl^-\right]$ is again equal to 1.8×10^{-10}. If a relatively large concentration of ammonia is added, the dissolving Ag⁺ ions are continuously removed from the system, so silver chloride keeps dissolving. We can see why this salt is so much more soluble in an aqueous solution of ammonia than in plain water. If enough ammonia is added, the solid silver chloride will completely dissolve, but the silver that is in solution will be almost entirely in the $Ag(NH_3)_2^+$ form, rather than free Ag⁺.

Example 17-2.

Consider a flask containing the following system at equilibrium:

$$Fe^{3+}(aq) + SCN^-(aq) \rightleftharpoons FeSCN^{2+}(aq)$$

What will be the effect on this equilibrium if a small portion of silver nitrate solution is added to the flask? Hint: AgSCN is an essentially insoluble salt.

Solution:

When the aqueous silver nitrate solution is added to the equilibrium system, the following reaction takes place:

$$Ag^+(aq) + SCN^-(aq) \longrightarrow AgSCN(s)$$

Because silver thiocyanate is essentially insoluble, we write this reaction with a single, forward arrow. The impact of this second reaction on our original equilibrium system is that it removes one of the reactants, SCN⁻, from the equilibrium. The iron-thiocyanate system will shift to the left to try to replenish the supply of aqueous SCN⁻.

---

3. The Common Ion Effect

In the phrase "the common ion effect," the word "common" is used in the same way it is used in a phrase such as, "you and I have so much in common." Two salts have a **common ion** if either the cation or anion is the same. The **common ion effect** language is specific to aqueous, ionic systems. Here are a couple of examples:

KCl and NaCl	common ion = Cl⁻
MgCl₂ and MgO	common ion = Mg²⁺

Remember that in an equilibrium system of iron thiocyanate the intensity of red color is a measure of how much of the product ion is present because it is the iron thiocyanate ion that is a dark red color (the reactants have little color).

$$Fe^{3+}(aq) + SCN^-(aq) \rightleftharpoons FeSCN^{2+}(aq) \quad \text{(dark red)}$$

Consider adding a solution of KSCN (K⁺ ions and SCN⁻ ions) to an equilibrium system described by the chemical equation above. We are adding the *common ion*, SCN⁻. This is, essentially, the same type of stress that we encountered in our very first scenario (Section A), where the amount of a reactant was increased. Notice that the presence of potassium ions from the potassium thiocyanate has no effect on the Fe³⁺/SCN⁻ equilibrium system, because it is not a component of the system, nor does it react in any way with any component of the system.

> *Adding a common ion to an aqueous system at equilibrium will cause the system to shift to eliminate some of the added ion.*

Adding NaNO₃ to the equilibrium system:

$$Fe^{3+}(aq)+SCN^-(aq)\rightleftharpoons FeSCN^{2+}(aq)$$

will not stress the system, because there is no "common ion" (and also no reaction).

There are two ways that a common ion problem might manifest:

1. A common ion is added to a system already at equilibrium.
      A solution containing 0.03 M FeCl₃ and 0.001 M KSCN is made and the following equilibrium is established: $Fe^{3+}(aq)+SCN^-(aq)\rightleftharpoons FeSCN^{2+}(aq)$. Then, enough solid NaSCN is added to increase the concentration of SCN⁻ to 0.011 M, causing the system to shift right so that the solution becomes a darker shade of red.

2. An equilibrium is established in a solution already containing a common ion.
      We start with a solution that is 0.01 M NaSCN, which is colorless. We add enough solid FeCl₃ to bring the concentration of Fe³⁺ ions to 0.03 M and enough solid KSCN to bring its concentration to 0.011 M. In short, we establish the following equilibrium in a solution that already contained one of the components, the SCN⁻ ion.
      $Fe^{3+}(aq)+SCN^-(aq)\rightleftharpoons FeSCN^{2+}(aq)$. Upon reaching equilibrium, this solution is the same color of red as the final solution in number 1, above.

The important point is that the order of the additions makes no difference to the final result.

Example 17-3.

Consider a flask containing a solution of 0.05 *M* AgNO₃ (a soluble silver salt). If we add solid silver chloride to the flask will more AgCl dissolve than normal? Less than normal? An identical amount?

Solution:

      This is an example of the common ion effect. We are trying to dissolve silver chloride in a system that already contains a large amount of dissolved silver ion. Because K_{sp} for the silver chloride system is only $1.8 \times 10^{-10} = \left[Ag^+\right]\left[Cl^-\right]$ and the *[Ag⁺] is already 0.05 M*, only very tiny amounts of the silver chloride will dissolve. Less silver chloride will dissolve than would have been the case in plain water.

F. Circumstances in which Systems are Not Stressed

      We have looked at a variety of ways to stress an equilibrium system. These all involve either temperature changes (Section B) or concentration changes (Sections A, C, D, E). As we have seen, some changes made to a system at equilibrium will not stress the system. Three of these circumstances have already been discussed:

1. *Changing the volume of a gas phase system that has the same number of gas particles in both the reactant and product.*

2. *Changing the volume of an aqueous system (by evaporation or dilution) that has the same number of dissolved particles in both the reactant and product.*

3. *Changing the pressure of a gas phase system without changing the concentrations of any of the gases in the equilibrium system (by adding an inert gas to a rigid container).*

The fourth situation that results in no stress to a system at equilibrium has not been discussed previously:

4. Using a Catalyst in a Reaction

Perhaps you have heard the word "catalyst" or the phrase "to catalyze." A speaker might be a "catalyst" for change in an organization. A coach might be able "to catalyze" the growth of his team. This kind of language borrows from the language of chemistry. Scientifically, a **catalyst** is a substance that speeds up a chemical reaction. Catalysts speed up the attainment of equilibrium. For our purposes, the most interesting thing about a catalyst is what it does not do: *the addition of a catalyst to a system at equilibrium will not stress the system because a catalyst does not change the K_{eq} value for a reaction, or alter any system concentrations. A catalyst only affects how quickly the equilibrium position can be established.* In the equilibrium state, both the forward and reverse reactions are proceeding at identical rates. A catalyst speeds up the rate of forward reactions and reverse reactions equally, so both are still proceeding at identical (but faster) rates once the catalyst has been added. Adding a catalyst to a system at equilibrium, or to a system approaching equilibrium, will have no effect on the value of the equilibrium constant.

> *A system containing a catalyst will attain its equilibrium position more quickly, but the equilibrium position will be the same as without the catalyst. If the system is already at equilibrium when the catalyst is added, no apparent changes will occur (though on a microscopic level the forward and reverse reactions will both speed up.)*

Biological catalysts are called **enzymes**. Enzymes are proteins that bind the reactant(s) of a desired cellular reaction and use a variety of strategies to speed up the process by which reactant(s) become product(s). The reactant in an enzyme-catalyzed reaction is usually called the **substrate**. Some enzymes are so good at catalysis that the rate of the catalyzed reaction is limited by the ability of the enzyme to find the next substrate molecule, a process that often is limited simply by the rate of diffusion of the molecules in the cell. In other words, the actual chemical change no longer limits the rate of the reaction! It is important to understand that enzymes, like all other catalysts, cannot alter the equilibrium constant of a reaction.

Exercise 17-7.

For each case, state whether or not the system will experience stress. Explain your answers.

    a. Increasing the pressure on the system $Zn(s) + Cu^{2+}(aq) \rightleftharpoons Zn^{2+}(aq) + Cu(s)$.

    b. Decreasing the volume of the system $PbSO_4(s) \rightleftharpoons Pb^{2+}(aq) + SO_4^{2-}(aq)$ by allowing water to evaporate.

    c. Decreasing the temperature of the system $S_3O_9(g) \rightleftharpoons 3SO_3(g)$

    d. Adding a catalyst to the system: $C_2H_2(g) + 2H_2(g) \rightleftharpoons C_2H_6(g)$

17-2. ANSWERING QUANTITATIVE QUESTIONS ABOUT REVERSIBLE SYSTEMS

We have done some quantitative equilibrium calculations already. In Chapter 16, we calculated the value of Q from reaction positions and the value of the K_{eq} from equilibrium positions. However, we have not yet asked how to calculate the equilibrium positions from initial positions. Consider Table 17-1, which will remind you of Tables 16-3 and 16-4. This time, however, we are concerned with how to calculate the values found in the "Equilibrium Position" column.

Table 17-1	$A(aq) \rightleftharpoons 2B(aq)$ 500 °C		
Experiment Number	Initial Position (M)	Equilibrium Position (M)	$K_{eq} = \dfrac{[B]_{eq}^2}{[A]_{eq}}$
1	$[A]_o = 1.000$ $[B]_o = 0$	$[A]_{eq} = ?$ $[B]_{eq} = ?$	$K_{eq} = \dfrac{[B]_{eq}^2}{[A]_{eq}} = 9.0$
2	$[A]_o = 2.000$ $[B]_o = 0$	$[A]_{eq} = ?$ $[B]_{eq} = ?$	$K_{eq} = \dfrac{[B]_{eq}^2}{[A]_{eq}} = 9.0$

Instead of using an equilibrium position to calculate the value of an equilibrium constant, how can we calculate the expected equilibrium concentrations when we know the initial concentrations and the equilibrium constant value?

A. Setting Up an Equilibrium Table

Let's begin with Experiment 1 of Table 17-1. Here, we note that we start with 1.000 M A and no B. We know that the value of the equilibrium constant is 9.0, and we want to calculate $[A]_{eq}$ and $[B]_{eq}$. In other words, we want to know how much reaction will actually occur. One tried and true method for solving a problem such as this is to create what we will call an **equilibrium table**.[131] The plan is to concisely display what we know and what we don't know, allowing us to see how best to proceed. We fill in the top row of the table:

	$A(g)$	$\rightleftharpoons$ $2B(g)$
Initial M	1.000	0
Changes in M	?	?
Equilibrium M	?	?

We use the balanced reaction to provide columns for each reaction species (just A and B in this case). We provide rows for initial concentrations of the species, changes in concentrations as the reaction occurs, and equilibrium concentrations of the species. In our case, we know the initial values, but not the changes or the equilibrium values. Because the equilibrium constant is defined in terms of concentrations, not numbers of moles, the table entries are concentrations.

We want to determine the equilibrium concentrations of the substances; the bottom row values. We know that at least some reaction will take place. We symbolize the amount of reaction that occurs with the variable, x:

Let x = change in concentration of A

Note that the units of x are molarity, and x can be defined in terms of any reactant or product in the system. The balanced reaction equation shows us that when the concentration of A drops by x M, the concentration of B increases by $2x$ M. We can update our table with this information:

	$A(g)$	$\rightleftharpoons$ $2B(g)$
Initial M	1.000	0
Changes in M	−x	+2x
Equilibrium M	?	?

---

[131] Some prefer to call these tables "**ICE**" tables due to the **I**nitial, **C**hange, and **E**quilibrium labels of the three rows.

Notice the negative sign for the change in concentration of A. We know that the concentration of A will decrease as this reaction proceeds because only the forward reaction can occur when no B is initially present.

The values for the changes that occur can now be applied to the initial concentrations. If x amount of the 1.000 M A reacts, the remaining concentration of A will be $(1.000 - x)$. If we begin with no B and then increase its amount by $2x$, we will end up with $2x$ B. We modify our equilibrium table with these expressions for the equilibrium concentrations:

	$A(g)$ $\rightleftharpoons$	$2B(g)$
Initial M	1.000	0
Changes in M	$-x$	$+2x$
Equilibrium M	$1.000 - x$	$2x$

This results in an equilibrium table with useful expressions for the equilibrium concentrations.

Example 17-4.

Set up an equilibrium table for each of the following problems. Use the variable "x" to represent the unknown amount of reaction that will occur.

    a. Dissolving bismuth(III) iodide (a minimally soluble salt) in plain water.

    b. Dissolving bismuth(III) iodide in a solution that is already 0.10 M in iodide ion (a *common ion* situation).

    c. The reaction $3O_2(g) \rightleftharpoons 2O_3(g)$ if you begin with 2.0 bar oxygen and no ozone.

Solutions:

    a. The reaction equation describing the solubility of bismuth(III) iodide is

$$BiI_3(s) \rightleftharpoons Bi^{3+}(aq) + 3I^-(aq)$$

When dissolving a salt in pure water, the starting concentrations of the ions are zero. If x amount of bismuth(III) iodide dissolves, the concentration of bismuth(III) ion will be x and the concentration of iodide ion will be $3x$. We construct the equilibrium table as follows:

	$BiI_3(s)$ $\rightleftharpoons$	$Bi^{3+}(aq)$ +	$3I^-(aq)$
Initial M	pure solid	0	0
Changes in M		$+x$	$+3x$
Equilibrium M		x	$3x$

There is no concentration information in the table for the reactant because it is a pure solid and does not appear in the equilibrium constant expression.

b. This problem is the same as the previous one except for the fact that the solution is 0.10 *M* in iodide ion before the bismuth(III) iodide is added. This changes the initial concentration of iodide ion from zero to 0.10 *M*. We construct the equilibrium table as follows:

	$BiI_3(s)$ ⇌	$Bi^{3+}(aq)$	+ $3I^-(aq)$
Initial M		0	0.10
Changes in M	pure solid	+x	+3x
Equilibrium M		x	0.10 + 3x

c. Here we have a gas phase reaction: $3O_2(g) \rightleftharpoons 2O_3(g)$. The stoichiometry tells us that for every 3 oxygen molecules that react, 2 ozone molecules are produced. So, if *x* amount of reaction occurs, 3*x* oxygen will disappear and 2*x* ozone will appear. We start with 2.0 bar oxygen and zero ozone, so the equilibrium table is constructed as follows:

	$3O_2(g)$ ⇌	$2O_3(g)$
Initial P (bar)	2.0	0
Changes in P (bar)	-3x	+2x
Equilibrium P (bar)	2.0 - 3x	2x

B. Using the Equilibrium Table to Calculate Equilibrium Concentrations

Equilibrium tables can help us set up the calculation of equilibrium concentrations of substances. Substitution of the **equilibrium concentration expressions** (bottom row, in terms of *x*) into the equilibrium constant expression leaves us an equation with only one unknown (if we know the value of *K*). For our example reaction, $A \rightleftharpoons 2B$ with an equilibrium constant of 9, we write:

$$K_c = \frac{[B]_{eq}^2}{[A]_{eq}} = \frac{(2x)^2}{1.000 - x} = 9$$

This is an equation that can be solved for *x* in a variety of ways.

1. Solving Rigorously for "x" by Hand

First, the equation $\qquad \dfrac{(2x)^2}{1.000 - x} = 9$

can be rearranged to a quadratic equation of the form, $ax^2 + bx + c = 0$:

$$4x^2 = 9(1.000 - x)$$
$$4x^2 = 9.000 - 9x$$
$$4x^2 + 9x - 9.000 = 0$$

The final equation, above, can be solved by use of the *quadratic formula*:

$$\frac{-b \pm \sqrt{b^2 - 4ac}}{2a} = x$$

The results are:

$$x = \frac{-9 \pm \sqrt{9^2 - 4(4)(-9)}}{2(4)} = 0.75 \ M \quad or \quad -3.0 \ M$$

We know that the result cannot be -3.0 M, because that would result in a negative concentration of B (equilibrium concentration is $2x$ which would be $2(-3.0 \ M) = -6.0 \ M$)! The 0.75 M answer makes sense, though. The amount of reaction that occurs (x) is 0.75 M. The equilibrium concentrations of A and B under these circumstances would be:

$$\left[A \right]_{eq} = 1.000 - x = 1.000 - 0.75 = 0.25 \ M$$
$$\left[B \right]_{eq} = 2x = 2(0.75) = 1.50 \ M$$

Notice that these equilibrium amounts lead to an equilibrium constant of 9:

$$K = \frac{[B]^2_{eq}}{[A]_{eq}} = \frac{(1.50)^2}{0.25} = 9$$

2. Solving by Making Simplifying Assumptions

A second method that is often useful in solving expressions such as

$$\frac{(2x)^2}{1.000 - x} = 9.0 \times 10^{-4}$$

is to assume that x is very small in relation to whatever number it is moderating, 1.000 in our case.

This assumption will be considered valid if it is found that x is less than 5% of 1.000.

If x is very small compared to 1.000, then one can assume that $1.000 - x$ is simply 1.000. For instance, if x turned out to be 2.3×10^{-4} then

$$1.000 - 2.3 \times 10^{-4} = 0.99977 \approx 1.000$$

The assumption of an insignificant x simplifies the arithmetic that must be done to solve our problem because instead of:

$$\frac{(2x)^2}{1.000 - x} = 9.0 \times 10^{-4} \qquad \text{we can write:} \qquad \frac{(2x)^2}{1.000} \approx 9.0 \times 10^{-4}$$

We solve for x:

$$4x^2 \approx 9.0 \times 10^{-4}$$
$$x \approx \sqrt{\frac{9.0 \times 10^{-4}}{4}} = 1.5 \times 10^{-2} \ M$$

This answer can be considered correct if our assumption that x is much smaller than 1.000 passes the 5% test:

$$5\%(1.000 \ M) = 0.05 \ M = 5 \times 10^{-2}$$

Because our value of x is less than 5% of 1.000 M, we can consider this our final answer. (Just to double check once, the actual answer to this problem, solved rigorously, is 0.015.)

When will making this simplifying assumption not work? A good indication of potential trouble occurs when the value of K_{eq} is not small enough. When K_{eq} is relatively large, more reaction occurs. Because x is a measure of how much reaction occurs, x is larger when K_{eq} is larger. Here's an example of a larger K_{eq} causing an assumption to not work:

$$\text{Solve the problem:} \qquad \frac{(2x)^2}{1.000 - x} = 9.0 \qquad (\text{instead of } 9.0 \times 10^{-4})$$

We try the assumption that x is very small in relation to 1.000, and the arithmetic seems simplified:

$$\frac{(2x)^2}{1.000} \approx 9.0 \qquad \text{thus} \qquad 4x^2 \approx 9.0 \qquad \text{and} \qquad x \approx \sqrt{\frac{9.0}{4}} = 1.5\ M$$

We check to see if our calculated value of x passes the 5% test:

$$5\% \,(1.000\ M) = 0.05\ M$$

Uh-oh! $x = 1.5\ M > 0.05\ M$

When x is greater than 5% of the number it is moderating (1.000 M in our case), the assumption has failed and the value of x that was calculated (1.5 M) is <u>not</u> the correct answer to the original problem. Making the assumption of a small x was not warranted in this case. The actual value of x (which we found earlier by rigorously applying the quadratic equation) is 0.75 M.

Important reminder: *If you are assuming that x is very small in comparison to some other number, it must turn out to be smaller than 5% of that number, otherwise the assumption is invalid and you must solve in a more rigorous fashion.*

Example 17-5.

At 500 K, gaseous iodine breaks down to iodine atoms with $K_c = 5.6 \times 10^{-12}$. If 0.020 M gaseous iodine is placed into a vessel and held at 500 K until equilibrium is reached, calculate the final concentration of iodine atoms.

Solution:

We can use an equilibrium table to find sensible expressions for the equilibrium concentrations of the iodine species:

	$I_2(g)$ $\rightleftharpoons$	$2I(g)$
Initial M	0.020	0
Changes in M	-x	+2x
Equilibrium M	0.020 − x	2x

Now we substitute the equilibrium concentration expressions from the table into the equilibrium constant expression:

$$K_c = \frac{[I]^2}{[I_2]} = \frac{(2x)^2}{(0.020 - x)} = 5.6 \times 10^{-12}$$

This arithmetic can be simplified by assuming that x is insignificant in comparison to 0.020 (symbolized as $x \ll 0.020$). We expect the assumption to be a good one because the K value is very small, so not much reaction will occur. The simplification results in the following:

$$K_c = \frac{[I]^2}{[I_2]} = \frac{(2x)^2}{(0.020 - x)} \approx \frac{(2x)^2}{(0.020)} = 5.6 \times 10^{-12}$$

This problem is easily solved:

$$4x^2 = \left(5.6 \times 10^{-12}\right)\left(0.020\right)$$

$$x^2 = \frac{\left(5.6 \times 10^{-12}\right)\left(0.020\right)}{4} = 2.8 \times 10^{-14}$$

$$x = \sqrt{2.8 \times 10^{-14}} = 1.67 \times 10^{-7} \ M$$

We check our assumption by making sure that $x \ll 0.020$ is true: $5\% \ (0.020 \ M) = 0.001 \ M$ and our x value is, indeed, much smaller than this.

Once a value for the variable x has been attained, always go back to the problem and determine whether or not x is the answer. In our case it is not. The problem asked us to find the concentration of iodine atoms in the equilibrium mixture. The equilibrium table tells us that $\left[I\right]_{eq} = 2x$. So to finish:

$$\left[I\right]_{eq} = 2x = 2\left(1.67 \times 10^{-7} \ M\right) = 3.34 \times 10^{-7} \ M$$

You can double check this result by using the quadratic formula to solve this problem. Two roots are found: $-0.167, 1.67 \times 10^{-7}$. Only the positive root is possible in this problem.

3. Solving Rigorously for "x" by Using an Equation Solving Calculator

So far we have considered two ways to solve for x in a problem such as:

$$\frac{\left(2x\right)^2}{\left(0.020 - x\right)} = 5.6 \times 10^{-12}$$

1. *rigorously solve the problem by hand, or*
2. *make an appropriate simplifying assumption (when possible), and solve a much simpler math problem.*

The third way to solve a problem of this type is to use the equation solving capability of a graphing calculator or a computer. Once mastered, this is certainly the quickest and most accurate method. Many different graphing calculators exist and their "solvers" do not all work the same.

We offer five tips for the use of calculators to solve equations:

1. Be sure to enter the equation properly. It may take more use of parentheses than you think. An equation that we might write as:

$$K_{eq} = \frac{(2x)^2}{0.020 - x}$$

   may need parentheses in the denominator, depending on the calculator:

   $$K_{eq} = (2x)^2/(0.020 - x)$$

   If the parentheses in the denominator are omitted, the calculator may interpret the equation as

   $$K_{eq} = \frac{(2x)^2}{0.020} - x$$

2. Equations can be saved in the calculator for later use in a different problem. Many equilibrium constant expressions are similar in form, so saving a few equations may help to avoid a lot of repetitive equation entering. Refer to the owner's manual for specific instructions.

3. Some calculators will not be able to return a correct value of x unless they are given a

ballpark value from which to start iterating. In this case, enter the K_{eq} value as an initial "guess" at the value of x.

4. Once the calculator has returned a value for x, that value is assigned to the variable "x" in doing further calculations, even outside of the solver. So, if the calculator has determined that $x = 1.2761715890373$, entering "$2 - x$"
    will yield: $2 - 1.2761715890373 = 0.723828410963$.

5. Calculators, as always, pay no attention to significant digits!

Example 17-6.

Here is the same problem as in Example 17-5, but posed in pressure units instead of concentration units.

At 500 K, gaseous iodine breaks down to iodine atoms with $K_{eq} = 2.3 \times 10^{-10}$. If 0.82 bar gaseous iodine is placed into a vessel and held at 500 K until equilibrium is reached, calculate the final partial pressure of iodine atoms.

Solution:

We can use an equilibrium table to find sensible expressions for the equilibrium partial pressures of the iodine species. We set up our equilibrium table in units of bars because we have a K_{eq} value rather than a K_c value.

	$I_2(g) \rightleftharpoons$	$2I(g)$
Initial P (bar)	0.82	0
Changes in P (bar)	-x	+2x
Equilibrium P (bar)	0.82 – x	2x

Substitute the equilibrium pressure expressions from the bottom row of the table into the equilibrium constant expression:

$$K_{eq} = \frac{\left(P_I\right)^2}{\left(P_{I_2}\right)} = \frac{\left(2x\right)^2}{\left(0.82 - x\right)} = 2.3 \times 10^{-10}$$

Use a solver to determine the value of x: $x = 6.8665570101013 \times 10^{-6}$ bar

The final pressure of iodine atoms is $2x = 1.4 \times 10^{-5}$ bar

---

Example 17-7.

Calculate the equilibrium concentrations of A and B for the second experiment in Table 17-1 (at the beginning of section 17-2). Start by setting up an equilibrium table. Use a mathematical method suggested by your instructor.

Solution:

First we set up the necessary equilibrium table. Because we know K_{eq} and all system components are solutes, we set up the table using molarities.

	$A \rightleftharpoons$	$2B$
Initial M	2.000	0
Changes in M	-x	+2x
Equilibrium M	2.000 – x	2x

Substitution of the equilibrium concentration expressions into the equilibrium constant expression yields;

$$K_{eq} = \frac{[B]_{eq}^2}{[A]_{eq}} = \frac{(2x)^2}{2.000 - x} = 9.0$$

A solver or the quadratic equation can be used to assess the value of x for the equation above. Either method yields: $x = 1.2762$ M (and many more digits). We use at least one extra digit to do our remaining work (in order to avoid rounding errors):

$[A]_{eq} = 2.000 - 1.2762 = 0.72 \, M$ and $[B]_{eq} = 2x = 2(1.2762) = 2.6 \, M.$

Note 1: The other root of the quadratic equation is −3.5262 M and cannot possibly be correct!

Note 2: This problem cannot be solved by assuming that $x \ll 2$; the equilibrium constant is not particularly small. If you tried that, x turns out to be 2.1 M which is (obviously!) not less than 5% of 2.

Example 17-8.

Determine the equilibrium concentration expected for each of the species in the following system. Use both of the methods **a** and **b** to solve for x:

    a. Make a simplifying assumption: solve for x by assuming that its subtraction from or addition to another number will not be noticeable, and so can be ignored. Make sure to check the assumption using the 5% rule.

    b. Solve for x by using an equation solver.

The value of K_c for the equilibrium $COCl_2(g) \rightleftharpoons CO(g) + Cl_2(g)$ at a particular temperature is 2.2×10^{-10}. If a 2.0 L flask is charged with 0.0864 moles of $COCl_2$ gas and the system is allowed to reach equilibrium, calculate the equilibrium concentrations of all three gas species.

Solutions:

First we need to set up our equilibrium table. Because we know K_c, we use molarity units in the table. We determine the initial molarity of the $COCl_2$ involved in our reaction:

$$[COCl_2]_0 = \frac{moles}{volume} = \frac{0.0864 \, mol}{2.0 \, L} = 0.0432 \, M$$

The table can now be constructed:

	$COCl_2(g)$ $\rightleftharpoons$	$CO(g)$ +	$Cl_2(aq)$
Initial M	0.0432	0	0
Changes in M	−x	+x	+3x
Equilibrium M	0.0432 − x	x	3x

We produce the equation to be solved by substituting the equilibrium concentration expressions (from the equilibrium table) into the equilibrium constant expression:

$$K_c = \frac{[CO]_{eq}[Cl_2]_{eq}}{[COCl_2]_{eq}} = 2.2 \times 10^{-10}$$

$$= \frac{(x)(x)}{0.0432 - x} = \frac{x^2}{0.0432 - x} = 2.2 \times 10^{-10}$$

a. We are asked to solve this problem by assuming that x is very small compared to 0.0432. (This will likely be the case due to the very small value of K.) We continue with our calculations:

$$K_c = \frac{(x)(x)}{0.0432 - x} \approx \frac{x^2}{0.0432} \approx 2.2 \times 10^{-10}$$

$$x^2 \approx (2.2 \times 10^{-10})(0.0432) = 9.5 \times 10^{-12}$$

$$x \approx \sqrt{9.504 \times 10^{-12}} = 3.08286 \times 10^{-6} \, M$$

Notice that the units of our equilibrium table supply the unit of our x value. We get help analyzing the sensibility of this result by checking the *5% rule:*

$$5\% \text{ of } 0.0432 = (0.05)(0.0432) = 2.2 \times 10^{-3}.$$

Since $x = 3.08 \times 10^{-6} < 2.2 \times 10^{-3}$, we can conclude that our assumption was acceptable.

The three gases are present as follows in the equilibrium mixture:

$$[COCl_2]_{eq} = 0.0432 - x = 0.0432 - 3.08 \times 10^{-6} = 0.0432 \, M$$

$$[CO]_{eq} = x = 3.1 \times 10^{-6} \, M \qquad [Cl_2]_{eq} = x = 3.1 \times 10^{-6} \, M$$

b. Practice the use of a calculator's equation solver. Enter the equation (without simplifying assumptions) into the solver:
$$K_{eq} = x^2/(0.0432 - x)$$

Note: For some calculators, the parentheses are necessary in the denominator. Some calculator users prefer to directly enter the value of K, instead of the variable "K."

When the equation is entered correctly, you can input the K value, clear the current x value, and ask the calculator to solve. The result is $x = 3.0827458208421E-6$ or we write $x = 3.08 \times 10^{-6} \, M$.

Having a value in hand (and in the calculator) for x lets us easily finish the task of calculating the equilibrium concentrations. Simply go back to the equilibrium table and substitute in the value of x.

$[COCl_2]_{eq} = 0.0432 - x = 0.0432 - 3.08 \times 10^{-6} = 0.0432 \, M$ (so little reaction occurs that the initial concentration and final concentration of this species are not measurably different.)

$[CO]_{eq} = [Cl_2]_{eq} = x = 3.1 \times 10^{-6} \, M.$

Example 17-9.

$COCl_2$ can be heated to establish the equilibrium: $COCl_2(g) \rightleftharpoons CO(g) + Cl_2(g)$. Suppose that a flask is charged with 0.75 bar CO and 0.56 bar Cl_2 and the system is allowed to reach equilibrium. If x = the increase in pressure of $COCl_2$, determine the following quantities in terms of x:

  a. the pressure of $COCl_2$ at equilibrium   **b.** the pressure of CO at equilibrium
  c. the pressure of Cl_2 at equilibrium   **d.** K_{eq}

Solutions:

Construct an equilibrium table with units of bars. The answers needed come directly from the entries in the table. Because we are starting with only products present, we know that the reverse reaction will occur.

	$COCl_2(g)$ $\rightleftharpoons$	$CO(g)$ +	$Cl_2(aq)$
Initial P (bar)	0	0.75	0.56
Changes in P (bar)	+x	–x	–x
Equilibrium P (bar)	x	0.75 – x	0.56 – x

  a. the equilibrium pressure of $COCl_2$ = x bars.
  b. the equilibrium pressure of CO = (0.75 – x) bars
  c. the equilibrium pressure of Cl_2 = (0.56 – x) bars
  d. substituting all of these equilibrium pressures into the K_{eq} expression gives a K_{eq} expression in terms of x:

$$K_{eq} = \frac{\left(P_{CO}\right)_{eq}\left(P_{Cl_2}\right)_{eq}}{\left(P_{COCl_2}\right)_{eq}}$$

$$K_{eq} = \frac{(0.75 - x)(0.56 - x)}{x}$$

IMPORTANT: notice that if we know K_{eq}, we are able to solve for x, and if we know x, we are able to solve for K_{eq}.

Exercise 17-8.

At 1000 K gaseous sulfur trioxide decomposes to gaseous sulfur dioxide and molecular oxygen with an equilibrium constant $K_{eq} = 0.293$. Determine the equilibrium partial pressures of the three gases if a flask originally contains 1.50 bar of sulfur trioxide and then is allowed o reach equilibrium at 1000 K.
Hint: remember to set up the equilibrium table in terms of "bars."

17-3. HEMOGLOBIN, LECHATELIER'S PRINCIPLE, AND EQUILIBRIUM CONSTANTS

We have learned previously that human hemoglobin is a tetrameric protein of $\alpha\alpha\beta\beta$ structure with a reasonably high affinity for binding oxygen (O_2) at its four heme groups. Oxygen forms a **reversible** *coordinate covalent* bond with the Fe^{2+} ion at the center of the heme. Because the role of hemoglobin is to transport oxygen, the reversibility of this bond-forming reaction is critical. Bonds between heme groups and O_2 must be made and broken to allow for delivery of O_2 from lung to tissue. We can depict the overall chemical reaction as

$$Hb + 4\,O_2 \rightleftharpoons Hb(O_2)_4 \qquad \text{with} \qquad K_{eq} = \frac{\left[Hb(O_2)_4\right]}{\left[Hb\right]\left[O_2\right]^4}$$

where "Hb" represents the hemoglobin tetramer (including the heme groups) and "Hb(O₂)₄" represents a hemoglobin molecule with 4 oxygen molecules bound. LeChatelier's principle plays a major role in helping hemoglobin bind oxygen in the lungs, and then release it in the tissues. Remember that O_2 is plentiful in the lungs. When a reactant is plentiful, the reaction shifts to the right and results in a high concentration of oxygenated hemoglobin. Then, when the hemoglobin moves into the tissues where the presence of free oxygen is considerably lower, the equilibrium shifts to the left. Oxygen is released into the tissues and the cycle can repeat as hemoglobin circulates back to the lungs.

LeChatelier's principle alone cannot account for the very large amount of oxygen that hemoglobin manages to deliver. Myoglobin is essentially a single subunit of hemoglobin; see Figure 17-2. Myoglobin binds oxygen too tightly to be able to deliver it to normal tissues. The

tetrameric form of hemoglobin is a structural feature whose importance to the task of oxygen delivery cannot be overstated.

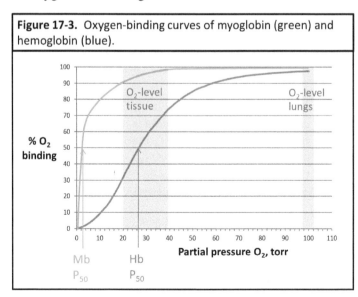

Figure 17-2. Left: Myoglobin with its heme cofactor. Ribbon style protein, space-filling heme. **Right:** Hemoglobin; a tetramer of myoglobin-like subunits. Each subunit is a different color, each has its own heme cofactor.

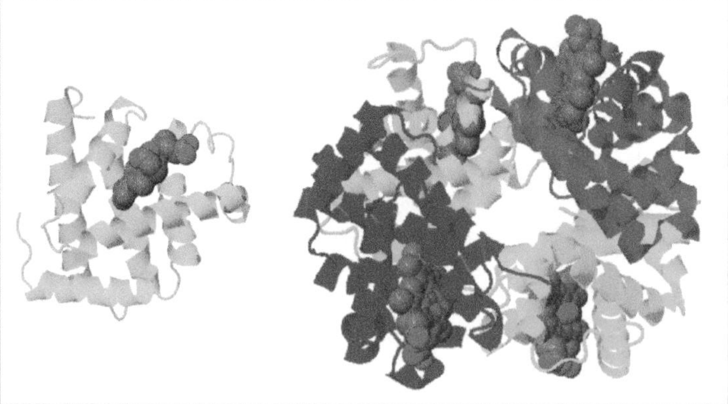

Myoglobin is an excellent oxygen storage molecule, but a very poor transporter. Why? It binds oxygen extremely well. Its oxygen binding curve is very different than that of hemoglobin, as shown in Figure 17-3. The hyperbolic myoglobin curve is consistent with the single binding site. It is noteworthy that the storage molecule (myoglobin) has a higher affinity for oxygen at nearly all oxygen partial pressures than the transport protein (hemoglobin). This is essential, because myoglobin gets its oxygen from hemoglobin.

Furthermore, if hemoglobin's binding curve was hyperbolic, it would either have to be a strong binder, similar to myoglobin, in which case it would be able to deliver very little of the oxygen it carried to the tissues (myoglobin is still > 90% bound under normal tissue conditions), or, it would have to be a weak binder having a hyperbolic binding curve with a much lower maximum. The net result would again be poor delivery, but this time because the binding in the lungs was not favorable enough. It is the tetrameric structure of hemoglobin that allows for the sigmoidal binding curve.

Figure 17-3. Oxygen-binding curves of myoglobin (green) and hemoglobin (blue).

What is so special about grouping multiple binding sites together? It allows for oxygen-binding that is "cooperative" in nature. **Cooperative binding** means that the binding of one oxygen molecule encourages the binding of the next oxygen molecule. In other words, the four oxygen ligands have different affinities for hemoglobin; there is <u>not</u> just one equilibrium constant for the binding of oxygen. This means that our previous thinking:

$$Hb + 4\,O_2 \rightleftharpoons Hb(O_2)_4 \qquad \text{with} \qquad K_{eq} = \frac{\left[Hb(O_2)_4\right]}{\left[Hb\right]\left[O_2\right]^4}$$

is an over-simplification. Instead, we need to think in terms of the sequential binding of 4 oxygen molecules; see box at right. The magic of hemoglobin is that these individual equilibrium constants are not the same, *even though the binding sites are essentially identical.* The value of K_1 is much smaller than that of an isolated subunit.[132] The equilibrium constants get larger as more oxygen is bound:

$$Hb + O_2 \xrightleftharpoons{K_1} Hb(O_2)$$
$$Hb(O_2) + O_2 \xrightleftharpoons{K_2} Hb(O_2)_2$$
$$Hb(O_2)_2 + O_2 \xrightleftharpoons{K_3} Hb(O_2)_3$$
$$Hb(O_2)_3 + O_2 \xrightleftharpoons{K_4} Hb(O_2)_4$$

$$K_1 < K_2 < K_3 < K_4$$

The feature that allows for cooperativity is the flexibility of the protein backbone which allows a conformational adjustment in the tertiary structure of a subunit when oxygen is bound. When this conformational adjustment takes place in one subunit, neighboring subunits in the tetrameric molecule are influenced, because they are "rubbing elbows" with each other. Crystal structures of the two primary subunit conformations are shown in Figure 17-4. The structure on the left has all four subunits in the conformation favoring the binding of O_2; we call this the **oxygenated conformation**. The

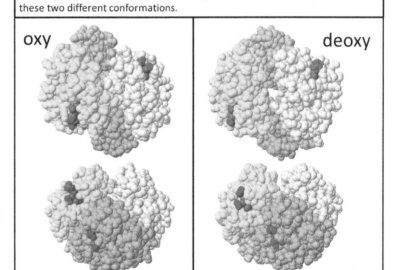

Figure 17-4. The oxygenated and deoxygenated conformations of hemoglobin, rendered in a space-filling scheme, two views of each. The edges of two hemes are visible in each view. Notice the change in size of the central open core in these two different conformations.

structure on the right shows all four subunits in the **deoxygenated conformation**. The binding of oxygen to one subunit causes it to switch from the deoxygenated to the oxygenated conformation. This changes interactions at the subunit-subunit boundaries making it easier for neighboring subunits to flip to the oxygenated conformation. This increases the affinity of remaining subunits for oxygen molecules. Each additional oxygen molecule bound to the tetramer causes a higher and higher affinity for adding more oxygen.

---

[132] An isolated subunit is very similar to the myoglobin molecule.

Let's look at this quantitatively. Under a particular set of conditions, an <u>isolated</u> subunit (a monomer) from a hemoglobin molecule has a K value for O_2 binding of about 2000-3000. Under the same conditions, the tetrameric structure displays first and last K values of approximately:

$$K_1 \approx 30 \qquad\qquad Hb + O_2 \xrightleftharpoons{K_1} Hb(O_2)$$

$$K_4 \approx 3000\text{-}5000 \qquad\qquad Hb(O_2)_3 + O_2 \xrightleftharpoons{K_4} Hb(O_2)_4$$

Because the K_4 value is only slightly larger than the isolated subunit value, it appears that the primary value of the tetramer is to <u>decrease</u> hemoglobin's affinity for small numbers of oxygen. Similarly, scrutiny of Figure 17-2 shows that tetrameric hemoglobin and monomeric myoglobin have similar abilities to bind oxygen at 100 torr (and higher). Differences in oxygen binding abilities of the monomer and tetramer arise as the partial pressure of oxygen drops. It appears that the strategy of the tetrameric structure is important to *helping hemoglobin let go*.

Let's view the process from a "letting go" perspective instead of a binding perspective. If we consider the reverse reactions, the K_{eq} values will be reciprocals and we can write the following K_D (dissociation constants) for oxygen and hemoglobin:

First letting go step: $\quad K_D \approx 1/4000 = 3 \times 10^{-4} \qquad Hb(O_2)_4 \xrightleftharpoons{K_D} Hb(O_2)_3 + O_2$

Final letting go step: $\quad K_D \approx 1/30 = 3 \times 10^{-2} \qquad Hb(O_2) \xrightleftharpoons{K_D} Hb + O_2$

The small dissociation constant for loss of the first O_2 indicates a poor ability to let go of any oxygen molecules. However, when the fully bound hemoglobin migrates into the low $[O_2]$ tissue region, LeChatelier's principle encourages the release of some oxygen. Then, as we see by the larger and larger successive K_D values, when some oxygen has been delivered (let go), the delivery of more is encouraged by a better and better dissociation constant.

This type of binding behavior is called **cooperativity**. The cooperativity of hemoglobin is a type of **positive cooperativity** because the binding of one ligand encourages the binding of additional ones. We could also say that the release of one ligand encourages the release of more. Either statement is a description of positive cooperativity. **Negative cooperativity**, on the other hand, occurs when the binding of one substrate/ligand[133] discourages the binding of additional ones. This is not as common in biological systems, but has been shown to occur in rare cases.

There are additional influences on hemoglobin's oxygen-binding capabilities. One of these, of which we will just scratch the surface, is that there are several **heterotropic allosteric effectors** of hemoglobin. Let's take a close look at all of those new words:

An **effector**	is a small molecule that binds to a protein in order to influence its activity.
Allosteric	effectors influence the protein's activity by adjusting the conformation (tertiary structure, shape) of the protein upon binding to a site that is not the normal substrate/ligand site.
Heterotropic	means that the small molecule serving as the effector is not the normal substrate/ligand.

---

[133] The small molecule that binds to the active site of a protein is called a **substrate** if the protein is an enzyme (that chemically alters the substrate), but is called a **ligand** (lye´-gand) if it binds and releases reversibly, with no chemical changes. A biologist would likely say that oxygen is a ligand (lye-gand) of hemoglobin; a chemist would likely say that oxygen is a ligand (rhymes with "pig") of hemoglobin, due to the covalent bond to a metal ion, as in Chapter 10.

Heterotropic allosteric effectors, then, are other species (not the normal substrate) that bind to a protein at sites other than the normal active site and that, by binding, affect the activity of the protein by influencing its shape. Heterotropic allosteric effectors of hemoglobin bind to the tetramer in places other than at the oxygen-binding position of the heme; one example is the molecule 2,3-bis-phosphoglycerate (BPG), which is shown in Figure 17-5.

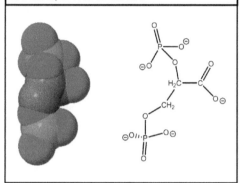

Figure 17-5. 2,3-Bisphosphoglycerate, an allosteric effector of hemoglobin, two views. Hydrogen atoms typically do not show in crystal structures, as seen on the left.

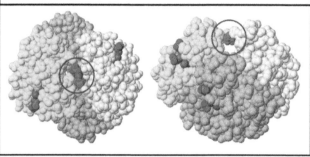

Figure 17-6. Two views of the binding of BPG (circled) to hemoglobin in the cleft between the two beta-subunits (green and yellow). The edges of hemes are also seen protruding from some subunits.

Where does BPG bind to hemoglobin? As can be seen in Figure 17-6, BPG wedges between the two beta-subunits of hemoglobin (remember that hemoglobin is an $\alpha\alpha\beta\beta$ tetramer). Take a close look at the oxygenated and deoxygenated conformations in Figure 17-4. Which of these conformations has enough room for BPG to bind? Only the deoxy conformation has room for BPG!

Allosteric effectors come in two different classes: **positive effectors** (whose binding increases the protein's activity, or increases its ability to bind substrate) and **negative effectors** (whose binding decreases the protein's activity, or decreases its ability to bind substrate). For hemoglobin, positive effectors stabilize the oxygenated conformation, thus encouraging oxygen to bind, and negative effectors stabilize the deoxygenated conformation, thus encouraging the release of bound oxygen. Thus, BPG is a negative heterotropic allosteric effector of hemoglobin. *Heterotropic* because it is not O_2, *negative* because the binding of BPG stabilizes the deoxy conformation and thus discourages the binding of oxygen, and *allosteric* because it binds to a site that is not the O_2-binding site and influences protein shape. Taken altogether, we see that BPG helps hemoglobin let go!

Exercise 17-9.

Why might the oxygen molecule be considered an example of a *positive homotropic effector* of hemoglobin?

There are many natural effectors of the hemoglobin molecule. Want to learn more about all the "tricks" that allow hemoglobin to do its job? A more complete study of the fascinating hemoglobin molecule is usually accomplished in upper level biochemistry courses!

17-4. LeChatelier's Principle and Metabolic Flux.

Biochemical reactions occurring in the cell are not isolated. Metabolic pathways are constructed from successive reactions. Each reaction is mediated by an enzyme (catalyst) so that transformations can be accomplished quickly. The product of the first reaction of a pathway serves as substrate for second reaction, and so on. The metabolic pathway from glucose to pyruvate is called **glycolysis**. Glycolysis is a 10-reaction pathway (under aerobic conditions) that leads to the production of small amounts of ATP and the pyruvate ion (which continues on to the citric acid cycle).

Table 17-2 gives an outline of reactants and products of the steps of the **glycolytic pathway**, including the equilibrium constant for each of the biochemical reactions. As can be seen, many of the equilibrium constants are less than 1.0, even far less than 1.0. It seems likely, then, that this metabolic pathway would not be able to make much of the ultimate product, pyruvate. Enzyme catalysts cannot solve this problem because catalysts cannot change the equilibrium constant. The answer to the problem of small equilibrium constants in a metabolic sequence lies in LeChatelier's principle. Let's see how this works.

Our explanation of the metabolic strategy will be based on the scheme shown in Figure 17-7 (next page). Notice that reversible arrows are used for reactions in the scheme with small equilibrium constants and single forward arrows are used for the reactions having

Table 17-2. Glycolytic reactions and their equilibrium constants.

Step	K_{eq}	reactants	products
1	650	Glucose	Glucose-6-phosphate
2	0.52	Glucose-6-phosphate	Fructose-6-phosphate
3	240	Fructose-6-phosphate	Fructose-1,6-bisphosphate
4	9.8×10^{-5}	Fructose-1,6-bisphosphate	Glyceraldehyde-3-phosphate <u>and</u> dihydroxyacetone phosphate
5	0.054	Dihydroxyacetone phosphate	Glyceraldehyde-3-phosphate
6	0.087	Glyceraldehyde-3-phosphate	1,3-Bisphosphoglycerate
7	1.5×10^3	1,3-Bisphosphoglycerate	3-Phosphoglycerate
8	0.17	3-Phosphoglycerate	2-Phosphoglycerate
9	0.52	2-Phosphoglycerate	Phosphoenolpyruvate
10	2.0×10^5	Phosphoenolpyruvate	Pyruvate

large equilibrium constants. The key to understanding the situation is to start at the end of the pathway (Reaction 10) and work toward the beginning. We note that the final step of glycolysis has an excellent equilibrium constant:

$$\text{Reaction 10:}\quad K_{eq} = 2.0\times10^5$$

Thus, at equilibrium, this reaction provides large concentrations of products compared to reactants. We see the use of a single forward arrow in Reaction 10. This indicates that the equilibrium constant is large, such that for all practical purposes the reaction seems to "go to completion." If Reaction 10 were alone in the cell, the concentrations of reactant (phosphoenolpyruvate and ADP) would be very low and the concentration of product (pyruvate and ATP) would be high.

We now consider the reaction that feeds Reaction 10:

$$\text{Reaction 9:}\quad K_{eq} = 0.52$$

This reaction has a small K_{eq} value (less than 1.0) and we note that it is represented with reversible arrows. If left on its own, the concentration of reactants at equilibrium would be larger than that of products. However, this reaction does not hinder flux through the pathway but rather provides a continual source of phosphoenolpyruvate, its product. How? Reaction 10 effectively consumes the phosphoenolpyruvate produced by Reaction 9. Thus Reaction 9 is continually pulled forward by the (bio)chemical removal of its product. Reaction 9 is not hindered by its poor equilibrium constant because it is continually pulled forward by LeChatelier's Principle. Reaction 9 does not achieve the equilibrium state because its product keeps "disappearing."

We can make a similar argument for Reaction 8 of the process. Because Reaction 9 is continually fluxing forward to try to achieve equilibrium, Reaction 8 must also be pulled forward as its product is consumed in Reaction 9. As we investigate each earlier glycolytic step, it becomes apparent that as long as the last step in the process has a large equilibrium constant, the sizes of the earlier equilibrium constants really don't matter much. Each reaction step has its product depleted by subsequent steps, so all reactions shift to the right, thus producing successful metabolic flux.

The glycolytic pathway is often represented in biochemistry textbooks similarly to the scheme offered above. We are particularly interested in how arrows are being used. Note that only K_{eq} values larger than 100 have been given single forward arrows.[134] LeChatelier's Principle provides the drive that allows metabolic sequences to efficiently flux toward product. Without this effect, many molecules would get "stuck" part way through a metabolic path, thus wasting a lot of material and energy.

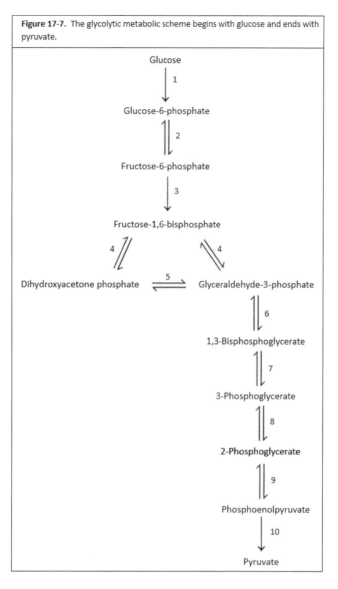

Figure 17-7. The glycolytic metabolic scheme begins with glucose and ends with pyruvate.

---

[134] There is no defined point at which K_{eq} is universally considered large enough to be represented by a single forward arrow. This is a judgement call.

Summary Points

Reaction Stresses:

Two ways to stress an equilibrium system:	Result of the stress:
Alter concentrations (or partial pressures) of system components.	The original value of K_{eq} must be regained.
Change the temperature of the system.	A new value for K_{eq} must be achieved.

1. Changing the temperature of a system at equilibrium (Section B)
   a. increased T will favor the endothermic direction of system
   b. decreased T will favor the exothermic direction of system

2. Changing the concentrations of one or more components of an equilibrium system.
   a. adding or removing a system component
      either physically (Section A) or chemically (Section E)
   b. changing the volume of a system
      *gas phase reactions: changing the container volume (Section C)
      *solution reactions: changing the volume of solvent (Section D)

3. Non-Stresses
   a. volume change when the reaction has same number of moles on each side
      gas phase or solution phase
   b. adding an inert gas to a rigid container
   c. adding a catalyst

LeChatelier's Principle: an equilibrium system will adjust to a **stress** by shifting so as to minimize the stressor, or alleviate the stress.

Solving Equilibrium Problems:

1. Use an equilibrium table in units of molarity (K_{eq} or K_c) or bars (K_{eq} or K_p). You cannot mix and match these units, so if you have a reaction with both dissolved substances and gases, use K_c, not K_{eq}.

2. Determine an equation in terms of x that is solvable by at least one method:
   use the solver on your calculator;
   use a simplifying assumption, solve the equation, check the assumption;
   solve outright, using the quadratic equation when possible.

4. Once the value of x has been determined, use it to calculate whatever quantity you were seeking.

CHAPTER 17 PROBLEMS

1. Suppose the equilibrium $PCl_3(g) + Cl_2(g) \rightleftharpoons PCl_5(g)$ has been established. If this is an endothermic reaction as written, predict whether the *number of moles of* Cl_2 will <u>increase</u>, <u>decrease</u>, or <u>stay the same</u> when:

   a. A catalyst is added.   **d.** The pressure of PCl_5 is decreased.
   b. The volume is increased.   **e.** The temperature is decreased.
   c. The pressure of PCl_3 is increased.   **f.** The total pressure is increased

2. Suppose the equilibrium $2\,NO_2(g) \rightleftharpoons N_2O_4(g)$ has been established. If this is an exothermic reaction, predict whether the *number of moles of* NO_2 will <u>increase</u>, <u>decrease</u>, or <u>stay the same</u> when:

   a. $P_{N_2O_4}$ is increased   **c.** The volume is decreased
   b. The temperature is increased   **d.** A catalyst is added

3. Consider the following exothermic reaction: $2NO(g) + O_2(g) \rightleftharpoons 2NO_2(g)$
   Predict the direction, if any, in which an established equilibrium will shift when:

   a. More O_2 is added
   b. NO_2 is removed   **d.** The temperature is reduced
   c. The pressure is reduced   **e.** A catalyst is added

4. The following equilibrium has been established:

   $$SbF_5(g) \rightleftharpoons SbF_3(g) + F_2(g)$$

   This is an endothermic reaction as written. Predict whether the *number of moles of* F_2 will <u>increase</u>, <u>decrease</u>, or <u>stay the same</u> when:

   a. A catalyst is added.   **b.** The partial pressure of SbF_5 is increased.
   c. The total pressure is decreased.   **d.** The temperature is increased.

5. Consider the sublimation of iodine occurring in a piston chamber: $I_2(s) \rightleftharpoons I_2(g)$
   Predict the direction (if any) of the shift in the equilibrium caused by the following.
   Briefly explain your answers.

   a. An increase in pressure on the piston (for example, adding a weight to the piston)
   b. An increase in temperature
   c. Addition of neon gas to the piston chamber at constant pressure
   d. Taking the piston chamber from Denver to Los Angeles (at constant temp)

6. For the equilibrium $H_2O(\ell) \rightleftharpoons H_2O(g)$ predict the direction of the shift in the equilibrium (if any) when:

    a. A catalyst is added
    b. The temperature is increased
    c. The total pressure is decreased
    d. $Cu(NO_3)_2$ is dissolved in the liquid water [note: Cu^{2+} reacts with H_2O to form the complex ion $[Cu(H_2O)_6]^{2+}$]

7. Consider the following equilibrium in aqueous solution:

$$Ni^{2+}(aq) + 6\,NH_3(aq) \rightleftharpoons Ni(NH_3)_6^{2+}(aq)$$

Indicate the direction the equilibrium will shift (if any), and briefly explain your reasoning, when:

    a. The concentration of Ni^{2+} is doubled.
    b. Water is added to the solution.
    c. Nitrogen is bubbled through the solution to displace (remove) dissolved ammonia.
    d. Ethylenediamine, which forms a more stable complex with Ni^{2+} than does NH_3, is added.

8. For AgCl : K_{sp} at $4.7\,°C = 0.21 \times 10^{-10}$
                    K_{sp} at $100\,°C = 215 \times 10^{-10}$

Is the reaction $Ag^+ + Cl^- \rightleftharpoons AgCl$ endothermic or exothermic? Explain briefly.

9. Lead(II) ions can be precipitated from aqueous solution by adding HCl. Addition of hot water causes the precipitate to dissolve. Is the reaction

$$PbCl_2(s) \longrightarrow Pb^{2+}(aq) + 2Cl^-(aq)$$

endothermic or exothermic? Explain briefly.

10. The following equilibrium has been observed: $2\,BrCl(g) \rightleftharpoons Br_2(g) + Cl_2(g)$
Suppose 0.200 bar of BrCl is placed in a container of fixed volume, and this equilibrium is established. Let x = increase in pressure of Br_2.

    a. Construct, and fill in, an equilibrium table using the definition of x.
    b. Write an expression for K_p in terms of x.

11. Antimony pentafluoride, SbF_5, can be heated to establish the equilibrium:

$$SbF_5(g) \rightleftharpoons SbF_3(g) + F_2(g)$$

Suppose 1.20 bar of SbF_5 is heated in a container of fixed volume, and this equilibrium is established. Let x = decrease in pressure of SbF_5.

    a. Construct, and fill in, an equilibrium table using the definition of x.
    b. Write an expression for K_p in terms of x.

12. Consider the reaction $C_2H_2(g) + Br_2(g) \rightleftharpoons C_2H_2Br_2(g)$. The initial pressure of C_2H_2 is 1.00 bar, the initial pressure of Br_2 is 0.20 bar, and the decrease in pressure of Br_2 as equilibrium is reached is z.

    a. Construct, and fill in, an equilibrium table in terms of z.
    b. Write an expression for K_p in terms of z.

13. The following equilibrium occurs in the gas phase :

$$2\,BrCl(g) \rightleftharpoons Br_2(g) + Cl_2(g)$$

Suppose an initial mixture in a sealed container has

$$P_{BrCl} = 0.300 \text{ bar}, \ P_{Br_2} = 0.100 \text{ bar}, \text{ and } P_{Cl_2} = 0.000 \text{ bar}.$$

Let x = pressure change in BrCl.

    a. Construct, and fill in, an equilibrium table using the definition of x.
    b. Write an expression for K_p in terms of your x.

14. Suppose 0.100 bar of ClF and 0.300 bar of SF_4 are mixed, and the following equilibrium is established: $ClF(g) + SF_4(g) \rightleftharpoons SF_5Cl(g)$

    a. Define a variable (x) to describe the change in pressure of a reactant or product that occurs as equilibrium is reached.
    b. Construct, and fill in, an equilibrium table using your definition of x.
    c. Write an expression for K_p in terms of your x.

15. Suppose 0.40 bar of SeO_2 and 0.10 bar of O_2 are mixed, and the following equilibrium is established: $2\,SeO_2(g) + O_2(g) \rightleftharpoons 2\,SeO_3(g)$

    a. Define a variable (x) to describe the change in pressure of a reactant or product that occurs as equilibrium is reached.
    b. Construct, and fill in, an equilibrium table using your definition of x.
    c. Write an expression for K_p in terms of your x.

16. Acetylene, C_2H_2, at 5.00 bar and benzene, C_6H_6, at 0.30 bar are mixed, and the following equilibrium is established in the presence of a catalyst: $3\,C_2H_2(g) \rightleftharpoons C_6H_6(g)$

    a. Define a variable (x) to describe the change in pressure of a reactant or product that occurs as equilibrium is reached.
    b. Construct, and fill in, an equilibrium table using your definition of x.
    c. Write an expression for K_p in terms of your x.

17. Consider the equilibrium : $C_{10}H_{12}(g) \rightleftharpoons 2\,C_5H_6(g)$

Suppose 0.30 bar of $C_{10}H_{12}$ and 0.10 bar of C_5H_6 are mixed, and equilibrium is established.

    a. Define a variable (x) to describe the extent of reaction that occurs.
    b. Construct, and fill in, an equilibrium table using your definition of x.
    c. Write an expression for K_p in terms of your x.

18. Consider the equilibrium : $C_{10}H_{12}(g) \rightleftharpoons 2\,C_5H_6(g)$

    a. At higher temperatures, C_5H_6 is favored. Is the reaction as written above exothermic or endothermic?

    b. Predict the effect on the equilibrium of:

        (1) A decrease in $P(C_{10}H_{12})$
        (2) An increase in total pressure
        (3) A decrease in temperature

19. At 700 K, the equilibrium $C(s) + 2 H_2(g) \rightleftharpoons CH_4(g)$ is established. The pressure of H_2 at equilibrium is 0.180 bar, and the pressure of CH_4 is 0.290 bar.

   a. Determine the value of K_p.

   b. To the equilibrium mixture is added 0.110 bar of H_2, and equilibrium is reestablished. What is the final pressure of H_2?

20. At 448 °C, the system $H_2(g) + I_2(g) \rightleftharpoons 2 HI(g)$ has $K_p = 50.53$. If 1.000 bar each of H_2 and I_2 are mixed in a glass bulb of fixed volume, and equilibrium with HI is achieved at this temperature, what is the pressure of H_2 at equilibrium?

21. Ammonium carbamate, $NH_4CO_2NH_2$, a solid, decomposes as follows :

$$NH_4CO_2NH_2(s) \rightleftharpoons 2NH_3(g) + CO_2(g)$$

   a. Predict the effect on the equilibrium of:

   (1) Increasing the pressure of CO_2
   (2) Decreasing the total pressure
   (3) Increasing the temperature

   b. At 40 °C, solid ammonium carbamate is allowed to come to equilibrium with NH_3 and CO_2, and a total pressure of these gases of 0.363 bar is reached. Calculate K_p, the equilibrium constant of the reaction as written above.

22. The equilibrium between brown NO_2 and colorless N_2O_4 is readily established at room temperature:

$$2 NO_2(g) \rightleftharpoons N_2O_4(g)$$

At 45 °C, $K_p = 1.073$ for the reaction as written. A sealed gas bulb contains only these two gases at 45 °C. The total pressure in the bulb is 1.000 bar.

   a. Calculate the partial pressure of NO_2 in the bulb.

   b. If the temperature is increased, more NO_2 is formed. Is the reaction as written above endothermic or exothermic?

   c. In a separate experiment, 0.250 bar of NO_2 and 0.750 bar of N_2O_4 are mixed, and equilibrium is established.

   (1) If x = change of pressure of NO_2 on establishment of equilibrium, what is the equilibrium pressure of N_2O_4 in terms of x?

   (2) Calculate the equilibrium pressures of both gases.

   d. What would you predict for the structure of NO_2 (show diagram) ?

   e. Why do you suppose there is a tendency for NO_2 molecules to "dimerize" to form N_2O_4 ?

   f. One of these molecules is diamagnetic. Which one?

23. The gas S_3O_9 is placed in a glass bulb, and the following equilibrium is established:

$$S_3O_9(g) \rightleftharpoons 3 SO_3(g)$$

The initial pressure of S_3O_9 is 0.1000 bar (initially no SO_3 is present). If the total equilibrium pressure in the bulb is 0.2360 bar, calculate the equilibrium partial pressures of S_3O_9 and SO_3. [HINT: Set up an equilibrium table and use Dalton's Law of Partial Pressures!]

CHAPTER 18: THE CHARACTERISTICS OF ACIDS AND BASES; FOCUS ON STRONG ACIDS, STRONG BASES, AND WATER

18-1. INTRODUCTION: ACIDS AND BASES

Many common products contain acids and bases. Acids are found in automobile batteries, bleach, and oven cleaner. Many foods contain acids—citric acid in citrus fruits, acetic acid in vinegar, and phosphoric acid in soft drinks. Bases are found in cleaning supplies such as lye and ammonia. Baking soda is a base. The reactions between acids and bases can be either subtle or obvious. Try pouring a little vinegar (acid) on some baking soda (base) and you will observe an obvious, gas-producing reaction. But, not all acid-base reactions evolve (give off) a gas. One of our goals in this chapter and the following chapter will be to understand the nature of the reactions between acids and bases. Before we get to this, however, we should explore the definitions of acids and bases and develop an understanding of the behavior of water in acid and base systems.

18-2. DEFINITIONS OF ACIDS AND BASES

Defining acids and bases is more complicated than might be expected. Three important definitions of acids and bases have followed the development of understandings within the field of chemistry. A particular chemical substance might be an acid according to all three definitions, or only according to one. We will begin with the oldest and narrowest definition and work through progressively newer and broader understandings.

A. The Arrhenius Definitions

The earliest conception of acids was physiological in nature: acids taste sour. Bases were first classified merely by their ability to neutralize an acid. Later it was noted that bases have a generally bitter flavor. The chemical understanding of acids grew when it was noted that the molecules that had acidic characteristics all contained dissociable hydrogen ions.[135] The dissociative process was noted to occur in aqueous solutions. So, acetic acid (CH_3CO_2H) was labeled an acid by virtue of the fact that one of its four hydrogens can dissociate from the molecule (as H^+) when the molecule is dissolved in water:

$$CH_3CO_2H(aq) \rightleftharpoons H^+(aq) + CH_3CO_2^-(aq)$$

The Lewis dot structures of the dissociation process are shown here. Notice that the bonding electrons to the dissociated hydrogen ion have stayed behind with the acetate ion:

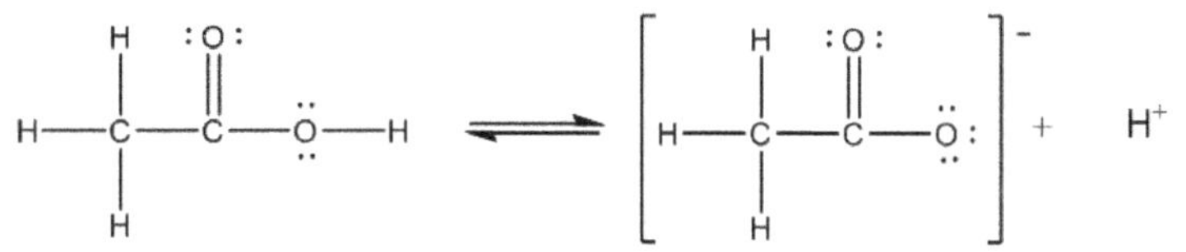

_____

[135] Dissociable hydrogen ions are those that can be removed rather easily from the rest of the structure, leaving both bonding electrons behind. Because a hydrogen atom *nucleus* is a single proton, H^+, the hydrogen ion is often called a proton.

All acids were understood to undergo a parallel dissociation in aqueous systems.

$$HCl(aq) \rightleftharpoons H^+(aq) + Cl^-(aq)$$

$$HCN(aq) \rightleftharpoons H^+(aq) + CN^-(aq)$$

Practice writing the Lewis dot structures of reactant and products. The observation that all acids were undergoing the same process was a valuable insight; it led to the first understanding of the distinction between "strong" and "weak" acids. Acid strength was seen to be dependent upon the equilibrium constant for the dissociation. Strong acids dissociated essentially completely (K_{eq} very large) while weak acid dissociations had smaller equilibrium constants ($K_{eq} < 1$). This view of the distinction between strong and weak acids has evolved only a little. We will look at the modern view later in the chapter. For now the most important point is that

> *an acid was understood to be a species capable of the dissociative liberation of a hydrogen ion (proton) in water solution.*

The acidic character of an acid solution is due to the released proton.

Similarly, bases were understood to be those substances that contained dissociable hydroxide ions (OH^-). The only recognized bases, then, were the hydroxide salts of various cations:

$$NaOH(s) \longrightarrow Na^+(aq) + OH^-(aq)$$

$$KOH(s) \longrightarrow K^+(aq) + OH^-(aq)$$

$$Ba(OH)_2(s) \longrightarrow Ba^{2+}(aq) + 2OH^-(aq)$$

All of these bases, by our current understanding, would be considered strong bases because they are strong electrolytes; complete dissociation of the ions accompanies the dissolving of these salts.[136]

> *A base was understood to be species capable of the dissociative liberation of hydroxide ions in aqueous solution.*

These hydroxide ions were believed to be responsible for the basic character of the solution.

Arrhenius Definitions	
Acid	Proton Liberator (in water solution)
Base	Hydroxide Ion Liberator (in water solution)

Eventually certain shortcomings of these understandings became problematic:

(1)   Only hydroxide salts were defined as bases. However, other species (such as ammonia, NH_3) cause the formation of hydroxide ions in water solution. These should be considered bases, but where did the OH^- come from?

(2)   Further experimentation led to a better understanding of the nature of the acid-liberated proton. The crux of the new understanding was that a bare proton could not exist in aqueous solution. Rather the liberated proton was strongly hydrated by at

---

[136] Some hydroxide salts are much less soluble than others, but remember that a limited solubility does not prevent a species from being a strong electrolyte.

least one water molecule. The energetically more stable *hydronium ion*, H_3O^+,[137] is a much better representation of the actual chemical species created in solution by the acid. Given this understanding, it became clear that "dissociation" was not an accurate representation of the acid system. Rather, the proton in question was not so much "dissociable" as it was "transferable," and the recipient was the water molecule. "Transfer" language is a better fit to the process than "dissociation" language.

In Arrhenius theory, reactions between acids and bases were understood as "neutralization" processes. The products of these reactions were salts and water (and the water wasn't noticeable):

$$\underline{Base} \quad + \quad \underline{Acid} \quad \rightarrow \quad \underline{Salt} \quad + \quad \underline{Water}$$

$$KOH(aq) + HCl(aq) \rightleftharpoons KCl(aq) + H_2O(\ell)$$

$$NaOH(aq) + HCN(aq) \rightleftharpoons NaCN(aq) + H_2O(\ell)$$

By the Arrhenius definitions salts were taken to be "neutral" species. Another problem arose:

(3) Growing evidence showed that many salts have acid and base properties. Solutions of sodium cyanide (product of the second reaction above) are weakly basic, not neutral.

Eventually the problems associated with what has come to be known as the Arrhenius concept of acids and bases led to the development of a more sophisticated understanding that resolved the problems noted above. The Arrhenius definitions served as an important stepping stone to the more modern Bronsted-Lowry definitions. The Arrhenius concept of acids and bases is still useful as an introduction to acid-base concepts.

B. The Bronsted-Lowry Definitions

1. "Transfer" Instead of "Dissociation"

The Bronsted-Lowry concept of acids and bases arose from the emerging understanding that *acids are capable of donating a proton* (H^+) to a water molecule, not just liberating a free proton. Instead of a "dissociation" process that is entirely a bond-breaking process, the Bronsted-Lowry concept introduces proton-transfer language and writes the reaction of an acid in water as a proton **transfer**:

$$acidH(aq) + H_2O(\ell) \rightleftharpoons \left[acid\right]^- (aq) + H_3O^+(aq)$$

or a common, more abbreviated generic form:

$$HA(aq) + H_2O(\ell) \rightleftharpoons A^-(aq) + H_3O^+(aq)$$

The proton transfer results in the formation of the **hydronium ion**, H_3O^+.[138] The transfer process involves both bond-breaking and bond-making steps.

The concept of bases expanded, similarly, to include any species capable of reacting with water in another proton transfer process to produce the **hydroxide ion**, OH^-. *A Bronsted-Lowry base can extract a proton from some other species, such as water*:

---

[137] Actually, the proton is certainly hydrated by more than one water molecule, creating species such as $H_5O_2^+$, $H_7O_3^+$, and $H_9O_4^+$ (with 2, 3 and 4 water molecules, respectively). We will continue to use the hydronium ion, H_3O^+, as a representation of any and all of these hydrated species.

[138] Again, see footnote 137, H_3O^+ is understood as an abbreviation for any hydrated proton.

$$base(aq) + H_2O(\ell) \rightleftharpoons Hbase^+(aq) + OH^-(aq)$$

or a common, more abbreviated form:

$$B{:}(aq) + H_2O(\ell) \rightleftharpoons BH^+(aq) + OH^-(aq)$$

In the abbreviated general reaction, above, a lone pair of electrons is sometimes shown on the base (B:). These are the electrons that are used to make the new bond to the proton taken from the water molecule. In Bronsted-Lowry theory, both acid and base behaviors are characterized by a proton transfer process.

Bronsted-Lowry Definitions	
Acid	Proton Donor
Base	Proton Acceptor

2. Acid and Base Behaviors Require Both an Acid and a Base

Consider the examples of acid and base behavior in Table 18-1. Notice that for HCl to donate its proton, a water molecule must accept the proton. Similarly, for ammonia (NH_3) to accept a proton, water must donate a proton.

Table 18-1. Bronsted-Lowry Acids and Bases in Water	
Acids	Production of H_3O^+
HCl	$HCl(g) + H_2O(\ell) \rightleftharpoons Cl^-(aq) + H_3O^+(aq)$
CH_3CO_2H	$CH_3CO_2H(\ell) + H_2O(\ell) \rightleftharpoons CH_3CO_2^-(aq) + H_3O^+(aq)$
Bases	Production of OH⁻
NH_3	$NH_3(g) + H_2O(\ell) \rightleftharpoons NH_4^+(aq) + OH^-(aq)$
CN⁻	$CN^-(aq) + H_2O(\ell) \rightleftharpoons HCN(aq) + OH^-(aq)$

> *The point is that acids cannot behave as acids in the absence of a base, and vice versa. Acid-base character is defined by the **transfer** of a proton so there must be both a <u>donor</u> and an <u>acceptor</u>.*

Is OH⁻ a base under the Bronsted-Lowry concept? Yes it is. A proton transfer reaction between hydroxide ion and water molecules undoubtedly occurs, but the products are indistinguishable from the reactants:

$$OH^-(aq) + H_2O(\ell) \rightleftharpoons H_2O(\ell) + OH^-(aq)$$

Hydroxide salts are not dependent on the reaction with water to place hydroxide ions into solution; the salt must just dissolve. Hydroxide salts are bases under the Bronsted-Lowry theory, just as they were in Arrhenius theory, but many other species that produce hydroxide ions in water are also recognized as bases by Bronsted-Lowry theory.

Example 18-1.

    a. Write the acid ionization reaction equation for the acid HOBr in water solution.
    b. Write the base ionization reaction equation for the base HSO_3^- in water solution.

Solutions:

The forms of acid ionization reaction equations and base ionization reaction equations are shown in Table 18-1. Acid ionizations always produce hydronium ion. Base ionizations always produce hydroxide ions.

    a. $HOBr(aq) + H_2O(\ell) \rightleftharpoons OBr^-(aq) + H_3O^+(aq)$

    b. $HSO_3^-(aq) + H_2O(\ell) \rightleftharpoons H_2SO_3(aq) + OH^-(aq)$

Exercise 18-1.

Write the acid ionization reaction equation for each of these acids in water.

    a. HBr   **b.** $HClO_4$ **c.** HOCl   **d.** $C_6H_5CO_2H$

(The structure of the acid in part **d** is shown below. It is the last H in the formula that is acidic; hydrogen atoms directly bonded to carbon atoms are only acidic under special circumstances, which will be considered in organic chemistry.)

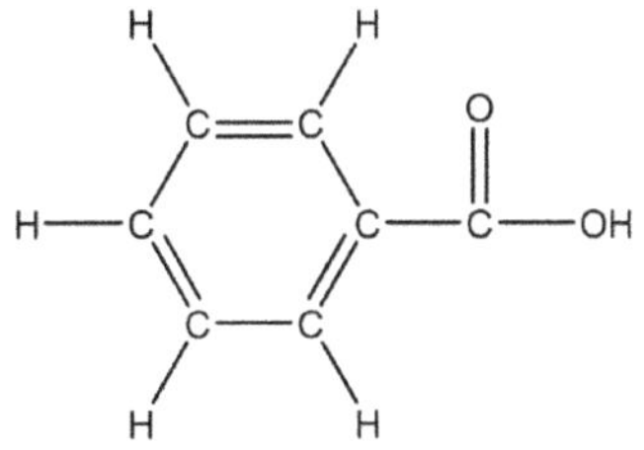

Exercise 18-2.

Write the base ionization reaction equation for each of these bases in water.

    a. NO_2^- **b.** $CH_3CO_2^-$ **c.** CH_3NH_2 **d.** $C_6H_5O^-$

Notice that you don't have to know much about these bases in order to write these reaction equations, although writing the formula in an acceptable way can be a challenge. Some acid formulas list the acidic proton(s) first (such as $HClO_4$ from Exercise 18-1), while others list the formula in a way that helps the reader decipher the structure (such as $C_6H_5CO_2H$ from Exercise 18-1). Chapter 6, Section 6-5, D.3 may be helpful to you.

3. Comparing Arrhenius and Bronsted-Lowry Definitions

    The Bronsted-Lowry concept of acids and bases is more satisfactory than the Arrhenius concept on many levels.

    (1) It eliminates thinking about bare protons in water solution, where evidence indicates they cannot exist.
    (2) It allows species other than hydroxide salts to be labeled as bases. This is encouraging,

because many species in addition to hydroxide salts have characteristics we expect of bases: the production of hydroxide ion in water, the neutralization of acidic solutions, etc.

(3) It eliminates the dependence on an aqueous system by defining acids and bases without reference to their specific behavior in water. *An acid is defined as a species that is capable of <u>donating a proton</u> to some otherspecies and a base is defined as a species that is capable of <u>accepting a proton</u> from some other species.* The other species can be a water molecule, but it can also be many other species.

Consider the following comments to build an appreciation of the relationship between Arrhenius and Bronsted-Lowry theories.

- *All species once considered to be Arrhenius acids and bases are still acids and bases under the Bronsted-Lowry concept.*

- *The nature of what causes acidic character has been revised from "proton dissociation in water" to "proton transfer."*

- *Most (but not all) Bronsted-Lowry acids would also be considered acidic by Arrhenius theory.* An important class of exceptions is non-aqueous reaction systems. Remember that Arrhenius acids are defined only in an aqueous system. So gas-phase proton transfers, or proton transfers in solvents other than water, would not have been recognized as acid-base reactions by Arrhenius theory. Consider the reaction

$$HCl(g) + NH_3(g) \rightleftharpoons NH_4Cl(s)$$

Arrhenius theory would not consider gaseous HCl an acid, because the proton does not dissociate under gaseous conditions. However, gaseous HCl is an acid according to Bronsted-Lowry theory because it is capable of transferring a proton to another species, gaseous NH_3 in this case, thus forming the ions NH_4^+ and Cl^-. These two ions attract each other in the gas phase, forming the solid white salt, NH_4Cl. Another example utilizes the Bronsted-Lowry acid HF dissolved in ammonia, rather than water:

$$HF(g) + NH_3(\ell) \rightleftharpoons F^- + NH_4^+ \quad \textit{in liquid ammonia}$$

Here we see a familiar proton transfer process, but Arrhenius theory would not recognize this as an acid-base reaction. More species are acids under the Bronsted-Lowry theory than under the Arrhenius theory.

- *Not all Bronsted-Lowry bases are bases under the Arrhenius theory.* There are many more bases under the Bronsted-Lowry theory than under the Arrhenius theory. As we will see, the Arrhenius bases were all strong bases. Bronsted-Lowry theory allows us to recognize the weak bases; these species produce OH^- only by chemical reaction with water.

- *The origin of basic character has been overhauled.* In the Arrhenius concept, only substances capable of hydroxide ion <u>dissociation</u> in water were considered to be bases. Under Bronsted-Lowry theory any substance capable of accepting a proton from water to create a hydroxide ion in solution is recognized as a base. In addition, the accepted proton need not come from a water molecule. The definition does not depend explicitly on hydroxide ion production and so is not tied directly to aqueous systems. Again, we can illustrate the broadening of our acid and base concepts by considering the reaction

$$HCl(g) + NH_3(g) \rightleftharpoons NH_4Cl(s)$$

Here ammonia is a base because it accepts a proton from HCl. There is never any hydroxide ion involved in this non-aqueous reaction.

Some examples of Bronsted-Lowry acid-base reactions are given in Table 18-2. Make sure that you can recognize the proton transfer nature of each of these processes.

Table 18-2. Bronsted-Lowry Acids and Bases		
Acid	**Base**	**Acid-Base Reaction**
CH_3CO_2H	H_2O	$CH_3CO_2H(aq) + H_2O(\ell) \rightleftharpoons H_3O^+(aq) + CH_3CO_2^-(aq)$
H_2O	NH_3	$NH_3(aq) + H_2O(\ell) \rightleftharpoons NH_4^+(aq) + OH^-(aq)$
HCN	OH^-	$HCN(aq) + OH^-(aq) \rightleftharpoons H_2O(\ell) + CN^-(aq)$
HCl	NH_3	$HCl(g) + NH_3(g) \rightleftharpoons NH_4Cl(s)$

Exercise 18-3.

Write Bronsted-Lowry acid-base reaction equations between these acid/base pairs.

    a. acid = HNO_2 base = H_2O **c.** acid = HBr   base = NH_3
    b. acid = H_3O^+ base = OCl^- **d.** acid = HNO_2 base = OCl^-

4. Keeping Reaction Equations Consistent with Behavior

None of the following reactions occur in aqueous solution:

$$NH_3(aq) + H_2O(\ell) \rightleftharpoons NH_2^-(aq) + H_3O^+(aq)$$

$$CH_4(g) + H_2O(\ell) \rightleftharpoons CH_3^-(aq) + H_3O^+(aq)$$

$$LiH(aq) + H_2O(\ell) \rightleftharpoons Li^-(aq) + H_3O^+(aq)$$

Ammonia, methane, and lithium hydride are NOT acidic. *Reaction equations* can be written showing proton transfers to water, but these proton transfers do not occur. Ammonia is a base, and takes a proton from water. Methane is neither an acid nor a base, unless the conditions are very severe. Lithium hydride releases H^- (the hydride ion), not H^+. *Being able to write a reaction equation does not mean that the behavior occurs.*

How can we know what substances are acids and what substances are bases? One answer is to do the experiment. Add these various substances to water and see if acidic, basic, or neutral solutions result.

A way to predict acidic or basic character is to become familiar with the preferred bonding characteristics of a wide range of substances. None of the products of the fictitious reactions above (NH_2^-, CH_3^-, or Li^-) are stable. Nitrogen atoms prefer either three bonds and no charge, or four bonds and a positive charge. Carbon atoms almost always make four bonds.[139] Lithium is a metal that would much prefer to lose an electron, than gain one.

> *An important key to predicting behavior is to assess the stability of proposed products. Products that violate the common bonding preferences of atoms are not likely to form.*

Here is an example. Lewis dot structures can help predict whether a particular species will be stable. When the Lewis dot structure for NH_2^- is drawn, we can see that the nitrogen does not have its more normal bonding characteristics (three bonds and a lone pair, or four bonds and a positive formal charge) such as in ammonia and the ammonium ion as shown below, right.

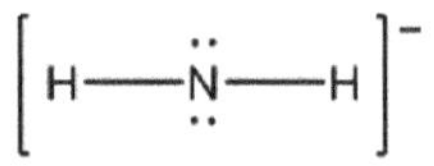

The recognition of common bonding patterns aids in the identification of unlikely species. Being familiar with common bonding patterns for particular atoms helps us to identify unusual bonding circumstances that may signal that the species cannot exist.

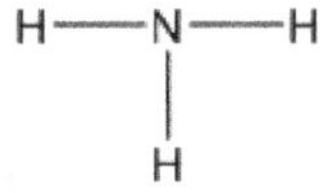

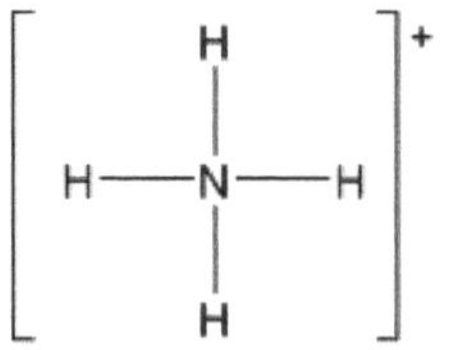

5. Conjugate Pairs

The proton transfer nature of Bronsted-Lowry acids and bases gives rise to pairs of related species called **conjugate pairs**. In a conjugate pair, one species is the acid and the other species is the base. The two species differ structurally by one proton. For example, NH_4^+ and NH_3 are a conjugate pair. In this pair, NH_4^+ is the acid (it is capable of donating a proton) and NH_3 is the base (it is capable of accepting the proton.)

Conjugate pairs always end up in the same acid-base reaction equations, but on opposite sides of the arrow. Notice that H_2O and OH^- are one of the conjugate pairs in the reaction equation, below. Here, H_2O is the acid (has the additional proton) and OH^- is the base (can accept a proton). So, overall, Bronsted-Lowry reaction equations involves two conjugate pairs. One pair is circled, the other is boxed:

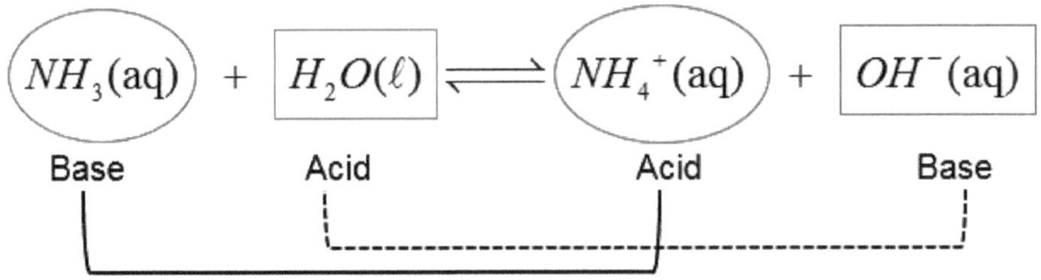

$$NH_3(aq) + H_2O(\ell) \rightleftharpoons NH_4^+(aq) + OH^-(aq)$$

Base   Acid   Acid   Base

---

[139] Common exceptions include CO and CN⁻.

Example 18-2.

Provide the formula of the missing conjugate partner. The first one is done for you.

Conjugate Acid	Conjugate Base
HCN	CN⁻
HBr	
	H_3C-NH_2
H_2SO_3	
	ClO_4^-
HSO_3^-	
	NO_2^-
H_3O^+	

Solutions:

Conjugate Acid	Conjugate Base
HCN	CN⁻
HBr	*Br⁻*
H_3C-NH_3^+	H_3C-NH_2
H_2SO_3	*HSO_3^-*
$HClO_4$	ClO_4^-
HSO_3^-	*SO_3^{2-}*
HNO_2	NO_2^-
H_3O^+	*H_2O*

- Notice that to produce the conjugate base of a particular acid, you must remove one proton (a hydrogen ion *with a positive charge*.) To produce the conjugate acid of a particular base you must add one proton (a hydrogen atom *with a positive charge*.) So the base of a conjugate pair is always one step more negative than its partner acid.
- Also notice that hydrogen atoms bonded to carbon atoms are not generally acidic. So for the acid, $CH_3NH_3^+$, the proton to be removed should come from the nitrogen end of the molecule.

C. The Lewis Definitions

One more concept of acid and base character remains. The Lewis concept of acids and bases is less utilized than the Bronsted-Lowry concept in the realm of the study of "acid-base chemistry." We introduced Lewis theory in Chapter 11, when we were studying coordination compounds. Lewis theory is geared toward understanding bond formation when one of the bonding partners brings both bonding electrons. Because new bonds are formed in exactly this way as a proton is transferred to a base, Bronsted-Lowry theory is really a subset of Lewis theory. It is instructive to review Lewis theory in this chapter, to see this broadening of the acid-base concept. The concept of Lewis acids and bases is also important in the study of organic chemistry.

1. Focus on Electrons

The Lewis concept of acids and bases looks at reactions from the standpoint of the electrons (and the bonds they make), rather than the position of a proton. A fundamental tenet of the Lewis concept centers on the idea that if a proton is transferred, one bond must be broken and a new bond must be made. Bonds arise from the sharing of electrons. Viewing acid-base reactions from an electron perspective is a chemist-friendly view. On a fundamental level chemists study chemical reactions, and all chemical reactions involve rearrangements of electrons (and their bonds). Lewis theory emphasizes these changes. Let's get started.

Lewis Definitions	
Acid	Electron Pair Acceptor
Base	Electron Pair Donor

If an electron pair acceptor reacts with an electron pair donor, a new bond will form. How do these definitions relate to a typical Bronsted-Lowry acid-base reaction? Consider this reaction:

$$HCN(aq) + OH^-(aq) \rightleftharpoons H_2O(\ell) + CN^-(aq)$$

In Bronsted-Lowry theory we see this reaction as a proton transfer. In Lewis theory we see the base, OH⁻ as an electron-rich species that donates a pair of electrons to make a new bond to an electron deficient species. That electron deficient species is the proton from the HCN species. Chemists show the rearrangement of electrons with a **mechanism diagram**. Curved arrows show rearrangements of electron pairs:

A lone pair from the oxygen of the hydroxide ion forms a new bond to the proton from HCN. The bonding electrons between the C and H of HCN become a lone pair on carbon. Notice that the hydrogen atom cannot end up bonded to both the carbon and the oxygen; hydrogen atoms commonly only make one covalent bond at a time. A mechanism diagram for the reverse reaction is shown here:

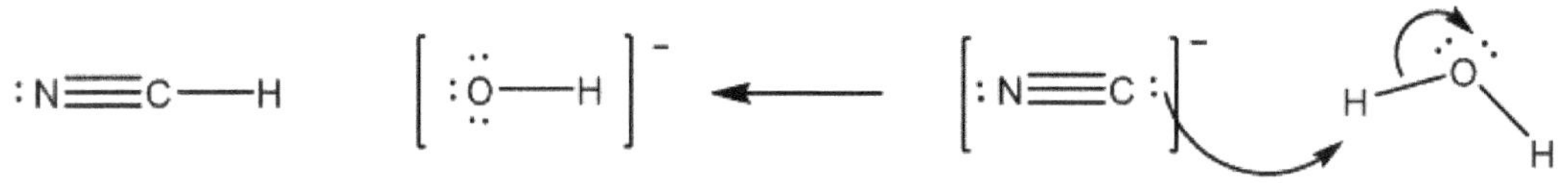

Instead of seeing the acid-base reaction in terms of the proton transfer, we are seeing it in terms of the use of electrons on the basic species to make a new bond to the electron deficient proton. This evokes a helpful tug-of-war analogy. The reaction

$$HCN(aq) + OH^-(aq) \rightleftharpoons H_2O(\ell) + CN^-(aq)$$

can be viewed as a tug-of-war between two electron rich species (OH⁻ and CN⁻) for the proton. Whichever electron rich species is better at donating its electrons to the proton will end up bonded to the proton. If OH⁻ wins (and binds more protons) we will end up predominantly with the products (H₂O and CN⁻) and if CN⁻ wins (and binds more protons) we will end up predominantly with the reactants (OH⁻ and HCN).

The equilibrium constant for the overall reaction will let the chemist know who the winner was, CN⁻ or OH⁻, and by what margin. The particular reaction under consideration has a large equilibrium constant ($K_{eq} = 6.2 \times 10^4$) and could be considered essentially irreversible. It could be written as (note the arrow):

$$HCN(aq) + OH^-(aq) \longrightarrow H_2O(\ell) + CN^-(aq)$$

but this tends to encourage us to forget that the reverse reaction does occur to a small extent. So we often use a lopsided reversable reaction arrow:

$$HCN(aq) + OH^-(aq) \rightleftharpoons H_2O(\ell) + CN^-(aq)$$

This arrow reminds us that even a very lopsided equilibrium is still an equilibrium. The arrow can be drawn either as $\underrightarrow{\rightleftharpoons}$ or $\underleftarrow{\rightleftharpoons}$ depending on which direction is favored in a lopsided reaction. It is never incorrect to use $\rightleftharpoons$, but if you know that the equilibrium is very skewed in one direction or the other, this additional information can be conveyed with the new arrows. In the case of

$$HCN(aq) + OH^-(aq) \underrightarrow{\rightleftharpoons} H_2O(\ell) + CN^-(aq)$$

we understand from the equilibrium constant value (and the arrow) that the OH^- species is a more successful electron donor than the CN^- species. Thus it is primarily the OH^- that ends up with the proton (giving the H_2O molecule). This is encouraging because we will discover that OH^- is a strong base and CN^- is a weak base.

2. Additional Reactions Can be Labeled as Acid-Base Reactions

Bronsted-Lowry acids and bases all fit the Lewis definitions:

Proton donors = electron acceptors
Proton acceptors = electron donors

However, Lewis definitions are broader than Bronsted-Lowry definitions, so some species are Lewis acids, but not Bronsted-Lowry acids and some species are Lewis bases, but not Bronsted-Lowry bases. Consider the formation of a **complex ion** upon the mixing of a silver(I) ion solution and an ammonia solution. We can write:

$$Ag^+(aq) + 2\,\ddot{N}H_3(aq) \rightleftharpoons [Ag(NH_3)_2]^+(aq)$$

or

$$H_3N: \quad Ag^+ \quad :NH_3 \longrightarrow [H_3N—Ag—NH_3]^+$$

Note that the electron deficient silver(I) ion accepts electron pairs from the nitrogens of both ammonia molecules to form new bonds. The positive charge initially on the silver ion is spread out over a larger number of atoms in the product. This is an acid-base reaction under the tenets of Lewis theory. The silver(I) ion is the Lewis acid; it accepts electron pairs. The ammonia molecules are Lewis bases; they donate electron pairs. This is not a Bronsted-Lowry acid-base reaction; there is no proton transfer.

In summary, the Lewis acid-base view is very broad, and encompasses the Bronsted-Lowry view. In the Lewis view, acid-base behavior is not tied exclusively to proton transfers. A wide variety of reactions can be categorized as Lewis acid-base reactions.

Summary Table of Acid-Base Definitions		
Theory	Acids	Bases
Arrhenius	H^+(aq)	OH^-(aq)
Bronsted-Lowry	proton donors	proton acceptors
Lewis	electron pair acceptors	electron pair donors

D. How Will We Define Acids and Bases?

The mainstream understanding of "acids" and "bases" depends on the Bronsted-Lowry concept. Topics such as pH, neutralization, and titrations all typically utilize Bronsted-Lowry ideas. This will be our focus in acid-base chapters of the following chapters. In addition, we will limit our further treatment of acids and bases to aqueous systems, where this behavior is most prevalent. Because our systems will be aqueous, we commence with an examination of the behavior of water with respect to acidic and basic systems.

18-3. THE CHARACTERISTICS AND BEHAVIOR OF WATER WITH RESPECT TO ACIDS AND BASES

A. Amphoterism

For such a common substance, water has some bizarre characteristics. It is difficult to appreciate water's uniqueness because its properties are so familiar. It is not until one begins to learn about the behaviors of many other materials that the expansion of water as it freezes seems out of the ordinary. Most substances lose volume upon freezing; their solids sink, rather than float, in their liquids. Similarly, it is not until one begins to learn a little about the chemistry of acids and bases that another odd characteristic of water crops up. Study the first two entries of Table 18-2, reproduced here:

Acid	Base	Acid-Base Reaction
CH_3CO_2H	H_2O	$CH_3CO_2H(\ell) + H_2O(\ell) \rightleftharpoons H_3O^+(aq) + CH_3CO_2^-(aq)$
H_2O	NH_3	$H_2O(\ell) + NH_3(g) \rightleftharpoons NH_4^+(aq) + OH^-(aq)$

What is odd about water? It acts as an acid in the presence of a base (by donating a proton to form OH^-) and it acts as a base in the presence of an acid (by accepting a proton to form H_3O^+). This is a property called **amphoterism**. Water is said to be **amphoteric** because it can act as either an acid or a base. (The prefixes "*amphi*" and "*ampho*" mean "both". Amphoteric substances can also be called **amphiprotic,** meaning that they behave in <u>both</u> ways with respect to <u>protons</u>—accepting them and donating them.) Water is not the only amphoteric substance; we will see more of them in the next chapter. Amphoterism is an odd characteristic to ponder. Take the time to judge your ability to make logical deductions by addressing Exercise 18-4 before continuing with your reading.

Exercise 18-4.

Using just your ability to think logically, make a determination about whether you think that an amphoteric substance is in general a pretty strong acid and a pretty strong base, or a pretty poor acid and a pretty poor base. Consider the Bronsted-Lowry definitions.

How did you do? Did you determine that an amphoteric substance is likely to be both a fairly poor acid and a fairly poor base? That is the most sensible conclusion.

Good proton acceptor = poor proton donor If a species wants more protons, it won't give protons away.
Good proton donor = poor proton acceptor If a species prefers to give protons away, it won't want protons.
Water cannot be good at both taking and giving protons, but it can be poor at both.

Indeed, we certainly don't normally think of water as being acidic or basic, but individual molecules do accept and donate protons. Learning more about this process will help us understand what it really means for a solution to be "neutral," not acidic or basic.

B. Autoionization

1. Definition of Autoionization

Because water molecules can act either as acids or as bases, one molecule of water can react with another molecule of water in an acid-base reaction. A proton transfer occurs:

$$H_2O(\ell) + H_2O(\ell) \rightleftharpoons OH^-(aq) + H_3O^+(aq)$$

Here, the first water molecule donates a proton to the second one. Because water is a particularly poor acid and a particularly poor base, not much of this process occurs in a sample of water. The process is called **autoionization** because it represents the automatic formation of ions in pure water. Autoionization is also called **self-ionization**.

> All water samples contain at least small concentrations of both hydroxide ion and hydronium ion.

2. The Ion Product Constant

The autoionization of water molecules in a sample of water is a reversible process. The forward and reverse processes are both occurring.

$$H_2O(\ell) + H_2O(\ell) \rightleftharpoons OH^-(aq) + H_3O^+(aq)$$

The equilibrium constant for this reaction is given the special symbol K_w, where the "w" reminds us that this is the equilibrium constant for the reaction of water with water. K_w is called the **ion product constant for water** (because it is the product of two ion concentrations):

$$K_w = [OH^-]_{eq}[H_3O^+]_{eq}$$

The value of K_w is 1.008×10^{-4} at room temperature (25 °C).[140] This very small K value tells us that writing the autoionization reaction equation with a different arrow might be instructive:

$$H_2O(\ell) + H_2O(\ell) \rightleftharpoons OH^-(aq) + H_3O^+(aq)$$

The forward reaction proceeds only a tiny amount. The reverse reaction could be considered **irreversible** for many purposes. The reverse reaction has $K_c = \dfrac{1}{1.008 \times 10^{-14}} = 9.921 \times 10^{13}$ (note the positive exponent). The size of this equilibrium constant implies that the hydronium ion reacts completely (essentially) with the hydroxide ion.

Consider the balanced reaction for autoionization. In pure water, the equilibrium concentration of OH^- will always be the same as the equilibrium concentration of H_3O^+ because the process that makes one of them makes both. We write

$$[OH^-]_{eq} = [H_3O^+]_{eq} \text{ in pure water}$$

This is the reason that pure water is **neutral**, not acidic or basic. Only when the relative amounts of OH^- and H_3O^+ get out of balance does acid or base character emerge.

---

[140] Commonly given to two significant figures as 1.0×10^{-14}, but this is not an exact number.

Relative Ion Concentrations	Acid/Base Character
$[OH^-]_{eq} = [H_3O^+]_{eq}$	Neutral
$[H_3O^+]_{eq} > [OH^-]_{eq}$	Acidic
$[OH^-]_{eq} > [H_3O^+]_{eq}$	Basic

Summarizing what we know about pure water at room temperature:

$$K_w = 1.0 \times 10^{-14} = [OH^-]_{eq}[H_3O^+]_{eq}$$
and
$$[OH^-]_{eq} = [H_3O^+]_{eq}$$

Letting x represent the concentrations of the ions, we can write:

$$1.0 \times 10^{-14} = x^2$$

$$x = \sqrt{1.0 \times 10^{-14}} = 1.0 \times 10^{-7}$$

> *The equilibrium concentrations of both OH^- and H_3O^+ in pure water at 25 °C are 1.0×10^{-7} M.*

3. Values for K_w at Various Temperatures

Like all equilibrium constants, K_w is temperature dependent. Table 18-3 gives experimental K_w values at a selection of temperatures. In <u>pure</u> water, at these temperatures, the concentrations of hydronium ion and hydroxide are always equal to the square root of the K_w value, as we saw in the previous section. Pure water, at any temperature, is neutral because the hydroxide ion concentration and the hydronium ion concentrations must be identical. Notice that more autoionization occurs as the temperature increases (larger K_w, higher ion concentrations).

Table 18-3.			
Temperature (°C)	**K_w value** $K_w = [H_3O^+]_{eq}[OH^-]_{eq}$	**$[H_3O^+]_{eq}$** in pure water	**$[OH^-]_{eq}$** in pure water
0	1.2×10^{-15}	3.5×10^{-8}	3.5×10^{-8}
24	1.000×10^{-14}	1.000×10^{-7}	1.000×10^{-7}
25	1.008×10^{-14}	1.004×10^{-7}	1.004×10^{-7}
60	9.6×10^{-14}	3.1×10^{-7}	3.1×10^{-7}
100	6.1×10^{-13}	7.8×10^{-7}	7.8×10^{-7}
200	5.0×10^{-12}	2.2×10^{-6}	2.2×10^{-6}

Example 18-3.

Determine the equilibrium concentrations of OH^- and H_3O^+ in pure water at normal body temperature (37 °C). K_w at 37 °C is 2.4×10^{-14}.

Solution:

In pure water, the only source of the ions in question is autoionization. Therefore, we know that $[OH^-]_{eq} = [H_3O^+]_{eq}$. Given that the value of K_w at 37 °C is 2.4×10^{-14} we can write:

$$K_w = 2.4 \times 10^{-14} = [OH^-]_{eq}[H_3O^+]_{eq}$$

$$2.4 \times 10^{-14} = x^2$$

$$x = \sqrt{2.4 \times 10^{-14}} = 1.5 \times 10^{-7}$$

So, in pure water at 37 °C, $[OH^-]_{eq} = [H_3O^+]_{eq} = 1.5 \times 10^{-7}\ M$.

C. Common Ion Effect and LeChatelier's Principle

The autoionization of water is an equilibrium process similar to any other equilibrium process we have studied.

$$H_2O(\ell) + H_2O(\ell) \rightleftharpoons OH^-(aq) + H_3O^+(aq) \quad K_{eq} = K_w = 1.0 \times 10^{-14} \text{ at } 25°C$$

The equilibrium constant always stays the same, if the temperature stays the same. If a *common ion* is added to the system, the system's equilibrium position will shift to preserve the value of the equilibrium constant. The only possible common ions are OH^- and H_3O^+. If an acid is added to an aqueous system, such that the $[H_3O^+]$ increases, the system will shift toward the left, using up some of the added H_3O^+ along with some of the original OH^- to create more water. This occurs until the remaining H_3O^+ and OH^- satisfy the requirement that $[OH^-]_{eq}[H_3O^+]_{eq} = 1.0 \times 10^{-14}$. It will no longer be true that $[OH^-]_{eq} = [H_3O^+]_{eq}$; rather $[H_3O^+]_{eq} > [OH^-]_{eq}$ and the solution will be acidic.

> STOP! Make sure this makes sense. When acid is added, the concentration of H_3O^+ rises. But then, with the shift to the left, why aren't $[H_3O^+]$ and $[OH^-]$ equalized again? The shift to the left must deplete both $[H_3O^+]$ and $[OH^-]$ equally. Because the acid addition made them unequal, they will remain unequal.

Likewise, if a base is added to water so that the concentration of OH^- increases, the system shifts to the left to remove OH^- (and some of the original H_3O^+). When equilibrium is reestablished $[OH^-]_{eq} > [H_3O^+]_{eq}$ and the solution is basic.

Example 18-4.

A substance is added to a water sample at normal body temperature (37 °C), and the resulting hydronium ion concentration is measured as $1.3 \times 10^{-7} M$.

    a. Calculate the hydroxide ion concentration of this solution. K_w (37 °C) $= 2.4 \times 10^{-14}$.

    b. Is the solution acidic or basic? (Was the added substance an acid or a base?)

Solutions:

    a. It is always true that $\quad\quad K_w = [OH^-]_{eq}[H_3O^+]_{eq}$

    We can write: $\quad\quad\quad\quad K_w = 2.4 \times 10^{-14} = [OH^-]_{eq}[H_3O^+]_{eq}$

$$2.4 \times 10^{-14} = [OH^-]_{eq}(1.3 \times 10^{-7})$$

$$\left[OH^- \right] = \frac{2.4 \times 10^{-14}}{1.3 \times 10^{-7}} = 1.9 \times 10^{-7} \, M$$

    b. $[OH^-]_{eq} > [H_3O^+]_{eq}$ so the solution is basic. The added substance was a base.

Exercise 18-5.

Either the $[OH^-]_{eq}$ or the $[H_3O^+]_{eq}$ of an aqueous solution is given. Calculate the other. All solutions are at room temperature (what does this mean about K_w?)

    a. $[H_3O^+]_{eq} = 3.7 \times 10^{-6} \, M$ **b.** $[OH^-]_{eq} = 9.2 \times 10^{-3} \, M$

    c. $[H_3O^+]_{eq} = 2.8 \times 10^{-11} \, M$ **d.** $[OH^-]_{eq} = 6.6 \times 10^{-9} \, M$

Exercise 18-6.

 a. Consider an aqueous solution, at room temperature, whose equilibrium concentration of H_3O^+ is 3.1×10^{-7} M. What must be the concentration of OH^- in the sample? Is this solution acidic or basic? Explain.

 b. If the solution in part **a** is at 60 °C instead of 25 °C, what must be the concentration of OH^- in the sample? Is this solution acidic or basic? Explain.

D. Degrees of Acidity and Basicity

  It should be clear from the previous section that, at any temperature, the more H_3O^+ in an aqueous system the less OH^- there must be in the same system. As the $[H_3O^+]_{eq}$ becomes larger and larger in comparison to the $[OH^-]_{eq}$ the degree of acidity of the solution increases. Likewise, in a solution where $[OH^-]_{eq}$ is larger than $[H_3O^+]_{eq}$, the degree of basicity depends on how different the two concentrations have become. See Table 18-4.

TABLE 18-4. Some Possible Ion Concentrations in Water at 25 °C.

$[H_3O^+]_{eq}$	$[OH^-]_{eq}$	$K_{w=}$ $[OH^-]_{eq} [H_3O^+]_{eq}$	acid/base character
1.0×10^1 M	1.0×10^{-15} M	1.0×10^{-14} M	very acidic
1.0×10^{-1} M	1.0×10^{-13} M	1.0×10^{-14} M	↑
1.0×10^{-3} M	1.0×10^{-11} M	1.0×10^{-14} M	
1.0×10^{-5} M	1.0×10^{-9} M	1.0×10^{-14} M	
1.0×10^{-7} M	1.0×10^{-7} M	1.0×10^{-14} M	neutral
1.0×10^{-9} M	1.0×10^{-5} M	1.0×10^{-14} M	
1.0×10^{-11} M	1.0×10^{-3} M	1.0×10^{-14} M	
1.0×10^{-13} M	1.0×10^{-1} M	1.0×10^{-14} M	↓
1.0×10^{-15} M	1.0×10^1 M	1.0×10^{-14} M	very basic

Table 18-4 contains some redundant information. The value of the equilibrium constant is the same in every case, and is a well-known constant at 25 °C. In addition, the value of $[H_3O^+]_{eq}$ implies a value of $[OH^-]_{eq}$. We really do not have to list both in order to describe an aqueous system. The relative acidities and basicities of various aqueous systems are fully described by reporting *either* the $[H_3O^+]_{eq}$ *or* the $[OH^-]_{eq}$. Usually the $[H_3O^+]_{eq}$ is reported.

 Make sure you understand why we don't have to list both [H_3O^+] and [OH^-] in order to fully describe an aqueous system!

E. The pH Scale

  We saw in the previous section that reporting just the $[H_3O^+]_{eq}$ is enough to fully describe the acid and base character of an aqueous system at room temperature. Historically, the reporting of this information has been made even more succinct by adopting the use of logarithms (exponential powers) to report the concentration of H_3O^+ in a solution. This is because the concentrations of H_3O^+ tend to be very small, and, before the advent of calculators, it was easier to work with logarithmic values than with the actual values. You may already be somewhat familiar with the **pH scale**. The small "p" stands for "power," as in "exponential power." The capital "H" stands for the hydronium ion. Listing pH values is simply another way of listing hydronium ion concentrations:

$$pH = -log\ [H_3O^+]_{eq}$$

or

$$[H_3O^+]_{eq} = (10)^{-pH}$$

The negative sign in the definition ensures that most pH values will be positive numbers—again for computational convenience. Table 18-5 lists the same hydronium ion concentrations as Table 18-4 but also includes pH values. Notice that the pH is only a negative number for a strongly acidic solution, with $[H_3O^+] > 1.0\ M$. Also, larger values of $[H_3O^+]$ produce smaller values of pH because of the negative sign in the definition.

TABLE 18-5. pH's and Acid-Base Characteristics in Water at 25 ^{0}C.

$[H_3O^+]_{eq}$ (M)	$[H_3O^+]_{eq}$ (as an exponent of 10)	pH $= -log[H_3O^+]_{eq}$	acid/base character
1.0×10^1	10^1	-1.00	very acidic
1.0×10^{-1}	10^{-1}	1.00	↑
1.0×10^{-3}	10^{-3}	3.00	
1.0×10^{-5}	10^{-5}	5.00	
1.0×10^{-7}	10^{-7}	7.00	neutral
1.0×10^{-9}	10^{-9}	9.00	
1.0×10^{-11}	10^{-11}	11.00	
1.0×10^{-13}	10^{-13}	13.00	↓
1.0×10^{-15}	10^{-15}	15.00	very basic

It takes fewer digits to report a pH than to report the concentrations of H_3O^+, compare the 1st and 3rd columns. In addition, pH values are unitless, but they are based on concentrations in molarity.

1. Significant Digits and Logarithms

It may appear that too many significant digits have been reported in the pH values in Table 18-5. These numbers look as if they have 3 or 4 significant digits. But think carefully. For what does the "7" in a pH of 7.00 stand?

It comes from the "7" in this number: $1.0 \times 10^{-7}\ M$ *(scientific notation)*
which could be written: $0.00000010\ M$ *(decimal notation)*

In translating from scientific notation to decimal notation, the "7" tells us how many leading zeros to use. Because the leading zeros are not significant, the "7" in a pH of 7.00 is also not significant.

The only digits that are significant in a logarithm occur to the right of the decimal.

In a pH of 7.00, or 4.56, there are only two significant digits. The concentrations in Table 18-5 each have two significant digits; the pH values are also reported to two significant digits.

2. A Primer on Logarithms

We can learn more about logarithms by looking at Table 18-6. This table explores pH values in the case that the concentration is not an *integer* exponent of 10. (In Table 18-5, all $[H_3O^+]_{eq}$ values were integer exponents of 10. All pH values were also, then, integers.)

TABLE 18-6. Mathematical Relationships for Logarithms

Row Number	$[H_3O^+]_{eq}$ (M)	$[H_3O^+]_{eq}$ (as an exponent of 10)	pH = $-\log[H_3O^+]_{eq}$
1	2.3×10^{-1}	$10^{-0.64}$	0.64
2	3.1×10^{-3}	$10^{-2.51}$	2.51
3	4.6×10^{-4}	$10^{-3.34}$	3.34
4	5.4×10^{-6}	$10^{-5.27}$	5.27
5	4.6×10^{-7}	$10^{-6.34}$	6.34
6	7.9×10^{-8}	$10^{-7.10}$	7.10
7	8.5×10^{-10}	$10^{-9.07}$	9.07
8	9.7×10^{-11}	$10^{-10.01}$	10.01
9	4.6×10^{-12}	$10^{-11.34}$	11.34

Note: the third column of the table can be calculated from the second column by solving equations such as $2.3 \times 10^{-1} = 10^x$, where x is the logarithm of 2.3×10^{-1}, and $x = -0.64$.

The part of the pH value to the left of the decimal (blue) comes from the exponent of 10 in the scientific notation form of the concentration (also blue). The digits to the right of the decimal in the pH (red) arise from the first part of the scientific notation value (also red). These digits describe how much larger the concentration is from the simple 1.0×10^{-x} M. Notice that entries in rows 3, 5, and 9 all have concentrations of 4.6×10^{-x} M and that all of the pH values have the same red digits. *The red digits are also the significant digits.*

Exercise 18-7.

State, for each of the following concentrations, the two whole number pH's you expect the actual pH to fall between. For example, a concentration of 1.2×10^{-8} should have a pH between 7 and 8. Do not use a calculator.

    a. $[H_3O^+]_{eq} = 3.5 \times 10^{-1}$ M   **b.** $[H_3O^+]_{eq} = 9.6 \times 10^{-10}$ M   **c.** $[H_3O^+]_{eq} = 7.7 \times 10^{-7}$ M

    d. $[H_3O^+]_{eq} = 0.0063$ M   **e.** $[H_3O^+]_{eq} = 1.8 \times 10^{0}$ M

Exercise 18-8.

For each solution, below, either the $[H_3O^+]_{eq}$ or the pH is provided. Calculate the missing value.

    a. $[H_3O^+]_{eq} = 2.8 \times 10^{-6}$ **b.** pH = 10.65

    c. pH = 3.92   **d.** $[H_3O^+]_{eq} = 4.2 \times 10^{-1}$ M

Knowing the pH of a solution tells us everything we need to know about the solution's acidity or basicity. Although the pH only directly reports the $[H_3O^+]_{eq}$, we can easily know the $[OH^-]_{eq}$ by reference to K_w.

solution character[141]	pH	relative ion concentrations
neutral	= 7.00	$[H_3O^+] = [OH^-]$
acidic	< 7.00	$[H_3O^+] > [OH^-]$
basic	> 7.00	$[H_3O^+] < [OH^-]$

The further a (room temp) solution is from pH 7.00, in either direction, the more out of balance the concentrations of the two ions have become.

Example 18-5.

The $[H_3O^+]_{eq}$, $[OH^-]_{eq}$, and pH are all related by simple mathematical operations. For a solution with $[OH^-]_{eq} = 3.6 \times 10^{-9}$ M, calculate the $[H_3O^+]_{eq}$ and pH for an aqueous solution at room temperature.

Solution:

We can write:

$$K_w = 1.0 \times 10^{-14} = [OH^-]_{eq} [H_3O^+]_{eq}$$

$$1.0 \times 10^{-14} = (3.6 \times 10^{-9})[H_3O^+]_{eq}$$

$$\left[H_3O^+\right] = \frac{1.0 \times 10^{-14}}{3.6 \times 10^{-9}} = 2.78 \times 10^{-6} \, M$$

$$pH = -\log(2.78 \times 10^{-6}) = 5.556$$

To the correct number of significant digits (2), the answers are:

$$\left[H_3O^+\right] = 2.8 \times 10^{-6} \, M \text{ and } pH = 5.56$$

Exercise 18-9.

The pH, $[H_3O^+]_{eq}$ and $[OH^-]_{eq}$ are all descriptors of the acid-base character of a solution. For each of the solutions below (at room temperature) one of the values is provided. Provide the remaining values.

    a. Solution A has a pH of 4.13. Calculate $[H_3O^+]_{eq}$ and $[OH^-]_{eq}$.

    b. Solution B has $[OH^-]_{eq} = 9.4 \times 10^{-3}$ M. Calculate $[H_3O^+]_{eq}$ and pH.

    c. Solution C has $[H_3O^+]_{eq} = 5.7 \times 10^{-6}$ M. Calculate $[OH^-]_{eq}$ and pH.

F. Other "Power" Functions

So far the only logarithmic function we have used in our study of the acid-base characteristics of solutions is the pH function. Other logarithmic functions are also used. They are all defined analogously to the pH. Two of these are the pOH and the pK_w.

---

[141] The notations in the first and third columns of this table are true at any temperature, but the pH values depends on the magnitude of K_w and, thus, are temperature dependent. This table reflects a temperature of 25 °C.

$$pOH = -\log[OH^-]_{eq} \quad \text{or} \quad [OH^-] = 10^{-pOH}$$

$$pK_w = -\log K_w \quad \text{or} \quad K_w = 10^{-pK_w}$$

Remember that at room temperature $K_w = 1.0 \times 10^{-14}$. This means that pK_w at room temperature is equal to 14.00. In tabulations of equilibrium constants it is common for the pK to be listed instead of the K. This is mostly a matter of history and the convenience of using less paper to present the same information.

Exercise 18-10.

Add a column filled with pK_w values to Table 18-3.

The pOH is another possible descriptor of the acid-base character of an aqueous solution (along with pH, $[H_3O^+]_{eq}$ and $[OH^-]_{eq}$). It does not add any new information but does give another format by which information can be shared. The pH is used far more often than the pOH to describe solutions. It is important to understand the relationships between the many possible descriptors of acid and base character. Consider Table 18-7.

TABLE 18-7. Relationships of Acid-Base Descriptors in Aqueous Solutions at 25 °C.

$[H_3O^+]_{eq}$ (M)	$[OH^-]_{eq}$ (M)	pH	pOH	acid/base character
1.0×10^1	1.0×10^{-15}	−1.00	15.00	very acidic
1.0×10^{-1}	1.0×10^{-13}	1.00	13.00	↑
1.0×10^{-3}	1.0×10^{-11}	3.00	11.00	
1.0×10^{-5}	1.0×10^{-9}	5.00	9.00	
1.0×10^{-7}	1.0×10^{-7}	7.00	7.00	neutral
1.0×10^{-9}	1.0×10^{-5}	9.00	5.00	
1.0×10^{-11}	1.0×10^{-3}	11.00	3.00	
1.0×10^{-13}	1.0×10^{-1}	13.00	1.00	↓
1.0×10^{-15}	1.0×10^1	15.00	−1.00	very basic

Because of the definition of pOH, it is likely to be easier to think of it as a measure of basicity rather than a measure of acidity. Values of pH are low when a solution is more acidic.

Likewise, pOH values are low when a solution is more basic. Some algebraic manipulations involving concentrations and equilibrium constant values might be instructive. Remember that

$$K_w = 1.0 \times 10^{-14} = [OH^-]_{eq}[H_3O^+]_{eq} \quad \text{(at 25 °C)}$$

If we take −log of both sides of this equation we will have:

$$-\log K_w = -\log(1.0 \times 10^{-14}) = -\log([OH^-]_{eq}[H_3O^+]_{eq})$$

Now, because $-\log (a \times b) = (-\log a) + (-\log b)$, we can write:

$$-\log K_w = -\log(1.0 \times 10^{-14}) = (-\log[OH^-]_{eq}) + (-\log[H_3O^+]_{eq})$$

This can be rewritten in terms of power functions:

$$pK_w = 14.00 = pOH + pH \quad (at \ 25 \ °C)$$

What does this show us? First, there is more than one way to calculate a pOH given a pH. One could take the long route:

$$pH \xrightarrow{10^{-pH}} \left[H_3O^+ \right] \xrightarrow{use \ K_w} \left[OH^- \right] \xrightarrow{-\log} pOH$$

or one could take the short route:

$$pOH = 14.00 - pH \quad (if \ at \ room \ temperature!)$$

Second, the two statements:

$$K_w = 1.0 \times 10^{-14} = [OH^-]_{eq}[H_3O^+]_{eq}$$
$$and$$
$$pK_w = 14.00 = pOH + pH$$

are identical statements made with different symbolism. Both indicate that as the concentration of one ion rises (and its power function decreases) the concentration of the other ion must decrease (and its power function increases). Finally, check out Table 18-7 one more time. Is it true that the pH + pOH = 14.00?

Exercise 18-11.

Return to Table 18-6. Add columns for the [OH⁻] and pOH of the solutions in this table. Fill out the new columns. Check to see that the requirements of the equations below are met:
$$K_w = 1.0 \times 10^{-14} = [OH^-]_{eq}[H_3O^+]_{eq}$$
$$pK_w = 14.00 = pOH + pH$$

Example 18-6.

Calculate the pH and $[OH^-]_{eq}$ of the solutions below. Label the solution as acidic, basic, or neutral.

    a. An aqueous solution, *at room temperature*, whose $[H_3O^+]_{eq} = 3.1 \times 10^{-7} \ M$.

    b. An aqueous solution, *at 60 °C*, whose $[H_3O^+]_{eq} = 3.1 \times 10^{-7} \ M$.

    c. What does this tell you about a pH scale centered at pH = 7.00?

Solutions:

    a. $pH = -\log (3.1 \times 10^{-7}) = 6.51 \quad [OH^-] = \dfrac{K_w}{\left[H_3O^+ \right]} = \dfrac{1.0 \times 10^{-14}}{3.1 \times 10^{-7}} = 3.2 \times 10^{-8} \ M$

    This solution is acidic (a pH less than 7.00 at 25 °C, an $[H_3O^+]_{eq} > [OH^-]_{eq}$).

    b. $pH = -\log (3.1 \times 10^{-7}) = 6.51 \quad [OH^-] = \dfrac{K_w}{\left[H_3O^+ \right]} = \dfrac{9.6 \times 10^{-14}}{3.1 \times 10^{-7}} = 3.1 \times 10^{-7} \ M$

    This solution is neutral ($[H_3O^+]_{eq} = [OH^-]_{eq}$).

    c. The "normal" pH scale where neutral is a pH of 7.00 only applies at room temperature (when $K_w = 1.0 \times 10^{-14}$). In a problem that is not at room temperature the only good way to know if the solution is acidic, basic or neutral is to calculate both $[H_3O^+]_{eq}$ and $[OH^-]_{eq}$.

18-4. STRONG ACIDS AND BASES

A. Which Acids and Bases are Strong?

We have spent some time exploring the acid and base properties of water as well as how to describe the relative acidity and basicity of aqueous solutions. We have been ignoring, for the most part, how the various species that change the acidity of water samples can be categorized and described. We conclude this chapter with a look at strong acids and bases. Remember that we are working within the Bronsted-Lowry definitions of acids and bases, so

Acid	Proton Donor
Base	Proton Acceptor

1. Identifying Strong Bases

Strong bases are salts (network solids) and **strong electrolytes**. That is, in water, they fully dissociate into ions to produce a **stoichiometric** equivalent of OH^-. It is a good idea to memorize the brief list of the common strong bases in aqueous solution:

Common Strong Bases
Inexpensive, soluble hydroxide salts:[1]   NaOH   KOH   Ba(OH)$_2$
Alkali metal oxides: Na$_2$O   K$_2$O

[1]LiOH, RbOH, Sr(OH)$_2$, and CsOH are strong bases, but are too expensive for common use. Less soluble hydroxide salts such as Mg(OH)$_2$ and Ca(OH)$_2$ are strong bases but are less convenient for many purposes due to their low solubility.

We considered the hydroxide salts as bases when we considered the Arrhenius concept of bases. The hydroxide salts differ considerably from one another in their water <u>solubility</u>, but whatever does dissolve <u>fully ionizes</u>. Magnesium hydroxide, $Mg(OH)_2$, is a common antacid (a base is an anti-acid). Its low solubility in water is responsible for the milky look of "milk of magnesia," and for the fact that it doesn't burn the linings of the digestive system upon contact. Low solubility does not stop $Mg(OH)_2$ from fully reacting with an acid that might be present. Consider the solubility equilibrium:

$$Mg(OH)_2(s) \rightleftharpoons Mg^{2+}(aq) + 2OH^-(aq) \quad (\text{small } K_{sp} = 5.6 \times 10^{-12})$$

Upon the addition of acid, the following reaction takes place:

$$OH^-(aq) + H_3O^+(aq) \longrightarrow 2H_2O(\ell) \quad (\text{large } K_{eq}, \text{ reverse of autoionization!})$$

This second process stresses the first solubility equilibrium by removing hydroxide anion from the system and causes more magnesium hydroxide to dissolve. LeChatelier's Principle results in the full use of the base, even though it had limited solubility.

The alkali metal oxides produce *stoichiometric* quantities of hydroxide ion in aqueous systems. The oxide anion is unstable in aqueous solution. It reacts immediately, with water, as a potent proton acceptor:

$$O^{2-}(aq) + H_2O(\ell) \longrightarrow OH^-(aq) + OH^-(aq)$$

Every mole of oxide ion places *two moles* of hydroxide ion into solution.

2. Identifying Strong Acids

Strong acids are <u>molecules</u>[142] that behave as **strong electrolytes**. That is, in water, they fully ionize (by reaction with water) to produce a stoichiometric equivalent of H_3O^+. It is a good idea to memorize the common strong acids in aqueous solution:

---

[142] Contrast this with the strong bases which are salts (network solids), not molecules.

Strong Acids (aq)	
HCl	hydrochloric acid
HBr	hydrobromic acid
HI	hydroiodic acid
HNO_3	nitric acid
H_2SO_4	sulfuric acid
$HClO_4$	perchloric acid
$HClO_3$	chloric acid

Acids are named differently depending on whether or not they are *oxo*acids. *In* **oxoacids**, *the acidic hydrogen atom(s) are bonded to one or more oxygen atom(s)*. Nitric acid, sulfuric acid, chloric acid and perchloric acid[143] are all oxoacids. We show nitric acid as a resonance hybrid of the two best resonance structures. The other three have only one best resonance structure.

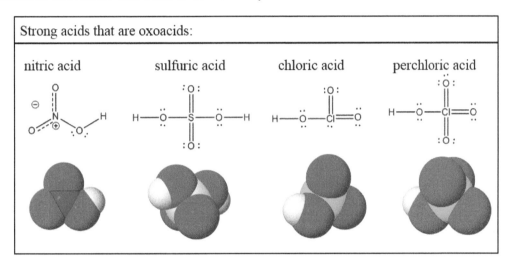

Strong acids that are oxoacids:

nitric acid   sulfuric acid   chloric acid   perchloric acid

The names of oxoacids start with the name of the anion around which the acid is built (nitrate, sulfate, chlorate, perchlorate) but with an *"-ic"* or *"-uric"* ending instead of the *"-ate"* ending of the anion. Beware! The order that the atoms are listed in the formulas makes it appear that the acidic hydrogens are bonded to the nitrogen (of nitric acid), the sulfur (of sulfuric acid) and the chlorine (of chloric acid or perchloric acid). You need to know that this is not really the case! The formulas of these acids list the acidic hydrogens first and then the anion formula.

The other three common strong acids are not oxoacids: HCl, HBr, HI. These are named with the "hydro" prefix followed by the name of the anion with the *"-ide"* ending of the anion changed to the *"-ic"* ending of an acid, such as "*hydro*chloric acid" (instead of hydrogen chlor*ide*). The HX (X = Cl, Br, I) acids are only named as acids when they are in aqueous solution. For example, HCl(g) would be named "hydrogen chloride."

Acidic hydrogens are usually bonded to atoms that can easily carry a negative charge, such as oxygen and the halogens.[144] Highly electronegative atoms promote the removal of a proton because the bond to hydrogen is already polarized and the electronegative atom is willing to take on the

---

[143] The chloric acid and perchloric acid molecules are unstable and cannot be isolated.

[144] Most of these atoms are considerably more electronegative than hydrogen (O, F, Cl, Br). Iodine is an interesting case; its electronegativity is very similar to hydrogen's (ENEG I = 2.36, H = 2.30). This means that the H-I bond is essential nonpolar. Iodine is able to carry negative charge primarily because of its large size, rather than its electronegativity.

negative charge left behind. Hydrogens bonded to carbon atoms are not generally acidic because carbon is particularly poor at carrying negative charge (a small atom that is not particularly electronegative).[145] Hydrofluoric acid, HF, is interesting in that, even though fluorine is one of the most electronegative elements, this is a weaker acid than the other hydrogen halides. Hydrogen and fluorine enjoy a particularly strong covalent bond due to the extensive overlaps of their bonding orbitals. The high bond strength of the H-F bond limits the acidity of the HF species.

3. Conjugates of Strong Acids and Strong Bases

The conjugate bases of strong acids (other than H_3O^+) are the anions left behind when the proton is released; see the table below.

Strong Acids (aq)	Conjugate Bases (aq)	Acid/base behavior of conjugate base
HCl	Cl^-	None
HBr	Br^-	None
HI	I^-	None
HNO_3	NO_3^-	None
H_2SO_4	HSO_4^-	Weak acid
$HClO_4$	ClO_4^-	None
$HClO_3$	ClO_3^-	None
H_3O^+	H_2O	Very weak base

The odd result is that the conjugate bases of strong acids are not basic (in fact, HSO_4^- is a weak acid!) Chloride ion, for instance, has no ability to take a proton away from water. It cannot even get a proton away from a hydronium ion (see reaction equation below)! The essence of a strong acid is that the reverse reaction of its ionization reaction does not noticeably occur. For example, the ionization reaction for HCl is given. The reverse reaction does not occur to any noticeable extent.

$$HCl(aq) + H_2O(\ell) \longrightarrow Cl^-(aq) + H_3O^+(aq)$$

The hydronium ion is the weakest of the strong acids. Its conjugate base, water, has a minimal ability to accept a proton. So, we label something that doesn't behave as a base, as a conjugate base! A conjugate base is simply the species that has one less H^+ than the acid, regardless of how it behaves.

The conjugate acids of strong bases are listed here:

Strong Bases (aq)	Conjugate Acids	Acid/base behavior of conjugate acid
OH^-	H_2O	Very weak acid
O^{2-}	OH^-	Strong base

We have a similar result. The conjugate acid of the oxide ion is the hydroxide ion. Clearly this conjugate acid is not acidic. The conjugate acid of hydroxide ion is the water molecule, which does have a minimal ability to donate a proton, as we have already noted. A conjugate acid is simply the species that has one more H^+ than its base-partner, regardless of how it behaves.

---

[145] Carbon's electronegativity is 2.54, which is just barely higher than that of hydrogen, 2.30. Carbon-hydrogen bonds behave in a non-polar manner.

The stronger the acid, the weaker the conjugate base, to the point that the conjugates of strong acids are not basic (and might even be acidic).

The stronger the base, the weaker the conjugate acid, to the point that the conjugates of strong bases are not acidic (and might even be basic).

4. The Strong Acids are "Leveled" in Water

The ionizations of strong acids in water are reactions that go essentially to completion. We usually write these processes with a single forward arrow instead of the reversible arrow. For example, we write the following for the ionization of hydroiodic acid:

$$HI(aq) + H_2O(\ell) \longrightarrow H_3O^+(aq) + I^-(aq)$$

This process goes essentially to completion for all strong acids, making their relative strengths difficult to establish. How does the acid strength of HI compare to HNO_3? Both of these acids are sufficiently strong to completely push their protons onto water; the resulting solutions are equally acidic, containing identical concentrations of H_3O^+. We say that the strengths of the different acids are *leveled* (made equal) by the reaction with water. Hydronium ion, H_3O^+, is the strongest acid that can exist in water. Any stronger acid reacts with water to produce H_3O^+.

Think about it this way. Given the task of picking up one chemistry textbook, everyone in your class would appear to be equally strong because they would all be successful. But that does not mean that all of your classmates are of equal strength. Once the task gets more difficult (picking up twenty textbooks?) we might start to see who is really the strongest. Here we would say that "carrying one book levels the strength of the students." We have to utilize a more difficult task in order to tell the difference between the students.

In order to assess the relative strengths of the strong acids, one must use a solvent other than water. This solvent must be *more difficult to protonate* than water; the solvent molecules must be poorer bases than water (and water is a very poor base). One solvent used for such determinations is the weak acid, acetic acid, CH_3CO_2H. It is very difficult, indeed, to protonate an acid (a species that would rather donate a proton than accept one).

$$HI + CH_3CO_2H(\ell) \rightleftharpoons CH_3CO_2H_2^+ + I^-$$

Measuring how well the various strong acids can force a proton onto acetic acid molecules can establish their respective strengths. The results of such studies indicate that the order of the strong acids from strongest to weakest may be (not all sources of information agree):

$$HI > HBr > HClO_4 > HCl > H_2SO_4 > HNO_3 > HClO_3 > H_3O^+$$

B. Determination of the pH of Strong Acid or Strong Base Solutions

It is relatively straightforward to determine the pH of a strong acid or strong base solution. This is because these species fully ionize. If you make a solution 0.45 M in HI, essentially all of the HI will ionize according to:

$$HI(aq) + H_2O(\ell) \longrightarrow H_3O^+(aq) + I^-(aq)$$

The tiny bit that doesn't ionize is not noticeable with, for instance, a pH meter. Thus, after the ionization process has occurred, essentially no molecular HI will remain and the solution will be 0.45 M in both H_3O^+ and I^-. The pH can be calculated as follows:

$$pH = -\log[H_3O^+]_{eq}$$
$$pH = -\log(0.45) = 0.35$$

Similarly, if a solution is 0.45 M in a strong base such as KOH, we know that the KOH is fully dissociated:

$$KOH(aq) \longrightarrow K^+(aq) + OH^-(aq)$$

The $[OH^-]_{eq}$ must be 0.45 M. We can calculate the pOH, and pH, of this solution:

$$pOH = -log[OH^-]_{eq}$$

$$pOH = -log(0.45) = 0.35$$

$$pH = 14.00 - 0.35 = 13.65$$

Notice that when working from $[OH^-]$ data, one additional step is necessary for the determination of the pH. Other computation strategies can be employed; if $[OH^-]_{eq}$ is 0.45 M we may use K_w to find $[H_3O^+]_{eq}$.

$$1.0 \times 10^{-14} = [OH^-]_{eq}[H_3O^+]_{eq} \quad \text{thus} \quad \frac{1.0 \times 10^{-14}}{0.45} = [H_3O^+]_{eq}$$

$$[H_3O^+]_{eq} = 2.22 \times 10^{-14} \text{ M} \quad \text{and} \quad pH = -log(2.22 \times 10^{-14}) = 13.65$$

Exercise 18-12.

Determine the pH of each solution described below.

    a. $[HCl] = 2.4 \times 10^{-3}\ M$ **b.** $[NaOH] = 0.0032\ M$ **c.** $[HClO_4] = 0.100\ M$

    d. $[Ba(OH)_2] = 4.51 \times 10^{-5}\ M$ **e.** $[K_2O] = 5.1 \times 10^{-4}\ M$

HINTS: In part d, think carefully about the stoichiometry. In part e, consider first the dissolution of the salt and identify which of the ions reacts with water.

C. Writing Reaction Equations for Strong Acids and Strong Bases

    Strong acids and bases react together in a very predictable manner. Because strong acids are very effective proton donors and strong bases are very effective proton acceptors, these reactions have very large equilibrium constants and are usually considered irreversible, not because they are strictly irreversible but because they are essentially irreversible. Consider the reaction between the two very common species HCl and NaOH in aqueous solution. We can write a molecular form of the reaction, a complete ionic reaction, and a net ionic reaction.

    molecular eq : $HCl(aq) + NaOH(aq) \longrightarrow H_2O(\ell) + NaCl(aq)$

    complete ionic eq : $H_3O^+(aq) + Cl^-(aq) + Na^+(aq) + OH^-(aq) \longrightarrow 2H_2O(\ell) + Na^+(aq) + Cl^-(aq)$

    net ionic eq : $H_3O^+(aq) + OH^-(aq) \longrightarrow 2H_2O(\ell)$

Notice that in keeping with Bronsted-Lowry theory we have written the ionic proton as a hydronium ion instead of as a bare proton. Even though it is generally accepted that this is a much more accurate depiction of the proton in solution, chemists often do abbreviate the ionic equations above so that they look as follows.

    molecular eq : $HCl(aq) + NaOH(aq) \longrightarrow H_2O(\ell) + NaCl(aq)$

    complete ionic eq : $H^+(aq) + Cl^-(aq) + Na^+(aq) + OH^-(aq) \longrightarrow H_2O(\ell) + Na^+(aq) + Cl^-(aq)$

    net ionic eq : $H^+(aq) + OH^-(aq) \longrightarrow H_2O(\ell)$

You should read "H^+(aq)" as an abbreviation for the hydronium ion,[146] not a return to the Arrhenius definitions. Chemists think beyond what is literally written when it comes to equations involving an aqueous proton. Some prefer the simplest possible representation for equations such as those above. Using the H^+(aq) depiction of an aqueous proton simplifies the rest of the equation by removing extra water molecules from consideration. The biggest problem with using H^+(aq) is that, for instance, the autoionization reaction then is written:

$$H_2O(\ell) \rightleftharpoons OH^-(aq) + H^+(aq)$$

which obscures the idea that a proton transfer is occurring! This oversimplified reaction equation makes it look as if a bond was simply broken, when in actuality a bond was also made! This book will avoid that issue by always using H_3O^+(aq)!

D. Equilibrium Constants for Reactions of Strong Acids and Strong Bases

Consider the net ionic equation for the reaction of a strong acid and a strong base:

$$H_3O^+(aq) + OH^-(aq) \longrightarrow 2H_2O(\ell)$$

This is the reverse of the autoionization of water:

$$2H_2O(\ell) \rightleftharpoons H_3O^+(aq) + OH^-(aq)$$

We know that the equilibrium constant for the autoionization of water at 25 °C is

$$K_w = [H_3O^+]_{eq}[OH^-]_{eq} = 1.0 \times 10^{-14}$$

We can compute the equilibrium constant for the reaction of hydronium ion with hydroxide ion:

$$K_{eq} = \frac{1}{\left[H_3O^+\right]_{eq}\left[OH^-\right]_{eq}} = \frac{1}{1.0 \times 10^{-14}} = 1.0 \times 10^{14}$$

This is a very large equilibrium constant, but it is not infinite. When we say that strong acids react completely with strong bases, we are technically overstating just a bit. The truth of the matter is that so little reactant remains that it is difficult to prove it is there. Reactions that can be treated as though they are irreversible (such as strong acid + strong base) have reverse reactions that proceed very little, but we are sometimes very interested in the (tiny) extent to which these unlikely processes do occur (such as the autoionization process).

The reactions of strong acids and strong bases produce salts and water. The identity of the salt produced depends on which strong acid and which strong base are reacting. The cation/anion possibilities are shown in the table at right.

Any of the cations could be paired with any of the anions. Bold cations are more common than the others. Note that the anions are all very stable species for several reasons:

1. the negative charge resides on an electronegative atom (such as O, Cl, Br, or I); and/or
2. the negative charge resides on a group of atoms with a high average electronegativity (ClO_4^-, HSO_4^-, NO_3^-); and/or

Cations from the base	Anions from the acid
Na$^+$	Cl$^-$
K$^+$	Br$^-$
Ba^{2+}	I$^-$
Mg^{2+}	NO$_3^-$
Ca^{2+}	HSO$_4^-$
Sr^{2+}	ClO$_4^-$
Li$^+$	ClO$_3^-$
Rb$^+$	
Cs$^+$	

---

[146] Which is, itself, an abbreviation for the reality of the situation wherein more than one water molecule is closely associated with the proton.

3. the anion is stabilized by spreading out the negative charge over a large atom (such as iodine); and/or

4. the anion is stabilized by spreading out the negative charge over many atoms via resonance (such as ClO_4^-, HSO_4^-, NO_3^-, consider the pi-delocalization available to these ions).[147]

As we have mentioned, these anions (though called "conjugate bases") have no propensity to act as bases; they are perfectly content to exist without the proton. The stability of the anions is what makes their conjugate acids "strong."

Example 18-7.

Which of the following salts can be created by the reaction of a strong acid with a strong base?

a. KI	**b.** $NaHSO_4$	**c.** $Mg(CN)_2$
d. $LiNO_3$	**e.** CsBr	**f.** CaF_2
g. $KClO_4$	**h.** $NaNO_3$	**i.** $CaBr_2$

Solutions:

The salts **a**, **b**, **d**, **e**, **g**, **h** and **i** can be created by a reaction of a strong acid with a strong base. The cation of the salt was paired with the hydroxide ion in the strong base, the anion of the salt is what remains of a strong acid after the proton is expelled:

a. *K*OH, H*I*	**b.** *Na*OH, *H₂SO₄*	**d.** *Li*OH, H*NO₃*
e. *Cs*OH, H*Br*	**g.** *K*OH, H*ClO₄*	**h.** *Na*OH, H*NO₃*
i. *Ca*(OH)₂, H*Br*		

The other two (**c** and **f**) contain an anion that does not come from a strong acid.

    c. *Mg*(OH)₂, H*CN* (a weak acid)   **f.** *Ca*(OH)₂, H*F* (a weak acid)

We will see later that salts such as $Mg(CN)_2$ and CaF_2 will themselves be basic.

E. Determination of the pH of a Solution After a Strong Acid and a Strong Base Have Reacted

When strong acids and strong bases react together, the equilibrium constant is very large. Consider that strong acids can (essentially) completely transfer their acidic proton to a very weak base, the water molecule. Most of the strong acids have K_a values larger than 1×10^3. Mathematically, we can treat these ionization reactions as if they go to completion. But, we know that the proton transfer from the same strong acid to a stronger base (such as OH^-) is even more favorable ($K_{eq} \approx 1 \times 10^{14}$). The language of irreversible reactions, such as the phrase "goes to completion," leaves out the detail that some "irreversible" reactions go further toward completion than others.

When we pour a strong acid solution and a strong base solution together we can assume, for all practical purposes, that they fully react. Calculations for such a reaction can utilize the concept of limiting reagent. If there is more H_3O^+ in the acid solution than there is OH^- in the base solution, the solution that results from combining these will be acidic due to the leftover H_3O^+. Similarly, if there is more OH^- in the base solution than there is H_3O^+ in the acid solution, the resulting solution will be basic due to the leftover OH^-. A **stoichiometry table** (see the Examples) can be used to determine which species is left over.

---

[147] The extra stability of spreading out negative charges by virtue of pi-delocalization is often referred to as "***resonance stability***." Anions with multiple resonance structures are said to be resonance stabilized.

> *Stoichiometry tables (in units of moles) may be used when a reaction is treated as irreversible. Equilibrium tables (in units of M or bar) are used when a reaction's reversible nature is under consideration.*

We will point out, in the examples worked below, complexities that occur due to the fact that none of these acid-base reactions actually go to completion.

Example 18-8.

Calculate the pH of the solution that results when 20.0 mL of 0.15 M HCl is added to 20.0 mL of 0.11 M NaOH.

Solution:

This answer is provided twice: first in its most rigorously complete form, then in the form that we will find most convenient. The rigorously solved problem shows us what all of the issues are, but makes us aware of how to simplify our work based on chemical logic.

Rigorously:

First calculate the number of moles of H_3O^+ and the number of moles of OH^-. These are the important species in a solution of HCl and a solution of NaOH.

$$H_3O^+ \text{ moles}: \quad 0.0200\, L \times \frac{0.15\, mol}{L} = 3.0 \times 10^{-3}\, mol$$

$$OH^- \text{ moles}: \quad 0.0200\, L \times \frac{0.11\, mol}{L} = 2.2 \times 10^{-3}\, mol$$

When we pour these solutions together the following reaction takes place:

$$H_3O^+(aq) + OH^-(aq) \longrightarrow 2H_2O(\ell)$$

We produce a *stoichiometry table* (in units of moles) to keep track of the reacting species:

	$H_3O^+(aq)$	+ $OH^-(aq)$ $\longrightarrow$	$2H_2O(\ell)$
Initial moles	3.0×10^{-3}	2.2×10^{-3}	Solvent (not measurable)
Changes	-2.2×10^{-3}	-2.2×10^{-3}	
Final moles	0.8×10^{-3}	0	

OH^- is the limiting reagent, so only 2.2×10^{-3} moles of H_3O^+ can react. Once the result of the reaction has been calculated (bottom row of table) we can proceed to our equilibrium problem. We know that there cannot really be zero OH^- in solution as the stoichiometry table suggests. The reaction doesn't really quite go to completion. We could think about it this way. Pretend that the reaction goes to completion, as in the stoichiometry table. Then, determine how much autoionization would occur in the remaining solution to put small amounts of OH^- and H_3O^+ back into solution. To do this we construct an equilibrium table (in units of molarity). First, let's determine the molarity of the leftover H_3O^+ that we found above.

$$[H_3O^+] = \frac{moles\ H_3O^+}{solution\ volume} = \frac{0.8 \times 10^{-3}\, mol}{0.0400\, L} = 2.0 \times 10^{-2}\, M$$

We have only one significant digit in 0.8×10^{-3}, but we carry an extra digit into the equilibrium table:

	$2H_2O(\ell) \rightleftharpoons$	$H_3O^+(aq)$ +	$OH^-(aq)$
Initial M	liquid	2.0×10^{-2}	0
Changes in M		$+x$	$+x$
Equilibrium M		$2.0 \times 10^{-2} + x$	x

Now we can solve the equilibrium problem using the K_w expression:

$$K_w = 1.0 \times 10^{-14} = [OH^-]_{eq}[H_3O^+]_{eq}$$

$$1.0 \times 10^{-14} = (2.0 \times 10^{-2} + x)(x)$$

Using our calculator's solver to solve for x yields:

$$x = 5.0 \times 10^{-13}$$

We can see from this value that at equilibrium we will have the following concentrations:

$$[OH^-]_{eq} = 5 \times 10^{-13} \, M$$

$$[H_3O^+]_{eq} = 2.0 \times 10^{-2} + 5.0 \times 10^{-13} = 2 \times 10^{-2} \, M$$

[Note: the tiny amount of autoionization that occurs does not, in this case, significantly alter the [H₃O⁺] present.]

We can calculate the pH as follows:

$$pH = -\log\left[H_3O^+\right] = -\log\left(2.0 \times 10^{-2}\right) = 1.7$$

Note the return to one significant digit in the final answers.

Now, you might have noticed that some of the work we have done was not significant to our final answer. If we had stopped our work after the stoichiometric calculations we would have already known as much as we needed to know about the concentration of H_3O^+. Adding in the tiny additional H_3O^+ due to autoionization did not change its overall concentration significantly. This is a general rule about strong acid and base calculations unless one of two criteria are met:

1. either the problem gives stoichiometrically identical amounts of strong acid and strong base so that the only source of ions in the resulting solution is autoionization (see Example 18-10), or,

2. such a tiny amount of strong acid or strong base is present in a solution that autoionization is an important player in the production of ions (see Example 18-11).

Usually autoionization can be ignored in strong acid-strong base pH determinations because the leftover strong acid or strong base is in overwhelming supply. Consider this: under the best of circumstances (pure water) autoionization only produces tiny quantities of OH⁻ and H₃O⁺.

$$2H_2O(\ell) \rightleftharpoons H_3O^+(aq) + OH^-(aq)$$

In any solution with added acids and bases (or leftover acids and bases), autoionization is suppressed by the common ion effect and LeChatelier's Principle (shifts left) so that even fewer ions can be contributed by the autoionization process. *Autoionization can be ignored unless the system under consideration is either pure water (or salt water), or has very tiny quantities of other acids and bases added.*

A more convenient calculation is shown below. This is the method to use (but it is important to understand why you are ignoring the autoionization process).

More conveniently:

When we ignore autoionization, solving the problem can be simplified: First (again) we calculate the number of moles of H_3O^+ and the number of moles of OH^-.

$$H_3O^+ \text{ moles}: \quad 0.0200 \, L \times \frac{0.15 \, mol}{L} = 3.0 \times 10^{-3} \, mol$$

$$OH^- \text{ moles}: \quad 0.0200 \, L \times \frac{0.11 \, mol}{L} = 2.2 \times 10^{-3} \, mol$$

Again, because strong acids completely ionize and strong bases completely dissociate, we know that the species above give us solutions that contain 3.0×10^{-3} moles of H_3O^+ and 2.2×10^{-3} moles of OH^-. When we pour these solutions together the following reaction takes place:

$$H_3O^+(aq) + OH^-(aq) \longrightarrow 2H_2O(\ell)$$

We can produce the stoichiometry table (in units of moles) to keep track of the reacting species:

	$H_3O^+(aq)$	$+ \quad OH^-(aq)$	$\longrightarrow \quad 2H_2O(\ell)$
Initial moles	3.0×10^{-3}	2.2×10^{-3}	Solvent (not measurable)
Changes	-2.2×10^{-3}	-2.2×10^{-3}	
Final moles	0.8×10^{-3}	0	

We determine the concentration of the leftover H_3O^+:

$$[H_3O^+] = \frac{moles \, H_3O^+}{solution \, volume} = \frac{0.8 \times 10^{-3} \, mol}{0.0400 \, L} = 2.0 \times 10^{-2} \, M$$

This is where we diverge from the previous path: we note that this value of $[H_3O^+]$ is a much larger concentration than autoionization could ever influence (several orders of magnitude), so we determine the pH:

$$pH = -\log[H_3O^+] = -\log(2.0 \times 10^{-2}) = 1.7$$

Notice the return to one significant digit (only the "7" in 1.7 is significant) in the final pH. If we care to know the OH^- concentration (which cannot really be zero as the stoichiometry table suggested) we can calculate it directly from the pH, rather than from an equilibrium table:

$$14.0 = pH + pOH$$
$$14.0 = 1.7 + pOH$$
$$pOH = 12.3$$
$$[OH^-] = 10^{-12.3} = 5 \times 10^{-13}$$

These are the same values for $[H_3O^+]$ and $[OH^-]$ that we arrived at with the more rigorous solution.

Example 18-9.

Calculate the pH of the solution that results when 35.5 mL of 0.034 M Ca(OH)$_2$ is added to 54.7 mL of 0.042 M HI.

Solution:

This time we solve the problem only in the most convenient fashion. The strong acid HI produces solutions featuring the H_3O^+ ion, not the HI molecule. In the strong base solution, we are interested in the OH$^-$ concentration. We calculate the number of moles of H_3O^+ and the number of moles of OH$^-$ as follows.

$$H_3O^+ \ moles: \quad 0.0547 \ L \times \frac{0.042 \ mol}{L} = 2.30 \times 10^{-3} \ mol$$

$$OH^- \ moles: \quad 0.0355 \ L \times \frac{0.034 \ mol \ Ca(OH)_2}{L} \times \frac{2 \ mol \ OH^-}{1 \ mol \ Ca(OH)_2} = 2.42 \times 10^{-3} \ mol \ OH^-$$

Notice that we are carrying an extra significant digit on each of these mole amounts, in order to avoid rounding errors. There should really be only two significant digits based on the concentrations of the solutions.

When we pour the acid and base solutions together the following reaction takes place:

$$H_3O^+(aq) + OH^-(aq) \rightarrow 2H_2O(\ell)$$

We can produce a stoichiometry table (in moles) to keep track of the reacting species:

	$H_3O^+(aq)$	+ $OH^-(aq)$	$\longrightarrow$ $2H_2O(\ell)$
Initial moles	2.30 × 10^{-3}	2.42 × 10^{-3}	Solvent (not measurable)
Changes	-2.30 × 10^{-3}	-2.30 × 10^{-3}	
Final moles	0	0.12 × 10^{-3}	

In the "final moles" row, we continue to carry an extra digit in the moles OH$^-$ value. There would only be one significant digit if this were the final answer. We see that the leftover OH$^-$ is in much larger supply than the autoionization process could influence, so we can skip production of the equilibrium table. The limiting reagent is H_3O^+. We expect a basic solution with pH greater than 7.00. The leftover OH$^-$ is found in a total volume of 0.0547 + 0.0355 = 0.0902 L. So we can calculate the [OH$^-$] and pOH as follows:

$$[OH^-] = \frac{moles \ OH^- \ remaining}{solution \ volume} = \frac{0.12 \times 10^{-3} \ mol}{0.0902 \ L} = 1.3 \times 10^{-3} \ M$$

$$pOH = -log[OH^-] = -log(1.3 \times 10^{-3}) = 2.9$$

We have been carrying an extra digit so as not to build up a series of rounding errors. In the last calculation we took the two-significant digit number, 1.3×10^{-3}, and wrote an answer with only one significant digit (the pOH of 2.9). This is really the number of significant digits that we are allowed at this point. We can determine the pH:

$$pH = 14.0 - pOH = 14.0 - 2.9 = 11.1$$

(Note: The concentration of H_3O^+ that goes with the calculated pH is $7.9 \times 10^{-12} \ M$. There really isn't zero H_3O^+ as the stoichiometry table suggested. This is a good method to determine how much autoionization occurred without the production of the equilibrium table. You can check this by producing the equilibrium table on your own to make sure that the results agree.)

Example 18-10.

Calculate the concentrations of H_3O^+, OH^-, Na^+, and ClO_4^- that result when the following solutions are combined: 50.0 mL of 0.100 M $HClO_4$ and 50.0 mL of 0.100 M NaOH.

Solution:

First, we calculate the final concentrations of the spectator ions, Na^+ and ClO_4^-. These ions do not react. We can determine the number of moles of each, and then divide by the final volume of the combined solution (100.0 mL) to obtain the final concentrations of these ions.

$$\left[Na^+ \right] = 0.0500 \, L \times \frac{0.100 \, mol \, Na^+}{L} \times \frac{1}{100.0 \, mL} \times \frac{1000 \, mL}{L} = 5.00 \times 10^{-2} \, M \, Na^+$$

$$\left[ClO_4^- \right] = 0.0500 \, L \times \frac{0.100 \, mol \, ClO_4^-}{L} \times \frac{1}{100.0 \, mL} \times \frac{1000 \, mL}{L} = 5.00 \times 10^{-2} \, M \, ClO_4^-$$

Next, we consider the ions that react, H_3O^+ (from the $HClO_4$ solution) and OH^- (from the NaOH solution). We calculate the number of moles of these two ions.

$$H_3O^+ \, moles: \quad 0.0500 \, L \times \frac{0.100 \, mol \, H_3O^+}{L} = 5.00 \times 10^{-3} \, mol \, H_3O^+$$

$$OH^- \, moles: \quad 0.0500 \, L \times \frac{0.100 \, mol \, OH^-}{L} = 5.00 \times 10^{-3} \, mol \, OH^-$$

When we pour these solutions together the following reaction takes place:

$$H_3O^+(aq) + OH^-(aq) \rightarrow 2H_2O(\ell)$$

We can produce a stoichiometry table to keep track of the reacting species:

	$H_3O^+(aq)$	+ $OH^-(aq)$	$\longrightarrow$ $2H_2O(\ell)$
Initial moles	5.00×10^{-3}	5.00×10^{-3}	Solvent (not measurable)
Changes	-5.00×10^{-3}	-5.00×10^{-3}	
Final moles	0	0	

Now we know that this cannot actually be the case. There cannot be zero H_3O^+ and zero OH^- in an aqueous solution. But, what has occurred here is a complete neutralization, which leaves a batch of salt water. The concentrations of $[H_3O^+]$ and $[OH^-]$ are 1.0×10^{-7} M and the pH is 7.00.

Example 18-11.

Determine the pH of a 1.0×10^{-8} M HCl solution.

Solution:

This is a common type of question at the end of acid-base chapters. This problem does not require a stoichiometry table because there is no acid-base reaction other than the ionization of the strong acid. However, it is not nearly as straightforward as it initially appears. Many students will proceed with the following logic:

HCl is a strong acid that ionizes completely.
The solution will, therefore, be 1.0×10^{-8} M in H_3O^+.
pH $= -\log[H_3O^+]_{eq} = -\log(1.0 \times 10^{-8}) = 8.00$.

Do you see the problem with this answer? Think about the pH scale before reading on!

Here we have calculated a basic pH for an aqueous solution of a strong acid: not very sensible. What went wrong?

The amount of strong acid in this solution is so tiny that it actually contributes less H_3O^+ than autoionization. We cannot discount the autoionization process in our determination of pH for this solution. The strong acid added is in such a small supply that autoionization is not effectively suppressed and remains an important source of H_3O^+ in the solution. We can solve this problem by using strategies developed in previous chapters for the analysis of equilibrium systems with a common ion effect. We start by creating an equilibrium table:

		$2H_2O(\ell) \rightleftharpoons H_3O^+(aq)\ +$	$OH^-(aq)$
Initial M		1.0×10^{-8}	0
Changes in M	solvent	+x	+x
Equilibrium M		$1.0 \times 10^{-8} + x$	x

We can now substitute the equilibrium concentrations into the K_w expression:

$$K_w = \left[H_3O^+\right]_{eq}\left[OH^-\right]_{eq} = \left(1.0 \times 10^{-8} + x\right)(x)$$

$$1.0 \times 10^{-14} = \left(1.0 \times 10^{-8} + x\right)(x)$$

We use the solver on our calculator to solve for x and find that $x = 9.5 \times 10^{-8}$ M. This is the contribution to $[H_3O^+]$ made by the autoionization process. The total $[H_3O^+]$ must be $1.0 \times 10^{-8} + 9.5 \times 10^{-8} = 1.05 \times 10^{-7}$ M. This gives a pH of 6.98, very slightly acidic, in line with a tiny addition of strong acid.

Note that autoionization has been slightly suppressed by the addition of the strong acid; autoionization in pure water would generate an $x = 1.0 \times 10^{-7}$ M.

Table 18-8 summarizes the types of solutions for which you should be able to calculate the pH. We will add to this table in Chapters 19 and 20 as we become able to perform these calculations on a wider variety of solutions.

Summary Table 18-8. Solutions for which we have calculated pH:

1	strong acid solution, H_3O^+	Use [strong acid] = $[H_3O^+]$, and pH = $-\log [H_3O^+]$	Chap 18-4B
2	strong base solution, OH^-	Use $[OH^-]$ = [strong base], or $[OH^-]$ = 2 × [strong base] (depending on the strong base); then pOH = $-\log [OH^-]$, then pH = 14 $-$ pOH.	Chap 18-4B
3	strong acid + strong base	Use stoichiometry table to determine composition of final solution (could be strong acid, strong base, or neutral) then find pH as indicated in Table entries 1 and 2, above.	Chap 18-4E

Chapter Summary

Summary Table of Acid-Base Definitions		
Theory	Acids	Bases
Arrhenius	H^+(aq)	OH^-(aq)
Bronsted-Lowry	proton donors	proton acceptors
Lewis	electron pair acceptors	electron pair donors

Within Bronsted-Lowry theory: Acids cannot behave as acids in the absence of a base, and vice versa. Acid-base character is defined by the **transfer** of a proton so there must be both a donor and an acceptor.

Within Lewis theory: Acids cannot behave as acids in the absence of a base, and vice versa. Lewis acid-base character depends on a **new bond** being formed, so there must be both a donor of electrons and an acceptor.

Lewis theory offers the broadest acid-base definitions. Arrhenius theory is the narrowest.

Strong acids and bases in aqueous systems:

1. Strong bases are salts of either the hydroxide or oxide anion.

2. Strong acids are molecules that react with water stoichiometrically to produce the hydronium ion.

3. The conjugate bases of strong acids are not basic. The conjugate acids of strong bases are not acidic.

Strong Acids (aq)	Conjugate Bases (aq)	Acid/base behavior of conjugate base
HCl	Cl^-	None
HBr	Br^-	None
HI	I^-	None
HNO_3	NO_3^-	None
H_2SO_4	HSO_4^-	Weak acid
$HClO_4$	ClO_4^-	None
$HClO_3$	ClO_3^-	None
H_3O^+	H_2O	Very weak base

Strong Bases (aq)	Conjugate Acids	Acid/base behavior of conjugate acid
OH^-	H_2O	Very weak acid
O^{2-}	OH^-	Strong base

4. Net ionic reaction equations for strong acids reacting with strong bases are all identical:

$$H_3O^+(aq) + OH^-(aq) \rightarrow 2H_2O(\ell)$$

5. pH determinations of strong acids and bases, see Summary Table 18-8, above. The autoionization process may be ignored unless the equilibrium concentration of H_3O^+ is very small (on the order of 10^{-7} M or below.)

CHAPTER 18 PROBLEMS

1.   Give chemical formulas of the conjugate bases of the following:

   a. H_2O **b.** perchloric acid   **c.** $H_2PO_4^-$ **d.** H_2
   e. $H_3SO_4^+$ **f.** $HClO_2$ **g.** CH_3COOH (acetic acid)

2.   Give chemical formulas of the conjugate acids of the following:

   a. OH^- **b.** thiosulfate ion   **c.** $HAsO_4^{2-}$ **d.** PH_3
   e. $C_2H_5NH_2$ **f.** SO_3^{2-} **g.** perchlorate ion

3.   Give the chemical formulas of both the conjugate acids and conjugate bases of the following:

   a. HPO_4^{2-} **b.** HSO_4^- **c.** SH^- **d.** NH_3

4.   In each of the following acid base reactions identify and label the conjugate acid/base pairs.

   a. $HF(aq) + NH_3(aq) \rightleftharpoons F^-(aq) + NH_4^+(aq)$

   b. $HCl(aq) + OH^-(aq) \rightleftharpoons Cl^-(aq) + H_2O(\ell)$

   c. $HPO_4^{2-}(aq) + HCN(aq) \rightleftharpoons H_2PO_4^-(aq) + CN^-(aq)$

   d. $HNO_3(aq) + CH_3CO_2^-(aq) \rightleftharpoons NO_3^-(aq) + CH_3CO_2H(aq)$

   e. $O^{2-}(aq) + H_2O(\ell) \rightleftharpoons 2\ OH^-(aq)$

   f. $HClO_2(aq) + NO_2^-(aq) \rightleftharpoons ClO_2^-(aq) + HNO_2(aq)$

5.   Write the molecular reaction equation and the net ionic reaction equation for the following reactants.

   a. NaOH and HNO_3 **b.** $HClO_4$ and $Ca(OH)_2$ **c.** MgO and HI

6.   Write the Bronsted-Lowry acid-base reaction equation for each set of reactants provided.

   a. acid = HCO_2H base = OH^-
   b. acid = C_6H_5OH base = H_2O
   c. acid = H_2O base = HPO_4^{2-}
   d. acid = HNO_2 base = $CH_3CO_2^-$
   e. acid = $HClO_2$ base = NH_3
   f. acid = H_2S base = ClO_2^-

7.   Write the acid ionization reaction equation for each of the following acids.
   a. HF   **b.** HCN   **c.** HPO_4^{2-}
   d. HI   **e.** NH_4^+ **f.** HClO

8.   Write the base ionization reaction equation for each of the following bases.
   a. NH_3 **b.** SH^- **c.** HPO_4^{2-}
   d. $CH_3CO_2^-$ **e.** BrO^- **f.** NO_2^-

9.   Match each arrow-type to its best interpretation:

      a. $\rightleftharpoons$ (1) A reaction with a very small K_{eq} value.

      b. $\rightleftharpoons$ (2) An irreversible reaction.

      c. $\longrightarrow$ (3) A reaction that is reversible.

      d. $\rightleftharpoons$ (4) A reaction with a very large K_{eq} value

10.   There are two principal categories of strong bases. What are these categories? Give two examples of each kind of strong base.

11.   There are six common strong acids. List them (and commit them to memory).

12.   Explain why the strong acids, though not equivalent in acid strength, are generally treated as though they are equivalent.

13.   Explain why the autoionization of water is not an important contributor of ions in the presence of a strong acid.

14.   At 37 °C (body temperature) $[H_3O^+][OH^-] = 2.4 \times 10^{-14}$. What is the pH of pure water at 37 °C?

15.   At 40 °C water has a pH of 6.77. Does water have more or fewer ions at 40 °C than at 25 °C? Explain briefly.

16. K_w for water is temperature dependent, as shown below:

T(°C)	K_w
25	1.0×10^{-14}
40	3.0×10^{-14}
60	9.6×10^{-14}

On the basis of these equilibrium constants, is the autoionization of water endothermic or exothermic? Explain.

17.   An aqueous solution of hydrochloric acid has pH = 3.88. What is the HCl concentration of this solution?

18.   What is the concentration of an aqueous sodium hydroxide solution if the pH is 10.50?

19.   The pH of an aqueous NaOH solution is 12.40. What is the concentration of sodium ions in this solution?

20. Calculate the desired quantities (aqueous solutions, T = 25 °C):

    a. 1.00×10^{-2} *M* HNO_3 pH =

    b. $10^{-2.50}$ *M* NaOH   pH =   pOH =

    c. $10^{-11.50}$ *M* HCl   pH =

    d. pH of an HNO_3 solution = 0.286 $[H_3O^+]$ =

    e. pure H_2O pK_w =

21. Calculate the desired quantities (aqueous solutions, T = 25 °C):

    a. $[H_3O^+] = 1.4 \times 10^{-3}$ *M*.   pH =

    b. $[OH^-] = 6.2 \times 10^{-4}$ *M*   pH =

    c. 1.00×10^{-3} *M* perchloric acid $[OH^-]$ =

    d. $[H_3O^+] = 10^{-9.62}$ pH =

    e. 1.27×10^{-13} *M* HBr $[H_3O^+]$ =

22. Calculate the desired quantities (aqueous solutions, T = 25 °C):

    a. $[OH^-] = 10^{-4.57}$ *M*   pH =

    b. $[H_3O^+] = 2.0$ *M*   pH =

    c. $[OH^-] = 4.5 \times 10^{-5}$ *M*   pH =

    d. 0.0160 *M* HI   pOH =

    e. 4.75×10^{-12} *M* NaOH $[H_3O^+]$ =

23. Calculate the desired quantities (aqueous solutions, T = 25 °C):

    a. The pH of a solution is 10.52. Calculate $[H_3O^+]$.

    b. What is the pH of 2.40×10^{-3} *M* KOH?

    c. What is the concentration of a perchloric acid solution if the pH is 1.86?

    d. Calculate the pH of 3.3×10^{-3} *M* NaOH solution.

    e. Calculate the pH of 4.2×10^{-4} *M* $Ba(OH)_2$ solution.

24. Calculate the pH of the solution that results from mixing 5.00 mL of 0.62 *M* LiOH and 6.70 mL of 0.40 *M* $HClO_4$.

25. Calculate the pH of the solution that results from mixing 23.0 mL of 0.17 *M* HBr and 32.0 mL of 0.23 *M* KOH.

26. 100.0 mL of 0.150 *M* HCl and 50.0 mL of 0.050 *M* NaOH are mixed at 25 °C. Determine the concentrations of the following ions in the final solution:

    a. Na^+ **b.** H_3O^+ **c.** Cl^- **d.** OH^-

27. A solution is prepared by mixing 20.0 mL of 0.100 *M* HNO_3 with 50.0 mL of 0.120 *M* $HClO_4$ at 25 °C. Determine the concentrations of the following ions in the final solution:

    a. NO_3^- **b.** ClO_4^- **c.** H_3O^+ **d.** OH^-

28. What volume of 0.40 *M* HCl must be added to 5.00 mL of 0.62 *M* NaOH to give a solution with a pH of 13.00?

29. What volume of 0.23 M KOH solution must be added to 23.0 mL of 0.17 M HBr to give a solution with a pH of 12.00?

30. Ethylenediamine is a common ligand. It is also a base according to at least two of our acid-base concepts. Illustrate the basic properties of ethylenediamine, showing that it satisfies two definitions of basic behavior. Illustrate both of your answers with balanced chemical equations.

31. A solution of barium hydroxide of concentration 0.100 M is available. What volume of this solution is necessary to prepare 500.0 mL of solution having pH of 11.00?

32. **a.** Set up an equilibrium table to determine the amount of autoionization that will occur in a 4.6×10^{-7} M HNO_3 solution.
b. Calculate the pH of the resulting solution.
c. Calculate the pH if autoionization is ignored.

33. **a.** Set up an equilibrium table to determine the amount of autoionization that will occur in a 6.1×10^{-9} M HNO_3 solution.
b. Calculate the pH of the resulting solution.
c. Calculate the pH if autoionization is ignored.

34. **a.** Set up an equilibrium table to determine the amount of autoionization that will occur in a 5.3×10^{-6} M HNO_3 solution.
b. Calculate the pH of the resulting solution.
c. Calculate the pH if autoionization is ignored.

35. **a.** Set up an equilibrium table to determine the amount of autoionization that will occur in a 2.9×10^{-5} M HNO_3 solution.
b. Calculate the pH of the resulting solution.
c. Calculate the pH if autoionization is ignored.

CHAPTER 19: UNDERSTANDING WEAK ACIDS AND BASES CONCEPT AND CALCULATIONS

19-1. INTRODUCTION: DEFINITIONS FOR THIS CHAPTER

A. Bronsted-Lowry Definition

As we begin to explore weak acids and bases we should reiterate that throughout this chapter (and the next) we will be confining ourselves to the realm of Bronsted-Lowry acids and bases. Therefore the useful definitions[148] to keep in mind are

Bronsted-Lowry Definitions	
Acid	Proton[149] Donor
Base	Proton Acceptor

We can write a generic reaction equation for the addition of a Bronsted-Lowry acid to water solution:

$$HA(aq) + H_2O(\ell) \rightleftharpoons A^-(aq) + H_3O^+(aq)$$

We can do the same for a Bronsted-Lowry base:[150]

$$B:(aq) + H_2O(\ell) \rightleftharpoons BH^+(aq) + OH^-(aq)$$

Both of these reaction equations show the proton-transfer nature of a Bronsted-Lowry acid-base reaction.

B. What are Weak Acids and Bases?

Weak acids and **weak bases** are **weak electrolytes**; whereas strong acids and bases are strong electrolytes. Salts are typical strong electrolytes that fully dissociate:

$$Ba(NO_3)_2(s) \longrightarrow Ba^{2+}(aq) + 2NO_3^-(aq)$$

Stoichiometric amounts of aqueous ions are produced and essentially no intact formula units of the solute exist. Strong acids are similar to salts in that they generate a stoichiometric number of ions in solution. For strong acids, the process is called ionization rather than dissociation, because new ions are made from neutral molecules:

$$HNO_3(aq) + H_2O(\ell) \longrightarrow NO_3^-(aq) + H_3O^+(aq)$$

A strong electrolyte is signified in a reaction equation by use of a single forward arrow. The equilibrium constants for these processes are large. In Chapter 18, we suggested that the it is useful to memorize the identities of the common strong acids.[151]

---

[148] Previously discussed in Chapter 18, Section 18-2.B.

[149] A proton is what is left of a hydrogen atom when the single electron has been removed, hence H+ is often called a proton.

[150] The "colon" with the B is the lone pair of electrons that will be used to make a new bond to H+.

[151] This list is short: HCl, HBr, HI, HNO$_3$, H$_2$SO$_4$, HClO$_4$, HClO$_3$.

Weak acids are molecular substances or ions[152] having a hydrogen atom that can be transferred to other molecules as a proton, thus leaving its valence electron behind. Weak acids do not react to completion with water to produce the hydronium ion. For example, one million weak acid molecules in aqueous solution might only transfer 50,000 protons to water. The rest of the weak acid molecules (950,000 of them) would remain intact. Because acidic character depends on the formation of H_3O^+, placing one million *strong acid* molecules in water results in a more acidic solution (essentially one million H_3O^+) than putting one million *weak acid* molecules in water (maybe ~50,000 H_3O^+).

Weak bases are generally either neutral molecules containing a nitrogen atom that has a lone pair of electrons (such as ammonia, or methyl amine, CH_3NH_2), or anions that are the conjugate base of a weak acid (such as CN^- or $CH_3CO_2^-$).[153] Putting one million formula units of the *strong base*, NaOH, in water will result in (essentially) one million OH^- in the solution. Putting one million molecules of a *weak base* into solution might result in 50,000 OH^- in solution. Only a small portion of the weak acid or the weak base is able to ionize in water.

We use <u>reversible arrows to depict the behavior of weak acids and bases in water</u>. Note that the weak acid (or base) is *already dissolved in water* on the reactant side of the equation. We are not describing the solubility of the weak acids and bases, but the degree to which proton transfer occurs. Here are a couple of examples of each:

Weak acids		
Acetic acid:	$CH_3CO_2H(aq) + H_2O(\ell) \rightleftharpoons CH_3CO_2^-(aq) + H_3O^+(aq)$
Hydrocyanic acid:	$HCN(aq) + H_2O(\ell) \rightleftharpoons CN^-(aq) + H_3O^+(aq)$

Weak bases		
Ammonia:	$NH_3(aq) + H_2O(\ell) \rightleftharpoons NH_4^+(aq) + OH^-(aq)$
Bicarbonate ion:	$HCO_3^-(aq) + H_2O(\ell) \rightleftharpoons H_2CO_3(aq) + OH^-(aq)$

Make sure to look for the proton transfer in each case. We have chosen to use the lop-sided reversible arrows to emphasize that the equilibrium constants for reactions such as these are generally very small, always less than one. At equilibrium, there are more reactants than products.

C. Conjugate Pairs and Relative Strengths within a Pair

Weak acids and bases have conjugates that differ from each other by one H^+ (or proton). The conjugate pairs from the four reactions above (in the order acid / base) are:

$$CH_3CO_2H \,/\, CH_3CO_2^- \qquad HCN \,/\, CN^- \qquad NH_4^+ \,/\, NH_3 \qquad H_2CO_3 \,/\, HCO_3^-$$

Exercise 19-1.

Each of the four acid/base reactions listed above (involving the ionizations of acetic acid, hydrocyanic acid, ammonia, and the bicarbonate ion) involves a second acid-base conjugate pair. List these in the order: acid / base.

---

[152] Some ions, such as HSO_4^- or NH_4^+, are weak acids. In the lab these come in the form of salts such as $NaHSO_4$, or NH_4NO_3. The counter ion (Na^+, NO_3^-) do not affect the acid character of the weak acid, unless the counter ion has its own acid or base qualities, such as $(NH_4)_2CO_3$, where CO_3^{2-} is a weak base.

[153] Weak bases that are anions come in the form of salts, such KCN or $NaCH_3CO_2$. The counter ion (K^+, Na^+) will not affect the base character of the weak base, unless the counter ion has its own acid or base properties (as in NH_4CN).

The conjugate base of a weak acid is a weak base. The conjugate acid of a weak base is a weak acid.[154] Not all "weak" acids are the same strength; some are better than others. *The more acidic a weak acid is, the less basic its conjugate base.* We have already seen the extreme of this trend: the conjugate bases of strong acids do not even manage to behave as bases under typical aqueous conditions. Consider, again, the reaction equations for acetic acid and hydrocyanic acid:

$$CH_3CO_2H(aq) + H_2O(\ell) \rightleftharpoons CH_3CO_2^-(aq) + H_3O^+(aq)$$

$$HCN(aq) + H_2O(\ell) \rightleftharpoons CN^-(aq) + H_3O^+(aq)$$

Notice that the two reaction equations have forward reactions that depend upon the abilities of the acids to push a proton onto the water molecule. Acetic acid is more successful and generates a solution of lower pH (more acidic) when equal concentrations of the two acids are compared. As we learned in Chapter 16, a more successful forward reaction means a less successful reverse reaction (the K_{eq}'s have a reciprocal relationship). The reverse reactions compare the ability of the conjugate bases, acetate ion and cyanide anion, to attract a proton from H_3O^+. The cyanide ion is more successful; it is the better weak base. Think about it this way: the equilibrium position of the acetic acid reaction equilibrium sits farther

Table 19-1. Conjugate acid-base pairs.			
Increasing acid strength ↑	Acid	Base	*Increasing* base strength ↓
	HCl	Cl⁻	
	HIO₃	IO₃⁻	
	HF	F⁻	
	CH₃CO₂H	CH₃CO₂⁻	
	HCN	CN⁻	
	NH₄⁺	NH₃	
	H₂O	OH⁻	

toward products than the equilibrium position of the HCN reaction. This must mean two things: acetic acid is better at being an acid (and so generates more ion products) AND acetate ion is the poorer base (and so cannot generate as much water and acetic acid). Table 19-1 shows these conjugate relationships, with acid strength highest at the top of the list, and base strength highest at the bottom.

19-2. STRENGTHS OF WEAK ACIDS AND BASES

In this section of the chapter we will explore two ways to specify the relative strengths of weak acids and bases. First, we take a look at percent ionization. We want to see what a percent ionization is, and how we can use a percent ionization to determine the pH of a weak acid or weak base solution. Then we move to a second entity that describes the strength of a weak acid or weak base–the equilibrium constants for their ionization reactions.

A. Strengths of Weak Acids and Bases: Percent Ionization

1. Determination of Fraction Ionized and Percent Ionization.

As we discussed with respect to the strong acids,[155] weak acids are not all the same strength; some are stronger than others. The key is that the weak acids are *unable* to fully push their protons onto water molecules, so they do not produce stoichiometric amounts of H_3O^+. Strong and weak bases share the same relationship: strong bases provide *stoichiometric* amounts of OH⁻ in solution, weak bases provide less than stoichiometric amounts.

---

[154] Remember, the conjugate base of a strong acid is not a strong base! This may seem inconsistent, but, as we shall see, it all follows the same trend.

[155] While the strengths of the strong acids are leveled in water (see Chapter 18, Section 18-4), they are not intrinsically equal to one another.

Consider the generic reaction equations for weak acids (HA) and weak bases (B:)

$$HA(aq) + H_2O(\ell) \rightleftharpoons A^-(aq) + H_3O^+(aq)$$

$$B:(aq) + H_2O(\ell) \rightleftharpoons BH^+(aq) + OH^-(aq)$$

Note that we have neutral molecules as reactants and ions as products, so these reactions can be described as **ionizations**. Most weak acids and bases ionize to an extent from less than 1% to about 10%. The fraction ionized is:

$$fraction\ ionized = \frac{amount\ ionized}{total\ amount} = \frac{moles\ A^-}{moles\left(A^- + HA\right)}\ or\ \frac{moles\ BH^+}{moles\left(BH^+ + B\right)}$$

Converting from fractions to percents gives:

$$percent\ ionization = \frac{amount\ ionized}{total\ amount} \times 100\%$$

In our example from the beginning of this chapter, we talked about one million weak acid molecules resulting in 50,000 hydronium ions[156] (at equilibrium). This would mean that 50,000 out of the million molecules were able to ionize. The fraction ionized is

$$\frac{50,000\ ionized}{1,000,000\ total} = 0.050$$

The percent ionization is

$$\frac{50,000\ ionized}{1,000,000\ total} \times 100\% = 5.0\%\ ionized$$

In practice, the fraction ionized may be calculated from numbers of particles, moles of particles, or concentrations of the particles:

$$fraction\ of\ a\ weak\ acid\ ionized = \frac{number\ of\ A^-}{number\ HA + A^-} = \frac{moles\ A^-}{moles\ HA + A^-} = \frac{\left[A^-\right]}{\left[HA\right] + \left[A^-\right]}$$

In each case the denominator is the amount of HA (number, moles or concentration) present *before* ionization.

Ratios of concentrations (on the right, above) are really just ratios of moles because all particles (HA and A⁻) are in the same solution, and thus the volume terms in the numerator and denominator cancel out.

The fraction ionized of a weak base can be calculated in analogous ways:

$$fraction\ of\ a\ weak\ base\ ionized = \frac{number\ of\ BH^+}{number\ B + BH^+} = \frac{moles\ BH^+}{moles\ B + BH^+} = \frac{\left[BH^+\right]}{\left[B\right] + \left[BH^+\right]}$$

In each case the denominator is the amount of B (number, moles or concentration) present *before* ionization.

Percent ionization of a weak acid or weak base may be calculated from the fraction ionized:

fraction ionized (from above) × 100%

---

[156] And the number of H_3O^+ is equal to the number of A⁻ because the same reaction equation produces one of each.

Note that when a solution is labeled as having a particular concentration of a weak acid or weak base, such as "0.10 M NH$_3$," this means that the total concentration of NH$_3$ originally added is 0.10 M. At equilibrium, a small percent of this will have ionized to NH$_4^+$. The total presence of NH$_3$ and NH$_4^+$ at equilibrium is 0.10 M; this would be the denominator of a calculation of fraction ionized.

Exercise 19-2.

Determine the percent ionization for each of the following weak acid solutions.

a. A solution of 1,000,000,000 weak acid molecules where 80,000,000 become ionized at equilibrium. Assume 2 significant digits.

b. A solution of 1.00 mole of weak acid molecules where 4.73×10^{21} become ionized at equilibrium.

c. A 0.44 M solution of HA where the concentration of A$^-$ is found to be 0.0063 M.

Exercise 19-3.

Determine the percent ionization of each of the following weak base solutions.

a. A solution of 3.0×10^{15} weak base molecules where at equilibrium 4.9×10^{13} have become ionized.

b. A 0.265 M solution of B that contains 0.00521 M BH$^+$ at equilibrium.

c. A weak base solution that, *at equilibrium*, contains 0.0021 M B and 2.2×10^{-4} M BH$^+$. Be careful here. What is the total concentration of B and BH$^+$ in this solution?

---

2. Using Fraction Ionized or Percent Ionized to Determine pH

If we know the fraction or percent ionized for a particular solution of a weak acid or base, we can determine the pH. Consider the ionization reaction equations:

$$HA + H_2O \rightleftharpoons A^- + H_3O^+$$

$$B: + H_2O \rightleftharpoons BH^+ + OH^-$$

The pH can be determined by either knowing [H$_3$O$^+$] or [OH$^-$]. If we know the fraction ionized, and the total concentration of the weak acid or weak base (the denominators of the fraction ionized), we can calculate the concentration of A$^-$ or BH$^+$:

$$\text{weak acid fraction ionized} = \frac{\left[A^- \right]}{\left[HA \right] + \left[A^- \right]}$$

$$\left[A^- \right] = (\text{fraction ionized}) \times \left(\left[HA \right] + \left[A^- \right] \right) = (\text{fraction ionized}) \times \left(\text{total concentration} \right)$$

$$\text{weak base fraction ionized} = \frac{\left[BH^+ \right]}{\left[B \right] + \left[BH^+ \right]}$$

$$\left[BH^+ \right] = (\text{fraction ionized}) \times \left(\left[B \right] + \left[BH^+ \right] \right) = (\text{fraction ionized}) \times \left(\text{total concentration} \right)$$

Looking at the ionization reaction equations again, we see that the product species are produced in equal amounts. Thus, for acids $\left[A^- \right] = \left[H_3O^+ \right]$ and for bases $\left[BH^+ \right] = \left[OH^- \right]$. Thus, the pH can be calculated from a knowledge of either $\left[A^-\right]$ or $\left[BH^+\right]$. The examples that follow illustrate this method.

Example 19-1.

A 0.14 M solution of a particular weak acid is 6.5% ionized. Calculate the pH.

Solution:

We don't need to know the identity of the weak acid, just the extent to which it is ionized. We write a generic reaction equation:

$$HA(aq) + H_2O(\ell) \rightleftharpoons A^-(aq) + H_3O^+(aq)$$

A concentration of 0.14 M refers to the original amount of weak acid placed into solution. We see that for every A^- formed there is also one H_3O^+ formed. So if we determine $[A^-]$, we will also know $[H_3O^+]$ and the pH.

We need to know, then, how much of the total concentration of HA is ionized to A^-. We use the idea of fraction ionized:

$$\text{fraction ionized} = \frac{\text{concentration ionized}}{\text{total concentration}}$$

so that

$$\text{concentration ionized} = \text{fraction ionized} \times \text{total concentration}$$

We first convert the 6.5% ionization into a fraction ionized: $\frac{6.5}{100} = 0.065$. Then we use the relationship above to solve for the concentration of A^-.

$$\text{concentration ionized} = \left[A^-\right] = (0.065)(0.14\ M) = 9.10 \times 10^{-3}\ M$$

Notice that we keep an extra digit, making sure to round off our answers only at the very end of a calculation.

Now, we have what we need to find the pH. Remember from our balanced, generic equation that the ionization process produces equivalent amounts of A^- ions and H_3O^+ ions. If we have

$$[A^-] = 9.10 \times 10^{-3}\ M$$

we also have

$$[H_3O^+] = 9.10 \times 10^{-3}\ M$$

The pH must then be

$$-\log(9.10 \times 10^{-3}) = 2.04$$

Notice that we end with just two significant figures, the "04" of the pH value.

The same procedures allow us to determine the pH of a weak base solution if we know the extent of ionization.

Example 19-2.

Calculate the pH of a 0.032 M solution of a weak base that is 9.3% ionized.

<u>Solution</u>:

We start by writing a generic reaction equation:

$$B:(aq)+H_2O(\ell)\rightleftharpoons BH^+(aq)+OH^-(aq)$$

We see that the molarity of ionized base formed is equal to the molarity of *hydroxide ion* formed (not the molarity of *hydronium ion* as was the case for a weak acid). We write:

$$[BH^+]=[OH^-]$$

So, if we can determine the concentration of ionized base, $[BH^+]$, we will be able to calculate the pH, but we will have to work from the pOH this time.

To begin, we utilize the definition of fraction ionized to write

concentration ionized = fraction ionized × total concentration

We substitute in what we know (and keep a couple extra digits for now):

$$\text{concentration ionized}=\left[BH^+\right]=0.093\times0.032\,M=2.976\times10^{-3}\,M$$

Because $\left[BH^+\right]=\left[OH^-\right]$, we know that $\left[OH^-\right]=2.976\times10^{-3}\,M$. We can calculate the pOH:

$$-\log[OH^-]=pOH$$

$$-\log(2.976\times10^{-3})=2.526$$

Finally, converting to pH (and ending with 2 significant digits):

$$pOH+pH=14.00$$

$$pH=14.00-2.526$$

$$pH=11.47$$

Exercise 19-4.

a. Determine the pH of a 0.14 M weak acid solution that is 9.3% ionized.

b. Determine the pH of a 0.032 M weak acid solution that is 6.5% ionized.

c. Determine the pH of a 0.032 M weak acid solution that is 9.3% ionized.

d. Compare your work to the work in Example 19-1. What determines the pH of a weak acid solution, the concentration, the percent ionization, or both? Support your answer.

Exercise 19-5.

Determine the pH of the following solutions:

      a. 0.045 M weak base that is 6.6% ionized. **b.** 0.28 M weak base that is 10.0% ionized.

B. Strengths of Weak Acids and Bases: Equilibrium Constants

While a knowledge of the percent ionization of a weak acid or weak base solution allows the straightforward calculation of pH, it is not possible to tabulate the percent ionizations of a list of weak acids and weak bases. Perhaps surprisingly, a particular weak acid (or weak base) will have different percent ionizations under different circumstances. We summarize in Table 19-2.

Table 19-2. Summary of percent ionization	
Percent ionization depends on:	because:
The identity of the weak acid or base	some are naturally stronger than others
the concentration of the weak acid or base	more concentrated solutions tend to have smaller percent ionizations (more ions, but smaller percent ionization)
the presence of other species in the solution	in the presence of a common ion, less of the weak acid or weak base will be able to ionize (LeChatelier's Principle)
the temperature	the extent of any reaction depends on the temperature; K_{eq} is temperature dependent

Chemists normally approach the comparison of strengths of various weak acids and weak bases by using the equilibrium constants for their ionization in water. The generic reactions of interest, along with their K_{eq} expressions, are:

$$HA(aq) + H_2O(\ell) \rightleftharpoons A^-(aq) + H_3O^+(aq) \qquad K_{eq} = \frac{\left[A^-\right]\left[H_3O^+\right]}{\left[HA\right]}$$

$$B{:}(aq) + H_2O(\ell) \rightleftharpoons BH^+(aq) + OH^-(aq) \qquad K_{eq} = \frac{\left[BH^+\right]\left[OH^-\right]}{\left[B{:}\right]}$$

Stronger acids and bases ionize more, and, therefore, have larger equilibrium constants. Both percent ionization and equilibrium constants are temperature dependent, so we must choose to list K_{eq} values at a particular temperature (usually room temperature, 25 °C). Unlike percent ionizations, equilibrium constants are <u>not</u> dependent on the initial concentrations of a solution, <u>nor</u> are they dependent on the presence of other species in solution. Other species in solution might influence the equilibrium *position*, but not the value of the equilibrium *constant*.

1. Particulars for Weak Acids

The equilibrium constant for the reaction of a weak acid with water is given the name **acid ionization constant** and the symbol, $\mathbf{K_a}$.[157] All weak acids have an acid ionization reaction equation similar to the generic one:

$$HA(aq) + H_2O(\ell) \rightleftharpoons A^-(aq) + H_3O^+(aq)$$

The equilibrium constant expression for the reaction is

$$K_a = \frac{\left[A^-\right]\left[H_3O^+\right]}{\left[HA\right]}$$

---

[157] This specially named equilibrium constant was first introduced in Section 16-5 at the end of Chapter 16. You can re-read that section for an introduction to named K_{eq}'s.

Recall that water (the solvent for this reaction system) does not appear in the equilibrium constant expression. *Larger values of K_a occur for stronger acids; stronger acids are able to produce more ions.*

Table 19-3 compares the relative strengths of some weak acids. Notice the range of values for the K_a's of these weak acids. The strongest of these "weak" acids are found at the top of this table.

Table 19-3. Weak acid ionizations			
Weak Acid Name	Weak acid formula	Acid ionization reaction equation	K_a value
Molecular acid or Cationic acid	HA HA$^+$	$HA(\text{aq}) + H_2O(\ell) \rightleftharpoons A^-(\text{aq}) + H_3O^+(\text{aq})$ $HA^+(\text{aq}) + H_2O(\ell) \rightleftharpoons A(\text{aq}) + H_3O^+(\text{aq})$	
Iodic acid	HIO_3		1.6×10^{-1}
Hydrofluoric acid	HF		6.3×10^{-4}
Nitrous acid	HNO_2		5.6×10^{-4}
Formic acid	HCO_2H		1.8×10^{-4}
Acetic acid	CH_3CO_2H		1.8×10^{-5}
Hypochlorous acid	HClO		4.0×10^{-8}
Hydrocyanic acid	HCN		6.2×10^{-10}
Ammonium Ion*	NH_4^+		5.6×10^{-10}
*Ammonium ion is available in the lab as the cation of a salt, such as NH_4Cl or NH_4NO_3.			

It may seem odd to call the reaction of a cationic acid such as the ammonium ion an "ionization;" see the general acid ionization reaction equation for HA$^+$ in Table 19-3. A cationic acid actually goes from being an ion to NOT being an ion during the reaction! It may help to understand that the word "ionization" means the production of <u>new</u> ions. When the weak acid HA$^+$ ionizes, the new ion, H_3O^+ is formed. We could say that weak acids promote the ionization of water molecules.

Exercise 19-6.

Fill out the column for acid ionization reaction equations in Table 19-3. Note that each one is a proton transfer to a water molecule.

---

2. *Particulars for Weak Bases*

The equilibrium constant for the reaction of a weak base with water is given the name **base ionization constant** and the symbol, $\mathbf{K_b}$.[158] All weak bases have a base ionization reaction equation similar to the generic one:

$$B{:}(\text{aq}) + H_2O(\ell) \rightleftharpoons BH^+(\text{aq}) + OH^-(\text{aq})$$

---

[158] This specially named equilibrium constant was first introduced in Section 16-5 at the end of Chapter 16.

The equilibrium constant expression for the reaction is

$$K_b = \frac{\left[BH^+\right]\left[OH^-\right]}{\left[B:\right]}$$

Larger values of K_b occur for stronger bases; stronger bases are able to produce more ions. *NOTE: It is not possible to speak of the K_a value of a weak <u>base</u>, or the K_b value of a weak <u>acid</u>.*

Table 19-4 is analogous to Table 19-3, but gives information about weak bases instead of weak acids. Notice the range of values for the K_b's of these weak bases. The largest values for K_b represent the strongest bases; these are at the top of the table.

Table 19-4. Weak base ionizations			
Weak Base Name	Weak base formula	Base ionization reaction equation	K_b value
Molecular base or Anionic base	B: B:$^-$	$B{:}(aq) + H_2O(\ell) \rightleftharpoons BH^+(aq) + OH^-(aq)$ $B{:}^-(aq) + H_2O(\ell) \rightleftharpoons BH(aq) + OH^-(aq)$	
Ammonia	NH_3		1.8×10^{-5}
Cyanide ion*	CN^-		1.6×10^{-5}
Hypochlorite ion	ClO^-		2.5×10^{-7}
Acetate ion	$CH_3CO_2^-$		5.7×10^{-10}
Formate ion	HCO_2^-		5.7×10^{-11}
Nitrite ion	NO_2^-		1.8×10^{-11}
Fluoride ion	F^-		1.6×10^{-11}
Iodate ion	IO_3^-		6.4×10^{-14}
*Anionic bases are available in the lab as salts such as NaCN or KClO.			

Exercise 19-7.

Fill out the column for base ionization reaction equations in Table 19-4. Note that each one features the transfer of a proton from water to the weak base.

Notice that when it comes to base behavior, the most stable anions, such as IO_3^-, are the poorest bases. Resonance delocalization of electron pairs, and of negative charge, offers considerable stability to ions such as IO_3^-.

We consider the fact that the job of a base is to attract a proton by utilizing a lone pair of electrons to make a new bond. Resonance offers the ability to stabilize negative charge by sharing it over multiple atoms. A lone pair that is highly delocalized due to resonance is not able to attract a proton as successfully as an electron pair that exists on one atom. Similarly, a more delocalized negative charge does not seek out a positive charge for neutralization with the same intensity as a more localized negative charge. Because IO_3^- is a very stable anion, it is a poor base. As we will see shortly, because the acid ionization of HIO_3 generates this stable base, HIO_3 is more successful at ionizing and is a stronger acid.

It may seem odd to call the reaction of an anionic base with water an "ionization," see the top box of generic reaction equations. An anionic base actually goes from being an ion to NOT being an ion during the reaction. However, the new ion, OH^- is formed! So, the weak base (anionic or neutral) promotes the ionization of the water molecule.

Exercise 19-8.

Consider the bases ClO^- and ClO_2^-. Which do you expect to be the stronger base? Why?

C. Relative Strengths of Acids

It is useful to be able to make predictions of strengths of acids on the basis of their molecular structures. While it is not possible to be exact about such predictions—for example, to predict the exact K_a value of an acid—some general guidelines do apply. There are many types of acids. We focus here on neutral, polyatomic **oxoacids**.[159] Examples of neutral oxoacids include H_2SO_3, HNO_2 and acetic acid, CH_3CO_2H.

1. Consideration of the structures of strong acids.

The "classic" strong acids include HNO_3 (nitric), H_2SO_4 (sulfuric), and $HClO_4$ (perchloric). Why are these particular acids so strong? We begin by reviewing the equations for the reactions of these acid molecules with water:

$$HNO_3(aq) + H_2O(\ell) \longrightarrow H_3O^+(aq) + NO_3^-(aq)$$

$$H_2SO_4(aq) + H_2O(\ell) \longrightarrow H_3O^+(aq) + HSO_4^-(aq)$$

$$HClO_4(aq) + H_2O(\ell) \longrightarrow H_3O^+(aq) + ClO_4^-(aq)$$

These reactions go to completion; there is no reverse reaction.

Now, consider the *conjugate bases* of these acids: what is similar about NO_3^-, HSO_4^-, and ClO_4^-? In other words, what structural similarity exists that makes these ions especially stable, and therefore unwilling to react at all with the hydronium ion, H_3O^+?[160] An important clue is that each of these conjugate bases contains multiple highly electronegative atoms. For reference, the most electronegative elements, omitting the noble gases, are shown at right with their electronegativity values. We note that the nitrate ion, NO_3^-, contains four of these atoms, having an average electronegativity of 3.48. The hydrogen sulfate ion, HSO_4^-, contains five highly electronegative atoms, plus a hydrogen atom (electronegativity = 2.30), for an average electronegativity of 3.22. The percholorate ion, ClO_4^-, contains five highly electronegative atoms, with an average electronegativity of

C 2.54	N 3.07	O 3.61	F 4.19
	P 2.25	S 2.59	Cl 2.87
		Se 2.42	Br 2.68
			I 2.36

3.46. When multiple atoms have a strong tendency to attract electrons there is, in essence, an opportunity to share the negative charge. It is not surprising that these anions are stable; they are comfortable carrying negative charge.

---

[159] *Oxoacid* is a designation for acids whose acidic hydrogen atom is bonded directly to an oxygen atom.
[160] Remember that the hydronium ion is the strongest acid that can exist in an aqueous solution. All of the strong acids are "leveled" in the presence of water.

2. Consideration of weak acids derived from strong acids.

Now, consider acids having one less oxygen atom than those above, hence, one fewer highly electronegative atom to stabilize the negative charge of the conjugate base. Would such acids (HNO_2, H_2SO_3, and $HClO_3$) be weaker? Let's examine them. The first two are in fact weaker and are classified as typical weak acids.

$$HNO_2(aq) + H_2O(\ell) \rightleftharpoons NO_2^-(aq) + H_3O^+(aq) \quad K_a = 5.6 \times 10^{-4}$$

$$H_2SO_3(aq) + H_2O(\ell) \rightleftharpoons HSO_3^-(aq) + H_3O^+(aq) \quad K_a = 1.4 \times 10^{-2}$$

However, even with one fewer oxygen atom, $HClO_3$ (with an average electronegativity of 3.42) is a strong acid.

$$HClO_3(aq) + H_2O(\ell) \longrightarrow ClO_3^-(aq) + H_3O^+(aq) \qquad strong$$

It is necessary to remove still another oxygen atom from $HClO_3$ to come up with an acid that is weak, $HClO_2$:

$$HClO_2(aq) + H_2O(\ell) \rightleftharpoons ClO_2^-(aq) + H_3O^+(aq) \qquad K_a = 1.1 \times 10^{-2}$$

The fourth acid in the $HClO_x$ series, $HClO$, is weaker than $HClO_2$ as expected. To summarize this information, the box, below, shows the three families of acids, with the parent strong acid at the top of each list.[161]

HNO_3	strong	H_2SO_4	strong	$HClO_4$	strong
HNO_2	$K_a = 5.6 \times 10^{-4}$	H_2SO_3	$K_a = 1.4 \times 10^{-2}$	$HClO_3$	strong
				$HClO_2$	$K_a = 1.1 \times 10^{-2}$
				$HClO$	$K_a = 4.0 \times 10^{-8}$

Exercise 19-9.

As we have seen, acid strength is largely determined by the stability of the conjugate base. This stability is affected both by the number of highly electronegative atoms present and by the opportunity for increased numbers of resonance structures between the acid and the base. Draw the Lewis dot structures of each of the weak acids in Table 19-3, and for its conjugate base. Which of these acids have conjugate bases with increased numbers of resonance forms? (Be careful with the skeletons you use for the acid molecules. In this table, any acid having one or more oxygen atoms is an oxoacid, so attach the acidic hydrogen atoms to oxygen atoms, where possible.)

3. Consideration of carboxylic acids

Many important acids, especially in the realm of biological systems, are carboxylic acids. Two well-known examples of carboxylic acids are formic acid (which is present in some ant venoms and in the secretion of stinging nettles) and acetic acid (which occurs in vinegar and as a metabolic product of ethanol).

---

[161] Note that species such as HNO and H_2SO_2 do not exist.

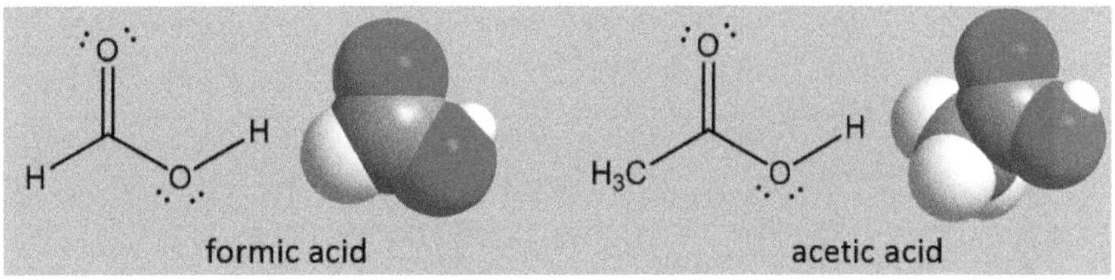

formic acid   acetic acid

Using acetic acid as a general case, when carboxylic acids react with water, the following equilibrium occurs:

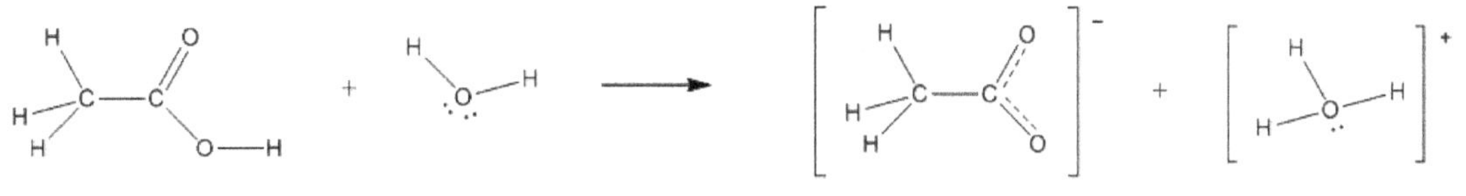

acetic acid   acetate ion
$K_a = 1.8 \times 10^{-5}$

Suppose that one of the H atoms of the CH_3 group (called a "methyl" group) was replaced by a more electronegative Cl atom. Would this make the acid stronger or weaker?

Again, we focus on the conjugate base. We have seen that more electronegative atoms are able to best accommodate negative charges, and thus help to stabilize conjugate bases. Stabilizing the conjugate base results in a shift of the equilibrium position toward the products. Replacing a hydrogen atom with the more electronegative chlorine atom produces a conjugate base having three highly electronegative atoms (two oxygen, one chlorine) instead of just two. Therefore, we expect chloroacetic acid to be a stronger acid than acetic acid. And it is!

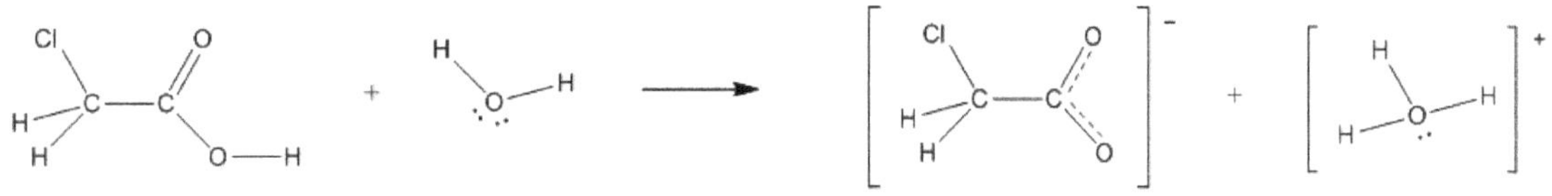

chloroacetic acid   chloroacetate ion
$K_a = 1.3 \times 10^{-3}$

Replacing additional methyl-group hydrogen atoms with chlorine atoms generates even stronger acids, as shown here.

So, again we see the connection between highly electronegative atoms and the stability of the conjugate base. A more stable conjugate base shifts the acid ionization equilibrium to the

Acid		K_a
acetic	$H_3C\text{-}CO_2H$	$1.8 \times 10^{-5} = 0.000018$
chloroacetic	$H_2ClC\text{-}CO_2H$	$1.3 \times 10^{-3} = 0.0013$
dichloroacetic	$HCl_2C\text{-}CO_2H$	$4.5 \times 10^{-2} = 0.045$
trichloroacetic	$Cl_3C\text{-}CO_2H$	$2.2 \times 10^{-1} = 0.22$

right, resulting in larger K_a values and stronger acids. Also important to these carboxylic acids is the existence of two resonance structures of the conjugate base. All-in-all we could say that the negative charge of the conjugate base is shared by the two oxygen atoms and that one or more chlorine atoms help to lessen the total electron density within the CO_2^- portion of the ion.

Exercise 19-10.

Select the strongest acid in each set.

    a. HIO HIO_2 HIO_3
    b. H_2SeO_4 H_2SeO_3 $HSeO_4^-$
    c. $H_2ClC\text{-}CO_2H$ $H_2FC\text{-}CO_2H$ $HF_2C\text{-}CO_2H$

Exercise 19-11.

We can utilize similar reasoning to judge the strengths of bases. Do you expect $CF_3CO_2^-$ to be a stronger or weaker base than $CH_3CO_2^-$? Explain briefly.

19-3. USING VALUES OF K_A AND K_B IN CALCULATIONS

A. Manipulations of K_a and K_b

We have already noted that K_a values are larger for stronger acids and the K_b values are larger for stronger bases. We have also learned that more successful acids, have less successful conjugate bases. But, how is the K_a for an acid related to the K_b for its conjugate base? First, note that the ionization reaction equations for a weak acid and its conjugate base are not reverses of one another; one involves the hydronium ion and the other involves the hydroxide ion.

$$HA(aq) + H_2O(\ell) \rightleftharpoons A^-(aq) + H_3O^+(aq) \qquad K_{eq} = K_a$$

and

$$A^-(aq) + H_2O(\ell) \rightleftharpoons HA(aq) + OH^-(aq) \qquad K_{eq} = K_b$$

Therefore, $K_a \neq \dfrac{1}{K_b}$. However, there is a reciprocal relationship between the strengths

of the members of a conjugate pair, so it is true that for a conjugate pair K_a is proportional to $\dfrac{1}{K_b}$.

This means that mathematically, $K_a \propto \dfrac{1}{K_b}$, or $K_a = m \times \dfrac{1}{K_b}$ where "m" is the proportionality

constant. Notice that if $K_a = m \times \dfrac{1}{K_b}$ then $K_a \times K_b = m$

Tables 19-3 and 19-4 provide K_a and K_b data for conjugate pairs. We can multiply these K_{eq}'s together to find the proportionality constant; see Table 19-5.

The proportionality constant must be 1.0×10^{-14}, a familiar number, the ion product constant for water. Why is this?

Table 19-5. The relationship between K_a and K_b

Conjugate pair	K_a	K_b	$K_a \times K_b$
HIO_3 / IO_3^-	1.6×10^{-1}	6.4×10^{-14}	1.0×10^{-14}
HF / F^-	6.3×10^{-4}	1.6×10^{-11}	1.0×10^{-14}
HNO_2 / NO_2^-	5.6×10^{-4}	1.8×10^{-11}	1.0×10^{-14}
HCO_2H / HCO_2^-	1.8×10^{-4}	5.7×10^{-11}	1.0×10^{-14}
$CH_3CO_2H / CH_3CO_2^-$	1.8×10^{-5}	5.7×10^{-10}	1.0×10^{-14}
$HClO / ClO^-$	4.0×10^{-8}	2.5×10^{-7}	1.0×10^{-14}
HCN / CN^-	6.2×10^{-10}	1.6×10^{-5}	1×10^{-14}
NH_4^+ / NH_3	5.6×10^{-10}	1.8×10^{-5}	1.0×10^{-14}

Let's approach the problem algebraically. Remember from Chapter 16 that when we add reactions together, we multiply their equilibrium constants. Thus, when we add an acid ionization reaction with the conjugate base ionization reaction, we multiply the K_a and K_b values to obtain the equilibrium constant for the summed reaction. So, for a *conjugate acid base pair* we can write:

$$HA(aq) + H_2O(\ell) \rightleftharpoons A^-(aq) + H_3O^+(aq) \qquad K_a = \frac{\left[A^-\right]\left[H_3O^+\right]}{\left[HA\right]}$$

$$A^-(aq) + H_2O(\ell) \rightleftharpoons HA(aq) + OH^-(aq) \qquad K_b = \frac{\left[HA\right]\left[OH^-\right]}{\left[A^-\right]}$$

$$2\,H_2O(\ell) \rightleftharpoons H_3O^+(aq) + OH^-\left(aq\right) \qquad K_{sum} = K_a \times K_b$$

We are not surprised that the summed reactions yield the autoionization reaction! Using the K_a and K_b expressions from above, we see that $K_{sum} = K_w$

$$K_{sum} = K_a \times K_b = \frac{\left[A^-\right]\left[H_3O^+\right]}{\left[HA\right]} \times \frac{\left[HA\right]\left[OH^-\right]}{\left[A^-\right]} = \left[H_3O^+\right]\left[OH^-\right] = K_w$$

Thus, we obtain the ion product constant of water when we multiply the K_a of a weak acid by the K_b of its conjugate base. *Note that the acid and base must be conjugates so that the HA and A⁻ terms cancel in the addition of the reaction equations!*

$$\boxed{\text{At 25 °C, } \; K_a\left(\text{HA}\right) \times K_b\left(\text{A}^-\right) = 1.0 \times 10^{-14} = K_w}$$

Values of K_a and K_b are often tabulated as power functions instead of decimal numbers. Consistent with previous use, we define

$$\boxed{\begin{array}{c} pK_a = -\log K_a \\ and \\ pK_b = -\log K_b \end{array}}$$

Applying these definitions to the algebra above gives

$$K_a \times K_b = \left[H_3O^+\right]\left[OH^-\right] = 1.0 \times 10^{-14}$$
$$-\log\left(K_a \times K_b\right) = -\log\left(1.0 \times 10^{-14}\right)$$
$$\left(-\log K_a\right) + \left(-\log K_b\right) = 14.00$$
$$\boxed{pK_a(\text{HA}) + pK_b(\text{A}^-) = 14.00 = pK_w}$$

Remember, *these relationships only hold for conjugate acid/base pairs*. *It is not true that any K_a multiplied by any K_b is 1.0×10^{-14}, or any pK_a added to any pK_b is 14.00.*

Let's expand our previous tables (19-3 and 19-4) to include pK data, and combine it all into one table (minus the ionization reaction equations). Notice that as the K_a gets bigger, the pK_a gets smaller. This is a direct result of the negative sign in the definition of a power function. It makes some sense that better acids have pK_a's that are at the more acidic end of the pH spectrum. Study the relationships in the table. Make sure (for conjugate pairs) that $K_a \times K_b = 1.0 \times 10^{-14}$ and that $pK_a + pK_b = 14.00$ (within rounding errors). Once you are comfortable with these relationships think about the table from the perspective of redundancy of information. What information in Table 19-6 would not have to be there if everyone understood the mathematical relationships? *Usually tables of either K_a for a weak acid, or K_b for a weak base are offered, but not both. This is because the K_b of any weak base can be calculated directly from the K_a of its conjugate acid; there is no need to tally both.*

Table 19-6. Data summary for weak conjugate pairs

Weak Acid Name	Weak acid formula	K_a value	pK_a value	Conjugate base formula	K_b value	pK_b value
Iodic acid	HIO_3	1.6×10^{-1}	0.80	IO_3^-	6.4×10^{-14}	13.20
Hydrofluoric acid	HF	6.3×10^{-4}	3.20	F^-	1.6×10^{-11}	10.80
Nitrous acid	HNO_2	5.6×10^{-4}	3.25	NO_2^-	1.8×10^{-11}	10.75
Formic acid	HCO_2H	1.8×10^{-4}	3.75	HCO_2^-	5.7×10^{-11}	10.25
Acetic acid	CH_3CO_2H	1.75×10^{-5}	4.756	$CH_3CO_2^-$	5.75×10^{-10}	9.241
Hypochlorous acid	HClO	4.0×10^{-8}	7.40	ClO^-	2.5×10^{-7}	6.60
Hydrocyanic acid	HCN	6.2×10^{-10}	9.21	CN^-	1.6×10^{-5}	4.79
Ammonium ion	NH_4^+	5.6×10^{-10}	9.25	NH_3	1.8×10^{-5}	4.75

All values in this table are derived from pK_a values as listed in the *CRC Handbook of Chemistry and Physics*. A K_w value of 1.008×10^{-14} was used in the conversion from K_a to K_b.

B. Related Equilibria

In Chapter 16, we introduced three mathematical relationships between the K_{eq} values of related reactions:

1. The K_{eq} values of reverse reactions are reciprocals.
2. When reaction equations can be added to give an overall reaction, their K_{eq} values can be multiplied to give the K_{eq} value of the overall process.
3. When one reaction equation is a multiple of another, the original K_{eq} value is raised to that power:
   if the reaction equation is doubled, square the K_{eq} value
   if the reaction equation is tripled, cube the K_{eq} value
   if the reaction equation is halved, take the square root of the K_{eq} value, etc.

These relationships allow the calculation of unknown equilibrium constants if reactions whose K_{eq} values are known can be manipulated to give the unknown reaction.

Example 19-3.

Use K_a and K_b values available in this chapter (and the K_w value, if needed) to determine the value of the equilibrium constant for the following reactions:

    a. $CH_3CO_2^-(aq) + H_3O^+(aq) \rightleftharpoons CH_3CO_2H(aq) + H_2O(\ell)$

    b. $CH_3CO_2H(aq) + F^-(aq) \rightleftharpoons CH_3CO_2^-(aq) + HF(aq)$

Solutions:

a. Studying this reaction shows that it is the *reverse* of the acid ionization reaction for acetic acid. Therefore, its K_{eq} value is the reciprocal of K_a:

$$K_{eq} = \frac{1}{K_a} = \frac{1}{1.8 \times 10^{-5}} = 5.6 \times 10^4$$

b. This reaction involves both the CH_3CO_2H / $CH_3CO_2^-$ and HF / F^- conjugate pairs. Looking for K_a and K_b reactions, we notice that the CH_3CO_2H / $CH_3CO_2^-$ conjugate pair is present with the acid as reactant and the base as product, similar to a K_a reaction. Additionally, the HF / F^- conjugate pair is present with the base as reactant and the acid as product, similar to a K_b reaction. It seems sensible to try adding these two reactions together:

$$CH_3CO_2H(aq) + H_2O(\ell) \rightleftharpoons CH_3CO_2^-(aq) + H_3O^+(aq) \qquad K_a = 1.8 \times 10^{-5}$$

$$F^-(aq) + H_2O(\ell) \rightleftharpoons HF(aq) + OH^-(aq) \qquad K_b = 1.6 \times 10^{-11}$$

$$\overline{CH_3CO_2H(aq) + F^-(aq) + 2H_2O(\ell) \rightleftharpoons CH_3CO_2^-(aq) + HF(aq) + OH^-(aq) + H_3O^+(aq)}$$

The summed reaction, above, has many species in the correct places, but has extra species compared to the target reaction. A study of the extras shows that these species make up the reaction for the autoionization of water. We need to add in the *opposite reaction* to cancel these species. Altogether:

$$CH_3CO_2H(aq) + H_2O(\ell) \rightleftharpoons CH_3CO_2^-(aq) + H_3O^+(aq) \qquad K_a = 1.8 \times 10^{-5}$$

$$F^-(aq) + H_2O(\ell) \rightleftharpoons HF(aq) + OH^-(aq) \qquad K_b = 1.6 \times 10^{-11}$$

$$H_3O^+(aq) + OH^-(aq) \rightleftharpoons 2H_2O(\ell) \qquad K = \frac{1}{K_w} = 1.0 \times 10^{14}$$

$$\overline{CH_3CO_2H(aq) + F^-(aq) \rightleftharpoons CH_3CO_2^-(aq) + HF(aq)} \qquad K = K_a \times K_b \times \frac{1}{K_w} = 2.9 \times 10^{-2}$$

You may enjoy seeing a second (slightly shorter) method for solving this problem:

As before, we use the K_a reaction to get the CH_3CO_2H / $CH_3CO_2^-$ species in the correct locations. This time, instead of using the K_b for F^-, we use the reverse of the K_a reaction for HF. This is another way to get the HF / F^- pair in the correct locations:

$$CH_3CO_2H(aq) + H_2O(\ell) \rightleftharpoons CH_3CO_2^-(aq) + H_3O^+(aq) \qquad K_1 = K_a = 1.8 \times 10^{-5}$$

$$F^-(aq) + H_3O^+(aq) \rightleftharpoons HF(aq) + H_2O(\ell) \qquad K_2 = \frac{1}{K_a} = \frac{1}{6.3 \times 10^{-4}}$$

$$\overline{CH_3CO_2H(aq) + F^-(aq) \rightleftharpoons CH_3CO_2^-(aq) + HF(aq)} \qquad K = K_1 \times K_2 = 2.9 \times 10^{-2}$$

Either method gives the same result. This second method avoids having to use the K_w reaction.

It may be surprising how many equilibrium constant values one can obtain starting with the K_a value of a weak acid. Here is a list:

1. The most obvious is that the K_a value is the equilibrium constant for the ionization of the weak acid.

$$HA(aq) + H_2O(\ell) \rightleftharpoons A^-(aq) + H_3O^+(aq) \qquad K_{eq} = K_a$$

2. Second, this K_a value leads to knowledge of the equilibrium constant for the reverse of the acid ionization reaction.

$$A^-(aq) + H_3O^+(aq) \rightleftharpoons HA(aq) + H_2O(\ell) \qquad K_{eq} = \frac{1}{K_a}$$

3. Third, this K_a value leads to knowledge of the equilibrium constant for the conjugate base ionization reaction.

$$A^-(aq) + H_2O(\ell) \rightleftharpoons HA(aq) + OH^-(aq) \qquad K_{eq} = \frac{K_w}{K_a}$$

4. And, finally, this K_a value leads to knowledge of the equilibrium constant for the reverse of the conjugate base ionization reaction.

$$HA(aq) + OH^-(aq) \rightleftharpoons A^-(aq) + H_2O(\ell) \qquad K_{eq} = \frac{K_a}{K_w}$$

Of course, all of these equilibrium constants could also be obtained from knowledge of just the base ionization constant!

Exercise 19-12.

The K_{eq} for reactions 1-4 (above) can also be expressed in terms related to K_b. Match each reaction to the correct K_{eq} expression:

Reaction 1	K_b
Reaction 2	$1/K_b$
Reaction 3	K_w/K_b
Reaction 4	K_b/K_w

Exercise 19-13.

Calculate the value of K_{eq} for each of the following reactions using data provided:

    a. $SO_4^{2-}(aq) + H_2O(\ell) \rightleftharpoons HSO_4^-(aq) + OH^-(aq)$ $K_a(HSO_4^-) = 1.02 \times 10^{-2}$

    b. $N_2H_4(aq) + H_3O^+(aq) \rightleftharpoons N_2H_5^+(aq) + H_2O(\ell)$ $K_a(N_2H_5^+) = 7.9 \times 10^{-9}$

    c. $HCrO_4^-(aq) + OH^-(aq) \rightleftharpoons CrO_4^{2-}(aq) + H_2O(\ell)$ $K_a(HCrO_4^-) = 3.2 \times 10^{-7}$

    d. $HN_3(aq) + H_2O(\ell) \rightleftharpoons N_3^-(aq) + H_3O^+(aq)$ $K_a(HN_3) = 2.5 \times 10^{-5}$

Exercise 19-14.

Which of the reactions in Exercise 19-13 featured a reactant that was either a strong acid or a strong base? How did that affect the size of the equilibrium constant for the reaction?

C. Calculation of the pH of a Weak Acid Solution

We have found that while percent ionization of a weak acid solution is able to lead us to the pH of the solution, it is not possible to tally percent ionizations for particular weak acids. Instead, the information on acid strength that can be tallied is the value of the acid ionization constant, K_a. Here, we learn how to calculate the pH of a weak acid solution, given the concentration of the weak acid and its K_a value.

The calculation method used is exactly the same as that used for the equilibrium problems that we solved in Chapter 17. Our strategy centers on the use of an equilibrium table. The best way to proceed may be through example. Studying the following example should help you understand the strategy.

Example 19-4.

Calculate the pH of a solution that is 0.34 M in acetic acid.

Solution:

We begin by using the reaction equation for the ionization process to develop an equilibrium table in units of molarity:

$CH_3CO_2H(aq)+H_2O(\ell)\rightleftharpoons CH_3CO_2^-(aq)+H_3O^+(aq)$				
Initial M	0.34	Pure liquid	0	0
Changes in M	$-x$		$+x$	$+x$
Equilibrium M	$0.34 - x$		x	x

Now we can substitute expressions for the equilibrium concentrations (bottom line from the table) into the equilibrium constant expression, and look up the value of the K_a needed:

$$K_a = 1.8\times10^{-5} = \frac{\left[CH_3CO_2^-\right]\left[H_3O^+\right]}{\left[CH_3CO_2H\right]}$$

$$1.8\times10^{-5} = \frac{x^2}{0.34 - x}$$

The solver on a graphing calculator can solve this equation for x.[162] We find that

$$x = 2.46 \times 10^{-3} \text{ M}$$

where the units come from the units of our equilibrium table. We remind ourselves that the variable x was assigned to represent the concentration of H_3O^+ and the concentration of $CH_3CO_2^-$. We can calculate the pH:

$$pH = -\log [H_3O^+]$$
$$= -\log (2.46 \times 10^{-3}) = 2.61$$

Exercise 19-15.

Calculate the pH's of the following weak acid solutions:

    a. 0.34 M HIO₃   **b.** 0.034 M HIO₃   **c.** 0.12 M NH₄⁺

D. Calculation of the pH of a Weak Base Solution

    Calculation of the pH of a weak base solution is completely analogous to our work in Example 19-4 for the weak acid solution. The only point of difference occurs after the value of x has been determined. Check out Example 19-5 for a complete treatment.

---

[162] Other methods may also be used to solve for x. One can make the assumption that x is much less than 0.34, or one can use a quadratic equation.

Example 19-5.

Calculate the pH of a 0.068 M solution of KNO_2.

Solution:

We must first recognize that the salt KNO_2 contains an anion with weak base properties. We can find the K_b of this anion in Table 19-6. Under other circumstances we might only be able to look up the K_a of the weak acid HNO_2 and find that it is 5.6×10^{-4}. The K_b for the conjugate base NO_2^- could then be calculated:

$$K_a(HNO_2) \times K_b(NO_2^-) = 1.0 \times 10^{-14}$$

$$K_b(NO_2^-) = \frac{1.0 \times 10^{-14}}{K_a(HNO_2)} = \frac{1.0 \times 10^{-14}}{5.6 \times 10^{-4}} = 1.8 \times 10^{-11}$$

We start the problem by setting up an equilibrium table based on the ionization reaction for the weak base:

$NO_2^-(aq) + H_2O(\ell) \rightleftharpoons HNO_2(aq) + OH^-(aq)$				
Initial M	0.068		0	0
Changes in M	$-x$	Pure liquid	$+x$	$+x$
Equilibrium M	$0.068 - x$		x	x

We substitute expressions for equilibrium concentrations found in the bottom line of the table into the equilibrium constant expression:

$$K_b = 1.8 \times 10^{-11} = \frac{[HNO_2][OH^-]}{[NO_2^-]}$$

$$1.8 \times 10^{-11} = \frac{x^2}{0.068 - x}$$

The solver on a graphing calculator can solve this equation for x. We find that

$$x = 1.11 \times 10^{-6} \text{ M}$$

We diverge, here, from our work in Example 19-4 with the weak acid. In that case x represented the $[H_3O^+]$, but in this case x represents the $[OH^-]$. Great care must always be taken when solving equilibrium problems to make note of what you know once the value of x has been determined.

In this case we can calculate the pH by first calculating the pOH:

$$pOH = -\log [OH^-]$$
$$= -\log (1.11 \times 10^{-6}) = 5.956$$

$$pH = 14.00 - pOH$$
$$= 14.00 - 5.956 = 8.04$$

Exercise 19-16.

Calculate the pH of each of the following weak base solutions:

a. 0.15 M NH_3 **b.** 0.080 M HCO_2^-

E. Calculation of the Percent Ionization of a Weak Acid or Weak Base Solution

The same process that allows the calculation of pH from equilibrium constant data also allows the calculation of the percent ionization in the solution. Recall the definition of percent ionization:

$$\text{percent ionization} = \frac{\text{amount ionized}}{\text{total amount}} \times 100\%$$

In the case of the solution from Example 19-4, we could write

$$\text{percent ionization} = \frac{\left[CH_3CO_2^-\right]_{eq}}{\left[CH_3CO_2H\right]_{eq} + \left[CH_3CO_2^-\right]_{eq}} \times 100\%$$

The value of the variable x, as calculated in Example 19-4 supplies the concentration of $CH_3CO_2^-$. The context of the problem supplies the value of the denominator: $0.34\,M$. So we calculate the percent ionization:

$$\text{percent ionization} = \frac{2.5 \times 10^{-3}\,M}{0.34\,M} \times 100\% = 0.74\%$$

Exercise 19-17.

Calculate the percent ionization of the weak base solution described in Example 19-5.

F. A Word About Polyprotic Acids

Polyprotic acids are those acids having more than one ionizable proton. Examples of polyprotic acids include sulfuric acid, H_2SO_4, carbonic acid H_2CO_3, and phosphoric acid, H_3PO_4. There are a host of biologically significant molecules that are polyprotic acids. One common example is citric acid, a **triprotic** carboxylic acid whose structure is shown here. Citric acid is the molecule for which the citric acid cycle, an important metabolic sequence of reactions, is named. This may be surprising, because citric acid cannot exist in its acid form at physiological pH's. In fact,

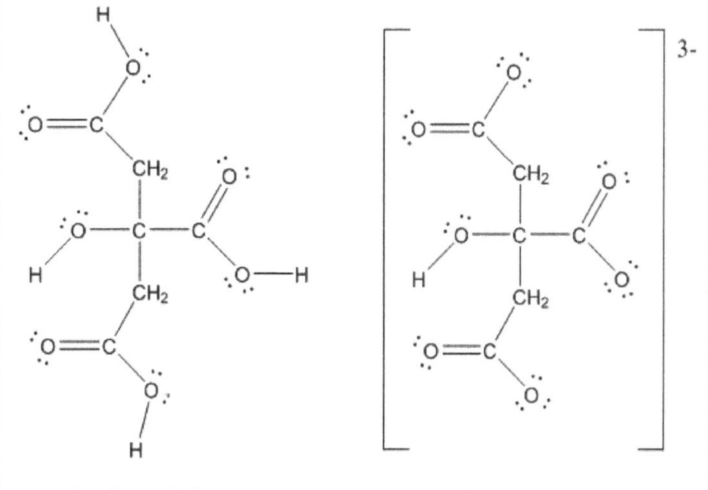

citric acid   citrate ion

the form of the molecule prevalent in living cells is the citrate ion (also shown, above). The citrate ion carries a -3 charge. Note that citric acid has three carboxylic acid groups and that, in the citrate ion, all three of these have lost their acidic proton. Because each of three groups has two possible resonance structures, there are eight possible resonance structures for the citrate ion!

One thing that is true of all polyprotic acids is that the loss of successive protons becomes more and more difficult. For instance, we can write the acid ionizations starting with the parent acid and removing one proton at a time. For citric acid we write

$$H_3C_6H_5O_7(aq) + H_2O(\ell) \rightleftharpoons H_2C_6H_5O_7^-(aq) + H_3O^+(aq) \quad K_a = 7.4 \times 10^{-4}$$

$$H_2C_6H_5O_7^-(aq) + H_2O(\ell) \rightleftharpoons HC_6H_5O_7^{2-}(aq) + H_3O^+(aq) \quad K_a = 1.7 \times 10^{-5}$$

$$HC_6H_5O_7^{2-}(aq) + H_2O(\ell) \rightleftharpoons C_6H_5O_7^{3-}(aq) + H_3O^+(aq) \quad K_a = 4.0 \times 10^{-7}$$

Notice, first, that we have written the formula of citric acid (the first reactant, above) in a way that highlights its three acidic protons. In formulas of carbon-based acids such as citric acid, formulas may list atoms in the order: acidic hydrogens, carbons, other hydrogens, other atoms (alphabetically). Acetic acid's formula is $HC_2H_3O_2$ when we follow this scheme. Second, notice that the product of the first ionization is the reactant for the second, and so on. Finally, notice the decreasing size of K_a as successive protons are removed. This trend, which exists for all polyprotic acids, is easily rationalized by the increasing magnitude of negative charge that the associated conjugate bases must carry. It is always more difficult to force the same atoms to carry larger magnitudes of charge. Negative charges repel one another and do not want to be exist in close proximity to one another.

1. Sulfuric Acid

You may recall from Chapter 18 that sulfuric acid, H_2SO_4, is a strong acid. It is also a **diprotic acid** because it has two ionizable protons. Only one of these protons behaves as a strong acid. We can write two successive acid ionization reaction equations for sulfuric acid:

$$H_2SO_4(aq) + H_2O(\ell) \longrightarrow HSO_4^-(aq) + H_3O^+(aq) \quad strong$$

$$HSO_4^-(aq) + H_2O(\ell) \rightleftharpoons SO_4^{2-}(aq) + H_3O^+(aq) \quad K_a = 1.02 \times 10^{-2}$$

In aqueous solution, the first proton is essentially completely transferred to water molecules. The second proton is more difficult to transfer. So, H_2SO_4 is a strong acid, but HSO_4^- (the hydrogen sulfate ion) is a weak acid.

Because it is more difficult to generate SO_4^{2-} than HSO_4^-, the second ionization is not as successful as the first. Notice the reversible arrows in the second ionization compared to the irreversible arrow in the first ionization.

We have an interesting occurrence with any polyprotic acid. There is more than one conjugate pair associated with the successive ionizations. Some of the language gets a little misleading—because some of the species are **amphiprotic**, they may behave either as an acid or as a base. For sulfuric acid we can list two conjugate pairs:

$$H_2SO_4 \, / \, HSO_4^-$$

and

$$HSO_4^- \, / \, SO_4^{2-}$$

Notice that in the top pair HSO_4^- is the base of the conjugate pair, but in the bottom pair it is the acid. This may seem confusing–how can one species be the acid of one pair and the base of another? Don't forget that we have seen a similar circumstance before with water. Not only is water sometimes the conjugate acid of a pair (H_2O/OH^-) and sometimes the conjugate base (H_3O^+/H_2O), but it actually <u>behaves</u> as an acid (in the presence of stronger bases) and *behaves* as a base (in the presence of stronger acids). With HSO_4^- we have a situation where it is sometimes *labeled* a conjugate base (in the H_2SO_4/HSO_4^- pair) and sometimes *labeled* a conjugate acid (in the HSO_4^-/SO_4^{2-} pair), but it always *behaves* as an acid.

How do we know that the hydrogen sulfate ion does not behave as a base? Remember that none of the conjugate bases of strong acids show appreciable basic behavior. The hydrogen sulfate ion fits this category. Look again at the reaction equation that forms HSO_4^-,

$$H_2SO_4(aq) + H_2O(\ell) \longrightarrow HSO_4^-(aq) + H_3O^+(aq)$$

The single forward arrow tells the story. The hydrogen sulfate ion is not even basic enough to react to any noticeable extent with the strongest acid available in aqueous solutions, H_3O^+. The reverse reaction does not occur. So, while HSO_4^- is the "conjugate base" of H_2SO_4, it does not display basic character.[163]

Calculation of the pH of a solution of sulfuric acid (H_2SO_4) is more difficult than for the other strong acids. For the others, if the solution has an overall concentration of 0.15 M, then you know that the final concentration of H_3O^+ is 0.15 M. Sulfuric acid will release a larger total number of protons due to its diprotic nature. But it will not produce double the number of protons ($2 \times 0.15 M = 0.30 M$) because the second ionization is not complete. Both ionization reactions occur; one completely and the other to some smaller extent. The K_a for the acid ionization of HSO_4^- is 1.02×10^{-2}, placing it at the strong end of the weak acids.

We might think that if we determine the concentration of H_3O^+ from the first ionization (0.15 M), and then add in the concentration of H_3O^+ we would expect from a 0.15 M solution of HSO_4^- based on its K_a, we could calculate the total. This does not work. The weak acid, HSO_4^- is unable to transfer as many protons as we expect because of the occurrence of the first ionization. Think about it this way:

$$H_2SO_4(aq) + H_2O(\ell) \longrightarrow HSO_4^-(aq) + H_3O^+(aq)$$

$$HSO_4^-(aq) + H_2O(\ell) \rightleftharpoons SO_4^{2-}(aq) + H_3O^+(aq)$$

The H_3O^+ formed in the first ionization causes the common ion effect to come into play for the second ionization. We can expect the hydrogen sulfate ion to be a poorer acid in a solution that already contains the common ion, H_3O^+.

How can we calculate the pH of solutions of sulfuric acid and/or hydrogen sulfate ion? First, if only hydrogen sulfate ion is placed in solution we are merely confronted with a normal weak acid calculation. Check out Example 19-6.

Example 19-6.

Calculate the pH of a 0.020 M solution of $NaHSO_4$.

Solution:

We must first recognize that the salt $NaHSO_4$ contains an anion with weak acid properties. The K_a of this anion according to the CRC Handbook is 1.02×10^{-2}. [note164]

---

[163] Assuming an aqueous system, there is no acid stronger than H_3O^+. In other types of systems an acid stronger than H_2SO_4 could force HSO_4^- to act as a base.

[164] There are many sources of information about equilibrium constant values in the case that you don't have it in a handy table. The internet is one possibility, but be careful to use a reliable source. The CRC Handbook, which may be available online via a library website, is a trusted reference for constants such as these, but it

We set up an equilibrium table based on the ionization reaction for the weak acid:

	$HSO_4^-(aq)$ + $H_2O(\ell)$	$\rightleftharpoons$	$SO_4^{2-}(aq)$ + $H_3O^+(aq)$	
Initial M	0.020		0	0
Changes in M	$-x$	Pure liquid	$+x$	$+x$
Equilibrium M	$0.020 - x$		x	x

Now we can substitute expressions for equilibrium concentrations from the table above into the equilibrium constant expression:

$$K_a = 1.02 \times 10^{-2} = \frac{\left[SO_4^{2-} \right]\left[H_3O^+ \right]}{\left[HSO_4^- \right]}$$

$$1.02 \times 10^{-2} = \frac{x^2}{0.020 - x}$$

The solver on a graphing calculator can solve this equation for x. We find that

$$x = 1.01 \times 10^{-2} \text{ M}$$

In this case x represents $[H_3O^+]$. So we can calculate the pH directly:

$$pH = -\log [H_3O^+]$$
$$= -\log (1.01 \times 10^{-2}) = 2.00$$

Things are a little more complicated for a solution of sulfuric acid. In this case, we must account for both ionizations. The simplest way to think about this problem is to consider the first (complete) ionization as a source of both the weak acid, HSO_4^- and the common ion, H_3O^+. Then, we can decide how the presence of the common ion will affect the ionization of the hydrogen sulfate ion. Check out Example 19-7.

Example 19-7.

Calculate the pH of a 0.020 M solution of sulfuric acid.

Solution:

We begin by considering the first ionization of sulfuric acid:

$$H_2SO_4(aq) + H_2O(\ell) \longrightarrow HSO_4^-(aq) + H_3O^+(aq)$$

The single forward arrow tells us that a 0.020 M solution of sulfuric acid will produce 0.020 M HSO_4^- and 0.020 M H_3O^+.

Now we consider the acid ionization of 0.020 M HSO_4^- by construction of an equilibrium table:

	$HSO_4^-(aq)$ + $H_2O(\ell)$	$\rightleftharpoons$	$SO_4^{2-}(aq)$ + $H_3O^+(aq)$	
Initial M	0.020		0	0.020
Changes in M	$-x$	Pure liquid	$+x$	$+x$
Equilibrium M	$0.020 - x$		x	$0.020 + x$

---

might take a little time to find the data in which you are interested. End-of-chapter problems use acids and bases for which the K_a or K_b values are available either within this chapter, or within the problem, itself.

Notice that the first ionization of sulfuric acid is accounted for by indicating an initial concentration (0.020 M) of the hydronium ion, H_3O^+, which was created in the first ionization. The equilibrium concentration expressions from the bottom row can be substituted into the equilibrium constant expression:

$$K_a = 1.02 \times 10^{-2} = \frac{\left[SO_4^{2-}\right]\left[H_3O^+\right]}{\left[HSO_4^-\right]} \qquad 1.02 \times 10^{-2} = \frac{x\left(0.020 + x\right)}{0.020 - x}$$

The solver on a graphing calculator can solve this equation for x. We find that

$$x = 5.68 \times 10^{-3} \text{ M}$$

In this case x does not simply represent $[H_3O^+]$. Instead, if we look back at the equilibrium table assignments, we see that:

$$[H_3O^+]_{eq} = 0.020 + x$$

x is the contribution of the HSO_4^- to the total $[H_3O^+]$. So

$$[H_3O^+] = 0.020 + 5.68 \times 10^{-3} = 2.568 \times 10^{-2} \, M$$

Now we can calculate the pH:

$$pH = -\log [H_3O^+] = -\log (2.568 \times 10^{-2}) = 1.59$$

Notice that 0.020 M HSO_4^- contributes less H_3O^+ in Example 19-7 than it did in Example 19-6 (x value of 5.68×10^{-3} instead of 1.01×10^{-2}). This is due to the common ion effect. We can also see this effect by exploring the percent ionizations of the hydrogen sulfate in both circumstances:

Using data from Example 19-6, a 0.020 M solution of HSO_4^- gave 0.010 M SO_4^{2-} for a percent ionization of 50%. (Very high for a weak acid!)

Using data from Example 19-7, a 0.020 M solution of HSO_4^- gave 0.00568 M SO_4^{2-} for a percent ionization of 28%. (Because the previous ionization of H_2SO_4 provided a substantial amount of the common ion, H_3O^+, thus limiting the ionization of the weak acid, HSO_4^-.)

To generalize: *the ionization of any weak acid will be greatly decreased in the presence of a significant concentration of a strong acid, due to the common ion effect. Similarly, the ionization of any weak base will be greatly decreased in the presence of a strong base.*

A corollary to this statement is that if a solution contains both a strong acid and a weak acid, the pH of the solution will depend almost entirely on the strong acid, the weak acid will not be able to contribute noticeable H_3O^+ ions. Similarly, if a solution contains both a strong base and a weak base, the pH of the solution will depend almost entirely on the strong base; the weak base will not be able to contribute noticeable OH^- ions. The hydrogen sulfate ion is an exception to this generalization, because (as weak acids go) it is very strong ($K_a = 0.0102$).[165]

Exercise 19-18.

Use only similarities to Examples 19-6 and 19-7 to decide how you would expect the following solution to behave. What do you expect the pH to be?

a solution that is 0.020 M HCl and 0.020 M NaHSO$_4$.

---

[165] As we saw in Example 19-7, the $[H_3O^+]$ in a strong acid solution (H_2SO_4) was noticeably increased by the presence of the weak acid, HSO_4^-. This is not usually the case for poorer weak acids. Often solutions containing both a strong and weak acid will have a pH as dictated by the strong acid present, with little to no contribution from the weak acid.

2. Other Polyprotic Acids

Sulfuric acid is the only common polyprotic acid whose first ionization is that of a strong acid. Other polyprotic acids include citric acid ($H_3C_6H_4O_7$), phosphoric acid (H_3PO_4), arsenic acid (H_3AsO_4), and carbonic acid (H_2CO_3). Consider phosphoric acid. This ***triprotic acid*** may exist in four different forms depending on how many of the acidic protons are present. This leads to three conjugate acid-base pairs.

CONJUGATE PAIRS

ACID	BASE
H_3PO_4	$H_2PO_4^-$
$H_2PO_4^-$	HPO_4^{2-}
HPO_4^{2-}	PO_4^{3-}

These three conjugate pairs are present in the three possible ionization reaction equations. Note that these are successive ionizations; reaction 2 begins with the product species of reaction 1 and reaction 3 begins with the product species of reaction 2.

1. $H_3PO_4(aq) + H_2O(\ell) \rightleftharpoons H_2PO_4^-(aq) + H_3O^+(aq)$

2. $H_2PO_4^-(aq) + H_2O(\ell) \rightleftharpoons HPO_4^{2-}(aq) + H_3O^+(aq)$

3. $HPO_4^{2-}(aq) + H_2O(\ell) \rightleftharpoons PO_4^{3-}(aq) + H_3O^+(aq)$

None of these is an irreversible process. Phosphoric acid is a weak acid, and the related acids are weaker still.

The dihydrogen phosphate ion, $H_2PO_4^-$, and the hydrogen phosphate ion, HPO_4^{2-}, are both amphoteric.[166] They can act as acids in the presence of appropriate bases and they can act as bases in the presence of appropriate acids. Tables of K_a values for polyprotic acids usually label the successive ionization constants "K_{a1}," "K_{a2}," and "K_{a3}" such as we see in Table 19-7.

Table 19-7. Acid ionization constants for some polyprotic acids				
Name	Formula	K_{a1}	K_{a2}	K_{a3}
Citric acid	$H_3C_6H_5O_7$	7.4×10^{-4}	1.7×10^{-5}	4.0×10^{-7}
Phosphoric acid	H_3PO_4	6.9×10^{-3}	6.2×10^{-8}	4.8×10^{-13}
Arsenic acid	H_3AsO_4	5.5×10^{-3}	1.7×10^{-7}	5.1×10^{-12}
Carbonic acid	H_2CO_3	4.5×10^{-7}	4.7×10^{-11}	

Exercise 19-19.

Why is there no value for K_{a3} for carbonic acid in Table 19-7?

Notice in Table 19-7 that when a polyprotic acid has fewer total atoms, the difference between successive K_a values becomes more exaggerated. Whereas citric acid (top of the list in Table 19-7) shows a decrease of approximately one order of magnitude per proton removed, the other polyprotics in the table show decreases of several orders of magnitude. This makes sense. In the considerably larger citric acid molecule, the negative charges left behind by the departure of a proton are separated by more atoms than in the smaller structures. Thus, there is less repulsion of like charges in the citrate ions than in the other families of ions shown in the table.

---

[166] Remember that water is also amphoteric.

Example 19-8.

a. Write the ionization reaction equation that is described by the K_{a2} for H_3AsO_4 in Table 19-7 above.

b. L-alanine is one of the 20 naturally occurring proteinogenic amino acids. Under appropriate conditions it is a diprotic acid with the formula $H_2C_3H_5NO_2$. The two pK_a values are 2.34 and 9.87. Write the two dissociation equations and label each one with the appropriate pK_a and K_a.

Solutions:

a. $H_2AsO_4^-(aq) + H_2O(\ell) \rightleftharpoons HAsO_4^{2-}(aq) + H_3O^+(aq)$

b. $H_2C_3H_5NO_2(aq) + H_2O(\ell) \rightleftharpoons HC_3H_5NO_2^-(aq) + H_3O^+(aq) \quad pK_{a1} = 2.34 \quad K_{a1} = 4.6 \times 10^{-3}$

$HC_3H_5NO_2^-(aq) + H_2O(\ell) \rightleftharpoons C_3H_5NO_2^{2-}(aq) + H_3O^+(aq) \quad pK_{a2} = 9.87 \quad K_{a2} = 1.3 \times 10^{-10}$

Similarly to H_2SO_4 and HSO_4^-, it is more difficult to remove protons from species carrying more negative charge.

19-4. STOICHIOMETRIC REACTIONS OF STRONG PLUS WEAK

In Exercise 19-14 we discovered that strong acids react with weak bases in irreversible reactions; the values of the equilibrium constants for such reactions are very large. The same is true of strong bases reacting with weak acids. As a final unit in this chapter we will study these reactions. What type of solution exists when *stoichiometric* amounts of a strong acid are added to a weak base? Thinking about reactions such as these will help us prepare for Chapter 20.

A. Strong Base + Weak Acid

If you think <u>qualitatively</u> about adding together equal moles of a strong base and a weak acid, do you expect the solution to be acidic, neutral, or basic when you are finished? Equal amounts of a <u>strong base</u> and a <u>weak acid</u> produce a basic solution. The effect of the <u>strong</u> base overwhelms the effect of the <u>weak</u> acid.

If we look at a generic net ionic reaction equation for a reaction of this nature:

$$OH^-(aq) + HA(aq) \longrightarrow H_2O(\ell) + A^-(aq)$$

we can understand on a different level.[167] First, notice that this is the reverse reaction of a weak base ionization and thus has an equilibrium constant that is the reciprocal of a K_b value. Because K_b values are small (by definition of *weak*), these equilibrium constants must be large. Reactions such as these go essentially to completion. Additionally, we see that when identical amounts of OH^- and HA are added together, both get (essentially) completely consumed. The result is an aqueous solution of A^-. Now if HA is a weak acid, then A^- is a weak base (remember the nature of conjugates) and we expect the solution to be basic.

Regardless of the single forward arrow just used for the reaction of the strong base with the weak acid, we know that the reaction between OH^- and HA is not <u>completely</u> irreversible. After all, the reverse reaction describes the ionization of the weak base, A^-, and so, must proceed to some small extent. It is, perhaps, the least confusing to portray the reaction of OH^- and HA as follows:

$$OH^-(aq) + HA(aq) \rightleftharpoons H_2O(\ell) + A^-(aq)$$

---

[167] Notice that in a net ionic equation, an aqueous weak electrolyte such as HA (perhaps CH_3CO_2H or HCN) is written as a molecule, not as separated ions. This is because a large majority of the species exist as the molecule; there is very little ionization.

with the lop-sided reversible arrow telling us that this reaction has a large equilibrium constant, while still acknowledging that the reverse reaction also occurs. We could say that the reaction between OH^- and HA goes <u>nearly</u> to completion. How close to completion it gets is governed by the K_b of the weak base, A^-. Labeling the equilibrium constant of the forward reaction as K_{fwd}, we can write:

$$K_{fwd} = \frac{1}{K_b}$$

because they are reverse reactions. So the size of K_b really does dictate the size of K_{fwd} !

How can we calculate the pH of a solution that results from a reaction such as this? The secret is to PRETEND that the original reaction really DOES go ALL THE WAY to COMPLETION. That is, pretend that the single forward arrow represents the behavior of this system and that *all* OH^- and HA are consumed. The resulting solution contains only the weak base, A^-. Its concentration depends on the original amount of HA. We know how to determine the pH of a weak base solution (see Example 19-5), so we utilize that kind of thinking again.

Emphasis: In reality the forward reaction <u>does not go to completion</u>. It stops just short, as dictated by K_b. The easiest logic for the calculations is to play the mind game of "letting" the forward reaction go to completion resulting in a solution containing only weak base, and then calculating the amount of ionization that would have to occur to achieve equilibrium as the weak base ionizes in that solution.

Here's an example of the logic and process:

Example 19-9.

Calculate the pH of the solution that results from pouring together 100.0 mL of 0.10 *M* NaOH and 100.0 mL of 0.10 *M* HClO.

Solution:

First, you must be able to write the reaction equation for the chemical process that will occur upon mixing these solutions. Can you?

$$OH^-(aq) \ + \ HClO(aq) \longrightarrow H_2O(\ell) \ + \ ClO^-(aq)$$

Then, we must work with the stoichiometry of the *nearly irreversible* weak acid-strong base reaction. We *assume* that it is, indeed, irreversible. We use a stoichiometry table (in moles). Each solution is 100.0 mL of 0.10 *M*, so the moles of each solute is:

$$100.0 \ mL \times \frac{1.0 \ L}{1000 \ mL} \times \frac{0.10 \ moles}{L} = 1.0 \times 10^{-2} \ moles$$

	$OH^-(aq)$	+ $HClO(aq)$	$\longrightarrow H_2O(\ell)$	+ $ClO^-(aq)$
Initial moles	0.010	0.010		0
Change	− 0.010	− 0.010	Pure liquid	+ 0.010
Final moles	0	0		0.010

This table shows us that after the initial reaction GOES TO COMPLETION we have a solution containing 0.010 moles of ClO^-, a weak base. Now, we just need to find the pH of this weak base solution.

We will use an equilibrium table set up in MOLARITIES. The molarity of the weak base is

$$\frac{0.010\ moles}{200.0\ mL} \times \frac{1000\ mL}{L} = 5.0 \times 10^{-2}\ M$$

Note that we are assuming that volumes of these solutions are additive; if we pour 100.0 mL into 100.0 mL we will have exactly 200.0 mL. This assumption is usually fine for relatively dilute aqueous systems. We set up the equilibrium table:

	$ClO^-(aq)$ +	$H_2O(\ell) \rightleftharpoons$	$HClO(aq)$ +	$OH^-(aq)$
Initial M	0.050		0	0
Changes in M	$-x$	Pure liquid	$+x$	$+x$
Equilibrium M	$0.050 - x$		x	x

We need to find the K_b of ClO^-. The K_a of HClO is 4.0×10^{-8}. We can calculate the K_b:

$$K_b = \frac{1.008 \times 10^{-14}}{4.0 \times 10^{-8}} = 2.5 \times 10^{-7}$$

We substitute the bottom-line expressions from the table into the equilibrium constant expression:

$$K_b = \frac{\left[HClO\right]_{eq}\left[OH^-\right]_{eq}}{\left[ClO^-\right]_{eq}} = \frac{x^2}{0.050 - x} = 2.5 \times 10^{-7}$$

This equation can be solved for x using the solver on a graphing calculator. We find that

$$x = 1.117 \times 10^{-4}\ M$$

This x represents the concentration of OH^- so we find the pH from the pOH:

$$pOH = -\log\left[OH^-\right]$$
$$pOH = -\log(1.117 \times 10^{-4}) = 3.952$$
$$pH = 14.00 - 3.952 = 10.05$$

B. Strong Acid + Weak Base

A discussion of strong acids reacting with weak bases is exactly analogous to the previous discussion of strong bases reacting with weak acids. One obtains a solution of a weak acid when *stoichiometric* amounts of strong acids and weak bases are combined. Here are two examples:

$$H_3O^+(aq) + NH_3(aq) \rightleftharpoons H_2O(\ell) + NH_4^+(aq)$$
$$H_3O^+(aq) + CN^-(aq) \rightleftharpoons H_2O(\ell) + HCN(aq)$$

Notice that in each case, if the same number of moles of hydronium ion and the weak base are present they will be (essentially) fully consumed. The result is a solution of a weak acid. We expect the final solution to have a pH less than 7.0. The calculation of the pH of a solution resulting from a reaction such as these is very similar to the calculation in Example 19-9. We must first solve the *stoichiometric* problem of the reaction that goes to completion, then we must solve the equilibrium problem. An example is offered here.

Example 19-10.

Calculate the pH of the solution that results from pouring together 200.0 mL of 0.10 M HCl and 100.0 mL of 0.20 M NH_3.

Solution:

First we work with the stoichiometry of the acid-base reaction presented. We can use a stoichiometry table (in moles). We must determine how many moles of each reactant are present:

$$200.0 \; mL \times \frac{1.0 \; L}{1000 \; mL} \times \frac{0.10 \; moles \; HCl}{L} = 2.0 \times 10^{-2} \; moles \; HCl$$

$$\left(this \; means \; 2.0 \times 10^{-2} \; moles \; H_3O^+ \right)$$

$$100.0 \; mL \times \frac{1.0 \; L}{1000 \; mL} \times \frac{0.20 \; moles \; NH_3}{L} = 2.0 \times 10^{-2} \; moles \; NH_3$$

Then we construct the stoichiometry table by assuming the reaction between weak base and strong acid really does go to completion:

	$H_3O^+(aq)$	+ $NH_3(aq)$	$\longrightarrow H_2O(\ell)$	+ $NH_4^+(aq)$
Initial moles	0.020	0.020		0
Change	-0.020	-0.020	Pure liquid	$+0.020$
Final moles	0	0		0.020

This table shows us that after the initial reaction GOES TO COMPLETION we have a solution containing 0.020 moles of NH_4^+, a weak acid. Now we need only find the pH of this weak acid solution:

We will use an equilibrium table set up in MOLARITIES. The molarity of the weak acid is

$$\frac{0.020 \; moles}{300.0 \; mL} \times \frac{1000 \; mL}{L} = 6.7 \times 10^{-2} \; M$$

We set up the equilibrium table using the acid ionization equilibrium:

	$NH_4^+(aq)$	+ $H_2O(\ell)$	$\rightleftharpoons$	$NH_3(aq)$	+ $H_3O^+(aq)$
Initial M	0.067			0	0
Changes in M	$-x$	Pure liquid		$+x$	$+x$
Equilibrium M	$0.067 - x$			x	x

The K_a of NH_4^+ is 5.6×10^{-10}. We can substitute the equilibrium concentration expressions from the table into the equilibrium constant expression:

$$K_a = \frac{\left[NH_3 \right]_{eq} \left[H_3O^+ \right]_{eq}}{\left[NH_4^+ \right]_{eq}} = \frac{x^2}{0.067 - x} = 5.6 \times 10^{-10}$$

This equation can be solved for x using the solver on a graphing calculator. We find that

$$x = 6.12 \times 10^{-6} \; M$$

This *x* represents the concentration of H₃O⁺ so we find the pH directly:

$$pH = -\log\left[H_3O^+\right]$$
$$pH = -\log(6.12\times10^{-6}) = 5.21$$

Table 19-8 summarizes the types of solutions for which we have learned how to calculate the pH so far. Compare to Table 18-8 at the end of Chapter 18 to see our progress. We have added the ability to calculate the pH of weak acid and base solutions, which can be made either by simply dissolving a weak acid or base, or by reaction of strong acids with weak bases or strong bases with weak acids.

Summary Table 19-8. Solutions for which we have calculated pH

1	strong acid solution, H₃O⁺	Use [strong acid] = [H₃O⁺], and pH = –log [H₃O⁺]	Chap 18-4B
2	strong base solution, OH⁻	Use [OH⁻] = [strong base], or [OH⁻] = 2 × [strong base] (depending on the strong base); then pOH = –log [OH⁻] , then pH = 14 – pOH.	Chap 18-4B
3	strong acid + strong base	Use stoichiometry table to determine composition of final solution (could be strong acid, strong base, or neutral) then find pH as indicated in Table entries 1 and 2, above.	Chap 18-4E
4	weak acid solution, HA	Use equilibrium table (in terms of *x*) and Kₐ expression to find [H₃O⁺], then pH = –log [H₃O⁺].	Chap 19-3C
5	weak base solution, A⁻	Use equilibrium table (in terms of *x*) and Kᵦ expression to find [OH⁻], then pOH = –log [OH⁻] , then pH = 14 – pOH.	Chap 19-3D
6	Stoichiometric additions of strong acid + weak base	Use stoichiometry table to determine moles of weak acid in final solution. Determine final weak acid concentration. Determine the pH of this final solution using method from entry 4 of this table.	Chap 19-4
	Stoichiometric additions of strong base + weak acid	Use stoichiometry table to determine moles of weak base in final solution. Determine final weak base concentration. Determine the pH of this final solution using method from entry 5 of this table.	Chap 19-4

Chapter Summary

Weak acids and weak bases are weak electrolytes: they do not produce stoichiometric amounts of ions in solution.

The percent ionization of a weak acid or weak base depends on:
- the identity of the weak acid or weak base (stronger ones ionize more),
- the concentration of the weak acid or weak base (more dilute solutions have larger percent ionizations, but fewer ions),
- the presence (or not) of common ions (common ions suppress ionization),
- the temperature.

Given the percent ionization of a weak acid or base, the pH can be determined.

Given the pH and total concentration of a weak acid or base, the percent ionization can be determined.

The relative strengths of weak acids and bases can be tabulated by K_a or K_b values.

Weak acids are strongest when their conjugate base is stable.

A stable weak base will be a relatively poor base, because it has little desire for a proton.

K_a and K_b values for <u>conjugate pairs</u> are related: $K_a \times K_b = 1.0 \times 10^{-14}$ or $pK_a + pK_b = 14.00$

The reverse reaction of an acid ionization reaction has $K_{eq} = \dfrac{1}{K_a}$.

The reverse reaction of a base ionization reaction has $K_{eq} = \dfrac{1}{K_b}$.

K_a and K_b values can be used to calculate the pH, or percent ionization, of a weak acid or weak base solution.

Polyprotic acids have more than one acidic hydrogen.

Sulfuric acid is unique in that its first ionization is "strong," while its second ionization is "weak."

The percent ionization of a weak acid will be decreased by the presence of a strong acid, due to the common ion effect. Considering $HA + H_2O \rightleftharpoons H_3O^+ + A^-$, by LeChatelier's Principle, the additional H_3O^+ will force the equilibrium to the left.

Polyprotic acids can be described by multiple K_a values: K_{a1}, K_{a2}, etc. The acids get successively weaker as more ionizations occur.

Equal moles of a weak acid and a strong base produce a weak base in solution.

Equal moles of a weak base and a strong acid produce a weak acid in solution.

CHAPTER 19: PROBLEMS

[Note: All problems are at a temperature of 25 °C unless noted otherwise.]

1.   Write the appropriate *net ionic* reaction equation for either the acid ionization or base ionization of the following species in aqueous solution.

a. HCN   **b.** NH_3 **c.** ClO^- **d.** HNO_2

e. HSO_4^- **f.** N_2H_4 (a base)   **g.** NH_4Cl **h.** CO_3^{2-}

2.   Draw the Lewis dot structure of N_2H_4. How does this structure tell you that this species is a base (see 1.f. above).

3.   Write the appropriate *net ionic* reaction equation for either the acid ionization or base ionization of the following species in aqueous solution.

a. C_5H_5N (a base)   **b.** NH_4^+ **c.** HClO   **d.** NO_2^-

e. SO_4^{2-} **f.** $N_2H_5^+$ **g.** KF   **h.** H_2CO_3

4.   **a.** Fill in the blanks with an appropriate chemical formula:

Acid	Conjugate Base	K_a
NH_4^+	_____	5.6×10^{-10}
_____	Cyanide	6.2×10^{-10}
HClO	_____	4.0×10^{-8}
$[Al(H_2O)_6]^{3+}$	_____	1.0×10^{-5}
_____	Nitrite	5.6×10^{-4}
_____	SO_4^{2-}	1.02×10^{-2}

b. Calculate pK_a for NH_4^+.

c. What is the weakest acid in part **a** (including those in the blanks)?

d. What is the weakest conjugate base in part **a** (including those in the blanks)?

5.   The pH of a weak acid solution is 5.88. The solution is 0.32 *M*. Determine the percent ionization of the weak acid.

6.   The pH of a 0.100 *M* solution of HNO_2 is 2.09. Determine the equilibrium concentration of NO_2^-.

7.   The pH of a 0.20 *M* weak base solution is 9.77. Determine the percent ionization of the weak base.

8.   **a.** Fill in the blanks to complete these reaction equations in aqueous solution:

Base	K_b
$NH_3 + H_2O \rightleftharpoons$ _____	1.8×10^{-5}
$N_2H_4 + H_2O \rightleftharpoons$ _____	1.3×10^{-6}
$C_5H_5N + H_2O \rightleftharpoons$ _____	1.7×10^{-9}

b. What is the weakest base in part **a**? The strongest conjugate acid?

c. Using the K_b values in the table, calculate the equilibrium constants for the following reactions:

(1) $C_5H_5NH^+ + OH^- \rightleftharpoons C_5H_5N + H_2O$

(2) $NH_4^+ + H_2O \rightleftharpoons H_3O^+ + NH_3$

(3) $N_2H_5^+ + NH_3 \rightleftharpoons N_2H_4 + NH_4^+$

9.   **a.** Fill in the blanks to complete these reaction equations in aqueous solution:

Acid	K_a
$HCN + H_2O \rightleftharpoons$ _____	6.2×10^{-10}
$HClO + H_2O \rightleftharpoons$ _____	4.0×10^{-8}
$HF + H_2O \rightleftharpoons$ _____	6.3×10^{-4}

b. What is the strongest acid in part **a**? The strongest conjugate base?

c. Using the K_a values in the table, calculate equilibrium constants for the following reactions:

(1) $H_3O^+ + ClO^- \rightleftharpoons H_2O + HClO$

(2) $CN^- + H_2O \rightleftharpoons HCN + OH^-$

(3) $HF + CN^- \rightleftharpoons HCN + F^-$

10.

Acid	K_a
HF	6.3×10^{-4}
HNO_2	5.6×10^{-4}
HCN	6.2×10^{-10}
HCO_3^-	4.7×10^{-11}

a. Select the strongest of the acids above.

b. Give the chemical formulas of the conjugate bases of these acids.

c. Select the strongest of the conjugate bases.

d. Determine the equilibrium constants for the following reactions in aqueous solution:

(1) $H_3O^+ + CO_3^{2-} \rightleftharpoons HCO_3^- + H_2O$

(2) $H_2O + CO_3^{2-} \rightleftharpoons OH^- + HCO_3^-$

11.

Acid	K_a (25 °C)
$HCN + H_2O \rightleftharpoons$ _____	6.2×10^{-10}
$HNO_2 + H_2O \rightleftharpoons$ _____	5.6×10^{-4}
$HSO_4^- + H_2O \rightleftharpoons$ _____	1.0×10^{-2}

  a. Fill in the blanks to complete the chemical reaction equations.

  b. Identify the strongest acid and the strongest conjugate base in these reactions (including items in the blanks).

  c. Determine the equilibrium constants for the following reactions at 25 °C :

      (1) $H_3O^+ + CN^- \rightleftharpoons HCN + H_2O$

      (2) $NO_2^- + H_2O \rightleftharpoons HNO_2 + OH^-$

  d. Determine the pH of :

      (1) 0.0500 M HCN

      (2) 0.0500 M HClO$_4$

12. Determine the pH of each of the following aqueous solutions:

    a. 1.00×10^{-2} M HCl   **d.** 1.00×10^{-3} M NaOH

    b. 1.00×10^{-2} M HCN   **e.** 1.00×10^{-3} M NH$_3$

    c. 1.00×10^{-11} M HCl

13. $K_{eq} = 7.5 \times 10^{-10}$ for the ionization of the weak base, aniline ($C_6H_5NH_2$). Aniline is an amine; the basic atom is the nitrogen atom.

      $C_6H_5NH_2 + H_2O \rightleftharpoons C_6H_5NH_3^+ + OH^-$

Determine K_a for $C_6H_5NH_3^+$.

14. The weak acid HF has $K_a = 6.3 \times 10^{-4}$. For a 0.0025 M aqueous HF solution, calculate:

    a. $[H_3O^+]$ **c.** pH

    b. [HF]   **d.** pOH

15. Calculate the pH of 0.15 M aqueous NH$_4$Cl. (For NH$_3$, $K_b = 1.8 \times 10^{-5}$.)

16. Aniline, $C_6H_5NH_2$, has $K_b = 7.5 \times 10^{-10}$. Calculate the concentrations of hydronium and hydroxide ions in a 0.0100 M aqueous solution of aniline.

17. Hydrazine, N_2H_4, has $K_b = 1.3 \times 10^{-6}$. For a 0.0100 M aqueous hydrazine solution, calculate:

    a. $[OH^-]$ **c.** pH

    b. $[N_2H_4]$ **d.** pOH

18.   Calculate the pH of 0.500 M aqueous NaCN. (For HCN, $K_a = 6.2 \times 10^{-10}$)

19.   Explain why the percent ionization of a weak acid is markedly decreased in the presence of a strong acid.

20.   Explain why the pH of a solution containing both a weak base and a strong base depends only on the concentration of the strong base.

21.   Explain why the percent ionization of HCN is markedly decreased in a solution containing KCN.

22.   Calculate the pH of a 0.085 M solution of H_2SO_4. (HINT: account for both protons!)

23.   **a.** Write the successive ionization reaction equations for carbonic acid (H_2CO_3).

        b. Write the K_a expression for each of your reactions in part a.

24.   Calculate the pH that should result if 0.200 moles of acetic acid and 0.200 moles of sodium hydroxide are both placed into 500.0 mL of solution.

25.   Calculate the pH that should result if 0.066 moles of ammonia and 0.066 moles of hydroiodic acid are both placed into 750.0 mL of solution.

26.   Calculate the pH that should result when 100.0 mL of 0.020 M KOH is poured into 200.0 mL of 0.010 M iodic acid.

27.   Calculate the pH that should result when 250.0 mL of 0.75 M HClO$_4$ is poured into 750.0 mL of 0.25 M KF.

CHAPTER 20: APPLICATIONS OF ACIDS AND BASES: BUFFERS, TITRATIONS, INDICATORS

20-1. BUFFER SOLUTIONS

A. Definition

The dictionary definition of a **buffer** is something that *lessens or absorbs the shock of an impact, or protects by intercepting or moderating adverse influences.* In acid-base chemistry these definitions of a buffer apply well.

> A buffer solution is a solution that resists large pH changes upon the addition of small quantities of strong acids or bases.

The addition of even small quantities of strong acids or bases will cause large pH changes in un-buffered systems (such as plain water). Example 20-1 illustrates a pH change that can occur when a small addition of strong acid is made to plain water.

Example 20-1.

A small amount of the strong acid $HClO_4$ (0.000020 moles) is added to 50.0 mL of water. Calculate the pH change that occurs.

Solution:

The initial solution is plain water and thus should have a pH of 7.00. The final solution has a hydronium ion concentration of

$$\frac{0.000020 \ mol}{0.0500 \ L} = 0.00040 \ M \ H_3O^+$$ and, thus, a pH of $-\log(0.00040) = 3.40$.

The change in pH that occurs is 3.40 – 7.00 = –3.60 pH units, where the negative sign indicates that the pH dropped from the initial value to the final value.

Note: the sign for any change will turn out correct if you calculate the magnitude of the change by taking the final circumstance minus the initial circumstance:

$$pH \ change = pH_{final} - pH_{initial}$$

Now, if the same addition of strong acid is made to a buffered solution, the pH change will be substantially less. The exact change will depend on the make-up of the buffering system, but might be on the order of –0.03 pH units. Clearly this is a meaningful difference in behaviors of the two systems. We would like to understand how the components of a buffered solution can accomplish this feat. In chemistry a system that is "buffered" is able to lessen the shock of added strong acid (or base). The adverse influence of added acid or base is minimized by the moderating effect of the buffer. The pH changes only minimally.

B. Why Buffers?

Before getting into the details of buffering components and their behavior, we should first make the case for the importance of buffers. Buffer solutions are found widely in nature and are used routinely in biochemical and molecular biological research. Your blood is a buffered solution at approximately pH 7.4. Any large change in pH of your blood would be catastrophic to your health.

Medically, blood plasma that is too acidic (pH below 7.35) is termed **acidosis**, while blood plasma that is too basic (pH above 7.45) is termed **alkalosis**. Yet quantities of acids and bases must fluctuate in the blood stream from location to location and time to time. For instance, strenuous exercise will liberate large quantities of lactic acid into the blood stream from the working muscles. This lactic acid needs to be recycled in the liver and must travel in the bloodstream in order to reach the liver. If the influx of lactic acid caused a significant decrease in blood pH, we would be in trouble; hemoglobin's ability to carry oxygen is very pH sensitive. In fact, the production of lactic acid does lower the pH of working muscles a little bit and the added H_3O^+ causes protonation of key sites on the hemoglobin molecule that stabilize the *deoxygenated conformation* of the subunits. Thus, this so-called "Bohr effect" is instrumental in encouraging the release of extra oxygen to working muscles. It would be catastrophic if the Bohr effect occurred system-wide, so that hemoglobin was unable to bind oxygen appropriately.

Additionally, enzymes and other biological molecules take on shapes and folded structures that are usually crucial to the function of the molecule. Many of the interactions that maintain the necessary shapes are disrupted by changes in pH. Therefore, cell fluids must be buffered to protect the enzymes and proteins therein. For similar reasons, researchers studying molecules such as enzymes must work in carefully buffered systems so that the denaturing (unfolding) of the enzyme does not cause a loss in the activity under study. These concepts are an important part of an education in the area of biochemistry. We begin here with an appreciation for how buffer systems work.

C. Buffer Components

A solution is a buffer solution when it contains both a weak acid and its conjugate base (or a weak base and its conjugate acid) in significant, and roughly equal, amounts. A solution containing these components will resist pH changes upon the addition of strong acids and bases.

1. Examples of Buffering Pairs

Any weak conjugate pair will serve as a buffering system, although some might be better than others for a particular task. At least one member of a conjugate pair will always be ionic (maybe both), and so will come as a salt. Examples are given in Table 20-1.

Table 20-1. Conjugate partners are necessary for the creation of buffer systems. Notice that any ions must be obtained from salts.	
Weak Acid Component	Weak Base Component
HF	F^- (possibly from NaF)
NH_4^+ (possibly from NH_4Cl)	NH_3
CH_3CO_2H	$CH_3CO_2^-$ (possibly from $NaCH_3CO_2$)
$H_2PO_4^-$ (possibly from KH_2PO_4)	HPO_4^{2-} (possibly from K_2HPO_4)

2. How Buffer Components Work.

Buffers succeed at minimizing pH changes by providing species that react with strong acids or strong bases, thus prohibiting the *stoichiometric* formation of OH^- or H_3O^+ in the solution. If the strong acid or base no longer produces stoichiometric concentrations of hydroxide or hydronium ion, the effect on the pH of the solution is minimized.

Remember (from section 19-4 of Chapter 19) that reactions between weak acids and strong bases (or weak bases and strong acids) go essentially to completion. We add the idea, now, that *any strong acid will transfer its proton to the best base present and any strong base will remove a proton from the strongest acid present.* When a solution is a buffer solution, the best acid or base present becomes the buffer pair, not the water molecule. Consider the ammonium/ammonia buffering system (NH_4^+ and NH_3) for which the following reactions would occur upon the addition of (1) strong base and (2) strong acid:

1. $OH^-(aq) + NH_4^+(aq) \rightleftharpoons H_2O(\ell) + NH_3(aq)$

2. $H_3O^+(aq) + NH_3(aq) \rightleftharpoons H_2O(\ell) + NH_4^+(aq)$

Notice (in line 1, above) that a strong base, when added to a solution containing both NH_4^+ and NH_3 reacts with the NH_4^+; bases react with acids! Similarly, when a strong acid is added to the buffer system, it only reacts with the NH_3 (line 2, above). In both cases, the other buffer component is present, but it is not reacting. Also, remember that the arrows used above indicate reactions that go essentially to completion. Notice that in the first reaction the strong base (OH^-) has been converted to the weak base ammonia (NH_3). In the second reaction the strong acid (H_3O^+) has been converted to the weak acid, ammonium ion (NH_4^+). Buffers minimize pH changes by converting strong bases into weak bases (by reaction with the acidic buffering component) and strong acids into weak acids (by reaction with the basic buffering component.)

In addition, the buffering reactions (1 and 2, above) generate a weak base or weak acid *that is already present in significant concentrations in the system*. These reactions result in the use of small amounts of one of the buffering components and the generation of small amounts of the other. For example, in reaction 1, above, a small amount of NH_4^+ is converted to NH_3, but both of these species are present in relatively large quantities. So the net result is a *change in the relative proportions of the two buffering components*. Because a small change in the relative proportions of the two components causes only a small change in pH, we have a successful buffer. We will explore this more in the next section.

Example 20-2.

Write the buffering reactions that occur for the following systems:

     a.   Addition of strong acid to an $H_2PO_4^-/HPO_4^{2-}$ buffer.
     b.   Addition of strong base to an HCO_2H/HCO_2^- buffer.

Solutions:

   a. strong acid transfers its proton to the basic component of the buffer (producing the acid
     component of the buffer): $H_3O^+(aq) + HPO_4^{2-}(aq) \longrightarrow H_2PO_4^-(aq) + H_2O(\ell)$

   b. strong base takes a proton from the acid component of the buffer (producing the base
     component of the buffer): $OH^-(aq) + HCO_2H(aq) \longrightarrow HCO_2^-(aq) + H_2O(\ell)$

Exercise 20-1.

Write the buffering reactions that occur for the following systems:

     a. an HCN/CN^- buffering system undergoing a small addition of strong base.
     b. an HCN/CN^- buffering system undergoing a small addition of strong acid.
     c. an acetic acid/acetate buffering system undergoing a small addition of strong base.
     d. an $H_2PO_4^-/HPO_4^{2-}$ buffering system undergoing a small addition of strong acid.

D. The pH of Buffers

Two variables dictate the pH of a buffer solution:

(1) the *identity* of the weak acid/weak base conjugate pair (a major influence);

(2) the *relative proportions* of the weak acid and weak base conjugate pair species (a minor influence).

(1) The major influence on the pH of a buffer is the identity of the conjugate pair used.

- Some conjugate pairs have a stronger weak acid and weaker conjugate base (for instance, HNO_2, $K_a = 5.6 \times 10^{-4}$ and NO_2^-, $K_b = 1.8 \times 10^{-11}$). If equal moles of these two are added to the same solution, the solution will be acidic (pH = 3.25).

- Some conjugate pairs have a stronger weak base and a weaker conjugate acid (for instance, NH_3, $K_b = 1.8 \times 10^{-5}$ and NH_4^+, $K_a = 5.6 \times 10^{-10}$). If equal moles of these two are added to the same solution, the solution will be basic (pH = 9.25).

- Some conjugate pairs have more balanced values of K_a and K_b (for instance, HClO, $K_a = 4.0 \times 10^{-8}$ and ClO^-, $K_b = 2.5 \times 10^{-7}$). If equal moles of HClO and ClO^- are added to the same solution, the pH will only be slightly on the basic side of neutral (pH = 7.40), because K_b is slightly larger in this case.

Because the K_b value *depends on* the K_a value, $K_b = \dfrac{K_w}{K_a}$, we can say that the pH of a buffer depends on the K_a value of the weak acid component. This is essentially the same as saying that the pH depends on the identity of the conjugate pair.

(2) The second (and lesser) contributor to buffer pH is the relative proportion of the two buffering components present. If more of the acid component is present, the pH will be more acidic; if more of the base component is present, the pH will be more basic. These differences are relatively small. For instance, a buffer with a 10:1 HClO to ClO^- ratio has a pH of 6.40 while a buffer with a 1:10 ratio of the same two components has a pH of 8.40. Note that this is one pH unit above and below the pH for a buffer with a 1:1 ratio of these components. Beyond these extremes the buffering effects are negligible.

It is easiest to understand these two influences by viewing information graphically. Figure 20-1 shows the pH of various mixtures of two different conjugate pairs, HClO/ClO$^-$ and HOAc/AcO$^-$.[168] All of the solutions have a total concentration of 0.10 *M*, so the "0% weak acid" solution is 0.10 *M* weak base and the "60% weak acid" solution is a buffer that is 0.060 *M* weak acid and 0.040 *M* weak base (for a total concentration of 0.10 M).

---

[168] HOAc is an abbreviation for acetic acid; OAc$^-$ is an abbreviation for the acetate ion.

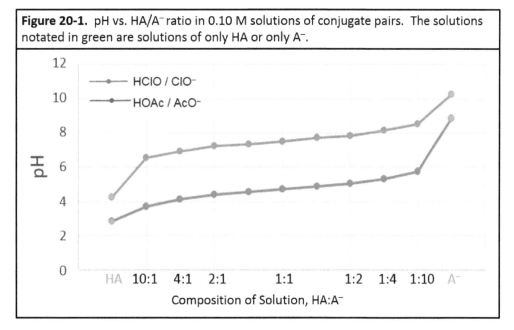

Figure 20-1. pH vs. HA/A⁻ ratio in 0.10 M solutions of conjugate pairs. The solutions notated in green are solutions of only HA or only A⁻.

There are four important points with respect to Figure 20-1.

1. The identity of the acid/base couple determines the vertical position of the curve on the pH axis, those acid-base couples with the strongest weak acids are found lower on the plot. This is the major influence on buffer pH. In Figure 20-1, we show data for two conjugate pairs: hypochlorous acid (HOCl) with the hypochlorite ion (OCl⁻) and acetic acid (HOAc) with the acetate ion (OAc⁻). We see that, because acetic acid is a stronger acid than hypochlorous acid, all of the HOAc/OAc⁻ solutions lie at lower pH than their HOCl/OCl⁻ counterparts.

2. The pH of <u>buffer</u> solutions (all data markers except the first and last green markers) also depends on the relative proportions of the acid and base components (as the relative amount of the weak base component increases, the pH increases). The whole point of a buffer is to limit changes in pH, hence the flatness of the curve indicates good buffering potential. An important point: *buffer regions have ratios of [HA]:[A⁻] from 10:1 at one extreme to 1:10 at the other*.

3. The middle point on each plot, where the solution is 0.050 M in weak acid and 0.050 M in weak base, displays a pH that is, perhaps surprisingly, equal to the pK_a of the weak acid component of the buffer pair. Thus, because HClO has a pK_a value of 7.40, we see that the 1:1 buffer pH is consistent with this value. Similarly, the HOAc/OAc⁻ plot is vertically centered at a pH of 4.76, the pK_a of acetic acid. In general, *the middle of the relatively flat "buffer region" of the plot is centered on the pK_a of the weak acid*. We will explore this more fully later in this chapter.

4. The solutions of only weak acid and only weak base (green markers) have pH values that differ more from the buffer region pH values. These solutions have ionized only to the extent of the ability of the weak acid or base component. No additional conjugate species is added. This suggests the reality of the buffer effect:

    the pH is most stable when the buffering components are present in a reasonably balanced ratio. Small changes in the ratio do not affect the pH much, when you are between ratios of 1:10 and 10:1.

As we have seen, two factors control the pH of a buffer solution: the pK_a of the weak acid and the concentration ratio of the conjugate pair components. The interplay of these two factors is easily seen in the mathematics of the equilibrium constant expression for the weak acid:

$$K_a = \frac{\left[H_3O^+\right]_{eq}\left[A^-\right]_{eq}}{\left[HA\right]_{eq}} \quad \textit{rearranged to} \quad \left[H_3O^+\right]_{eq} = K_a \times \frac{\left[HA\right]_{eq}}{\left[A^-\right]_{eq}}$$

Here we see that the concentration of H_3O^+ (and, therefore the pH) of an aqueous system at equilibrium is dependent on the value of K_a and the relative proportions of the HA and A^- components. What we learned from the analysis of Figure 20-1, is that the ratio should be somewhere between 1/10 and 10/1 in order for a solution to be a buffer solution.

Exercise 20-2.

Which of the following solutions fit the definition of a buffer solution?

    a. 0.12 M HCN and 0.10 M KCN   **b.** 0.20 M NH_3 and 0.0060 M NH_4^+

    c. 0.10 M HCO_2H and 0.050 M ClO_3^- **d.** 0.040 M HF and 0.0050 M NaF

---

1. Calculating Buffer pH

The findings of the previous section point to a mathematical method for calculation of the pH of a buffer system. You will recall that using the K_a expression to determine the pH of a weak acid system involves utilizing a variable (such as x) to describe the extent to which the weak acid ionizes in solubtion. However, for buffer solutions, *neither the weak acid nor the weak base component can significantly ionize*.

To understand why, consider dissolving 0.1 mole HCN and 0.1 mole KCN in the same solution.[169] The weak acid, HCN, tries to ionize:

$$HCN(aq) + H_2O(\ell) \rightleftharpoons CN^-(aq) + H_3O^+(aq)$$

but this ionization reaction is suppressed by the 0.1 mole of CN^- already present in the solution (which shifts the equilibrium to the left via the common ion effect). The weak base, CN^- tries to ionize:

$$CN^-(aq) + H_2O(\ell) \rightleftharpoons HCN(aq) + OH^-(aq)$$

but this ionization is suppressed by the 0.1 mole of HCN already present in the solution (which shifts this equilibrium to the left via LeChatelier's Principle). This effect leads to the general result:

Weak acid and weak base species in a buffer solution are not able to ionize significantly if they are conjugates.[170]

For buffer solutions, therefore, if the original [HA] is 0.10 M, not enough will ionize to significantly decrease this concentration, so $[HA]_{eq}$ is also 0.10 M. The same is true of the conjugate base; $[A^-]_{eq}$ equals the original $[A^-]$. This result is very helpful when it comes to calculating the pH of a buffer solution:

For buffer solutions, there is no need to use an equilibrium table to determine equilibrium concentrations. The extent of ionization, "x," in a buffer solution will always be insignificant, so that the equilibrium concentrations of the buffering species are essentially equal to the initial concentrations.

---

[169] A buffer solution results: HCN and CN^- are a conjugate pair.

[170] The common ion effect and LeChatelier's Principle fail if the pair is not a conjugate pair.

a. pH determination for buffers

The pH of a buffer solution can simply be calculated by using this relationship

$$\left[H_3O^+ \right]_{eq} = K_a \times \frac{\left[HA \right]_{eq}}{\left[A^- \right]_{eq}}$$

which is just a rearrangement of the K_a expression. As discussed above, the major player in the value of $[H_3O^+]_{eq}$ (and therefore, the pH) is the K_a term. The K_a magnitude sets the vertical positioning of the buffer region on a plot, as we saw in Figure 20-1. Then, the ratio of the two components, $[HA]/[A^-]$ controls where on the flat region of the plot the solution exists.

Example 20-3.

Calculate the pH of a buffer that is 0.040 M in acetic acid and 0.12 M in acetate ion.

Solution:

We find the K_a of acetic acid, 1.75×10^{-5}, in Table 19-6. We know that

$$\left[H_3O^+ \right]_{eq} = K_a \times \frac{\left[HA \right]_{eq}}{\left[A^- \right]_{eq}}$$

and we know that $[HA]_{eq} = [HA]_{orig}$ and $[A^-]_{eq} = [A^-]_{orig}$.

We substitute our values:

$$\left[H_3O^+ \right]_{eq} = 1.75 \times 10^{-5} \times \frac{0.040 \ M}{0.12 \ M}$$

$$\left[H_3O^+ \right]_{eq} = 5.83 \times 10^{-6} \ M = 5.8 \times 10^{-6} \ M$$

$$pH = -\log(5.83 \times 10^{-6}) = 5.23$$

Important: we could solve buffer pH problems in the same way that we solved weak acid and weak base problems. Here is what we would do:

Choose a reaction equation to head the equilibrium table. The weak acid ionization reaction works best:

	$CH_3CO_2H(aq) + H_2O(\ell) \rightleftharpoons$		$CH_3CO_2^-(aq)$	+	$H_3O^+(aq)$
Initial M	0.040		0.12		0
Change M	−x	Pure liquid	+x		+x
Equilibrium M	0.040 − x		0.12 + x		x

Solve for x using the K_a expression:

$$1.75 \times 10^{-5} = \frac{\left[A^- \right]_{eq}\left[H_3O^+ \right]_{eq}}{\left[HA \right]_{eq}} = \frac{(0.12 + x)(x)}{(0.040 - x)}$$

The solver determines that $x = 5.832 \times 10^{-6}$.

So $\left[H_3O^+ \right]_{eq} = x = 5.83 \times 10^{-6}\,M$ and $pH = -\log\left(5.832 \times 10^{-6} \right) = 5.23$ SAME ANSWER!

Notice, particularly, that $\left[A^- \right]_{eq} = (0.12 + x) = 0.12 + 5.832 \times 10^{-6} = 0.12\,M$

And, $\left[HA \right]_{eq} = (0.040 - x) = 0.040 - 5.832 \times 10^{-6} = 0.040\,M$

The amount of ionization, $5.83 \times 10^{-6}\,M$, is not large enough to significantly alter the equilibrium concentrations of the buffering species. (The value of x is insignificant in comparison to both 0.12 and 0.040.) We calculate a pH of 5.23 either way, so we might as well do it the shorter way!

b. pH determination for the special buffer circumstance where [HA] = [A⁻]

Consider the rearranged K_a expression, again:

$$\left[H_3O^+ \right]_{eq} = K_a \times \frac{\left[HA \right]_{eq}}{\left[A^- \right]_{eq}}$$

We see that: $\left[H_3O^+ \right]_{eq} = K_a$ whenever $\left[A^- \right]_{eq} = \left[HA \right]_{eq}$.

In that case: $-\log\left[H_3O^+ \right]_{eq} = -\log K_a$ and $pH = pK_a$

This means, that for a particular buffering pair, the pH of a buffer solution will be equal to the pK_a of the weak acid component whenever the buffer contains equal concentrations of the two components. Consider Figure 20-1 again. The middle point in the buffer region of those plots is the point where the solution components are 50% weak acid and 50% conjugate base. At this point, for either buffering system, the weak acid and weak base have the same concentrations. Remember, in point 3 of the analysis of Figure 20-1, we concluded that the pH of the middle point was equal to the pK_a of the weak acid component of the buffer!

Exercise 20-3.

Consider a mythical buffering pair, HA and A⁻, where the K_a of HA is 1.0×10^{-5}. Calculate the pH range of the buffer region by answering the following.

    a. Calculate the pH of a solution of HA and A⁻ when [HA] = [A⁻]. This is the middle of the buffer range.

    b. Calculate the pH of a solution of HA and A⁻ when [HA] / [A⁻] = 10/1. This is the acidic end of the buffer range.

    c. Calculate the pH of a solution of HA and A⁻ when [HA] / [A⁻] = 1/10. This is the basic end of the buffer range.

    Consider the results of your work in Exercise 20-3. The pH range of a buffer region is 2 pH units, and this region is centered at the pK_a of the weak acid. Thus, we could say that the *buffer region is ± 1 pH unit from the pKₐ*.

Example 20-4.

Calculate the pH of a buffer that is 0.12 M in both acetic acid and acetate ion.

Solution:

From Table 19-6, K_a of acetic acid is 1.75×10^{-5} and $\left[H_3O^+ \right]_{eq} = K_a \times \dfrac{\left[HA \right]_{eq}}{\left[A^- \right]_{eq}}$.

We substitute our values:

$$\left[H_3O^+ \right]_{eq} = 1.75 \times 10^{-5} \times \frac{0.12\ M}{0.12\ M}$$

$$\left[H_3O^+ \right]_{eq} = 1.75 \times 10^{-5}\ M$$

$$pH = -\log(1.75 \times 10^{-5}) = 4.76 = pK_{a\ (acetic\ acid)}$$

In summary: It is much simpler to determine the pH of a buffer solution than of a weak acid or weak base solution; there is no need to use an equilibrium table.

Exercise 20-4.

Use the relationship $\left[H_3O^+ \right]_{eq} = K_a \times \dfrac{\left[HA \right]_{eq}}{\left[A^- \right]_{eq}}$

to determine the pH of each of the following buffer solutions.

   a. A buffer that is 0.42 M in both HClO and ClO⁻.
   b. A buffer that is 0.20 M in HClO and 0.15 M in ClO⁻.
   c. A buffer that is 0.060 M in both formic acid and formate ion.
   d. A buffer that is 0.060 M in formic acid and 0.14 M in formate ion.

---

2. The Henderson-Hasselbalch Equation

The Henderson-Hasselbalch equation is an algebraic rearrangement of the K_a expression. It is often used for the calculation of pH problems, though the calculation is really no different than using

$$\left[H_3O^+ \right]_{eq} = K_a \times \frac{\left[HA \right]_{eq}}{\left[A^- \right]_{eq}}$$

Nonetheless, it is important to know about the Henderson-Hasselbalch equation because it is so widely used, especially in the biological and biochemical sciences. Here is the derivation of the Henderson-Hasselbalch equation. It is a good idea to be able to derive it, because relying on memorizing it leads to many mistakes.

$$\left[H_3O^+\right]_{eq} = K_a \times \frac{\left[HA\right]_{eq}}{\left[A^-\right]_{eq}}$$

Take –log of both sides:

$$-\log\left[H_3O^+\right]_{eq} = -\log K_a - \log\left(\frac{\left[HA\right]_{eq}}{\left[A^-\right]_{eq}}\right)$$

Convert to power functions:

$$pH = pK_a - \log\left(\frac{\left[HA\right]_{eq}}{\left[A^-\right]_{eq}}\right)$$

Rearrange the ratio in order to convert a subtraction into an addition:

$$pH = pK_a + \log\left(\frac{\left[A^-\right]_{eq}}{\left[HA\right]_{eq}}\right)$$

The boxed result is the **Henderson-Hasselbalch Equation**. Using it to determine the pH of a buffer solution is essentially the same as using the equation from which it was derived. It simply puts the step of taking the "–log" earlier in the calculation. Of course, like any equation, these equations can be used in other ways as well. For instance, if you know the pH of a solution of a particular weak acid (and its pK_a), you can use this equation to determine the ratio of the ionized to unionized forms of the weak acid molecule.

Example 20-5.

Use the Henderson-Hasselbalch equation to determine the pH of a buffer when the pK_a of the weak acid is 4.80, and the buffer includes 0.12 M HA and 0.46 M A⁻.

Solution:

We substitute known values into the Henderson-Hasselbalch equation:

$$pH = 4.80 + \log\left(\frac{0.46\,M}{0.12\,M}\right) = 5.35$$

The use of the Henderson-Hasselbalch equation instead of the K_a expression is really a matter of convenience. Because much information about acids, bases, and their solutions is communicated in the form of power functions (pH, pK_a) instead of the root numbers ($[H_3O^+]$, K_a), the Henderson-Hasselbalch equation can save the effort of obtaining the needed values. Additionally, it is sometimes more convenient to use a ratio of moles instead of a ratio of molarities in these expressions, as shown in the following equations.

$$\left[H_3O^+\right]_{eq} = K_a \times \left(\frac{moles\ HA}{moles\ A^-}\right) \quad or \quad pH = pK_a + \log\left(\frac{moles\ A^-}{moles\ HA}\right)$$

Utilizing "moles" instead of "molarities" is mathematically equivalent because the two components, HA and A⁻ are in the same solution, so both are at the same volume. Because concentrations are $\frac{moles}{volume}$, a ratio of two concentrations is the same as a ratio of moles when both species are in the same solution.

Exercise 20-5.

Use the Henderson-Hasselbalch equation to solve the following problems.

    a. Determine the pH of a buffer that is 0.24 M HClO and 0.20 M ClO⁻.

    b. Determine the K_a of an acid buffer component that gives a solution of pH 6.50 when the base component is present at twice the mole amount as the acid component.

    c. Determine the pH of a buffer made by dissolving 0.0032 moles ammonium nitrate and 0.0020 moles ammonia in 100.0 mL of solution.

    d. Histidine is an amino acid with a basic side chain that can become protonated under acidic enough conditions. The pK_a of the protonated side chain is about 6.1. (i) Determine the ratio of deprotonated histidine side chains (*his*) to protonated histidine side chains (*hisH⁺*) in a cell whose pH is 7.4. (ii) What percent of the sidechains are protonated at pH 7.4?

If you really want to see how all of this works together, try solving the problems above by using the K_a expression instead of the Henderson-Hasselbalch equation. Which method do you prefer?

E. Changes to a buffer solution upon the addition of strong acid or strong base

    Buffer solutions are able to minimize changes in pH upon the addition of small amounts of strong acid or strong base. But, the pH does change in a predictable fashion. If a strong acid is added to a buffer the pH drops and if a strong base is added to a buffer the pH increases. In either case it is important to be able to write the balanced reaction equation for the reaction that occurs when the strong acid or base is added (see section 20-1C2). It is also important to be able to construct a stoichiometry table to describe the addition of strong acid or strong base to a buffer, as this will lead to an understanding of the degree to which the buffer solution is altered.

1. Addition of strong acid (small amount) to a buffer

    When a strong acid (H_3O^+) is added to an HA/A⁻ buffer, the strong acid reacts with the weak base component of the buffer in a reaction that goes essentially to completion:

$$H_3O^+(aq) + A^-(aq) \rightleftharpoons H_2O(\ell) + HA(aq)$$

Notice that (if H_3O^+ is the limiting reagent) this reaction converts *some* of the weak base buffer component into the weak acid component. The resulting solution under these circumstances will still be a buffer solution, but the pH will be lower because the relative proportions of the weak acid and weak base buffering components will be changed. Return to a consideration of Figure 20-1. As long as the resulting solution maintains an HA/A⁻ ratio between 1/10 (0.10) and 10/1 (10), the solution will not undergo a major change in pH!

    Consider the addition of 0.00040 moles of strong acid to a buffer solution containing 0.0025 moles of each component, HA and A⁻. The initial buffer has an A⁻ to HA ratio of 1.0, which places it exactly in the middle of the flat buffer region in a graph such as those in Figure 20-1. Buffers such as this one are able to handle modest additions of either strong acid or strong base because there is a reasonably extensive region of minimal pH changes on both the more acidic and the more basic side of the starting solution.

    In the case of the addition of strong acid, the buffer offers a base that is a stronger base than water so that the A⁻ takes the proton from the strong acid instead of water. We say that the strong acid reacts with the best base available, and that is the weak base of the buffering pair. Because the reaction that occurs involves a strong acid, it goes *essentially* to completion. We can use a stoichiometry table to determine the final moles of each substance[171] based on the concept of limiting reagents. We use the balanced reaction equation as the headings for the columns of the stoichiometry table:

	$H_3O^+(aq)$	+ $A^-(aq)$	$\longrightarrow$ $HA(aq)$	+ $H_2O(\ell)$
Initial moles	0.00040	0.0025	0.0025	
change	−0.00040	−0.00040	+0.00040	Pure liquid
Final moles	0	0.0021	0.0029	

Note that in a stoichiometry table, the limiting reagent *defines* the amount of reaction that will occur; see the row labeled "change." The top row of the table, above, indicates that the strong acid is the limiting reagent. When the "final moles" row (green cells) is analyzed, we see that the resulting solution is a buffer solution. Two components are present, A^- and HA. Their mole ratio has changed from

$$\frac{0.0025\ HA}{0.0025\ A^-} = 1.0 \qquad \text{to} \qquad \frac{0.0029\ HA}{0.0021\ A^-} = 1.38$$

well within the requirements of a buffer solution.[172] This new buffer composition has a lower pH because the HA component is in larger supply. When the ratio HA/A⁻ increases, the $[H_3O^+]$ increases, and the pH decreases.

2. Addition of strong base (small amount) to a buffer

When a strong base (OH⁻) is added to an HA/A⁻ buffer, the strong base reacts with the best acid present. That is the weak acid component of the buffer, not water molecules! The reaction goes essentially to completion, driven by the strong base:

$$OH^-(aq) + HA(aq) \rightleftharpoons H_2O(\ell) + A^-(aq)$$

Notice that (if OH⁻ is the limiting reagent) this reaction converts *some* of the weak acid buffer component into the weak base component. The resulting solution is still a buffer solution, but the pH is *higher* than the original buffer because the relative proportions of the weak acid and weak base buffering components are changed. Consider the addition of 0.00040 moles of strong base to a buffer containing 0.0030 moles of each component, HA and A⁻. Again, we use the reaction that occurs as the column headings for a stoichiometry table:

	$OH^-(aq)$	+ $HA(aq)$	$\longrightarrow$ $A^-(aq)$	+ $H_2O(\ell)$
Initial moles	0.00040	0.0030	0.0030	
change	−0.00040	−0.00040	+0.00040	Pure liquid
Final moles	0	0.0026	0.0034	

In the top row of the table, we see that the strong base is the limiting reagent; thus it controls the amount of reaction that occurs. Analysis of the bottom line (green) shows that the resulting solution

---

[171] Stoichiometry tables must feature a reaction that "goes to completion" or at least a reaction that we are treating "as if it goes to completion."

[172] Remember that a buffer solution requires the ratio to be between 10 and 0.1 (or 10/1 and 1/10).

is still a buffer solution; only HA and A⁻ are present, there is no leftover strong base. The relative proportions of the buffering components have changed from

$$\frac{0.0030\ HA}{0.0030\ A^-}=1.0 \qquad \text{to} \qquad \frac{0.0026\ HA}{0.0034\ A^-}=0.76$$

Because 0.76 is between 0.1 and 10, this is still a buffer solution. When the ratio HA/ A⁻ decreases, the [H₃O⁺] decreases, and the pH increases.

3. Addition of strong acid and base do not always result in a new buffer solution

In the two sections above we considered the effects of adding a *small amount* of strong acid or base to a buffer solution. This results in a slightly changed buffer solution, with a minimally changed pH. This is the basis upon which a buffer solution does its job. But, if larger amounts of strong acid or base are added to a buffer solution, it is possible to overwhelm the buffering ability of the solution. Two possibilities exist:

- a. a **stoichiometric**[173] amount of strong acid or base is added, so as to just use up one of the buffer components; or
- b. an excess amount of strong acid or base is added, so that some is left over.

In either of these cases, the change in pH that occurs for the buffer solution is still readily predictable: add a strong acid and the pH decreases, add a strong base and the pH increases. But in the case of additions that overwhelm the buffer solution, the pH changes are more significant. In these cases the end result is no longer a buffer solution.

<u>a.</u> <u>Consider the following stoichiometric possibilities</u>

- Addition of 0.0025 moles of strong acid to a buffer that contains 0.0025 moles of each component, HA and A⁻. The strong acid reacts with the base partner of the conjugate pair. A stoichiometry table for this addition is provided here:

	$H_3O^+(aq)$ +	$A^-(aq)$ ⟶	$HA(aq)$ +	$H_2O(\ell)$
Initial moles	0.0025	0.0025	0.0025	
change	−0.0025	−0.0025	+0.0025	Pure liquid
Final moles	0	0	0.0050	

The bottom line (green) shows that the resulting solution contains only a weak acid. There is no conjugate base present because we treated this reaction (that has a large K_{eq}) as if it went all the way to completion. In reality, the reaction does not *quite* go to completion. We know that in an actual solution of weak acid, there will be small amounts of the conjugate base and H₃O⁺ due to the limited ionization of the weak acid. The zeros in the green cells under H₃O⁺ and A⁻ are not quite true! Nonetheless, we have determined that we now have a solution of weak acid, not a buffer solution.

- Addition of 0.0030 moles of strong base to a buffer that contains 0.0030 moles HA and 0.0015 moles of A⁻. The strong base reacts with the acid partner of the conjugate pair. A stoichiometry table is provided here:

---

[173] A stoichiometric amount is exactly the correct number of moles to completely react with another available reactant.

	OH⁻(aq) +	HA(aq) ⟶	A⁻(aq) +	H₂O(ℓ)
Initial moles	0.0030	0.0030	0.0015	
change	−0.0030	−0.0030	+0.0030	Pure liquid
Final moles	0	0	0.0045	

The bottom line (green) shows that the resulting solution contains only a weak base. Again, the zeros in the green cells under OH⁻ and HA are not quite true. The weak base ionizes to place small amounts of OH⁻ and HA into solution (in reality, the reaction in the table doesn't quite go to completion)!

We see in the tables, above, that stoichiometric additions of strong acids or base can transform an original buffer solution into a solution of a weak acid or weak base. This will usually alter the pH in a more significant way than a **sub-stoichiometric** addition.

b. Consider the following additions of excess strong acid or base

- Addition of 0.0030 moles of strong acid to a buffer that contains 0.0025 moles of each component, HA and A⁻. The strong acid reacts with the basic buffer component. A stoichiometry table for this addition is provided below, *notice that the buffer component, A⁻, is now the limiting reactant.*

	H_3O^+(aq) +	A⁻(aq) ⟶	HA(aq) +	H₂O(ℓ)
Initial moles	0.0030	0.0025	0.0025	
change	−0.0025	−0.0025	+0.0025	Pure liquid
Final moles	0.0005	0	0.0050	

The bottom line (green) shows that the resulting solution contains both a strong acid and a weak acid. We classify such a solution as a "strong acid" solution because its pH is usually dictated by the strong acid.

To understand why the weak acid in the resulting solution, above, is unimportant to the pH of the solution, consider the ionization reaction of the weak acid:

$$HA(aq) + H_2O(\ell) \rightleftharpoons A^-(aq) + H_3O^+(aq)$$

Remember that pH is a measure of the concentration of H_3O^+ ions. Under even the best of circumstances, a weak acid does not provide very many H_3O^+ ions. Now, however, there is already a significant number of H_3O^+ ions in the solution, and these cause the ionization equilibrium of the weak acid to shift left, by LeChatelier's Principle. Hence, if a solution contains both a strong acid and a weak acid, usually only the strong acid will contribute significant numbers of H_3O^+ ions.

- Addition of 0.0050 moles of strong base to a buffer that contains 0.0030 moles of HA and 0.0015 moles of A⁻:

	OH⁻(aq) +	HA(aq) ⟶	A⁻(aq) +	H₂O(ℓ)
Initial moles	0.0050	0.0030	0.0015	
change	−0.0030	−0.0030	+0.0030	Pure liquid
Final moles	0.0020	0	0.0045	

Here, the weak acid is the limiting reagent. The bottom line (green) shows that the resulting solution contains both a strong base and a weak base. We classify such a solution as a "strong base" solution because its pH is usually dictated by the strong base.

The presence of a weak base in a solution containing a strong base is usually unimportant. The ionization reaction for the weak base is suppressed in the presence of a strong base due to the significant numbers of OH^- present, which causes the weak base ionization reaction to shift left.

$$A^-(aq) + H_2O(\ell) \rightleftharpoons HA(aq) + OH^-(aq)$$

Excess additions of strong acids and bases change the original buffer solution into a solution of a strong acid or strong base. The pH will be drastically altered. The amount of strong acid or strong base that is "excess" depends on the original make-up of the buffer. Buffers that contain larger original concentrations of the buffer components are said to have a higher **buffer capacity** than buffers with smaller concentrations of components. For example, consider two buffer solutions, one that is 0.10 M in both HClO and ClO^- and one that is 0.50 M in both HClO and ClO^-. These two buffers both have the same pH (same 1:1 ratio of HClO/ClO^-), but the second one will have a considerably larger **buffer capacity**. Its pH will stay more consistent with small additions of strong acids or bases, and it will take five times more strong acid or base to completely overwhelm its buffering ability.

Example 20-6.

Consider each of the following buffer solutions and the circumstance described. Construct a stoichiometry table that describes the changes occurring. Determine if the resulting solution will be a buffer solution, a weak acid solution, a weak base solution, a strong acid solution, or a strong base solution. State the direction of the expected pH change.

a. To a 25.0 mL portion of a buffer that is 0.10 M HClO and 0.10 M ClO^- is added 0.00010 moles of strong base.

b. To a 25.0 mL portion of a buffer that is 0.10 M HClO and 0.10 M ClO^- is added 0.0025 moles of strong acid.

c. To a 25.0 mL portion of a buffer that is 0.10 M HCO_2H and 0.010 M HCO_2^- is added 0.00040 moles of strong base.

d. To a 25.0 mL portion of a buffer that is 0.10 M HCO_2H and 0.010 M HCO_2^- is added 0.00040 moles of strong acid.

Solutions:

a. This buffer contains equal numbers of moles of the buffering components:

$$25.0\ mL \times \frac{1\ L}{1000\ mL} \times \frac{0.10\ mol}{L} = 0.0025\ moles$$

A stoichiometry table can be constructed for the strong base addition:

	$OH^-(aq)$ +	$HClO(aq)$ $\longrightarrow$	$ClO^-(aq)$ +	$H_2O(\ell)$
Initial moles	0.00010	0.0025	0.0025	
change	−0.00010	−0.00010	+0.00010	Pure liquid
Final moles	0	0.0024	0.0026	

Strong base is the limiting reactant, a buffer solution results. The moles of buffering components present in the final solution are found in the green row of the stoichiometry table. The pH increases because the buffer now has a higher proportion of the conjugate base species.

b. This buffer starts out the same as the previous buffer, 0.0025 moles of each component. A stoichiometry table for the strong acid addition can be constructed:

	$H_3O^+(aq)$ +	$ClO^-(aq)$	⟶ $HClO(aq)$ +	$H_2O(\ell)$
Initial moles	0.0025	0.0025	0.0025	
change	−0.0025	−0.0025	+0.0025	Pure liquid
Final moles	0	0	0.0050	

Strong acid has been added in a stoichiometric amount; a weak acid solution results. All ClO⁻ has been converted to HClO, but no strong acid remains in the solution. The pH decreases because the buffer solution has become a weak acid solution.

c. This buffer contains unequal amounts of the buffering components in a 1:10 ratio:

$$25.0\ mL \times \frac{1\ L}{1000\ mL} \times \frac{0.010\ mol\ HCO_2^-}{L} = 0.00025\ moles\ HCO_2^-$$

$$25.0\ mL \times \frac{1\ L}{1000\ mL} \times \frac{0.10\ mol\ HCO_2H}{L} = 0.0025\ moles\ HCO_2H$$

Thus, this solution is at the edge of its buffer region and would not be able to buffer the addition of strong acid because the ratio of the buffering components would then be outside of the 1:10 ratio limits. However, a solution such as this one can buffer the addition of strong base; there is plenty of the weak acid component! We set up a stoichiometry table for the addition of the strong base:

	$OH^-(aq)$ +	$HCO_2H(aq)$	⟶ $HCO_2^-(aq)$ +	$H_2O(\ell)$
Initial moles	0.00040	0.0025	0.00025	
change	−0.00040	−0.00040	+0.00040	Pure liquid
Final moles	0	0.0021	0.00065	

Strong base is the limiting reactant, a buffer solution results. The final solution (green) contains both a weak acid and its conjugate base with an HA/A⁻ ratio of 3.23. The pH increases because more of the weak base (and less of the weak acid) is present.

d. This buffer contains the same starting moles of weak acid and weak base components as the reaction in part c. While 0.00040 moles of strong base was successfully managed by this buffer solution, we have a different result with the addition of the same number of moles of strong acid. We set up a stoichiometry table for the addition of the strong acid:

	$H_3O^+(aq)$ +	$HCO_2^-(aq)$	⟶ $HCO_2H(aq)$ +	$H_2O(\ell)$
Initial moles	0.00040	0.00025	0.0025	
change	−0.00025	−0.00025	+0.00025	Pure liquid
Final moles	0.00015	0	0.00275	

Strong acid is added in excess due to the relatively small amount of the weak base buffer component. The buffer is completely overwhelmed. Strong acid is left-over in the resulting solution and we expect a considerably lower pH. There is also weak acid in the solution (the formic acid) but it cannot contribute any significant acid character because its ionization

$$HCO_2H(aq) + H_2O(\ell) \rightleftharpoons HCO_2^-(aq) + H_3O^+(aq)$$

is suppressed by the strong acid (H_3O^+) present. Therefore, the pH depends on the 0.00015 moles of H_3O^+ present.

Exercise 20-6.

Consider each of the following buffer solutions and the circumstance described. Construct a stoichiometry table that describes the changes occurring. Determine if the resulting solution will be a buffer solution, a weak acid solution, a weak base solution, a strong acid solution, or a strong base solution. State the direction of the expected pH change.

    a. The addition of 0.0010 moles of OH^- to 100.0 mL of a buffer solution that is 0.35 M HCO_2H and 0.15 M HCO_2^-.

    b. The addition of 0.0010 moles of H_3O^+ to 25.0 mL of a buffer solution that is 0.035 M CH_3CO_2H and 0.010 M $CH_3CO_2^-$.

F. Making a Buffer of a Particular pH

    Because the pH of a buffer solution is determined principally by which buffer components one chooses, this turns out to be a crucial decision in making a buffer. It will be best to choose buffering components for which the pK_a of the weak acid is approximately equal to the pH desired for the buffer solution. It is generally <u>unacceptable</u> to use a buffer system whose pK_a is more than a full pH unit from the desired pH because this would necessitate a component ratio larger than 10:1, and solutions with ratios this large are ineffective buffers.[174] A buffer made from equimolar amounts of the weak acid and weak base (a 1:1 ratio) will be able to buffer additions of strong acids and bases equally well.

Example 20-7.

Given the choices in Table 19-6 of Chapter 19, which buffering components would produce a reasonably balanced buffer at pH 7.30?

<u>Solution</u>:

We want to choose a weak acid buffering component with a pK_a close to 7.30. The best choice would be HClO with a K_a of 4.0×10^{-8} and, therefore, a pK_a = 7.40.

Exercise 20-7.

In each case, choose the best buffering components from Table 19-6 in Chapter 19.

    a. A buffer with pH 3.40.   **b.** A buffer with pH 9.30.

---

[174] A more extreme ratio than 10:1 (or 1:10) means you are not working within the pH plateau of the buffer!

Surprisingly, it is rarely practical to make up a buffer based on calculations of expected pH. A buffer produced this way will generally not have *exactly* the desired pH. This is due to some assumptions that we make about the behavior of species in solution that are untrue. For instance, a species present in solution at 0.500 *M* may only *act as if* it is present at 0.422 *M*. We say that solutes behave non-ideally. A full understanding of these issues is not important here, but the result is important:

> *The best way to make a buffer is to dissolve <u>one</u> of the buffering components at the concentration you desire for the total concentration.[175] Then, add a strong acid (if you dissolved the base component), or strong base (if you dissolved the acid component) to this solution until the desired pH is achieved by indication of a pH meter.*

So, if a buffer at pH 7.30 is desired (as in Example 20-7), we could dissolve NaClO, the weak base of the buffer pair, to a concentration of, say, 0.10 *M*. Then, drip in a concentrated strong acid to convert some of the ClO⁻ to HClO:

$$H_3O^+(aq) + ClO^-(aq) \longrightarrow HClO(aq) + H_2O(\ell)$$

As long as the strong acid used is a highly concentrated solution, the volume change that occurs during this addition will not affect the total volume of the solution enough to cause concern. Add the acid slowly, with stirring, while watching the display on a pH meter, so that the addition can be halted when the desired pH is achieved. The final solution is a buffer whose total concentration of ClO⁻ and HClO is 0.10 *M*. If a buffer is desired with a higher buffer capacity, the original solution of NaClO could be 0.40 *M* instead of 0.10 *M*. Again, strong acid can be added until a pH meter registers the desired pH. The pH dictates the ratio of the components, so the solution ends up with the correct ratio. One component was generated *in situ*[176] from the other one.

How can you decide if you should dissolve the weak acid or the weak base component to get started? Either will work, but it is often easiest to start with a salt. Salts are solids that can often be weighed out accurately, to as many significant digits as desired. So, for instance, if you want to make an acetic acid/acetate buffer, you might consider the fact that acetic acid is a liquid, while acetate comes in salt form (sodium acetate, for example). It may be easiest to start with the weak base in this case.

On the other hand, if your buffer pair will be ammonium ion/ammonia, the opposite is true. This time the weak base is a gas and the weak acid comes as a salt (ammonium chloride, for example). You may want to begin with a solution of ammonium ion, and add strong base to convert some of the weak acid into the conjugate base (ammonia), thus creating the buffer solution *in situ*.

$$OH^-(aq) + NH_4^+(aq) \longrightarrow NH_3(aq) + H_2O(\ell)$$

Sometimes both buffer components are salts, such is the case for KH_2PO_4 (potassium dihydrogen phosphate) and K_2HPO_4 (potassium hydrogen phosphate); you could begin making a buffer with either one.

Buffer solutions found in laboratories are rarely labeled with the concentrations of both buffer components. More likely is a label such as "0.10*M* HClO buffer, pH 7.30." The designated concentration (0.10 *M*) is the total concentration of both the weak acid and its conjugate base. Only the word "buffer" indicates that both HClO and ClO⁻ are present in significant amounts. The pH value indicates, indirectly, the relative proportions of the weak acid and conjugate base. In order to be a butter solution, the pH must be within ±1 pH unit of the pK_a of the weak acid.

---

[175] This concentration will depend on the buffer capacity needed.

[176] *in situ* means "in the reaction mixture."

Example 20-8.

Describe the procedure you would use to make 1.0 L of a buffer of pH 5.00 and a total buffer component concentration of 0.20 M. What buffering components would work well? (Choose from the possibilities in Table 19-6.) How would you proceed?

Solution:

The weak acid in Table 19-6 with pK_a closest to 5.00 is acetic acid, so a good buffer pair to choose is the acetic acid/acetate pair. For a 1.0 liter volume of buffer one could weigh out sodium acetate to obtain 0.20 moles of acetate salt.

$$0.20 \ mol \ NaC_2H_3O_2 \times \frac{82.034 \ g \ NaC_2H_3O_2}{1 \ mol \ NaC_2H_3O_2} = 16 \ g \ NaC_2H_3O_2$$

Dissolve this to a total volume of a little less than 1.0 L and drip in concentrated HCl until a pH meter reads 5.00. Add deionized water to bring the volume to 1.0 L, adjusting the pH as necessary.

Exercise 20-8.

Describe the procedure you would use to make 500. mL of a buffer of pH 7.00 and a total buffer component concentration of 0.15 M. What buffering components will you use (Table 19-6). How will you proceed?

20-2. CALCULATION OF PH: STRONG ACID/BASE PLUS WEAK BASE/ACID

We have calculated the pH of a wide variety of solutions: strong acids, strong bases, weak acids, weak bases, and buffers. We have also seen how the addition of a strong acid or base affects buffer composition. In this section, we will revisit many of these skills by addressing, in general, the reactions of a strong acid and a weak base, or a strong base and a weak acid. By altering the relative amounts of the two reactants, a wide variety of situations result. In section 19-4 we studied the *stoichiometric* addition of a strong species to a weak species. We will review that, and add the elements of **non-stoichiometric** additions. In other words, we will consider the circumstances when the strong species is the limiting reagent and when the weak species is the limiting reagent.

We start with a general overview in Table 20-2. We represent a strong acid/weak base reaction as:

$$H_3O^+(aq) + B(aq) \longrightarrow BH^+(aq) + H_2O(\ell)$$

and a strong base/weak acid reaction as:

$$OH^-(aq) + HA(aq) \longrightarrow A^-(aq) + H_2O(\ell)$$

Notice that the use of a single forward arrow in the representation of these reactions is perfectly acceptable. These are reactions with very large equilibrium constants and they can be treated as if they go to completion. This means that the concept of limiting reagents will apply. Table 20-2 outlines each possible outcome for these types of reactions (*stoichiometric* and *non-stoichiometric*). Think about relative mole amounts of substances as you consider each of the six possible results in the boxes of the table. The results listed should seem logical.

Table 20-2. Possible results when strong acids react with weak bases (top) or strong bases react with weak acids (bottom).

$$H_3O^+(aq) + B(aq) \longrightarrow BH^+(aq) + H_2O(\ell)$$

1. If H_3O^+ limits, the result is a buffer solution: some B remains and some BH^+ is formed.	2. If B limits, the result is a strong acid solution; all B is converted to BH^+, H_3O^+ is leftover. The strong acid controls the resulting pH.	3. If stoichiometric, the result is a weak acid solution: all B has been converted to BH^+, all H_3O^+ has been consumed.

$$OH^-(aq) + HA(aq) \longrightarrow A^-(aq) + H_2O(\ell)$$

4. If OH^- limits, the result is a buffer solution: some HA remains and some A^- is formed.	5. If HA limits, the result is a strong base solution; all HA is converted to A^-, OH^- is leftover. The strong base controls the resulting pH.	6. If stoichiometric, the result is a weak base solution: all HA has been converted to A^-, all OH^- has been consumed.

The secret to the successful analysis of problems having to do with strong/weak reaction systems is to remember that the reaction goes (essentially) to completion. This means that the use of a **stoichiometry table** (in units of moles) will be valuable for deciding what type of solution results from a particular reaction system. The six examples that follow represent each of the six numbered boxes in Table 20-2. In each case a three-point procedure is used to analyze the resulting solution:

> 1. Construct a stoichiometry table.
> 2. Interpret the bottom entries of the stoichiometry table to decide if the resulting solution is classified as a strong acid, strong base, weak acid, weak base, or buffer.
> 3. Determine the pH of the resulting solution based on its classification.
>   a. if strong acid or base: find $[H_3O^+]$ or $[OH^-]$ and then pH.
>   b. if weak acid or base: find concentration of the weak species and use an equilibrium table to evaluate pH.
>   c. if a buffer solution: use the equilibrium constant expression (or Henderson Hasselbalch equation) to evaluate pH.

The following examples serve as an excellent review of many of the concepts covered in the study of equilibrium systems and, in particular, acid/base systems. Use these examples to review each of the following:

> Use of **stoichiometry tables**
>   (units of moles, use when the reaction goes essentially to completion).
> Use of **equilibrium tables**
>   (units of molarity, use when the reaction is a reversible reaction).
> Determination of the pH of weak acid or base solutions.
> Determination of the pH of strong acid or base solutions.
> Determination of the pH of a buffer solution.

Example 20-9.

Addition of a sub-stoichiometric amount of strong acid to a weak base, Table 20-2, Box 1.

Calculate the pH of the solution that results from the combining of the following two solutions:

100.0 mL of 0.012 M HCl with 100.0 mL of 0.084 M NH_3.

Solution:

Step 1: First, remember that in an aqueous solution of a strong acid such as HCl, the acid species present will be H_3O^+. A solution described as "100.0 mL of 0.012 M HCl," is really 100.0 mL of 0.012 M H_3O^+. The reaction that occurs can be written:

$$H_3O^+(aq) + NH_3(aq) \longrightarrow NH_4^+(aq) + H_2O(\ell)$$

In order to fill out the stoichiometry table we need to know how many moles of each species are present when we pour the solutions together.

Moles H_3O^+: $0.1000 \, L \times \dfrac{0.012 \, mol \, H_3O^+}{L} = 0.0012 \, mol \, H_3O^+$

Moles NH_3: $0.1000 \, L \times \dfrac{0.084 \, mol \, NH_3}{L} = 0.0084 \, mol \, NH_3$

Stoichiometry Table:

	$H_3O^+(aq)$ +	$NH_3(aq)$	$\longrightarrow NH_4^+(aq)$ +	$H_2O(\ell)$
Initial moles	0.0012	0.0084	0	Pure liquid
change	−0.0012	−0.0012	+0.0012	
Final moles	0	0.0072	0.0012	

Step 2: Analyze the green line of the stoichiometry table to determine the type of solution that results from the reaction. Here we see that the strong acid was the limiting reagent and both NH_3 and NH_4^+ are present after the reaction is completed. These species are a weak base and its conjugate acid in a mole ratio of $\frac{0.0072}{0.0012} = 6.0$. This is a buffer solution.

Step 3: Determine the pH of the buffer solution. We will use the K_a expression for NH_4^+, which is based on the acid ionization reaction:

$$NH_4^+(aq) + H_2O(aq) \rightleftharpoons NH_3(aq) + H_3O^+(aq)$$

So we can write: $K_a = \dfrac{[NH_3]_{eq}[H_3O^+]_{eq}}{[NH_4^+]_{eq}}$

And rearrange to give: $[H_3O^+]_{eq} = K_a \times \dfrac{[NH_4^+]_{eq}}{[NH_3]_{eq}}$

We remember that we can substitute the mole ratio of the buffer components for the concentration ratio and write:

$$[H_3O^+] = K_a \times \frac{moles\ NH_4^+}{moles\ NH_3}$$

The K_a for NH_4^+ is 5.6×10^{-10}; see Table 19-6. Substitution of the known quantities into the equation gives:

$$[H_3O^+] = 5.6 \times 10^{-10} \times \frac{0.0012}{0.0072}$$

$$[H_3O^+] = 9.33 \times 10^{-11} \qquad pH = 10.03$$

Example 20-10.

Addition of an excess amount of strong acid to a weak base, Table 20-2, Box 2.

Calculate the pH of the solution that results from the combining of the following two solutions: 50.0 mL of 0.13 M HCl with 100.0 mL of 0.025 M NH_3.

Solution:

Step 1: The reaction that occurs can be written:

$$H_3O^+(aq) + NH_3(aq) \longrightarrow NH_4^+(aq) + H_2O(\ell)$$

(Remember that an HCl solution is really an H_3O^+ solution.) Set up a stoichiometry table to analyze for the result of the reaction between the strong acid, H_3O^+ and the weak base, NH_3. In order to fill out the table we will need to know how many moles of each species are present when we pour the solutions together.

Moles H$_3$O$^+$: $\quad 0.0500\ L \times \dfrac{0.13\ mol\ H_3O^+}{L} = 0.0065\ mol\ H_3O^+$

Moles NH$_3$: $\quad 0.1000\ L \times \dfrac{0.025\ mol\ NH_3}{L} = 0.0025\ mol\ NH_3$

Stoichiometry Table:

	$H_3O^+(aq) + NH_3(aq) \longrightarrow NH_4^+(aq) + H_2O(\ell)$			
Initial moles	0.0065	0.0025	0	
change	−0.0025	−0.0025	+0.0025	Pure liquid
Final moles	0.0040	0	0.0025	

Step 2: Analyze the green line of the stoichiometry table in order to classify the resulting solution. Here we see that the strong acid, H_3O^+ is left over. The final solution also contains the weak acid, NH_4^+. Solutions containing both a strong acid and a weak acid can generally be classified as strong acid solutions. The pHs of such solutions are determined by the concentration of the strong acid (unless it is present in very small amounts!)

Step 3: Determine the pH of the strong acid solution. We need to know the concentration of the leftover strong acid. Concentration is moles/volume and we assume that the volumes of the two solutions are additive for a total of 150.0 mL:

$$[H_3O^+] = \frac{0.0040 \; moles}{0.1500 \; L} = 2.67 \times 10^{-2} \; M \qquad pH = 1.57$$

Example 20-11.

Addition of a stoichiometric amount of strong acid to a weak base, Table 20-2, Box 3.

Calculate the pH of the solution that results from the combining of the following two solutions: 100.0 mL of 0.012 M HCl with 50.0 mL of 0.024 M NH$_3$.

Solution:

Step 1: The reaction that occurs can be written:

$$H_3O^+(aq) + NH_3(aq) \longrightarrow NH_4^+(aq) + H_2O(aq)$$

(Remember that an HCl solution is really an H$_3$O$^+$ solution.) Set up a stoichiometry table to analyze for the result of the reaction between the strong acid, H$_3$O$^+$ and the weak base, NH$_3$. We determine the moles of strong acid and weak base present:

Moles H$_3$O$^+$: $\quad 0.1000 \; L \times \dfrac{0.012 \; mol \; H_3O^+}{L} = 0.0012 \; mol \; H_3O^+$

Moles NH$_3$: $\quad 0.0500 \; L \times \dfrac{0.024 \; mol \; NH_3}{L} = 0.0012 \; mol \; NH_3$

Stoichiometry Table:

	$H_3O^+(aq) + NH_3(aq) \longrightarrow NH_4^+(aq) + H_2O(\ell)$			
Initial moles	0.0012	0.0012	0	
change	−0.0012	−0.0012	+0.0012	Pure liquid
Final moles	0	0	0.0012	

Step 2: Analyze the green line to determine the type of solution that results from the reaction when *stoichiometric* amounts of reagents were used. Here we see that only the weak acid, NH$_4^+$ is present in the final solution. This solution is a weak acid solution.

Step 3: Determine the pH of the weak acid solution. We use the K$_a$ expression for NH$_4^+$, which is based on the acid ionization reaction:

$$NH_4^+(aq) + H_2O(\ell) \rightleftharpoons NH_3(aq) + H_3O^+(aq)$$

So we can write: $\qquad K_a = \dfrac{[NH_3]_{eq}[H_3O^+]_{eq}}{[NH_4^+]_{eq}}$

The K_a for NH_4^+ is 5.6×10^{-10} (See Table 19-6).

$$5.6 \times 10^{-10} = \frac{[NH_3]_{eq}[H_3O^+]_{eq}}{[NH_4^+]_{eq}}$$

To set up an equilibrium table, in units of molarity, we must determine the concentration of the weak acid in our final solution (assuming additive volumes):

$$[NH_4^+] = \frac{0.0012 \ moles}{0.1500 \ L} = 8.00 \times 10^{-3} \ M$$

Equilibrium Table:

	$NH_4^+(aq) + H_2O(\ell) \rightleftharpoons NH_3(aq) + H_3O^+(aq)$			
Initial M	8.00×10^{-3}	Pure liquid	0	0
Change M	$-x$		$+x$	$+x$
Equilibrium M	$8.00 \times 10^{-3} - x$		x	x

Substitute the equilibrium concentrations into the equilibrium constant expression:

$$5.6 \times 10^{-10} = \frac{x^2}{8.00 \times 10^{-3} - x}$$

Using the solver function of a calculator yields:

$$x = 2.12 \times 10^{-6} \ M = [H_3O^+] \qquad pH = 5.67$$

Example 20-12.

Addition of a sub-stoichiometric amount of strong base to a weak acid, Table 20-2, Box 4.

Calculate the pH of the solution that results from the combining of the following two solutions:

100.0 mL of 0.026 M NaOH with 100.0 mL of 0.044 M CH$_3$CO$_2$H.

Solution:

Step 1: Set up a stoichiometry table to analyze for the result of the reaction between the strong base, OH⁻ and the weak acid, CH$_3$CO$_2$H. The reaction that occurs can be written:

$$OH^-(aq) \ + \ CH_3CO_2H(aq) \ \longrightarrow \ CH_3CO_2^-(aq) \ + \ H_2O(\ell)$$

In order to fill out the table we need to know how many moles of each species are present when we pour the solutions together.

Moles OH⁻: $0.1000 \ L \times \dfrac{0.026 \ mol \ OH^-}{L} = 0.0026 \ mol \ OH^-$

Moles CH$_3$CO$_2$H: $0.1000 \ L \times \dfrac{0.044 \ mol \ CH_3CO_2H}{L} = 0.0044 \ mol \ CH_3CO_2H$

Stoichiometry Table:

	$OH^-(aq) + CH_3CO_2H(aq) \longrightarrow CH_3CO_2^-(aq) + H_2O(\ell)$			
Initial moles	0.0026	0.0044	0	
change	−0.0026	−0.0026	+0.0026	Pure liquid
Final moles	0	0.0018	0.0026	

Step 2: Analyze the green line to determine the type of solution that results from the reaction. Here we see that the strong base is the limiting reagent, so that both acetic acid and acetate ion are present in the final solution. With an HA to A⁻ ratio of $\frac{0.0018}{0.0026} = 0.7$, this is a buffer solution.

Step 3: Determine the pH of the buffer solution. We use the K_a expression for CH_3CO_2H, which is based on the acid ionization reaction:

$$CH_3CO_2H(aq) + H_2O(\ell) \rightleftharpoons CH_3CO_2^-(aq) + H_3O^+(aq)$$

We write:
$$K_a = \frac{[CH_3CO_2^-]_{eq}[H_3O^+]_{eq}}{[CH_3CO_2H]_{eq}}$$

And rearrange to give:
$$[H_3O^+]_{eq} = K_a \times \frac{[CH_3CO_2H]_{eq}}{[CH_3CO_2^-]_{eq}}$$

We substitute the mole ratio of the buffer components for the concentration ratio and write:

$$[H_3O^+] = K_a \times \frac{moles\ CH_3CO_2H}{moles\ CH_3CO_2^-}$$

The K_a for CH_3CO_2H is 1.75×10^{-5} (See Table 19-6).
Substitution of the known quantities into the equation gives:

$$[H_3O^+] = 1.75 \times 10^{-5} \times \frac{0.0018}{0.0026}$$

$$[H_3O^+] = 1.212 \times 10^{-5} \qquad pH = 4.92$$

Example 20-13.

Addition of an excess amount of strong base to a weak acid, Table 20-2, Box 5.

Calculate the pH of the solution that results from the combining of the following two solutions:

75.0 mL of 0.220 M KOH with 50.0 mL of 0.280 M HF.

Solution:

Step 1: The reaction that occurs can be written:

$$OH^-(aq) + HF(aq) \longrightarrow F^-(aq) + H_2O(\ell)$$

Set up a stoichiometry table to analyze for the result of the reaction between the strong base, OH⁻ and the weak acid, HF. In order to fill out the table we will need to know how many moles of each species are present when we pour the solutions together.

$$\text{Moles OH}^-: \quad 0.0750\,L \times \frac{0.220\,mol\,OH^-}{L} = 0.0165\,mol\,OH^-$$

$$\text{Moles HF:} \quad 0.0500\,L \times \frac{0.280\,mol\,HF}{L} = 0.0140\,mol\,HF$$

Stoichiometry Table:

	$OH^-(aq) + HF(aq) \longrightarrow F^-(aq) + H_2O(\ell)$			
Initial moles	0.0165	0.0140	0	
change	−0.0140	−0.0140	+0.0140	Pure liquid
Final moles	0.0025	0	0.0140	

Step 2: Analyze the green line in order to classify the resulting solution. Here we see that the strong base, OH⁻ is left over. The final solution also contains the weak base, F⁻. As with acids, the pH of any solution containing both a strong base and a weak base will be determined by the concentration of the strong base. The weak base will not contribute to the overall basicity of the solution because of the suppression of its ionization by the strong base already present.

Step 3: Determine the pH of the strong base solution. We need to know the concentration of the leftover strong base. Assume that the volumes of the two solutions are additive for a total of 125.0 mL:

$$[OH^-] = \frac{0.0025\,moles}{0.1250\,L} = 2.00 \times 10^{-2}\,M$$

$$pOH = 1.70, \text{ thus } pH = 14.00 - 1.70 = 12.30$$

Example 20-14.

Addition of a stoichiometric amount of strong base to a weak acid, Table 20-2, Box 6.

Calculate the pH of the solution that results from the combining of the following two solutions:

250.0 mL of 0.12 M KOH with 125.0 mL of 0.24 M HClO.

Solution:

Step 1: The reaction that occurs can be written:

$$OH^-(aq) + HClO(aq) \longrightarrow ClO^-(aq) + H_2O(\ell)$$

Set up a stoichiometry table to analyze for the result of the reaction between the strong base, OH⁻ and the weak acid, HClO. In order to fill out the table we will need to know how many moles of each species are present when we pour the solutions together.

$$\text{Moles OH}^-: \quad 0.2500\,L \times \frac{0.12\,mol\,OH^-}{L} = 0.0300\,mol\,OH^-$$

$$\text{Moles HClO:} \quad 0.1250\,L \times \frac{0.24\,mol\,HClO}{L} = 0.0300\,mol\,HClO$$

Stoichiometry Table:

	$OH^-(aq) + HClO(aq) \longrightarrow ClO^-(aq) + H_2O(\ell)$			
Initial moles	0.0300	0.0300	0	
change	−0.0300	−0.0300	+0.0300	Pure liquid
Final moles	0	0	0.0300	

Step 2: Analyze the green line in order to classify the resulting solution. Here we see that only the weak base, ClO⁻ is present in the final solution. This solution is a weak base solution.

Step 3: Determine the pH of the weak base solution. We use the K_b expression for ClO⁻, whose base ionization reaction is:

$$ClO^-(aq) + H_2O(\ell) \rightleftharpoons HClO(aq) + OH^-(aq)$$

We can write:

$$K_b = \frac{[HClO]_{eq}[OH^-]_{eq}}{[ClO^-]_{eq}}$$

We look up the K_b for the hypochlorite ion (Table 19-6) and substitute it into the equation:

$$2.5 \times 10^{-7} = \frac{[HClO]_{eq}[OH^-]_{eq}}{[ClO^-]_{eq}}$$

To set up an equilibrium table, in units of molarity, we must determine the concentration of the weak base in the bottom line solution from the stoichiometry table. We assume additive volumes in this work:

$$[ClO^-] = \frac{0.0300\ moles}{0.3750\ L} = 8.00 \times 10^{-2}\ M$$

Equilibrium Table:

	$ClO^-(aq) + H_2O(\ell) \rightleftharpoons HClO(aq) + OH^-(aq)$			
Initial M	8.00×10^{-2}		0	0
Change M	−x	Pure liquid	+x	+x
Equilibrium M	$8.00 \times 10^{-2} - x$		x	x

Substitute the equilibrium concentrations into the equilibrium constant expression:

$$2.5 \times 10^{-7} = \frac{x^2}{8.00 \times 10^{-2} - x}$$

Using the solver function of a calculator yields:

$$x = 1.413 \times 10^{-4}\ M = [OH^-]$$
$$pOH = 3.850,\ thus\ pH = 14.00 - 3.850 = 10.15$$

At this point we have addressed methods for calculating the pH of most types of solutions normally encountered in acid-base chemistry. Be sure to notice that it is the result of the stoichiometry table that steers the rest of the work. You must begin the problem without yet being aware of the complete path of the necessary calculations.

In section 20-1E, we did not show calculations of the pH values of solutions that resulted from the addition of strong acids or bases to buffer solutions. But, if desired, the same three point techniques introduced above can be applied to these problems. You will recall that we set up the stoichiometry tables and analyzed the bottom lines with respect to the important species present. All that was left to do is the final determination of pH of the buffer solution, the weak acid or base solution, or the strong acid or base solution. Success with the following Exercise should demonstrate that one has a very good grasp on acid-base pH determinations, even for instances for which a complete Example problem has not been provided.

Exercise 20-9.

Calculate the final pH of the solution that results when 3.0 mL of 12 M HCl is added to 100.0 mL of a buffer that is 0.070 M in both HCO_2H and HCO_2^-. (HINT: because the conjugate acid of the weak base reactant is already present at the beginning of the reaction, it must be accounted for in the top line of your stoichiometry table.)

Table 20-3 reviews all the types of solutions for which pH calculations have been addressed. Notice that the sixth entry has been altered from previous versions of this table (Chapters 18 and 19 have versions of this table). The sixth entry now includes all possibilities for the addition of a strong acid or base to a weak base or acid, not just at stoichiometric amounts.

Table 20-3: pH Calculation Summary		
1	strong acid solution, H_3O^+	Use [strong acid] = [H_3O^+], and pH = −log [H_3O^+]	Chap 18-4B
2	strong base solution, OH^-	Use [OH^-] = [strong base], or [OH^-] = 2 × [strong base] (depending on the strong base); then pOH = −log [OH^-] , then pH = 14 − pOH.	Chap 18-4B
3	strong acid + strong base	Use stoichiometry table to determine composition of final solution (could be strong acid, strong base, or neutral) then find pH as indicated in Table entries 1 and 2, above.	Chap 18-4E
4	weak acid solution, HA	Use equilibrium table (in terms of x) and K_a expression to find [H_3O^+], then pH = −log [H_3O^+].	Chap 19-3C
5	weak base solution, A^-	Use equilibrium table (in terms of x) and K_b expression to find [OH^-], then pOH = −log [OH^-] , then pH = 14 − pOH.	Chap 19-3D
6	additions of strong acid + weak base	Use stoichiometry table to determine composition of final solution: if strong acid limits, get a buffer solution if weak base limits, get a strong acid solution if addition is stoichiometric, get a weak acid solution. Determine the pH of the final solution using established methods from the rest of this table.	Chaps 19-4, 20-2
	Additions of strong base + weak acid	Use stoichiometry table to determine composition of final solution: if strong base limits, get a buffer solution if weak acid limits, get a strong base solution if addition is stoichiometric, get a weak base solution. Determine the pH of the final solution using established methods from the rest of this table.	Chaps 19-4, 20-2

7	buffer solution HA/A⁻	Use K_a expression, or Henderson-Hasselbalch equation.	Chap 20-1D
8	HA/A⁻ buffer with added strong acid: $H_3O^+ + A^-$	Use stoichiometry table to determine make-up of final solution if strong acid limits, solution remains a buffer if weak base component limits, get strong acid solution if stoichiometric addition, get a weak acid (HA) solution *[Determine the pH of the final solution using established methods from the rest of this table.]*	Chap 20-1E
	HA/A⁻ buffer with added strong base: $OH^- + HA$	Use stoichiometry table to determine make-up of final solution if strong base limits, solution remains a buffer if weak acid component limits, get strong base solution if stoichiometric addition, get a weak base (A⁻) solution *[Determine the pH of the final solution using established methods from the rest of this table.]*	Chap 20-1E

20-3. ACID-BASE TITRATIONS

Titrations are a common analytical tool used to determine the amount of a dissolved species in solution. In a titration, one reactant at a known concentration is added dropwise (usually from a buret) into a solution of an unknown number of moles of a second reactant. The volume of the first reactant required to completely react with the unknown moles of the second reactant allows the calculation of the moles of the second reactant, as long as the balanced reaction equation is known. A wide variety of chemical reactions can be used for titrations, but one common titration type is the acid-base titration. Over the course of an acid-base titration many different types of solutions may exist: weak acid and weak base solutions, strong acid and strong base solutions, and buffer solutions.

A. Introduction and Terms

Titration is a quantitative analytical technique. This means that it attempts to answer numerical questions about a sample. In particular, titration can inform the researcher about the amount of a particular species in a solution. Acids and bases lend themselves to analysis by titration because:

1. they are soluble in water,
2. the reactions between them are well documented,
3. the reactions are generally very fast, and
4. at least some acids and bases can be placed into solution at an accurately known concentration.

Figure 20-2 introduces the apparatus used in typical titration experiments. A solution whose concentration is accurately known is called a **standard solution**. The standard solution is used as the analytical tool and is usually placed in the buret. The solution in the buret is called the **titrant**. In an acid-base titration, the titrant is always a strong acid or base. The solution to be analyzed is usually placed in the titration flask, under the buret. This solution can be a strong acid, strong base, weak acid or weak base. In the language of titration, the phrase "solution A was titrated with solution B" indicates that a solution of A of unknown concentration is in the flask and a standard solution of B is in the buret.

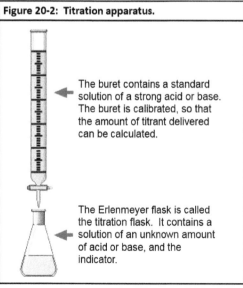

Figure 20-2: Titration apparatus.

The buret contains a standard solution of a strong acid or base. The buret is calibrated, so that the amount of titrant delivered can be calculated.

The Erlenmeyer flask is called the titration flask. It contains a solution of an unknown amount of acid or base, and the indicator.

Successful titrations depend on the presence of some kind of signal to tell the researcher when enough titrant has been added from the buret to the flask so that the reaction is complete, with no leftover reagents. For instance, in the case of the titration of 50.00 mL of an NaOH solution of unknown concentration with a 0.4500 M HCl solution, we want to stop the titration when the HCl addition has completely neutralized the NaOH solution, but no excess HCl has been added. At this point, called the **equivalence point**[177] of the titration, the reaction between the two species:

$$H_3O^+(aq) + OH^-(aq) \longrightarrow 2H_2O(\ell)$$

is complete with no leftover reactants of either type. Assuming that it is possible to identify the equivalence point, the researcher can determine how many moles of H_3O^+ were delivered for the neutralization by noting the volume used from the buret. If the volume used was 45.58 mL, the researcher calculates the moles of acid used:

$$45.58\ mL \times \frac{1\ L}{1000\ mL} \times \frac{0.4500\ mol\ H_3O^+}{L} = 2.051 \times 10^{-2}\ mol\ H_3O^+$$

Because the acid reacts in a one-to-one mole ratio with the base, the researcher knows that the amount of OH^- present in the original solution in the flask was also 2.051×10^{-2} moles. Therefore, the original concentration of the base can be established by dividing the moles of the base present by the <u>original</u> volume of the base solution:

$$[OH^-] = \frac{2.051 \times 10^{-2}\ mol}{0.05000\ L} = 0.4102\ M$$

An **indicator** molecule usually provides the signal used for identifying the **equivalence point** in acid-base titrations. The indicator is a substance whose color changes at, or very near, the equivalence point of the titration. The point at which the indicator changes color is known as the **end point** of the titration. More on indicators will be presented later in the chapter. For now, we will just point out the distinction between two similar terms:

> ### Equivalence point versus End point

The **equivalence point** of a titration is the point at which a stoichiometric amount of titrant has been added to the titration flask. Unfortunately, no indicator molecule can possibly "know" when this has exactly been achieved. Careful selection of an indicator can ensure that its color change will coincide closely with the equivalence point of the titration. The **end point** of a titration is the point identified by the color change of the indicator. A poorly planned titration might reach its end point (color change) significantly before (or after) the equivalence point. The trick is to choose an indicator whose color change will correspond very closely with the expected equivalence point. The end point and the equivalence point of a well-planned titration will coincide closely enough that the researcher need not be concerned about the difference.

To summarize:

> **Equivalence point:** *the theoretical point of stoichiometric equivalence for the reactants.*
> **End point:** *the point at which the indicator signals to stop the titration; this signal must coincide well with the equivalence point if the experiment is to succeed.*

---

[177] At this point the moles of acid and the moles of base are equivalent.

Example 20-15.

Determine the original concentration of acetic acid in vinegar if a 50.00 mL sample of vinegar is titrated with 0.998 M NaOH and the end point is reached after the addition of 41.88 mL of the base.

Solution:

The titration reaction is between acetic acid and hydroxide ion:

$$OH^-(aq) \ + \ HOAc(aq) \ \longrightarrow \ OAc^-(aq) \ + \ H_2O(\ell)$$

If we determine the moles of hydroxide used in the reaction, we will know the moles of acetic acid originally present in the vinegar; they react in a 1:1 mole ratio.

$$\frac{0.998 \ mol \ OH^-}{L} \times 0.04188 \ L = 0.04179 \ mol \ OH^-$$

So, the original moles of HOAc was also 0.04179 moles. The original concentration of acetic acid in the vinegar is the moles acid found in a particular volume of vinegar:

$$[HOAc] = \frac{0.04179 \ moles}{0.05000 \ L} = 0.836 \ M$$

Exercise 20-10.

Calculate the original concentration of NaOCl in a solution if a 25.00 mL sample is titrated with 1.093 M HCl and the end point occurs after the addition of 20.64 mL titrant.

B. pH Plots of Titration Data

During an acid-base titration, the pH of the solution being analyzed changes continually as the titrant is added. Graphs of pH changes (y-axis) versus the volume of added tritrant (x-axis), often called **titrations curves** or **pH plots**, can help us think about these changes. The shapes of titration curves vary depending on the details of a particular titration.

In order to understand the shapes of these plots we will focus on five attributes:

① the original pH, before any titrant is added,

② the pH at the **half-equivalence point** of the titration (when half of the stoichiometric amount of titrant has been added),

③ the pH at the **equivalence point** of the titration (when a stoichiometric amount of titrant has been added),

④ the pH well beyond the equivalence point, and

⑤ the length of the horizontal region of the plot, especially the volume of titrant necessary to the reach the equivalence point.

1. Titration Curve for the Titration of a Strong Acid with a Strong Base

We start our analyses by focusing on the titration of a strong acid with a strong base; see Figure 20-3. The five attributes of the curve are highlighted on the plot according to the numbers in the list above.

① The pH of the original solution of strong acid is very low, and depends only on the concentration of that strong acid solution. For any solution of strong acid at a concentration of 0.1 *M* or higher, the pH will be 1.0 or below.

② The pH at the half-equivalence point is only slightly higher than the original pH. Note that the **half-equivalence point** is defined as the point along the *x*-axis that is exactly halfway to the equivalence point. At this point the solution in the titration flask is still a solution of a strong acid. Referring to the titration reaction equation:

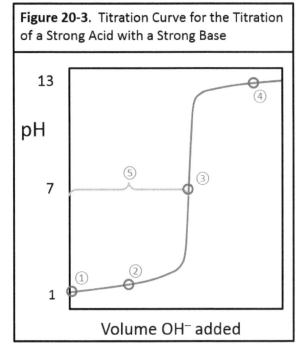

Figure 20-3. Titration Curve for the Titration of a Strong Acid with a Strong Base

$$H_3O^+(aq) + OH^-(aq) \longrightarrow 2\ H_2O(\ell)$$

at the half-equivalence point, enough base has been added to neutralize half of the strong acid. Additionally, the whole acid solution has been diluted by the addition of base solution. So, while exactly half of the original H_3O^+ remains, its concentration is less than half of its original concentration. For example, consider the titration of 30.00 mL of 0.10 *M* H_3O^+ (0.0030 moles H_3O^+) with 0.1000 *M* NaOH. The original pH of the H_3O^+ solution is 1.00. The half equivalence point occurs when 15.00 mL of the titrant has been added. At this point 0.0015 moles of H_3O^+ remain in a solution that has a total volume of 45.00 mL. The concentration of H_3O^+ is 0.033 *M*, for a pH of 1.48.

③ The pH at the **equivalence point** must be 7.0. Remember the reaction occurring:

$$H_3O^+(aq) + OH^-(aq) \longrightarrow 2\ H_2O(\ell)$$
$$\text{flask} \qquad\quad \text{buret}$$

When the OH^- moles added is equivalent to the original H_3O^+ moles, neither will be left over and the solution will be neutral. Note that the pH of the titrated solution is changing very steeply around the equivalence point. This occurs because the solution is changing from being a solution of a strong acid (before the equivalence point) to being a solution of a strong base (after the equivalence point). It only takes a small volume of titrant to drastically change the pH of the titration solution at and around the equivalence point.

④ The pH anywhere beyond the equivalence point is governed by the fact that there is leftover strong base in the solution. Refer, again to the reaction equation in number 3, above. Beyond the equivalence point, the H_3O^+ has all reacted and any added OH^- will simply persist in solution. At first this causes a steep increase in pH from 7.00. However, eventually the concentration of leftover OH^- in the flask begins to approach the concentration of OH^- in the buret. The concentration of OH^- in the flask can never reach the concentration of OH^- in the buret, though, because the buret solution is always diluted upon addition to the flask. Hence the curve becomes very flat as it asymptotically approaches the pH of the solution in the buret.

⑤ The length of the horizontal section of the plot is governed by the relationship between the moles of H_3O^+ originally present and the concentration of the OH^- in the buret. The volume of titrant

needed to react with all of the acid determines the horizontal placement of the equivalence point. For comparisons sake, consider Figure 20-4, which features two titration curves. The solutions are of the same strong acid. The solution providing the green data started at double the concentration of the solution providing the blue data. The base solution used was identical in each experiment. The equivalence point occurs at twice the volume of OH^- solution, as demonstrated by the red arrows. The beginning horizontal stretch of the plot is twice as long because twice as many hydronium ions must be neutralized.

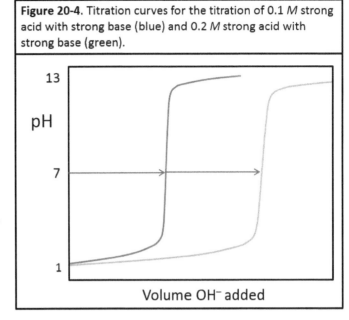

Figure 20-4. Titration curves for the titration of 0.1 *M* strong acid with strong base (blue) and 0.2 *M* strong acid with strong base (green).

Oftentimes, when considering a particular acid-base titration, volumes of base are defined in terms of "equivalents." With respect to the titration of a monoprotic strong acid, an "equivalent of base" is the volume necessary to neutralize the solution. We could say that half of an equivalent of base has been added when we are at the half-equivalence point, and that one equivalent of base has been added when we are at the equivalence point.

The pH at any point along one of these titration curves can be calculated according to methods already covered. All of the solutions are either strong acid solutions (before the equivalence point), a neutral solution (at the equivalence point), or a strong base solution (after the equivalence point). See Table 20-3, boxes 1, 2, and 3 for a summary.

2. *Titration Curve for the Titration of a Strong Base with a Strong Acid*

The ideas here are very similar to those for the titration of a strong acid with a strong base. The same five attributes are marked on the curve in Figure 20-5.

① The pH of the original solution of strong base is very high, and depends only on the concentration of that strong base solution. For any solution of strong base at an OH^- concentration of 0.1 *M* or higher, the pH will be 13.0 or above.

② The pH at the **half-equivalence** point is only slightly lower than the original pH. At the half-equivalence point, the solution in the titration flask is still a solution of a strong base, just not as concentrated as it was in the beginning of the titration. Half of the original hydroxide ions have been neutralized and the volume of the solution has increased due to the addition of titrant. Thus the $[OH^-]$ is less than half of the original concentration.

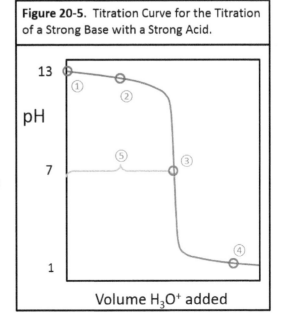

Figure 20-5. Titration Curve for the Titration of a Strong Base with a Strong Acid.

We could say that half an equivalent of acid has been added at this point.

③ The pH at the **equivalence point** must be 7.0. The reaction occurring during this titration is:

$$OH^-(aq) + H_3O^+(aq) \longrightarrow 2\ H_2O(\ell)$$
$$\text{flask} \qquad \text{buret}$$

When moles H_3O^+ added is equivalent to the original OH^- moles, neither will be left over and the solution must be neutral. In this case, the only H_3O^+ and OH^- present are due to autoionization of water. We could say that one equivalence of acid has been added at this point.

④ The pH anywhere on the curve beyond the equivalence point is governed by the excess strong acid in the solution. Beyond the equivalence point, the OH^- has all reacted and any added H_3O^+ simply persists in solution. At first this causes a steep decrease in pH from 7.00. However, eventually the concentration of the excess H_3O^+ in the flask begins to approach the concentration of H_3O^+ in the buret and the curve becomes very flat as it asymptotically approaches the pH of the solution in the buret.

⑤ The length of the horizontal section of the plot is governed by the relationship between the moles of OH^- originally present and the concentration of the H_3O^+ in the buret. The volume of the titrant needed to react with all of the acid determines the horizontal placement of the equivalence point. If twice as many moles of base start out in the titration flask, it will take twice as much of the titrant to reach the equivalence point.

The pH at any point along this titration curve can be calculated according to methods already covered. All solutions are either strong base solutions, neutral, or strong acid solutions. See Table 20-3, boxes 1, 2, and 3 for a summary.

3. Titration Curves for Titrations of Weak Acids with a Strong Base

There is a bit more variation in the graphs of titrations of various weak acids than those of strong acids. While all strong acids are equally strong in aqueous solutions (so pH depends only on concentration) not all weak acids are equally weak, and this becomes apparent in their titration plots. The most important difference between the titrations of a strong acid versus a weak acid are the details associated with the horizontal plateau region of the plot. When a strong acid is being titrated with a strong base, the pH of the solution before the equivalence point reflects a strong acid solution. However, when a weak acid is titrated with a strong base, the flat region of the plot (centered at point ② in Figure 20-6) is called the buffer region of the titration curve.[178] Consider the titration reaction equation when starting with the weak acid, HA:

$$HA(aq) + OH^-(aq) \longrightarrow A^-(aq) + H_2O(\ell)$$
$$\text{flask} \qquad \text{buret}$$

Early in the titration, when OH^- is limiting, the solution in the titration flask contains both unreacted HA and product A^-. This is a buffer solution. Hence, the pH changes that occur during this period of the titration are very modest due to the buffering behavior of the solution. This region of the plot extends from an HA/A^- ratio of ~10 to a ratio of ~0.1.

---

[178] Notice that this flat region of the pH plot is reminiscent of Figure 20-1, which we analyzed early in this chapter.

We now consider the five attributes of a titration curve of a typical weak acid, as marked in Figure 20-6.

① The pH of the original solution of weak acid depends on the identity of the weak acid (its K_a value) and its concentration. In general, the original pH of a solution of a weak acid is not as low as the pH of a strong acid solution. See Table 20-3, box 4.

② Consider the titration reaction equation:

$$HA(aq) + OH^-(aq) \longrightarrow A^-(aq) + H_2O(\ell)$$
flask   buret

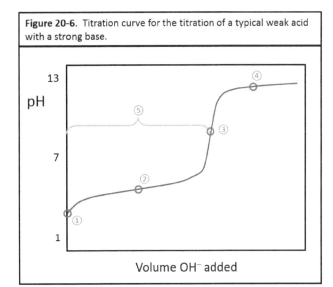

Figure 20-6. Titration curve for the titration of a typical weak acid with a strong base.

Point ② on the graph in Figure 20-6 is the **half-equivalence point**, which means that half of the original weak acid has been converted into its conjugate base. At this point, we have a 1:1 buffer solution because [HA] = [A⁻]. The pH at this point is equal to the pK_a of the weak acid, and thus can have a value less than, greater than, or equal to 7.0. The vertical placement of the buffer region depends on the strength of the weak acid. Figure 20-7 shows titration curves for a series of weak acids. The vertical gray lines and horizontal gray arrows mark the half-equivalence points and the equivalence points. The colored tick marks along the y-axis indicate the pH of the half-equivalence points of the corresponding curves. These pH's are the pK_a's of the associated weak acids. The buffer regions show vertical ranges of about ±1 pH unit from the pH of the half-equivalence point.

A final feature to notice in some of these curves is the initial steep rise at small volumes of titrant. These rises are more exaggerated for weaker acids. Notice that all initial pH's are below 7.0; even the weakest acid must produce a solution with pH less than 7.0. However, very weak acids have pK's considerably above 7.0, and thus, once a buffer is established, the pH is considerably higher. In these cases, the initial steep rise is quite severe. As the buffer regions move to more acidic pH's, these initial rises gradually disappear.

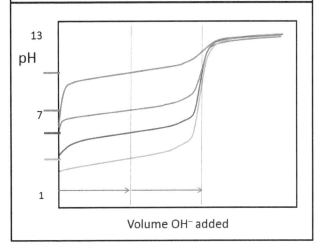

Figure 20-7. Titration curves for a series of weak acids at the same concentration but different pK_a values, which are marked on the y-axis. All are titrated with the same base solution.

③ In Figure 20-6 this marks the equivalence point of the titration. Consider, again, the titration reaction equation: $HA(aq) + OH^-(aq) \longrightarrow A^-(aq) + H_2O(\ell)$
flask   buret

At the equivalence point, all of the weak acid has been converted to its conjugate base. Thus the solution has become a weak base solution and has a pH higher than 7.0. The exact pH depends on the strength of the weak base (its K_b value) and its concentration. See Table 20-3, box 6 for a reminder about calculations of pH when strong base and weak acid solutions are combined.

④ The pH anywhere on the curve beyond the equivalence point is governed by the excess strong base in the solution. Beyond the equivalence point, the HA has all reacted and any added OH⁻ simply persists in solution. Weak base (A⁻) is also present in these solutions, but usually does not contribute enough OH⁻ to affect the pH. The OH⁻ building up in the solution initially causes a steep increase in pH. However, eventually the concentration of the excess OH⁻ in the flask begins to approach the concentration of OH⁻ in the buret and the curve becomes very flat as it asymptotically approaches the pH of the solution in the buret.

⑤ The length of the buffer region of any plot is governed by the relationship between the moles of weak acid originally present and the concentration of the OH⁻ in the buret. The volume of the titrant needed to react with all of the acid determines the horizontal placement of the equivalence point. Consider Figure 20-8. The green data arise from a titration of twice as many moles of weak acid as the blue data. The green equivalence point occurs at twice the volume of OH⁻ solution due to the need to convert twice as much HA into A⁻. The buffer region of the plot is twice as long. Notice that the pH at the equivalence point is greater than 7.0; the solution is a weak base (A⁻) solution.

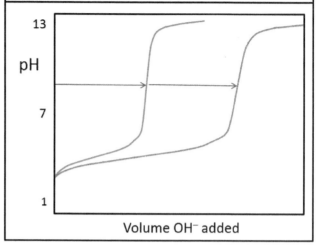

Figure 20-8. Titration curves for the titrations of 0.1 M HA (blue) and 0.2 M HA (green) with the identical OH⁻ solutions. Red arrows mark the equivalence points of the titrations.

Example 20-16.

Determine the K_a of a weak acid from the following titration data. In a titration of the weak acid with the strong base NaOH, the equivalence point is reached after the addition of 32.42 mL of base. The pH after the addition of 16.21 mL of base is 4.73.

Solution:

The 20.21 mL mark in the titration is the half-equivalence point $\left(\dfrac{32.42\ mL}{2} = 16.21\ mL \right)$. At this point, the weak acid has been half-converted into its conjugate base, so the pH = pK_a. Hence, the pK_a of the weak acid is 4.73 and the $K_a = 10^{-4.73} = 1.9 \times 10^{-5}$. note 179

---

4. Titration Curves for Titrations of Weak Bases with a Strong Acid

These titrations are related to the titrations of weak acids in the same way that titration curves for strong bases are related to those of strong acids. Once again we consider the five chosen attributes, as shown in Figure 20-9.

---

[179] In practice, the K_a values determined from experimental data in this way are not usually very accurate due to non-ideal behaviors of solutes. If you generate titration curves, remember to be flexible in the interpretation of the pK_a that is determined from the titration data.

① The pH of the original solution of weak base depends on the identity of the weak base (its K_b value) and its concentration. In general, the original pH of a solution of a weak base is not as high as the pH of a strong base solution. See Table 20-3, box 5.

② The pH at the half-equivalence point is the pH of a buffer having [HA] = [A⁻] because, at the half-equivalence point, exactly half of the original A⁻ has been converted to HA. The pH at this point is equal to the pK_a of the (conjugate) weak acid. Remember, this relationship comes from the mathematics of the K_a expression:

$$\left[H_3O^+ \right]_{eq} = K_a \times \frac{\left[HA \right]_{eq}}{\left[A^- \right]_{eq}}$$

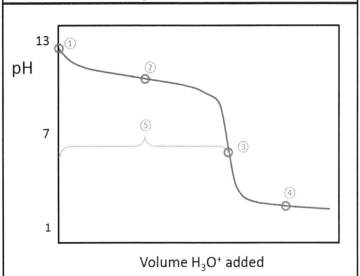

Figure 20-9. Titration curve for the titration of a typical weak base with a strong acid.

It is a mistake to think that because we are now considering the titration of a weak base, the pH at the half-equivalence point will be equal to the pK_b instead of the pK_a. The K_b expression is shown below, along with a similar rearrangement of it.

$$K_b = \frac{\left[HA \right]_{eq}\left[OH^- \right]_{eq}}{\left[A^- \right]_{eq}} \qquad \left[OH^- \right]_{eq} = K_b \times \frac{\left[A^- \right]_{eq}}{\left[HA \right]_{eq}}$$

Notice that the expressions above cannot be rearranged to give direct information about [H₃O⁺], and therefore, pH. Rather, they give information about [OH⁻] and pOH, which is not quite as useful to us. Therefore, the pH value at the half-equivalence point indicates the pK_a of the conjugate acid of the base being titrated. These pH values can be less than, greater than, or equal to 7.0. The vertical placement of this plateau, then, depends on the strength of the (conjugate) weak acid. If the titrations of a series of weak bases are plotted on the same set of axes we can see the differences easily; see Figure 20-10. The vertical dotted lines mark the half-equivalence points and the equivalence points.

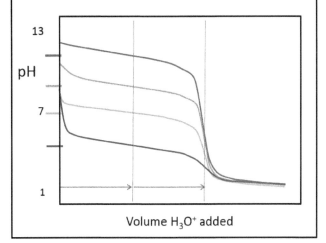

Figure 20-10. Titration curves for a series of weak bases at the same concentration but different pK_b values. All are titrated with the same acid solution. The pK_a's of the conjugate acids are marked on the y-axis.

In Figure 20-10, notice:

- the strongest weak bases have the highest K_b values (and hence the lowest pK_b values, thus their conjugate acids have the highest pK_a values) so their buffer regions are found higher on the plot,

- poor weak bases have stronger conjugate acids with lower pK$_a$ values; poor weak bases have buffer regions that are found lower on the plot.

- the inflection point at the beginning of the plot becomes more and more pronounced as the bases get weaker. In all cases the original pH has to be above 7.0, but for the very weak bases the buffer region occurs well below pH 7.0.

- all equivalence points have pH values less than 7.0 because these solutions are weak acid solutions.

③ Consider the titration reaction equation: $B(aq) + H_3O^+(aq) \longrightarrow BH^+(aq) + H_2O(\ell)$
                                              flask   buret

At the equivalence point all weak base has been converted to its conjugate acid. Thus the solution is a weak acid solution <u>and has a pH lower than 7.0.</u> The exact pH depends on the strength of the weak acid (its K$_a$ value) and its concentration. See Table 20-3, box 6 for a reminder on the calculation of the pH of solution made by adding a strong acid to a weak base.

④ The pH anywhere on the curve beyond the equivalence point is governed by the excess strong acid in the solution. Beyond the equivalence point, the A⁻ has all reacted and any added H$_3$O⁺ simply persists in solution. Weak acid (HA) is also present in these solutions, but usually does not contribute enough H$_3$O⁺ to affect the pH. The H$_3$O⁺ building up in the solution initially causes a steep decrease in pH. However, eventually the concentration of the excess H$_3$O⁺ in the flask begins to approach the concentration of H$_3$O⁺ in the buret and the curve becomes very flat as it asymptotically approaches the pH of the solution in the buret.

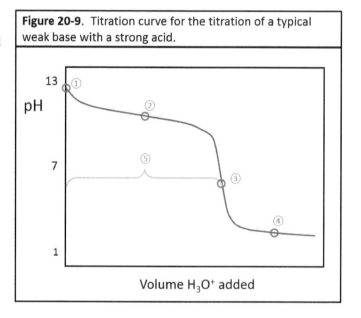

Figure 20-9. Titration curve for the titration of a typical weak base with a strong acid.

⑤ The length of the buffer region of the plot is governed by the relationship between the moles of weak base originally present and the concentration of the H$_3$O⁺ in the buret. The volume of the titrant needed to react with all of the base determines the horizontal placement of the equivalence point. In Figure 20-10, the four titrated weak base solutions started with the same number of moles of weak base (same volume of same concentration). Thus, these titrations all required the same volume of titrant. If twice as many moles of base are titrated with the same acid solution, the equivalence point occurs at twice the volume of H$_3$O⁺ solution and the buffer region of the plot is twice as long.

5. *Titration Curves for Titrations of Conjugate Pairs*

How do the titration curves for conjugate species compare? Consider the titrations of identical amounts of a weak acid and its conjugate base with 0.10 *M* strong base or strong acid. We see an example in Figure 20-11. Notice that the buffer region is centered at the same pH for both titrations. This is a necessary result because the buffer solutions contain the same conjugate pair, and in both cases pH = pK_a of the weak acid species. Note that in the case depicted in Figure 20-11, the buffer region occurs at basic pH values. This tells us that this particular conjugate pair has a stronger base than acid. In the two titration plots shown, the half-equivalence points and equivalence points are at the same volumes because the two experiments started with the same number of moles of weak acid or base AND utilized the same concentrations of strong base or acid in the burets.

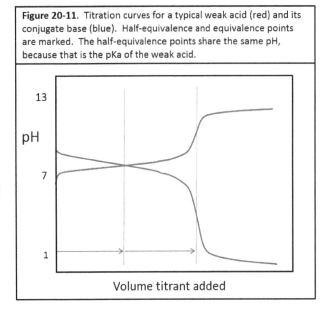

Figure 20-11. Titration curves for a typical weak acid (red) and its conjugate base (blue). Half-equivalence and equivalence points are marked. The half-equivalence points share the same pH, because that is the pKa of the weak acid.

20-4. PH INDICATORS

A. The Job to be Done

Most acid-base titrations are performed without a pH meter. The equivalence point is determined by the inclusion of an "indicator" molecule. The indicator is a species that undergoes a color change over a particular pH range. As long as the color change occurs in the steep region around the equivalence point, the signal will be a reasonably good indicator of the equivalence point. This is true because of the drastic pH changes occurring with very small volumes of titrant in the region surrounding the equivalence point. If the color changes at a pH very slightly above or below the pH of the actual equivalence point, the error in the titration determination will be very small. The end point of the titration occurs when the color of the indicator molecule changes. A well-planned titration has an **end point** in good agreement with the **equivalence point**, but, these terms are not interchangeable (see the beginning of section 20-3).

B. The Molecules for the Job

Acid-base indicators are themselves weak acids and bases. They are special in that the two conjugate species have different colors. For example, methyl red is a weak acid whose acid form is red and whose conjugate base form is yellow. An equimolar solution of the two forms of methyl red looks orange. With a pK_a of approximately 5.1, the buffer region for methyl red is from approximately pH 4.1 to 6.1. At these pH's, various shades of orange may be seen due to the presence of various ratios of red and yellow species. Phenolphthalein, on the other hand, is a colorless weak acid whose conjugate base is magenta. The buffer region of phenolphthalein solutions is centered at about pH 9.4, which is its pK_a. Most people can start to see very pale pink colors at pH's in the low 8's. For any titration to be successfully analyzed via an indicator, the color change must occur in the immediate vicinity of the equivalence point.

Consider Figure 20-12, which shows a pH plot for the titration of a typical weak acid. The approximate color change regions for methyl red and phenolphthalein are shown in the background. The color change for phenolphthalein coincides well with the equivalence point of the titration. Methyl red would not be helpful here; its color change occurs throughout the buffer region of the titration.

Now we turn our attention to a titration of a weak base. Figure 20-13 shows the color change regions for the same two indicators behind a plot of the titration curve for a typical weak base. This time the phenolphthalein changes color along the buffer region of the titration and is therefore useless as an equivalence point indicator. The methyl red color change now coincides nicely with the equivalence point of the titration, so this end point is a useful approximation of the equivalence point. Because of the steep nature of the curve at the equivalence point, the solution changes color from yellow to red with the addition of very little base, maybe just one drop from the buret.

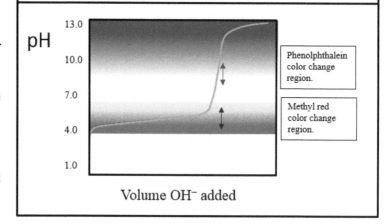

Figure 20-12. Titration of a weak acid with a strong base. Methyl red turns from red to yellow at approximately pH 5.1. Phenolphthalein turns from colorless to magenta at approximately pH 9.4.

Volume OH⁻ added

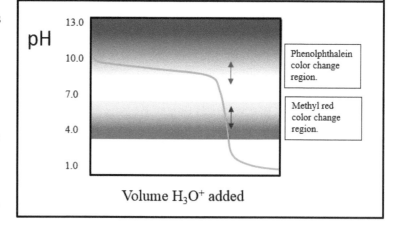

Figure 20-13. Titration of a weak base with a strong acid. Methyl red turns from red to yellow at approximately pH 5.1. Phenolphthalein turns from colorless to magenta at approximately pH 9.4.

Volume H₃O⁺ added

C. Structures of Indicator Molecules

Indicator molecules are dye molecules. They absorb some wavelengths of visible light so that the wavelengths transmitted by their solutions are only a subset of white light wavelengths. Molecules that are capable of the absorption of visible light wavelengths tend to be rather large organic (carbon-based) molecules with extensive conjugated double bond systems.[180] A **conjugated double bond system** is one in which double bonds alternate with single bonds, so that there is a whole string of trigonal planar (sp^2) atoms. This allows for planarity and thus extensive delocalization of pi-electrons. Figure 20-14 shows the structures of both the acid and conjugate base forms of methyl red.

---

[180] Conjugated systems were first introduced in Chapter 8, section 4 of this text.

Figure 20-14. Methyl Red indicator. **Left:** Conjugate acid form is red, pK_a = 5.1. **Right:** Conjugate base form is yellow.

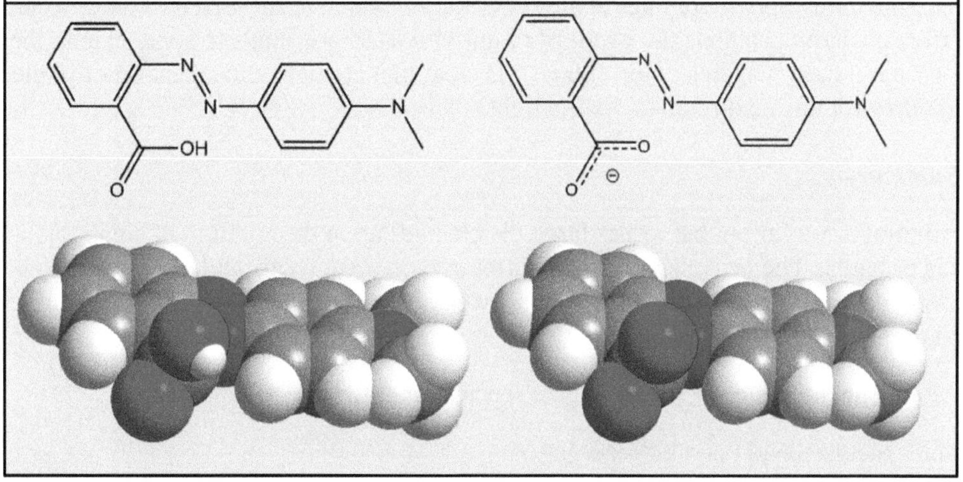

The conjugated system of bonds in the two forms of methyl red are essentially the same, thus both species are colored. The difference in color can be explained by the increased electron density in the pi-system of the anion compared to the neutral molecule.

Phenolphthalein has a more complicated system of bonds that leads to a more drastic color change upon deprotonation. Figure 20-15 shows the two most prevalent structures of phenolphthalein. These are the two dominant structures in solutions between pH 0 and 13.

The conjugate acid form (that we see on the left in Figure 20-15) has three isolated benzene-like rings. By "isolated," we mean that these rings are separated from each other by a tetrahedral carbon, thus interrupting an otherwise continuous conjugated system of bonding. This isolation causes the acid form to be colorless. The ball-and-stick model of the conjugate acid species shows us that its three rings all lie in different planes, almost like the blades of a fan.

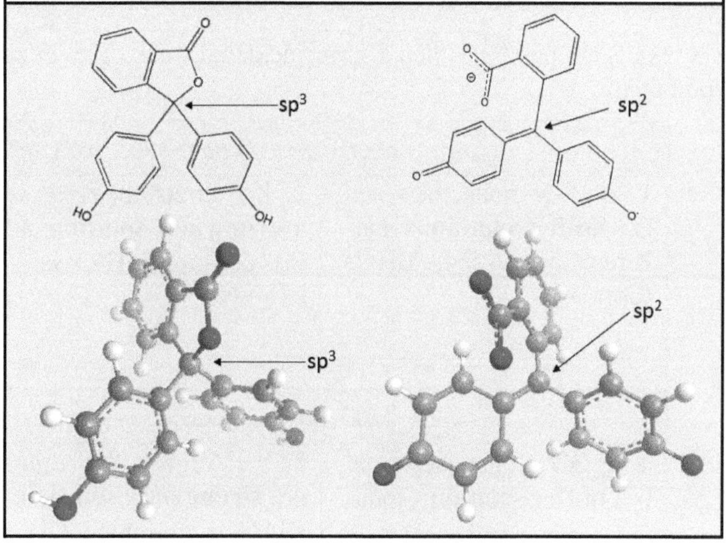

We expect that a somewhat drastic structural change must occur upon deprotonation, given that the conjugate base form of the molecule is colored. As we see on the right in Figure 20-15, deprotonation of one of the –OH hydrogens[181] leads to a major structural change. The most important outcome of the change is that the central carbon atom of the molecule transforms from tetrahedral (sp^3) to planar (sp^2). This leads to a more extensive conjugated system. Extended pi-systems depend on both conjugation and co-planarity in order to offer orbital lobe overlaps

Figure 20-15. Phenolphthalein Indicator. **Left:** Conjugate acid form is colorless, pK_a = 9.4. **Right:** Conjugate base form is magenta.

between the unhybridized *p* orbitals on each carbon atom. In the conjugate base form of phenolphthalein, the sheer bulk of the six-membered rings arranged around one central carbon atom

---

[181] The hydrogen attached to an –OH group that is bonded to a benzene ring is acidic, unlike other –OH groups such as the one on the methanol molecule, CH_3OH.

prohibits the planarity that we might expect when just looking at the Lewis dot structure. The ball-and-stick model of the conjugate base in Figure 20-15 shows that the two "lower" rings are nearly planar, while the third "upper" ring lies at almost a 90° angle due to its need for space. While the lack of perfect planarity prohibits the overlaps of unhybridized *p*-orbitals to some extent, the conjugate base is a deep magenta color. Thus, it is clear that enough delocalization of pi-electrons is possible to allow for the absorption of visible light.

Chapter Summary

A buffer solution is a solution that resists large pH changes upon the addition of small quantities of strong acids or bases. The active species in a buffer system are a weak acid and its conjugate base. The weak acid can react with strong base to make weak base instead. The weak base can react with strong acid to make weak acid instead.

Buffer solutions feature ratios of the conjugate species ranging from 10:1 to 1:10.

Two variables dictate the pH of a buffer solution:

       (1) the *identity* of the weak acid/weak base conjugate pair (major influence)
       (2) the *relative proportions* of the weak acid and weak base species (minor influence).

The pH of a buffer solution can be found without an equilibrium table, using either:

$$\left[H_3O^+\right]_{eq} = K_a \times \frac{\left[HA\right]_{eq}}{\left[A^-\right]_{eq}} \qquad\qquad pH = pK_a + \log\left(\frac{\left[A^-\right]_{eq}}{\left[HA\right]_{eq}}\right)$$

Buffer capacity increases as the concentration of the buffering species increase. Higher capacity means that larger additions of strong acids or bases can be buffered.

Buffers are most accurately made by either

1. dissolving the weak acid at the total concentration desired and adding concentrated strong base until the desired pH is achieved, or
2. dissolving the weak base at the total concentration desired and adding concentrated strong acid until the desired pH is achieved.

Six results are possible when a strong acid and weak base (or strong base and weak acid) are combined:

$H_3O^+(aq) + B(aq) \longrightarrow BH^+(aq) + H_2O(\ell)$		
1. If H_3O^+ limits, the *result* is a **buffer solution**: some B remains and some BH^+ is formed.	**2.** If B limits, the *result* is a **strong acid solution**: all B is consumed, H_3O^+ is leftover.	**3.** If stoichiometric, the *result* is a **weak acid solution**: all B has been converted to BH^+, all H_3O^+ has been consumed.

$OH^-(aq) + HA(aq) \longrightarrow A^-(aq) + H_2O(\ell)$		
4. If OH^- limits, the *result* is a **buffer solution**: some HA remains and some A^- is formed.	**5.** If HA limits, the *result* is a **strong base solution**: all HA is consumed, OH^- is leftover.	**6.** If stoichiometric, the *result* is a **weak base solution**: all HA has been converted to A^-, all OH^- has been consumed.

A three-step procedure can be used to calculate the pH of the resulting solutions:

> 1. *Construct a stoichiometry table.*
> 2. *Interpret the bottom-line entries of the stoichiometry table to decide whether the resulting solution is a strong acid, strong base, weak acid, weak base, or buffer solution.*
> 3. *Determine the pH of the resulting solution based on the result of number 2:*
>   *a. if strong acid or base: find [H_3O^+] or [OH^-] and then pH.*
>   *b. if weak acid or base: find concentration of the weak species and use an equilibrium table to evaluate pH.*
>   *c. if a buffer solution: use the equilibrium constant expression (or Henderson Hasselbalch equation) to evaluate pH.*

Plots of "pH" versus "titrant added" let us visualize the pH changes that occur over the course of a titration.

1. The original pH reflects the nature and concentration of the solution to be titrated.
2. If a weak species is titrated, a buffer region is present, during which the pH changes very slowly as titrant is added.
3. In this case, the half-equivalence point falls in the center of the buffer region. The buffer region extends from a pH 1 unit less than the pK_a to a pH 1 unit higher than the pK_a.
4. The pH changes sharply as the equivalence point is reached. This is the pH change that should trigger the color change of the indicator molecule.
5. The pH of a titration solution following the equivalence point depends on the pH of the titrant, though it can never quite reach that value due to dilution effects.

Acid-base indicators are weak acid molecules whose conjugate base is a different color.

Different indicators change color over different pH ranges.

Careful selection of the proper indicator for a titration will ensure that the end point and the equivalence point coincide.

CHAPTER 20 PROBLEMS

1. Hydrofluoric acid, HF, has $K_a = 6.3 \times 10^{-4}$ at 25 °C.

    a. What would be the pH of a solution containing 15.0 g of HF (20.006 g/mol) and 25.0 g of NaF (41.988 g/mol) dissolved in a total volume of 0.500 L?

    b. What ratio of $\frac{[HF]}{[F^-]}$ would be found in a buffer of pH 3.50?

    c. Show, using balanced net ionic chemical equations, how the solution in part a would behave as a buffer:

          (1) on the addition of aqueous HCl

          (2) on the addition of aqueous sodium hydroxide

2. Ammonia, NH_3, has $K_b = 1.8 \times 10^{-5}$.

    a. What would be the pH of a solution containing 20.0 g of NH_3 and 30.0 g of NH_4Cl dissolved in a total volume of 250.0 mL?

    b. What ratio of $\frac{[NH_3]}{[NH_4^+]}$ would be found in a buffer of pH 9.00?

    c. Show, using balanced net ionic chemical equations, how the solution in part a would behave as a buffer:

          (1) on the addition of aqueous nitric acid.

          (2) on the addition of aqueous potassium hydroxide

3. For HNO_2, $pK_a = 3.25$ at 25 °C.

    a. Calculate the equilibrium constant at 25 °C for the reaction:

    $$NO_2^- + H_3O^+ \rightleftharpoons H_2O + HNO_2$$

    (Hint: how does this reaction compare to the weak acid ionization reaction for HNO_2?)

    b. Calculate the equilibrium constant at 25 °C for the reaction:

    $$OH^- + HNO_2 \rightleftharpoons H_2O + NO_2^-$$

    (Hint: how does this reaction compare to the weak base ionization for NO_2^-?)

    c. Would you predict an aqueous solution of KNO_2 to be acidic, basic, or neutral? Explain.

    d. What ratio of $\frac{[HNO_2]}{[NO_2^-]}$ would be found in a buffer having pH = 3.00?

4. The following six acids are available:

		K_a
H_2SO_3	sulfurous	1.4×10^{-2}
HF	hydrofluoric	6.3×10^{-4}
HNO_2	nitrous	5.6×10^{-4}
$HC_7H_5O_2$	benzoic	6.3×10^{-5}
$HC_2H_3O_2$	acetic	1.8×10^{-5}
HCN	hydrocyanic	6.2×10^{-10}

   a. To calibrate a pH meter for acidic solutions a buffer of pH 4.00 is needed.

      (1) Which of the above acids would you select for use in this buffer? Why?

      (2) What would be the $\frac{[conjugate\ base]}{[conjugate\ acid]}$ ratio in your buffer?

   b. What is the chemical formula of the strongest conjugate base of the acids in the above table?

   c. Determine equilibrium constants for the following reactions in aqueous solution. Also fill in the blanks to indicate products, where necessary.

      (1) $H_3O^+ + F^- \rightleftharpoons$ _____ + _____ $K_{eq}=$

      (2) $NO_2^- + H_2O \rightleftharpoons$ _____ + _____ $K_{eq}=$

      (3) $HCN + F^- \rightleftharpoons HF + CN^-$ $K_{eq}=$

5. A buffer solution of pH 4.50 is needed. The four acids listed below and their sodium salts are available.

Acid	K_a	pK_a
HF	6.3×10^{-4}	3.20
HCOOH	1.8×10^{-4}	3.75
C_6H_5COOH	6.3×10^{-5}	4.20
CH_3COOH	1.8×10^{-5}	4.76

   a. Any of these acids could be used as the basis for the desired buffer, but one of these (plus its sodium salt) would be more effective than the others at maintaining the desired pH. Which one?

   b. For the acid you have selected, what [weak acid][conjugate base] ratio would be found in a buffer of pH 4.50?

   c. Write balanced chemical equations (net ionic equations) to explain how your buffer could neutralize:

      (1) An addition of hydrochloric acid

      (2) An addition of potassium hydroxide solution

6. A solution is prepared containing 0.100 mole of HF and 0.100 mole of NaF in a total volume of 500.0 mL.

   a. Determine the pH of this solution.

   b. Produce a stoichiometry table for the addition of 10.0 mL of 1.00 M $HClO_4$. What type of solution results? In what direction does the pH change upon this addition?

   c. Calculate the expected pH of the resulting solution after the addition made in part b.

7. **a.** What is the pH of the solution that results from addition of 100.0 mL of a 0.200 M solution of KOH to an equal volume of 0.200 M acetic acid solution? ($K_a = 1.75 \times 10^{-5}$ for acetic acid.)

   b. What would be the pH if only 50.0 mL of the KOH solution had been added to the acetic acid solution in part a?

8. **a.** What is the pH of a solution that results when 30.0 mL of 0.200 M HCl solution is added to 50.0 mL of 0.100 M NH₃? ($K_b = 1.8 \times 10^{-5}$ for NH₃)

   b. What would be the pH if only 15.0 mL of the HCl solution had been added to the NH₃ solution in part a?

9. Ammonia, NH₃, has $K_b = 1.8 \times 10^{-5}$ at 25 °C.

   a. What is the pH of a 0.125 M solution of NH₃?

   b. Determine the equilibrium constant for the following reaction in aqueous solution at 25 °C.

   $$NH_4^+ + H_2O \rightleftharpoons NH_3 + H_3O^+$$

   c. What is the chemical equation (net ionic equation) for the reaction of NH₃ with nitric acid in aqueous solution?

   d. What is the pH of the solution that results when 100.0 mL of the 0.125 M NH₃ solution is added to 50.0 mL of 0.125 M nitric acid solution?

10. The questions below are based on the data shown. The titration data were obtained by adding 0.100 M NaOH solution to 50.0 mL of a solution containing a weak acid.

Vol of 0.100 M NaOH Solution (mL)	pH
0.00	2.37
12.00	3.22
24.00	3.70
36.00	4.17
44.00	4.74
47.00	5.37
49.00	11.00
52.00	11.59
60.00	11.96

    a. Plot the titration data (pH vs. volume of NaOH solution). Use Excel.
    b. What was the initial concentration of the acid?
    c. Determine the pK_a and K_a for the acid.
    d. Determine the pH at the equivalence point (Note: calculate this value, do not just estimate from the graph.)

11. A solution containing 100.0 mL of 0.100 M formic acid (HCOOH, $K_a = 1.8 \times 10^{-4}$) is titrated with 0.200 M KOH solution. Calculate the pH at the following points in the titration:

    a. After addition of 25.0 mL of KOH solution
    b. At the equivalence point

12. The questions below are based on the data shown. The titration data were obtained by adding 0.0200 M NaOH solution to 100.0 mL of a solution containing acetylsalicylic acid (aspirin), a weak acid.

Volume of 0.0200 M NaOH Solution (mL)	pH
0.00	2.76
10.00	2.82
20.00	3.22
30.00	3.52
40.00	3.82
50.00	4.22
58.00	4.98
62.00	10.39
70.00	11.07

a. Plot the titration data (pH vs. volume of NaOH solution). Use Excel.

b. What was the initial concentration of the acetylsalicylic acid ($C_9H_8O_4$)?

c. Determine the pK_a and K_a for the acid.

d. Determine the pH at the equivalence point (Note: calculate this value, do not just estimate from the graph.)

13. HNO_2 (nitrous acid) has $K_a = 5.6 \times 10^{-4}$ at 25 °C. A 50.00 mL solution of 0.100 M HNO_2 is titrated with 0.125 M NaOH solution at 25 °C.

a. What volume of NaOH solution must be added to reach the equivalence point?

b. Calculate the pH:

(**1**) of the original HNO_2 solution

(**2**) after addition of 20.0 mL of the NaOH solution

(**3**) after addition of 25.0 mL (total) of the NaOH solution

(**4**) at the equivalence point

(**5**) after addition of 50.0 mL of the NaOH solution

14. NH_3 has $K_b = 1.8 \times 10^{-5}$ at 25 °C. A 25.00 mL solution of 0.200 M NH_4Cl is titrated with 0.150 M KOH solution at 25 °C.

a. What volume of KOH solution must be added to reach the equivalence point?

b. Calculate the pH:

(**1**) of the original NH_4Cl solution

(**2**) after addition of 20.0 mL of the KOH solution

(**3**) at the equivalence point

(**4**) at the half equivalence point

(**5**) after addition of 40.0 mL of the KOH solution

15.

Acid	Conjugate Base	K_a	pK_a
HCN	_____	6.2×10^{-10}	_____
_____	NH_3	_____	9.25
HClO	_____	4.0×10^{-8}	_____
HNO_2	_____	5.6×10^{-4}	_____

a. Fill in the blanks in the table above. Use a calculator, don't just look up values in another table.

b. What is the strongest conjugate base in the table?

c. Calculate numerical values for equilibrium constants for the following: (aqueous solutions, 25 °C)

(1) $HClO + OH^- \rightleftharpoons ClO^- + H_2O$

(2) $HCN + NH_3 \rightleftharpoons NH_4^+ + CN^-$

d. A solution is prepared containing 140.0 mL of 0.100 M ammonium chloride.

(1) This solution is transferred to a 250.0 mL volumetric flask and diluted to the mark. After dilution what is the concentration of ammonium chloride?

(2) The solution from the volumetric flask is transferred to an Erlenmeyer flask, and 35.0 mL of 0.200 M NaOH solution is added. What is the final pH?

e. What ratio of $\frac{[HNO_2]}{[NO_2^-]}$ would be found in a buffer having pH 3.50?

f. Unfortunately, this buffer would not be satisfactory in the presence of oxidizing agents. For example, addition of I_2 to the buffer would cause a brown gas to be liberated. Write a net ionic equation to describe formation of this gas.

16. What ratio of acetate to acetic acid would you expect to find in a buffer of pH 5.15?

17. What ratio of formate to formic acid would you expect to find in a buffer whose hydronium ion concentration equals 5.2×10^{-5} M?

18. Suppose you wanted to prepare 500.0 mL of a buffer with a total concentration of 0.20 M and pH = 5.40. You have bottles of solid potassium iodate and solid potassium acetate on hand. You also have concentrated HCl and KOH solutions.

a. Would it be better to use an acetic acid/acetate buffer or an iodic acid/iodate buffer? Why?

b. How many grams of which salt would you weigh out to get started?

c. You dissolve the weighed out salt to a total volume of 500.0 mL. What would you do next?

d. What ratio of [HA] to [A⁻] would you expect to find in the finished buffer?

19. Sketch titration curves for titrations of 50.00 mL 0.10 M iodic acid and acetic acid with 0.1000 M NaOH on the same set of axes. Label the axes appropriately. You need not calculate any pH values, but your curves should be placed reasonably on the axes. Show the half-equivalence and equivalence points on both axes.

20. Sketch titration curves for titrations of 40.00 mL 0.20 M sodium nitrite and 40.00 mL 0.20 M ammonia with 0.1000 M HNO_3 on the same set of axes. Label the axes appropriately. You need not calculate any pH values, but your curves should be placed reasonably on the axes. Show the half-equivalence and equivalence points on both axes.

21. Sketch titration curves for titrations of 50.00 mL 0.10 M iodic acid with 0.1000 M NaOH and 0.2000 M NaOH on the same set of axes. Label the axes appropriately. You need not calculate any pH values, but your curves should be placed reasonably on the axes. Show the half-equivalence and equivalence points on both axes.

22. A chemistry student volunteered to determine the concentration of HNO_2, a weak acid, in an ancient, dust-covered bottle which had been discovered during the renovation of a chemical storeroom. She carefully pipetted 50.00 mL of the acid into an Erlenmeyer flask. Then she added, by buret, 0.2200 M KOH solution, monitoring with a pH meter. The equivalence point was reached when 37.50 mL of the KOH solution had been added.

  a. What was the concentration of the acid?

  b. What is the pK_a of HNO_2? (K_a for $HNO_2 = 5.6 \times 10^{-4}$)

  c. What was the pH at the half equivalence point?

  d. The student took a pH reading after 18.75 mL of the KOH solution had been added. What should the meter have read at this point (provide 2 decimal places)?

23. An unknown weak acid (0.2500 g) is dissolved in water and titrated with 0.1000 M NaOH solution. The pH changes most rapidly at 20.00 mL of added base solution. What is the molecular weight of the acid?

24. Consider an acid-base titration with a pH of 5.00 at the equivalence point.
  a. What type of species is being titrated: strong acid, strong base, weak acid or weak base?
  b. What general properties would an indicator need to have in order to be a useful indicator for this titration?

25. In general, do you expect a wider choice of indicators for the titration of a strong base or a weak base? Explain.

GLOSSARY OF TERMS

Italicized terms within definitions are defined in this glossary.

Absorbance, A: A measure of the *absorption* of a particular *wavelength* of energy by a sample, often described in terms of the *Beer-Lambert law*, A = εℓc.

Absorbed: Light that enters, but does not pass through a *transparent* material or *solution*. This light (energy) was used to energize *electron*s or some other particle associated with the material or *solution*. Compare to *transmitted*.

Absorption: (of energy) The taking-up of energy by a material. Different *wavelengths* of *energy* can be *absorbed* by *matter* in a number of ways. The energy is used to excite the *matter* in some way: increasing its translational energy, increasing its rotational energy, increasing its vibrational energy, or moving its *electrons* further from the nuclei of the particle (increasing the energy of one or more *electron*s). The opposite of *transmitted* energy.

Absorption spectrum: A plot of either *molar absorptivity* or *absorbance* vs. *wavelength* for a *solute*.

Absorptivity constant, a_λ: A measure of how well a *solute* absorbs a particular *wavelength* of light, used when the *concentration* of the *solute* is described in units other than *molarity*. Compare to *molar absorptivity*.

Acceptor: In *hydrogen bonding*, the species whose lone pair of *electrons* attracts the partially positive hydrogen *atom* of another *molecule*. Compare to *Donor*. In *Bronsted-Lowry theory* the *base* is the acceptor of an H$^+$. In Lewis *theory* the *Lewis acid* is the acceptor of a lone pair of *electrons*. In *oxidation-reduction chemistry* the *oxidizing agent* is the acceptor of *electron*s.

Accuracy: The agreement (or lack thereof) between a measured value and the "true" value. Of course, in scientific research the "true" value is an unknown, so the average of a large set of measurements often replaces the "true" value. Accuracy is limited by *systematic error*.

Acetylene: A *hydrocarbon* with formula C_2H_2.

Acid Ionization Constant, K_a: An *equilibrium constant* for the reaction of an acid with water to produce the *hydronium ion*. Larger values imply a stronger acid, more *hydronium ion* formed.

Acidic hydrogen atom: Any covalently bonded hydrogen *atom* that has a tendency to be transferred to an *acceptor molecule* (such as water) as an H$^+$ *ion* (a *proton*).

Acidosis: A pathological blood condition that has a variety of causes. The pH of the blood drops to below 7.35. See also *Alkalosis*.

Aconitase: An *enzyme* of the citric acid cycle that is rendered useless during the action of the poison, *fluoroacetate*.

Actinides: The *elements* with *atomic number*s 90-103, in the *f block* of the *periodic table*.

Actual yield: The amount of one *product* (usually measured by mass) that is obtained from a *chemical reaction*.

Adenosine diphosphate, ADP: A precursor and metabolite of *adenosine triphosphate* (*ATP*). ADP is a more stable *molecule* than *ATP* and can be formed via the *hydrolysis* of ATP.

Adenosine triphosphate, ATP: A large *ion* that serves as energy currency for living cells.

Alcohol: Any *molecule* containing one or more –OH *functional groups*. See *Alcohol group*.

Alcohol group: One of many *functional groups* in *organic chemistry*, the –OH *group*.

Alkali metals: The *Group* 1 *elements*.

Alkaline earth metals: The *Group* 2 *elements*.

Alkalosis: A pathological blood condition that has a variety of causes. The pH of the blood rises to above 7.45. See also *Acidosis*.

Alkane: *Molecules* containing C–C *single bond*s, which can be considered a *functional group*.

Alkene: *Molecules* containing C=C *bond*s, which can be considered a *functional group*.

Allosteric: Relating to the change in *shape*, and activity, of a *protein* brought about by the binding of an *effector molecule*.

Allotropes: Different forms of the same *element*, characterized by different bonding patterns of the *atom*s of the *element*, for example, diamond and graphite.

Alloy: A *homogeneous mixture* of one *solid* in another (usually *metal*s), thus alloys are *solid phase solutions*. For example, bronze is an alloy of copper and tin.

Alpha-carbon: (of *amino acid*s) The carbon between the C of the *carboxylic acid group* and the N of the *amine group* of an *amino acid*. The site of attachment of the amino acid side chain.

Alpha decay: See *alpha emission*.

Alpha emission: *Radioactivity* characterized by the loss of an alpha particle from the *nucleus* of an unstable *nuclide*. This event results in the loss of 4 *atomic mass* units from the *nucleus*. Also called *alpha decay*.

Alpha particle, $_2^4He$ or $_2^4\alpha$: A nuclear particle that is equivalent to the *nucleus* of a helium *atom*, and that is lost by some unstable *nuclide*s undergoing *radioactive* decay. The high energy alpha particle carries a +2 charge.

Alpha helix: A very common *secondary structure* in *proteins* that is stabilized by *hydrogen bonds* between the "n" and "n+4" *residues*.

Alveolar: Of or relating to the air-containing cells of the lungs.

Ambidentate (pronounced as in "pig"): Any *polyatomic ligand* that has more than one *atom* that can serve as the point of attachment to the central metal *cation*. Only one point of attachment is used in any given circumstance. Compare to *polydentate ligand*s, where more than one concurrent attachment is made.

Amide: A *functional group*, R-(C=O)NH-R. The chemical identity of a *peptide bond*. Produced via reaction of *amine* and *carboxylic acid*.

Amine: A *functional group*, R-NH₂. Reacts to make an *amide*.

Amino acid: Any *organic molecule* with both an *amine group* and a *carboxylic acid group*.

Amino acid residue: The structure of an *amino acid* that remains after the *amino acid* has been incorporated into a *peptide* or *protein polymer*. Usually three *atom*s smaller than the original *amino acid* due to the loss of the *atom*s of H_2O during the polymerization process.

Amphiphile: A species that has both a *polar* and a *nonpolar* region.

Amphiphilic: The characteristic of being an *amphiphile*.

Amphipathic: See *Amphiphilic*.

Amphiprotic: A species that can either give up a *proton* that it already has, or bind a *proton* from another source, and thus, acts as either a *Bronsted-Lowry acid* or a *Bronsted-Lowry base*. Another word for *amphoteric*.

Amphoteric: An adjective that indicates the ability to act as either a *Bronsted-Lowry acid* or a *Bronsted-Lowry base*.

Amphoterism: The property or characteristic of being able to act as either a *Bronsted-Lowry acid* or a *Bronsted-Lowry base*. Water is a good example.

Amplitude: Half of the height between trough and crest of an electromagnetic wave. Distance from calm water level to crest of a water wave.

Anabolic: Of or relating to *anabolism*.

Anabolism: The subset of *metabolism* that accomplishes the synthesis of *molecule*s necessary to life. Compare to *catabolism*.

Analyte: The *substance* that is the subject of an analysis such as a *titration*.

Angular function: A mathematical function describing how a particular *electron*-wave changes as its position in three-dimensional space changes.

Angular momentum quantum number, ℓ: Also called the *Azimuthal quantum number*. Its value determines the shape of the *atomic orbital* because it specifies the number of *angular nodes* present. Historically known as the "*subshell*" of an *electron*.

Angular node: A *planar* surface on which the probability of finding an *electron* is zero.

Anion: A negatively charged *ion*.

Annihilation event: A post-*radioactive* event that occurs when a *beta particle* collides with an *electron* to produce a pair of gamma *photon*s.

Antibond: In molecular *orbital theory*, an *antibonding orbital* populated by 2 *electron*s.

Antibonding interactions: The destructive overlap of *atomic orbitals* on different *atom*s (one with positive *amplitude* and one with negative *amplitude*) producing a *molecular orbital* that places a *node* between the two nuclei. The overlap of *orbital* lobes of opposite sign.

Antibonding orbitals: *Molecular orbitals* that arise from *antibonding interactions*. *Electron*s in antibonding *orbital*s destabilize the *molecule*.

Antiparallel: Neighboring polymeric strands of a *protein* or nucleic acid that are running in opposite directions.

Aqueous: A *solution* in which the *solvent* is water. Designated (aq) in *chemical reaction* equations.

Arrhenius acid: A chemical species that was understood to liberate a *proton*, H^+, in *water solution*.

Arrhenius base: A chemical species that was understood to liberate a *hydroxide ion*, OH^-, in water *solution*.

Association: The act of joining or connecting together. In *chemistry* and biochemistry, this word is usually used in the context of connections made via weak bonding or *bond*s that are particularly *reversible* in character.

Association constant, K_A: An *equilibrium constant* for the *association* of a biological complex from its component parts, such as a *protein* + hormone or a *protein* + *substrate* binding step. Larger values imply a complex with stronger bonding. The reciprocal of the *dissociation constant*.

Asymmetric: Any *molecule* with a *nonsuperimposable* mirror image. Also called *chiral*.

Atmosphere: (atm) Common unit of *gas* pressure now being phased out by the IUPAC in favor of the *bar*.

Atom: The fundamental building blocks of *matter*. A positively charged, heavy *nucleus* surrounded by negatively charged *electrons*. Each *element* is distinguished by *atoms* having a particular structure. (sizes of *atoms*, see also *Covalent radius*).

Atomic mass: The mass of a particular *atom* in *atomic mass units*, or the mass of a *mole* of *atoms* of the same *element* in grams. In the case of a *mole* of *atoms* of an *element* it is often the *average atomic mass* due to the presence of various *isotopes*.

Atomic mass unit: (Abbreviations: u or Da or amu) The modern version became the "unified atomic mass unit" when it was redefined on the basis of the carbon-12 *atom*. A mass unit of very small magnitude so that it is useful for describing the masses of single *atoms*, *molecules*, and *subatomic particles*. One *atomic mass unit* is equal to 1/12 of the mass of a carbon-12 *atom*. One gram is equivalent to 6.022×10^{23} u. The "Da" unit honors John Dalton and is used most often in the field of biochemistry. Not an SI unit, but approved for use by the International Committee for Weights and Measures.

Atomic number, Z: The number of *protons* in the *nucleus* of a particular *atom*. This property defines an *element*.

Atomic orbitals: The three-dimensional spatial region (specified by *n, ℓ, and m_ℓ*) around an atomic *nucleus*, in which a particular *electron* is believed to be located. The mathematical result of the *Schrodinger wave equation*.

Atomic Theory: A set of postulates describing the nature of *atoms*.

ATP: See *Adenosine triphosphate*.

Autoionization: Also called *self-ionization*. The ability of an *amphiprotic* (or *amphoteric*) species to *transfer* a *proton* between two particles of itself. For instance, in the *autoionization* of water, two water *molecules transfer* a *proton* between them, so that one (the *acceptor*) becomes a *hydronium ion* and the other (the *donor*) becomes a *hydroxide ion*.

Average atomic mass: The mass, in grams, of one *mole* of *atoms* of a particular *element*, from a naturally occurring sample. Since many *elements* consist of two or more *isotopes*, a *mole* of *atoms* from a natural sample will consist of *atoms* of differing masses in some proportion. In this case the mass of any particular *atom* (in *atomic mass units*) will not be the same as the *average atomic mass*. This is the number found in the *periodic table*.

Average deviation: $\dfrac{\sum\limits_{i=1}^{n}(X_i - \overline{X})}{n}$ Where n = the number of measurements in a data set, X_i = the individual measurements and $\overline{X}$ = the average of the individual measurements. A value related to the *precision* (reproducibility) of a data set.

Avogadro's Hypothesis: See *Avogadro's Law*.

Avogadro's Law: Equal volumes of *gases* contain equal numbers of particles when the pressures and temperatures are the same. V/n = constant, where n = number of particles.

Avogadro's number: (Abbreviation: N_A) A counting number equal to 6.022×10^{23} items. One *mole* of a *substance* contains 6.022×10^{23} formula units of material.

Axial: The two positions in a *trigonal bipyramidal* system that form a linear arrangement with the central *atom*.

Azimuthal quantum number: See *Angular momentum quantum number*.

Backbone: All regularly repeating *atoms* of a *peptide* or *protein polymer* that are not the *side chains* of *amino acids*.

Balmer series: *Emission* lines of the hydrogen atom that occur when the *electron* moves from an upper energy level down to the n = 2 level. Four of these lines are in the *visible* region of the *electromagnetic spectrum*.

Bar: The IUPAC-preferred unit of *gas* pressure.

Base Ionization Constant, K_b: An *equilibrium constant* for the reaction of a base with water to produce the *hydroxide ion*. Larger values imply a stronger base, more *hydroxide ion* formed.

Beer-Lambert Law: The mathematical relationship between *absorbance*, *molar absorptivity*, *pathlength*, and *concentration*: $A = \varepsilon \ell c$.

Bent: A *molecular shape* that results either around a *trigonal planar* central *atom* having one lone pair of *electron*s or a *tetrahedral* central *atom* having two lone pairs of *electron*s. These two types of bent *molecules* are characterized by different approximate *bond* angles. In the *trigonal planar* case the resulting *bond* angle will be slightly less than 120° and in the *tetrahedral* case the resulting *bond* angle will be slightly less than 109.5°.

Benzene: A *hydrocarbon molecule* with formula C_6H_6 that is a *liquid* at room temperature. A classic example of pi *delocalization* and *resonance*.

Beta-barrel: A *protein* structural *motif*, resulting from the rolling up of a *beta-sheet* so that the first and last strands of the sheet can *hydrogen bond* to each other. This creates a hollow tube-like structure that may serve as a pore in a *membrane*, for instance.

Beta emission: *Radioactive* decay via the loss of a *beta particle* from the *nucleus* of an *atom*; the result is a *neutron* becoming a *proton*.

Beta particle, β^-: A high energy *electron* that emanates from the *nucleus* of an *atom*, resulting in the conversion of a *neutron* into a *proton*. Symbol = $_{-1}^{0}e$.

Beta-sheet: The *protein* structure that results when multiple *beta-strands* line up length-wise and *hydrogen bond* to each other to make a sheet-like entity.

Beta-strand: A common *secondary structure* of *proteins*, in which the *polymer* chain exists as if it were being pulled straight at each end, without any appreciable twisted nature. See also: *fully extended*. The components of a *beta-sheet*. Compare to *alpha-helix*.

Bidentate ligand (*pronounced as in "pig"*)***:*** A *polydentate ligand* for which there are two simultaneous bonding interactions to the central *metal cation* or *atom*.

Bilayer: The two associated layers of a *phospholipid membrane*; each layer is one *molecule* thick. The *hydrophobic* parts of the phospholipid *molecule* are in the center of the *bilayer*.

Binary: A *compound* containing two types of *atoms*, such as H_2O or $AlCl_3$. Compare to *diatomic*.

Blunder: An avoidable experimental mistake that should discount any measurements made during the experiment.

Body-centered cubic: One of the common three-dimensional geometries utilized by *metal atoms* in *pure* metals. The *unit cell* of this geometry is a cube.

Bohr equation: $E_n = -\frac{1}{n^2}(R_H)$. Allows calculation of the allowed energies of the hydrogen *atom*'s *electron*.

Boil: (verb) To heat a *liquid* to the point where its *vapor pressure* is equal to *atmospheric pressure* and it bubbles.

Boiling: (noun) The act of bringing a *liquid* to a *boil*. The *phase change* from *liquid* to gas occurring at the temperature at which the *vapor pressure* of a *liquid* equals the atmospheric pressure.

Bond: In *molecular orbital theory*, a *bonding orbital* populated by two *electrons*. See also *Chemical Bond*.

Bond dissociation energy, BDE: The energy required to break a particular *chemical bond*. Also, the energy released when a particular *chemical bond* is formed. Often tabulated as average values for particular *bonds* existing in different *molecules*. Also called *bond energy*.

Bond energy: See *Bond dissociation energy*.

Bond order: The number of *bonds* between two *atoms* (in the *molecular orbital* model). BO = ½(bonding *electrons* – antibonding *electrons*).

Bonding interactions: The constructive overlap of *atomic orbitals* on separate *atoms* (both of positive *amplitude*, or both of negative *amplitude*). This produces a *molecular orbital* that increases *electron density* between the two nuclei. The overlap of *orbital* lobes of the same sign.

Bonding orbitals: *Molecular orbitals* that arise from *bonding interactions*. *Electrons* in bonding *orbitals* stabilize the *molecule*.

Boyle's Law: The volume of a *gas* sample is inversely proportional to the pressure when temperature is held constant. PV = constant.

Branched chain: A feature of some *polymers* that arises when two *polymer* chains depart from the same *monomer* so that the chain is no longer a simple linear form.

Bridging ligand *(pronounced as in "pig")***:** A *ligand* making *bonds* to two or more central *metal* cations or *atoms* at the same time, and thus, forming a bridge between these *metal* atoms.

Bronsted-Lowry acid: A species capable of donating a *proton* to some other species, so that a *proton transfer* occurs. Usually a species with a polarized *bond*, such that the hydrogen carries considerable positive character.

Bronsted-Lowry base: A species capable of accepting a *proton* from some other species, so that a *proton transfer* occurs. A species with an *electron* pair available for forming a new *bond* to a *proton*.

Buffer: Something that lessens or absorbs the shock of an impact, or protects by intercepting or moderating adverse influences. In acid-base *chemistry*, a *solution* whose *pH* is protected from large changes by the presence of both a *weak acid* and its *conjugate base* in the *solution*. Both members of the *conjugate pair* must be present in significant and roughly equal amounts. The buffering species react with *strong acids and bases* to moderate their influences on the *pH* of the *solution*.

Buffer capacity: The property of a *buffer solution* having to do with the concentrations of buffering components present. This property controls the amount of *strong acid* or *strong base* the *buffer* is able to moderate.

C-terminus: The end of a *peptide* or *protein polymer* that has an unbonded *carboxylic acid group*. When listing the *primary structure* of a *protein*, this is the last *amino acid* listed.

Calmodulin: Calcium-*modulating protein* found in many cells. An important part of some *signal-transduction cascades*.

Carbon dioxide: CO_2.

Carboxylate: The *carboxylic acid group* after losing its *acidic hydrogen* as H^+. The CO_2^- group.

Carboxylic acid: A *functional group*, -CO_2H. Reacts with *amine* to produce *Amide*.

Catabolism: The subset of *metabolism* that accomplishes the transformation of food *molecules* into cellular energy. Compare to *anabolism*.

Catalyst: A chemical species or material that speeds up the attainment of *equilibrium*. Both the forward and reverse reactions are affected equally.

Catalytic cycle: The stages of a reaction occurring in an *enzyme* active site; includes bonding the *substrate*, altering the *substrate*, and releasing the *substrate*. Then the *enzyme* may begin the process (the cycle) again.

Cathode ray: A beam of *electron*s emitted by the negative terminal of a power supply (the cathode) in a vacuum.

Cation: A positively charged *ion*.

Cellular respiration: The sum total of the biochemical reaction sequences necessary for the processing of food to obtain energy in the form of *ATP*.

Chain reaction: A chemical or nuclear reaction that requires an initiation event, but whose *product*s include other particles capable of initiating future events, so that the reaction sustains itself through many cycles.

Charge delocalization: The phenomenon that occurs when an increment of electric charge, such as −1, is shared between multiple *atoms* so that none of the *atoms* carries the full charge. A result of *delocalization* of *electron*s.

Charge gradient: The separation of charge across a membrane. Typical cell *membranes* have more positive charge on the outside and more negative charge on the inside. *Charge gradient*s function as an energy storage device for cells.

Charles' Law: The volume of a *gas* sample is proportional to its absolute temperature when the pressure is held constant. V/T = constant.

Chelate: Any *coordination complex* utilizing a *polydentate ligand (pronounced as in "pig")*. This word arises from the Latin word "chela" meaning pincer-like claws.

Chelating agent: Any *polydentate ligand* (particularly *hexadentate*, such as *EDTA*) that can *sequester* a *metal ion* in *solution*, thus preventing it from reacting with any other *ligand*s.

Chelating ligands (pronounced as in "pig"): See *Polydentate ligands*, or *Chelating agent*.

Chelation therapy: Medical use of a *chelating agent* to detoxify poisonous *metal ion*s until they can be excreted from the body.

Chemical bonds: The strong forces that hold *atoms* to one another in *elements* (*metal* networks, *covalent networks* like diamond, *molecules* such as H_2 or S_8) or *compounds*. Range from perfectly *covalent*, to *polar* covalent, to *ionic*, depending on the difference in *electronegativity* of the two *atoms*. Compare to *Intermolecular attraction*. Also includes *metallic bonds*.

Chemical change: Also called a "*chemical reaction*". A process resulting in at least one *substance* changing into a different *substance*, thus a *chemical formula* must change (exception: if one *isomer* changes into another the formula does not necessarily change). *Chemical bonds* must be broken, formed, or both.

Chemical equation: The chemist's shorthand notation describing the overall changes occurring to *substance*s during a *chemical reaction*. This notation can also be used to describe a variety of *physical changes* (*phase changes*).

Chemical equilibrium: See *Equilibrium*.

Chemical formula: A representation of a *substance* that indicates the relative numbers of different *atoms* present using atomic symbols and numeric subscripts.

Chemical property: Any property of *matter* that describes its reactivity.

Chemical reaction: See *Chemical change*.

Chemical reaction equation: See *Chemical equation*.

Chemistry: The science of *matter* and the changes that *matter* undergoes.

Chiral: The circumstance of having a *nonsuperimposable* mirror image. Also called *asymmetric*.

Cis: A description of a chemical structure indicating that a *geometric isomer* has like *group*s side-by-side rather than opposite of each other. Compare to *trans*.

Cisplatin: The *cis* isomer of the *square planar* complex, $PtCl_2(NH_3)_2$. A widely used chemotherapeutic agent. Crosslinks DNA, causing *distortion*s in its structure that prevent *replication*.

Cofactor: A non-*protein* species that is an integral part of a working *protein molecule*, but is usually not covalently bonded to the *protein*. Example: *heme molecule* of *hemoglobin*.

Colligative property: Any property of a *solution* that depends on the number of dissolved particles rather than the identity of the dissolved particles. For example, boiling point elevation and *freezing* point depression.

Combustion: A type of *chemical reaction* characterized by the use of molecular oxygen as a *reactant* and an *exothermic* nature (giving off both heat and light). These reactions are often described as "burning."

Combustion analysis: May also be called "*elemental analysis*." The process of combusting a *pure* unknown *substance* in a sealed container and trapping *combustion product*s such as CO_2 and H_2O in preweighed traps to determine the *empirical formula* of the *substance*.

Common ion: An *ion* that is part of a reaction system, but comes from some source other than the reaction system.

Common Ion Effect: The effect, via *LeChatelier's Principle*, of a *common ion* on a reaction system's *equilibrium position*.

Complete ionic equation: See *Ionic equation*. The use of the word "complete" emphasizes the case wherein no species have been cancelled in order to produce a *net ionic equation*.

Complex ion: An *ionic* species containing a central *metal ion* or *atom* bonded to one or more *ligands* (*pronounced as in "pig"*). Also called a *coordination complex*.

Complementary colors: Any two colors directly across from each other on a traditional color wheel.

Compound: A *substance* composed of two or more *elements* in a fixed ratio. Can have either a molecular or network structure.

Concentration factor: For a *dilution* process, the ratio of the final concentration/initial concentration or initial volume/final volume; a value less than 1.0 that when multiplied by the concentration of an initial *solution* gives the concentration of the *diluted* solution. The reciprocal of the *dilution factor*.

Concentration gradient: The existence of different concentrations of a particular species on the two sides of a *membrane*. *Concentration gradient*s function as an energy storage device for cells. If the species is an *ion*, the *concentration gradient* may contribute to a *charge gradient*.

Condensation: The *phase change* from *gas* to *liquid*, or *gas* to *solid* (this case can also be called *vapor deposition*).

Configuration: Two *nonsuperimposable shape*s of a bonded system that can only be interchanged by breaking and re-forming a *covalent bond*, thus these two *shape*s are represent different *substances*. Compare to *Conformation*.

Conformation: Any of an infinite number of possible spatial arrangements of a *molecule* that result from *internal rotations* of *single bond*s and thus can be accessed without breaking any *covalent bonds*. An aspect of *molecular shape* that is in constant *flux* at any reasonable temperature.

Conjugate acid: The member of a *conjugate pair* that has the *proton*. This species is one increment more positive than the *conjugate base*.

Conjugate base: The member of a *conjugate pair* that does not have the *proton*. This species carries the *electron* pair that can form a *bond* to the *proton*. This species is one increment more negative than the *conjugate acid*.

Conjugate pair: Two chemical species whose structures differ by a single *proton* (and therefore, also a single charge increment). The members of a *conjugate pair* are known as the *conjugate acid* and the *conjugate base*.

Conjugated: The structural characteristic of having alternating single and *double bond*s, such as: $-C=C-C=C-$. Large *conjugated* systems are necessary for the *absorption* of *visible light* by *organic molecule*s.

Conserved residue: A particular *amino acid residue* that exists at the same position in a variety of related *proteins*, such as *alpha-* and *beta-chains* of *hemoglobin* or *myoglobin* from different species. When a particular *amino acid* is in the same position in many versions of the same *protein polymer*, the assumption is made that the structure and/or function of the *protein* is disrupted by any *mutation* that results in a different *amino acid* at that position.

Constructive interference: The overlap of waves of the same sign, such that the overall *amplitude* of the resulting wave is enhanced.

Continuum: a continuous sequence in which adjacent items are not perceptively different from one another, although the extremes are distinct. A number line (of real numbers) is a *continuum*, but the set of whole numbers is not. The opposite of *quantization*.

Conversion factor: A ratio with a value equivalent to 1.0 because the numerator and the denominator have the same value, but different units.

Cooperative binding: A phenomenon associated with *proteins* composed of multiple *subunits*, wherein the binding of *substrate* to one *subunit* causes structural rearrangements that make it easier for the *substrate* to bind to the other *subunit*(s). Of O_2 by *hemoglobin*: The phenomenon that is characterized by an increase in affinity between a multi-*subunit protein* and its binding partner as more of the binding partner binds. *Hemoglobin* has four oxygen-binding sites per *molecule*. The affinity of a *hemoglobin molecule* for molecular oxygen increases as the more of the sites are utilized.

Cooperativity: The phenomenon wherein the binding of one *substrate* or *ligand* (*lye'-gand*) makes it either easier or more difficult for the next *substrate* or *ligand* to bind. *Cooperativity* requires multi-*subunit* structures (*quaternary structure*). See *positive cooperativity* and *negative cooperativity*.

Coordinate covalent bond: A covalent *bond* that arises when an *orbital* containing 2 *electrons* on one species interacts with an empty *orbital* on another species, creating a 2-*electron bond*. This covalent *bond* is indistinguishable from one in which each species supplies one of the bonding *electrons*. Also called *Dative bond*.

Coordination chemistry: The study of structures, properties, and reactivity of *coordination complexes*.

Coordination complex: *Covalently* bonded *molecule*s or *ions*, usually consisting of a *transition metal* center with one or more bonded *ligands (pronounced as in "pig")*. The covalent bonds are *coordinate covalent bonds*, with the bonding *electrons* supplied by the *ligands*.

Coordination compound: Neutral *compounds* comprised of a central *metal cation* or *atom* surrounded by attached *groups* (*ligands, pronounced as in "pig"*).

Coordination number: (CN) The number of *atoms* (from *ligands, pronounced as in "pig"*) attached to the central *metal atom* or *cation*.

Co-polymer: A *polymer* made from a least two different *monomers*.

Correction factor: A value that is added or subtracted when a unit conversion is performed. This is necessary when the zero points of the two unit systems do not coincide—such as occurs for many temperature conversions.

Coulomb's constant, k_e: The proportionality constant found in the equation describing the energy of interaction of two point charges: $E = k_e \frac{Q_1 Q_2}{r}$, $k_e = 2.31 \times 10^{-28}$ J·m.

Coupled: Two biological or biochemical processes that require each other in order to achieve an end result.

Covalent bonds: *Chemical bonds* arising from the sharing of *electron*s, found primarily in *molecules*, *covalent networks*, and *polyatomic ions*. For contrast, see *Ionic bonds*.

Covalent crystal: A regularly repeating three-dimensional arrangement of atoms that are bonded utilizing an uninterrupted series of *covalent bonds*, for example the carbon *atoms* in diamond. Compare to *molecular crystal* and *ionic crystal*.

Covalent network: A three-dimensional arrangement of *atoms* that are bonded utilizing an uninterrupted series of *covalent bonds*, for example carbon *atoms* in coal.

Covalent radius: A measure of the size of neutral *atoms*. Usually measured as half of a *nucleus*-to-*nucleus* value in a variety of bonding situations and averaged.

Covalent solid: Any *covalent network* or *covalent crystal*.

Crystal: A *solid* material having a regularly repeating three-dimensional array of fundamental building units, either *atoms*, *molecules* or *ions*. See *covalent crystal*, *metallic crystal*, *molecular crystal*, *ionic crystal*.

Crystallization: The formation of *crystals* when a *solid* comes out of *solution*.

Cuvette: Sample cells of particular *path lengths* for use in *spectrophotometry* experiments.

Cytochrome c: A small *protein* (~12,000 g/mol) that is involved in the *electron* transport system of the mitochondria. It carries *electron*s from one multi*enzyme* complex to another by traveling along the outer surface of the mitochondria.

Cytoplasm: The complex gel-like *solution* making up the contents of a living cell.

d block elements: Any *element* whose highest energy ground state *electron* is in a *d orbital*. *Elements* in *group*s 3-12 of the *periodic table*, also called the *transition metals*.

Daughter nuclide: The *product nuclide(s)* of *radioactive* decay; compare to *parent nuclide*.

Dalton's Law (of Partial Pressures): The sum of the *partial pressures* of the components of a *gas mixture* is equal to the total pressure of the system.

Dative bond: See *Coordinate covalent bonds*.

de Broglie Wavelength: The *wavelength* of energy associated with the motion of a particle. $\lambda = h / mv$.

Debye: A small unit of measure of a *dipole moment*. 3×10^{29} *debye* = 1 C·m. The magnitude of a *dipole moment* is related to the amount of charge separated (coulomb, C) and the distance over which the separation occurs (meter, m).

Decomposition: A reaction featuring the loss of one or more strong *bonds* so that the *reactant* is broken into two (or more) smaller pieces.

Degenerate: An adjective indicating that different *orbitals*, *electrons*, etc. are energetically identical.

Delayed neutrons: *Neutrons* released upon the *radioactive* decay of *daughter nuclides* during an *induced fission chain reaction*.

Delocalized: Not concentrated in a particular area; distributed over a broad area, often used with "*electron*" or "charge."

Delocalization: A phenomenon that can refer to either *electron*s or charge and is characterized by the distribution of the *electron* or charge over more than two *atoms* in a bonded system.

Delta bond: A *bonding interaction* formed by the side-by-side interaction of two *d orbital*s. There are four regions of *electron density* surrounding, but not including, the line between the two nuclei.

Density: The mass of a sample of *matter* divided by its volume. Or, a number that represents the probability of finding a particle at a particular point in space, as in *electron density*.

Deoxygenated conformation: The *tertiary structure* of the *hemoglobin tetramer* that is less favorable for oxygen bonding. Compare to *Oxygenated conformation*.

Dependent variable: A category of measurement whose value depends on some other variable. On a graph, the *dependent variable* is usually found on the y-axis. See also: *Independent variable*.

Destructive interference: The overlap of waves such that where one has positive *amplitude*, the other has negative *amplitude*. Thus, the waves cancel each other out.

Diamagnetic: A species with zero unpaired *electron*s. These species are slightly repelled by a magnetic field.

Diatomic: Having a *covalent* structure featuring just two *atoms* (compare to *binary*). The two atoms can be of the same *element* or different *element*s. The diatomic particle can be either a neutral particle (a *molecule*, such as HCl or N_2) or a charged particle (a diatomic *ion*, such as O_2^{2-}). See also *homonuclear diatomics* and *heteronuclear diatomics*.

Diffuse: The movement of the particles of two or more *gases*, allowing them to mix with one another. See also *Graham's Law*. Also, the movement of *solute* particles in a *solution*.

Dilute: A verb meaning to add *solvent*, thus decreasing the concentration of a *solute*. Sometimes used as a *qualitative* way of indicating a *solution* containing only a small amount of dissolved material. Can be a *saturated solution*, if the *solute* has a very limited *solubility*.

Dilution: The addition of more *solvent* to a *solution*, rendering the *solution* less concentrated. $M_1V_1 = M_2V_2$. See also *Serial dilution*.

Dilution factor: For a *dilution* process, the ratio of the initial concentration to final concentration or final volume over initial volume; a value greater than 1.0 provides the concentration of a *dilute*d *solution* when the initial concentration is divided by the *dilution factor*. The reciprocal of the *concentration factor*.

Dimensional analysis: The use of *conversion factor* ratios to communicate the logic of a mathematical transformation.

Dimer: A single particle made by joining two identical (or similar) pieces.

Dipeptide: A *dimer* that is made by joining two *amino acids* with a *peptide bond*.

Dipolar (adj.): The property of being a *dipole*.

Dipole: Any particle that maintains a separation of charge, such that there is a positively charged region and a negatively charged region.

Dipole-dipole attraction or dipole-dipole interaction: A mid-strength *intermolecular attraction* arising when *dipolar* particles attract each other. An *electrostatic* attraction of permanent *dipole*s.

Dipole-induced dipole: An attraction between a permanent *dipole* and an *induced dipole* such as might occur when a *polarizable molecule* is placed into water.

Dipole moment: A measure of the degree of *polarity* of a *molecule*. See *Debye*.

Diprotic acid: A *Bronsted-Lowry acid* with two acidic *protons*.

Dispersion force: Also called *London dispersion force*. The weakest type of *intermolecular attraction*. Arise from the formation of *instantaneous dipoles* and *induced dipoles* in otherwise *nonpolar* particles. A weak, short-lived *electrostatic* attraction between neighboring particles.

Dissipate: To disperse, as a *gas* into the *atmosphere*.

Dissociate: The loss of a bonding interaction of some type, allowing particles that had been bonded to move independently, or creating two particles out of one particle. When a *salt* dissolves in water, for instance, the ions *dissociate* from one another.

Dissociation: The process of a larger chemical species breaking into smaller pieces by loss of at least one *bond*.

Dissociation constant, K$_D$: An *equilibrium constant* for the *dissociation* of a biological complex into its component parts, such as a *protein*-hormone complex or a *protein-substrate* complex. Larger values imply a complex with weaker bonding. The reciprocal of the *association constant*.

Distortions: (from ideal geometries) Small deviations from the ideal geometries indicated by the *steric number* due to some *electron* sets taking up more space than others.

Divalent cation: Any *cation* having a charge of +2.

Donor: The species that gives something away. In *hydrogen bonding*, the *molecule* whose hydrogen *atom* is at the center of the *hydrogen bond*. Compare to *Acceptor*. In *Bronsted-Lowry theory* the *acid* is the *donor* of an H$^+$. In Lewis *theory* the *Lewis base* is a *donor* of a lone pair of *electrons*. In *oxidation-reduction chemistry* the *reducing agent* is the *donor* of *electrons*.

Donor atom: The *atom* of a *ligand (pronounced as in "pig")* that acts like a *Lewis base* by donating a pair of *electrons* to make the *coordinate covalent bond* to the *metal atom* center of a *coordination complex*.

Dosage rate: The number of *radioactive* decay events occurring in a specific period of time. Related to the *half-life* of the decay process.

Double bond: A *bond* that results from the sharing of four *electrons*. Usually one *sigma* and one *pi bond*. Double bonds prohibit *internal rotation*. May display *cis* and *trans* character.

Double displacement: A *chemical reaction* wherein two *salts* rearrange *anion-cation* partners. Alos called *metathesis*.

Dual nature: The characteristic of having properties of both waves and particles. Applies to *electromagnetic radiation* and very small particles, such as the *electron*.

Ductile: A property of *metals* indicating that they can be pulled into wires.

Duet: A term describing hydrogen *atom*'s need to be surrounded only by two *valence electrons* in a bonded system. Compare to *Octet*.

Duplex DNA: The most familiar double-helical form of DNA; it utilizes *pi-stacking* and *hydrogen bonding* for stabilization.

Dynamic equilibrium: The state that a *reversible chemical reaction* achieves wherein no net change in concentrations is occurring over time, even though both the forward and reverse reactions are proceeding. The forward and reverse reactions are proceeding at identical rates.

Eclipsed conformation: A *conformation* in which the *atoms* bonded to one *atom* are exactly lined up with the *atoms* bonded to a neighboring *atom* when viewed along the *bond* axis. Compare to *Staggered conformation*.

Effective nuclear charge, Z_{eff}: The positive charge actually experienced by any particular *electron* in an *atom*. For one-*electron atoms*, $Z_{eff} = Z$ (the nuclear charge). In the case of multiple *electron* systems, $Z_{eff} < Z$ due to *screening/shielding* effects.

Effector: A small *molecule* that binds to a *protein* and affects its activity.

Effuse: Movement of *gas* particles through a small opening, into a vacuum. See also *Graham's Law*.

Electric, or Electrical: Of, or pertaining to electricity. Charges flowing in wires. Compare to *Electronic*.

Electrolyte: A *compound* that releases *ions* in *aqueous solution*, and, thus, forms a *solution* that is capable of conducting an electric current.

Electromagnetic (EM) radiation: Energy that propagates through space as magnetic and electrical field waves.

Electromagnetic spectrum: The wide array of *electromagnetic radiation* types arranged by *wavelength* (or *frequency* or energy) and often grouped by family, such as *ultraviolet, infrared, visible* or *microwave*.

Electron: A *subatomic particle* carrying negative charge and found outside of the *nucleus* of an *atom*. *Electrons* are responsible for the *bonds* formed between *atoms*; rearrangements of *electrons* are responsible for *chemical changes*. Mass = 9.1094×10^{-31} kg.

Electron affinity: The amount of energy necessary to remove an *electron* from a *gas phase*, *monatomic ion* of –1 charge. The amount of energy necessary to achieve the following:

$$A^-(g) \longrightarrow A(g) + e^-$$

Electron capture: A nuclear change event wherein a core *electron* of the *atom* is captured by the *nucleus*, thus converting a *proton* into a *neutron*; compare to *positron emission*. The *atom*'s *elemental* identity is changed by the decrease in Z. The new *atom* is still uncharged because the decrease in Z is accompanied by the loss of a core *electron*.

Electron configuration: A listing of the arrangement of *electrons* in an *atom* without specifying the arrangement of *electrons* within a *subshell*. Compare to *Orbital diagram*.

Electron pair geometry: The geometries that occur around a central *atom* based on the number of *atoms* bonded to the central *atom* and the number of lone pairs on the central *atom*.

Electron transfer: A chemical event featuring one or more *electrons* moving from a *donor* particle to an *acceptor* particle. *Electron transfer* is also called *oxidation-reduction*, where the *donor* of the *electrons* becomes *oxidized* and the *acceptor* becomes *reduced*.

Electronegative: An adjective used in describing *atoms* having a high degree of *electronegativity*. *Atoms* that more strongly attract shared *electrons* are said to be more electronegative.

Electronegativity: The ability of an *atom* to attract shared *electrons* when in a bonded situation.

Electronic: Of, or pertaining to, one or more *electrons*. Compare to *Electric*.

Electrostatic: Having to do with interactions of stationary charges.

Element: *Substances* that cannot be converted into simpler *substances* by *chemical changes*. *Atoms* with a particular number of *protons* in the *nucleus* represent distinct chemical *elements*. So, for instance, any *atom* with six *protons* in the *nucleus* is a carbon *atom*. Carbon is one of the (about) 118 different known *elements*.

Elemental: Of, or pertaining to, an *element*.

Elemental analysis: See *combustion analysis*.

Elementary charge: The magnitude of *electronic* charge carried by a single *proton* or *electron*, $1.60217662 \times 10^{-19}$ coulombs, C. First measured via the oil drop experiments of Robert Millikan. Because all charges have this charge as the fundamental base, charges are often referred to simply by the multiple of the base charge that is appropriate. Thus a charge of +2 means to multiply the *elementary charge* by +2, while a charge of −1 means to multiple the *elementary charge* by −1.

Elimination reaction: A *chemical reaction* that is characterized by the formation of a small stable *molecule* such as HCl or H_2O. The formation of *esters* (from *alcohol* and *carboxylic acid*) and *amides* (from *amine* and *carboxylic acid*) are examples.

Emission: The discharge or release of *electromagnetic radiation* (energy) that occurs when *electrons* move from higher to lower energy levels. Compare to *absorption* and *transmission*.

Empirical formula: The *chemical formula* that represents the simplest whole number ratio of the *atoms* of each *element* in a *substance*. This formula may, or may not, be the actual formula of the *substance*.

Enantiomers: See *Optical isomers*.

End point: The point during a *titration* at which the *indicator* changes colors. Compare to *equivalence point*.

Endothermic: A process that absorbs heat from the surroundings as it occurs.

Enzyme: Any *protein* whose biological task is to catalyze a *chemical reaction*.

Equilibrium: A stage reached by a *reversible* reaction or process, when the forward reaction and the reverse reaction are occurring at identical rates, so that no net change is taking place. See *dynamic equilibrium*.

Equilibrium composition: See *equilibrium position*.

Equilibrium concentration expression: The entries in the bottom row of an *equilibrium table* that give expected *equilibrium concentrations* in terms of a variable "x."

Equilibrium concentration: The concentration of a reaction component once the equilibrium state has been achieved. Used to calculate the value of the *equilibrium constant*.

Equilibrium Constant, K_{eq}: The final achievable value of the *reaction quotient*, Q for a particular reaction at a particular temperature. This value is independent of the amount of material in the system but dependent on temperature. The value of Q when *equilibrium* status has been achieved.

For the reaction: $aA(g) + bB(aq) \rightleftharpoons cC(aq) + dD(g)$, $K_{eq} = \dfrac{[C]_{eq}^{c}(P_D)_{eq}^{d}}{(P_A)_{eq}^{a}[B]_{eq}^{b}}$.

Comparison to Q value. Other versions include K_c (where molarities are used for both *solutes* and *gases*) and K_p (where only *partial pressures* are used, thus there cannot be any *solutes*).

Equilibrium constant expression: The formula for K_{eq} (or K_c or K_p) for a given reaction, in terms of products divided by reactants. The general form of such an expression is $K_{eq} = \dfrac{[C]_{eq}^c (P_D)_{eq}^d}{(P_A)_{eq}^a [B]_{eq}^b}$ for the reaction equation, $aA(g) + bB(aq) \rightleftharpoons cC(aq) + dD(g)$.

Equilibrium position: A list of the *concentrations* or *partial pressures* of each reaction species (except for *pure solids* or *pure liquids*) when a reaction system has attained *equilibrium* status.

Equilibrium table: Can also be called an *ICE table*. A tool for use in the determination of the extent of reaction that will occur for a *reversible* system. This tool allows the calculation of *equilibrium concentrations* from a knowledge of the *equilibrium constant*. Table entries are in units of *molarity* or *bars*.

Equivalence point: The point during a *titration* at which the *titrant* has been added to the reaction flask in exactly *stoichiometric* amounts.

Equivalent structures: *Resonance* structures that are identical except for spatial *orientation*.

Essentially insoluble: A *substance* that is so poorly soluble that the amount that dissolves cannot be determined in any straightforward way.

Ester: A *functional group*, R-(C=O)-O-R that can be made by reaction of *alcohol* + *carboxylic acid*.

Ethane: A *hydrocarbon* with formula C_2H_6.

Ether: A *functional group*, R-O-R.

Ethylene: A *hydrocarbon* with formula C_2H_4.

Evacuate: The act of removing all *substances*, including *gases*, from a container, thus producing an *evacuated* container. An *evacuated* container is a vacuum.

Evaporation: The *phase change* from *liquid* to *gas* that occurs below the boiling temperature of the liquid.

Excited states: Any *electronic* energy that is not the *ground electronic state*.

Exothermic: A process that liberates heat to the surroundings as it occurs.

Extract: The act of performing an *extraction*.

Extraction: The spontaneous movement of a *solute* from one *solvent* to another.

Extrapolation: The inference of an unknown value using trends in a data set or graph that does not include the value being pursued. See also: *Interpolation*.

f block elements: Also called the *lanthanides* and *actinides*. Any *element* whose highest energy ground state *electron* is placed in an *f orbital*. *Element*s 58-71 (*lanthanides*) and 90-103 (*actinides*).

Face-centered cubic: One of the common three-dimensional geometries utilized by *metal atoms* in *pure metals*. The *unit cell* of this geometry is a cube.

Facial (fac) isomer: *Octahedral isomer* of a MY_3Z_3 complex in which three identical *ligands* (*pronounced as in "pig"*) are found on the same triangular face of the structure. Compare to *Meridional (mer) isomer*.

Fatty acid: A naturally occurring relatively simple *amphiphile* having a *nonpolar hydrocarbon* chain ending in a *polar carboxylic acid group*.

First messenger: Any *molecule* or *ion*, such as hormones, that is produced by a gland and travels to particular cells to deliver a message by bonding to a component of the outer cell membrane. Compare to *second messenger*.

Fission: Any nuclear event in which a parent *nuclide* breaks into two or more less massive *nuclides*.

Flip-flop: See *Trans bilayer movement*.

Fluid Mosaic Model: A model that describes the structure of cell *membranes* as flexible *bilayers* made up of *phospholipid molecules* that can meander about in their own layer of the *bilayer* and interspersed with large *protein molecules* that do the work of the membrane and that can also *diffuse* through the *bilayer*.

Fluoroacetate: Acetate *ion* with one hydrogen *atom* replaced with a fluorine *atom*. A poison, $FCH_2CO_2^-$.

Flux: Biochemical *flux* involves the sequential performance of a series of *enzymes* to accomplish the overall transformation of a *substrate* into some necessary *product*. The word "flux" implies a *continuum* of change, which is accurate in that all of the *enzymes* in the process tend to be engaged with their own transformation at the same time as *substrates* move from one to the next.

Formal charge: A number assigned to *atoms* in a *Lewis dot structure*. Each *atom* is assigned all of its lone pair *electrons* and half of its bonding *electrons*. These *valence electrons* are subtracted from the number of *valence electrons* the neutral *atom* should have. *Formal charge* magnitudes are used as a tool to evaluate whether a particular structure is likely a good match to reality.

Formation Constant, K_f: An *equilibrium constant* for the reaction of a *metal cation* with a *ligand* (*pronounced as in "pig"*) to form a *complex ion*. The reciprocal of the *stability constant*. Larger values imply a more stable *complex ion*.

Formula mass: The sum of the *atomic masses* of the *atoms* in a *chemical formula*. Can be in *atomic mass units* or grams per *mole*. In the case of grams per *mole* the average *formula mass* will result.

Frequency, v: The number of waves (mechanical or electromagnetic) passing a particular point in a period of time. Units = 1/time.

Freezing: The *phase change* from *liquid* to *solid*.

Frontier orbitals: The *HOMO* and *LUMO molecular orbitals*.

Fully extended: Related to the *bond* angles of a *molecule* or *polymer* that exists as if its ends are being pulled hard in opposite directions; the lack of coiling in a *polymer*.

Functional group: Any of several common sets of *atoms* bonded in a particular *motif* that is found in a wide variety of *molecules*.

Gas: One of the common states, or *phases*, of *matter*, that is characterized by completely filling any container and having relatively large distances between neighboring *particles*.

Gay-Lussac's Law: See *Charles' Law*.

Geometric isomerism: A type of *stereoisomerism* characterized by same set of *bonds*, but a different spatial arrangement of the *bonds*. Being *nonsuperimposable*, but not mirror images. Compare to *optical isomerism*.

Geometric isomers: *Stereoisomers* (in which the all of the same *bonds* exist) having different spatial relationships between various *atoms*. *Cis* and *trans isomers*, for example.

Globin: A general name for any single *protein* chain that has the same general structure as a *myoglobin* chain.

Globular protein: A *protein* whose *polymer* chain is folded back on itself multiple times so that a compact, roughly spherical overall shape is achieved.

Glycolysis: A pathway within *catabolism* wherein *glucose* is converted to pyruvate and *ATP* is produced.

Glycolytic pathway: A series of 10-11 biochemical reactions starting with glucose and ending with either pyruvate (aerobic conditions) or lactic acid (anaerobic conditions) and producing a modest amount of *ATP* for the cell.

Graham's Law: The inverse relationship between the average speeds of *gas* particles and their molar masses. $\dfrac{u_1}{u_2} = \sqrt{\dfrac{M_2}{M_1}}$ Alternate form: $\dfrac{t_2}{t_1} = \sqrt{\dfrac{M_2}{M_1}}$ where t is the time necessary for traveling a particular distance.

Ground electronic state: (or just **ground state**) The lowest possible energy of an *electron* associated with a chemical structure, such as an *atom*. An *atom* or *molecule* having every *electron* is in the lowest energy state possible.

Group: Sets of *elements* related by similar properties and found in the same column of the *periodic table*. Also, reoccurring sets of atoms found in a large variety of *molecules*, such as in *functional group*.

Group numbers: The numbers 1-18 displayed over the columns of a *periodic table*. Some *groups* have a name in addition to the *group* number.

Half-equivalence point: The point during a *titration* at which the *titrant* has been added to the reaction flask in exactly half of the *stoichiometric* amount. At the *half-equivalence* point of the *titration* of a *weak acid* or a *weak base*, pH = pK$_a$.

Half-life: The amount of time (measured in years, hours, minutes) that it takes for half of a sample of a specific *radioactive nuclide* to undergo the decay event. See also: *dosage rate*.

Half reaction: A *reaction equation* that describes only the *reduction* half, or *oxidation* half, of an *oxidation-reduction reaction*. These reaction equations always show *electrons* (e^-) as either a *reactant (reduction half reaction)* or *product (oxidation half reaction)*.

Halide: A negatively charged *halogen ion* such as F^-, Cl^-, Br^-, I^-, whose names are fluoride, chloride, bromide, and iodide. Compare to *halogen*.

Halogen: Any *element* of *Group* 17 (F_2, Cl_2, Br_2, I_2) whose individual names are fluorine, chlorine, bromine, and iodine.

Haworth projection: A style of drawing cyclized sugars that simplifies the geometries and promotes ease of comparison between structures.

Heisenberg Uncertainty Principle: $\Delta p \Delta x \geq \dfrac{h}{4\pi}$. There is an absolute limit $\left(\dfrac{h}{4\pi} = 1.0546 \times 10^{-34} \dfrac{kg \cdot m^2}{s} \right)$ to how well the position and momentum of an *electron* can be known. The *product* of the uncertainties cannot be zero, or anything less than $\dfrac{h}{4\pi}$.

Heme: The *square-planar coordination complex* that serves as a *cofactor* to *hemoglobin* and *myoglobin*. The complex is centered on an Fe^{2+} *ion*. One *coordinate covalent bond* connects the *heme* to the *protein* utilizing the side chain of a histidine *residue* as the fifth *ligand (pronounced as in "pig")*. The sixth *ligand* is the oxygen *molecule* that is reversibly bonded.

Hemoglobin: A *protein* in the *globin* family. An oxygen-delivery *protein molecule* that is present in large supplies in red blood cells. Hemoglobin presents all four levels of *protein* architecture: *primary*, *secondary*, *tertiary* and *quaternary*. It has a tetrameric *subunit* structure.

Henderson-Hasselbalch Equation: An equation derived from a K_a expression by taking –log of both sides and rearranging: $pH = pK_a + \log\left(\dfrac{\left[A^-\right]}{\left[HA\right]}\right)$.

Henry's Law: The mathematical relationship between the concentration of a dissolved *gas* and the *partial pressure* of that *gas* in the *atmosphere* over the *solution*.

Henry's Law constant: The proportionality constant, k_H, found in *Henry's Law*.

Heteroatom: Any atom other than C or H in a carbon-based *molecule*.

Heterogeneous: Any material whose composition is not the same for multiple samples. A *mixture* that does not have a uniform composition throughout.

Heteronuclear diatomic: A diatomic *molecule* whose two *atoms* are not of the same *element*.

Heterotropic: Describing an *effector* that is not the normal *substrate*, or *ligand (lye'-gand)*, of a protein.

Hexadentate ligand: A *ligand (pronounced as in "pig")* that makes six simultaneous bonding interactions with a central *metal atom*, thus producing an *octahedral complex*.

Hexagonal close-packed: One of the common geometries of *metal atoms* in *solid metals* wherein the nuclei of neighboring *atoms* trace out the corners of a hexagon.

H-FON attraction: An alternative name for a *hydrogen bond* that emphasizes the need for fluorine, oxygen or nitrogen *atoms* in both *molecules* of the *hydrogen bond*.

High spin case: When the t_{2g} and e_g *molecular orbitals* of an *octahedral coordination complex* fill as though they were all at the same energy. Caused by a *weak field ligand (pronounced as in "pig")* and results in maximizing the number of unpaired *electrons*. Compare to *low spin case*.

HOMO: Highest occupied *molecular orbital*. The highest energy *molecular orbital* that holds at least one *electron*. Sometimes called a *frontier orbital*. Compare to *LUMO*.

Homogeneous: Having a uniform composition throughout, such that any sample has the same composition as any other sample. *Pure elements* (such as nitrogen *gas*, N_2) and *pure compounds* (such as water, H_2O) are always *homogeneous*.

Homogeneous mixture: Any *mixture* having a uniform composition throughout; *homogeneous mixtures* are also called *solutions*. Table *salt* dissolved in water is an example of a *homogeneous solution*.

Homologous: *Proteins* having the same *amino acid* at a particular position are said to be *homologous* at that site.

Homonuclear diatomic: A diatomic *molecule* or *ion* wherein both *atoms* are the same *element*.

Homopolymer: A *polymer* made from just a single *monomer* unit, repeating.

Hund's Rule: *Electrons* tend to occupy separate *orbitals* in a *subshell* and to have *parallel spins*.

Hybrid atomic orbitals (or just hybrid orbitals): A hypothesized "new" set of *atomic orbitals* acquired by "mixing" of some number of *s*, *p*, and/or *d atomic orbitals*. Not the best description of covalent bonding available (see *Molecular orbital theory*) but historically useful in explaining the geometries of many *molecules*.

Hybridize: The process of forming *hybrid atomic orbitals* from *atomic orbitals*.

Hydracid: A *Bronsted-Lowry acid* whose acidic hydrogen *atom* is not covalently bonded to an oxygen *atom*, but to some other electronegative *atom* instead.

Hydrated: Existing in close *association* with one or more water *molecules*.

Hydration: The process of becoming closely associated with one or more water *molecules*.

Hydration shell: A *solvation shell* when the *solvent* is water.

Hydrocarbon: Any *compound* containing only carbon and hydrogen *atoms*.

Hydrogen bond: Also called "*H-FON attraction.*" One type of *intermolecular attraction* characterized by a strong *electrostatic* attraction between the positively charged hydrogen of one *molecule* with the negatively charged fluorine, oxygen, or nitrogen *atom* of another *molecule*. The hydrogen *atom* involved must be bonded to a fluorine, oxygen, or nitrogen *atom* in order for the *polarity* of the *bond* to be large enough to lead to a *hydrogen bond*.

Hydrogenation: The addition of hydrogen *atoms* to a *molecule* by reaction with H_2.

Hydrolysis: Any *chemical reaction* utilizing water *molecules* to cause breakage of one or more *bonds* in another *molecule* or *ion*.

Hydrolyze: The process by which a reaction with a water *molecule* causes the removal of a group of *atoms* from another species.

Hydronium ion: The H_3O^+ *ion* formed when a *proton bonds* with a water *molecule*. The species responsible for acidic properties of *aqueous solutions*.

Hydrophobic: An adjective describing a species that is *nonpolar* and therefore does not interact well with water. Literally, water hating.

Hydrophobic effect: The force by which *hydrophobic* particles in *aqueous* systems are pushed together by water in order to limit the poor interactions between *polar* water and the *hydrophobic* material.

Hydrophobic interaction: The conglomeration of *nonpolar* species in *aqueous* systems caused by water trying to minimize its own contact area with the *hydrophobic* species.

Hydrophobic tail: The long *nonpolar hydrocarbon* chain of a *fatty acid* or phospholipid *molecule*.

Hydroxide ion: The OH^- *ion* formed from a water *molecule* when it loses a *proton* to a base. The species responsible for basic properties of *aqueous solutions*.

Hygroscopic: A material that absorbs water *molecules* from the *atmosphere* into its crystal structure, thus forming a hydrate. It is very difficult to obtain an accurate mass measurement on a hygroscopic *substance* because its mass keeps increasing as water *molecules* are attracted into the structure.

Hypocalemia: Having too few calcium *ions* in one's cells. Can lead to cardiac arrest.

Hypothesis: A possible explanation for a phenomenon that must undergo testing before being accepted as *theory*.

ICE table: See *Equilibrium table*.

Ideal gas: A *gas* that behaves as if there are no attractive or repulsive forces between *particles* and as if the particles have no volume.

Ideal gas law: PV = nRT. *Ideal gases* show behavior consistent with this mathematical relationship. Variant form: PM = dRT.

Immiscible: The adjective describing two *liquids* that are unable to dissolve in one another; thus forming layers, with the denser *liquid* at the bottom.

Independent variable: A category of measurement whose value does not depend on other types of measurements. A scientist may decide to study how some other variable's values depend on that of the *independent variable*. On a graph, the *independent variable* is usually found on the *x*-axis. See also: *Dependent variable*.

Indicator: In acid-base *chemistry*, a species whose color changes over a small pH range, useful for the identification of the *equivalence point* of an acid-base *titration*.

Induced dipole: A short-lived *dipole* produced by proximity to another *dipolar* species.

Induced fission: A nuclear *fission* event (a large *parent nuclide* breaking to produce two smaller *nuclides*) that occurs only when initiated by bombardment with *neutrons* from some other source. Compare to *spontaneous fission*.

Inert: An essentially non-reactive *substance*. The *noble gases* are usually *inert*.

Infrared (IR) radiation: *Electromagnetic radiation* with *wavelengths* generally between 700 nm and 1 mm. IR radiation is less energetic than *ultraviolet* or *visible radiation*. *Absorption* of IR radiation by chemical *substances* may cause *bonds* to vibrate. IR radiation is synonymous with heat.

Inner leaf: The layer of a lipid *bilayer* that is in contact with the interior compartment of the cell or *vesicle*.

Instantaneous dipole: A short-lived *dipole* produced by the momentary lack of balance in the placement of *electrons* in a chemical species. Occurs more easily for species with higher *polarizability*.

Instantaneous dipole moment: A short-lived *dipole moment* in a usually *nonpolar molecule*. See *Instantaneous dipole*.

Intensity: Of sound—a measure of the rate at which a sound wave's energy can be transferred. Related to the speed, *frequency* and *amplitude* of the sound wave. Of *electromagnetic radiation*—a measure of the "brightness" of light, related to the *amplitude* of the wave (the speed of EM radiation is essentially a constant).

Inter-: A prefix meaning "between," such as *intermolecular* meaning between different *molecules*.

Intermembrane space: The space between the outer and inner membranes of the mitochondria. The contents of this gel-like *solution* are very similar to the contents of the cell *cytoplasm* due to the leaky outer membrane.

Intermolecular attraction: Also "intermolecular force." The relatively weak attractive forces that cause *molecules* to associate with neighboring *molecules*. Not strong *chemical bonds*. These forces vary tremendously in strength from *dispersion forces* (weakest) to *dipole-dipole attractions* to *hydrogen bonds* (strongest).

Internal redox reaction: An *oxidation-reduction reaction* wherein both the *oxidation* and the *reduction* occur in the same *molecule*.

Internal rotation: A motion available to many *molecules* that involves spinning one end of a *molecule* with respect to the other end of the *molecule*, thus causing different *conformations* of the *molecule*. The spinning must cause one or more *atoms* to sweep out circular paths of motion. *Pi bonds* prohibit this type of motion.

Internuclear distance: The distance between two nuclei.

Interpolation: The inference of an unknown value using trends in a data set or graph that includes the value being pursued. See also: *Extrapolation*.

Interstitial alloy: A *homogeneous solid mixture* in which much smaller *atom*s occupy interstitial positions within a three-dimensional array of larger (usually *metal*) *atom*s.

Interstitial positions: The empty spaces between packed spheres.

Intracellular: Inside the cell.

Intra-: A prefix meaning "within," such as *intramolecular* meaning within one *molecule*.

Intramolecular hydrogen bond: A *hydrogen bond* in which both the *donor* and the *acceptor* sites are in the same *molecule*.

Ion: Any chemical particle carrying a net charge. These species have unequal numbers of *protons* and *electrons*. If there are extra *electron*s, the species carries a negative charge. If there are too few *electron*s, the species carries a positive charge.

Ion Product Constant (for water, K_w): The *equilibrium constant* for the *autoionization* of water. The *product* of the concentrations of the *hydronium ion* and *hydroxide ion* in any water sample. At 25 °C, $K_w = 1.0 \times 10^{-14} = \left[H_3O^+ \right]_{eq} \left[OH^- \right]_{eq}$.

Ion-dipole attraction: The attraction between an *ion* and the opposite charged end of a *dipole*.

Ionic: Of, or pertaining to, *ions*.

Ionic bonds: *Chemical bonds* resulting primarily from the *transfer* of electrons between two *atom*s, creating a *cation* and an *anion*, which then attract each other.

Ionic compound: A chemical *compound* that utilizes the *electrostatic* attraction of oppositely charged *ion*s as its primary attraction.

Ionic crystal: A *solid ionic compound* that features a regularly repeating array of *anion*s and *cation*s.

Ionic equation: Also called *complete ionic equation*. A *chemical reaction* equation that shows *soluble salts* and *strong acids* as *ions* in *solution* rather than as neutral formulas. All *ion*s are shown. Compare to *Net ionic equation*.

Ionic radius: A measurement of the size of a *cation* (smaller than the parent *atom*) or *anion* (larger than the parent *atom*). Generally measured as the *nucleus*-to-*nucleus* distance in an *ionic* lattice followed by using various methods to proportionally assign that distance to the two involved *ions*.

Ionic solid: See *Ionic crystal*.

Ionization energy: The energy that must be exceeded to remove a particular *electron* from a *gas phase atom*, thus creating the +1 *monatomic ion* (*first ionization energy*). The energy exceeded to accomplish: $A(g) \longrightarrow A^+(g) + e^-$.

Ionization: (noun) The process by which *ions* are created from neutral *molecule*s by either adding or removing one or more *electron*s.

Ionize: (verb) The act of creating *ion*s from neutral *atom*s or *molecule*s.

Irreversible reaction: A reaction that produces a *gas* that *dissipates* into the atmosphere and therefore is not available as a *reactant* for the reverse reaction. A reaction that can be treated as if it proceeds to completion, the reverse reaction is unimportant. A reaction that has a very large value of K_{eq}. A reaction that can be analyzed using the concepts of limiting *reagent*s.

Iso-: Prefix meaning "the same."

Isoelectronic: Having identical *electron configurations*.

Isomer: *Molecules* having the same formulas, but different structures. *Isomer*s are always *nonsuperimposable*.

Isomerization: A reaction featuring the conversion of a *molecule* into a different *isomer*ic form.

Isotone: Any *nuclide* having the same number of *neutrons*, but different numbers of *protons*.

Isotope: Any *atom* or *nuclide* of the same *element*, differing in the number of *neutrons* in the *nucleus* (and, therefore, differing in mass).

K_a: See *Acid Ionization Constant*.

K_b: See *Base Ionization Constant*.

K_c: A version of an *equilibrium constant* calculated from molar concentrations of both *solute*s and

gases. For the reaction, $aA(g) + bB(aq) \rightleftharpoons cC(aq) + dD(g)$, we write $K_c = \dfrac{\left[C\right]_{eq}^{c}\left[D\right]_{eq}^{d}}{\left[A\right]_{eq}^{a}\left[B\right]_{eq}^{b}}$.

K_{eq}: See *Equilibrium Constant*.

K_f: See *Formation Constant*.

Kinetic energy: Energy of motion.

Kinetic-Molecular Theory: The underlying *theory* describing the behavior of *gas* particles.

K_P: A version of an *equilibrium constant* calculated from *partial pressure*s of gases; this version of K_{eq} is undefined for any reaction equation that contains dissolved species. For the *gas phase* reaction,

$aA(g) + bB(g) \rightleftharpoons cC(g) + dD(g)$, we write $K_P = \dfrac{\left(P_C\right)_{eq}^{c}\left(P_D\right)_{eq}^{d}}{\left(P_A\right)_{eq}^{a}\left(P_B\right)_{eq}^{b}}$.

K_s: See *Stability Constant*.

K_{sp}: See *Solubility Product Constant*.

K_w: See *Ion Product Constant (for water)*.

Lambda-max, λ_{max}: The *most-absorbed wavelength* of *electromagnetic radiation* in a *visible spectrophotometry* experiment.

Lanthanides: Any *element* with *atomic number* 58-71, in the *f block* of the *periodic table*. Also called a rare earth *metal*.

Lattice energy, $E_{lattice}$: The amount of energy lost when *gas phase ions* come together to form a *solid crystal* lattice.

Law of Chemical Equilibrium: The final value of the *reaction quotient*, for a particular reaction at a particular temperature, is constant.

Law of Conservation of Matter: The fundamental idea that in chemical systems, *atom*s retain their identities even though bonding patterns may rearrange.

LCAO approximation: Linear Combination of Atomic Orbitals. An approximation that allows *molecular orbitals* of *molecules* to be calculated. The assumption that *molecular orbital*s arise directly from interactions of appropriate *atomic orbital*s.

LeChatelier's Principle: The principle stating that an *equilibrium* system will react to a *stress* by *shift*ing to minimize the *stress*.

Leveling: The inability to distinguish the relative strengths of *strong acid*s in water because they are all capable of completely transferring their *protons* to water.

Lewis acid: A species capable of accepting an *electron* pair from another species in order to form a *bond* between them.

Lewis base: A species capable of donating an *electron* pair to another species in order to form a *bond* between them. In *coordination compounds*. See also *Ligand*.

Lewis dot structure: A representation of a *molecule* showing all *valence electrons* either as bonding pairs or as lone pairs.

Lewis dot symbol: A notation featuring an *elemental* symbol surrounded by dots representing the *valence electrons*. Dots are kept unpaired around the four sides of the symbol until pairing is required because the number of dots is greater than 4. Useful for the prediction of bonding preferences of the *element* and of *ions* likely to be formed by the *element*.

Ligand: *Chemistry:* Pronounced with a short "i" sound, as in the word "pig." A species that can donate an *electron* pair to a *metal ion* (or *metal atom*) center to form a new *bond*, such as in a *complex ion* or *coordination complex*. See also *Lewis base*. Biology: Pronounced with a long "i" sound, as in the word "time." A species that binds to a *protein* but is not chemically changed, such as O_2 and myoglobin. Compare to *substrate*.

Limiting reactant: Also called "*limiting reagent*." A *reactant* that is completely consumed by a *chemical reaction*, while others leave leftovers. The *limiting reactant* determines the amount of *product* that may be produced.

Limiting reagent: See *limiting reactant*.

Linear geometry: The geometry resulting from a *steric number* of two around the central *atom*. A *molecular shape* that arises when a central *atom* has *steric number* = 2 and no lone pairs, or *steric number* = 5 with three lone pairs on the central *atom*, so that only *axial* positions of *a trigonal bipyramidal* system contain *atoms*.

Linkage isomerism: A type of *structural isomerism* specific to *coordination complexes*, wherein a *ligand (pronounced as in "pig")* is bonded to the central *atom* using a different *donor atom* in the two *isomers*. Only *ligands* having more than one different *Lewis base* site can produce this type of *isomerism*. These are not *bidentate ligands*; in the case of *linkage isomerism*, only one of the sites may be used at a time.

Linkage isomers: *Coordination complexes* or *coordination compounds* differing only in the *atom* used by a particular *ligand (pronounced as in "pig")* as a point of attachment to the central *metal cation* or *atom*.

Liquid: One of the common states, or *phases*, of *matter*, that is characterized by taking the shape of its container, having neighboring particles in close contact with one another, but not having the particles in a rigid three-dimensional array.

Localization: Refers to *electrons* that belong to a single *atom* as a lone pair, or are a part of a *covalent bond* that is shared by two *atoms*.

Localized electron model: An oversimplification in thinking about *chemical bond*ing that assumes that valence *electron* pairs "belong" to either one *atom* (as a lone pair) or two *atoms* (as a shared covalent *bond*).

London dispersion forces: Also called *dispersion force*. The weakest type of *intermolecular attraction*. Arise from the formation of *instantaneous dipoles* and *induced dipoles* in otherwise *nonpolar* particles. A weak, short-lived *electrostatic* attraction between neighboring particles.

Low spin case: When the t_{2g} *molecular orbitals* completely fill before any *electrons* populate the e_g *molecular orbitals* of an *octahedral coordination complex*. Caused by a *strong field ligand* *(pronounced as in "pig")* and results in minimizing the number of unpaired *electron*s. Compare to *high spin case*.

LUMO: Lowest unoccupied *molecular orbital*. The lowest energy *molecular orbital* that contains no *electron*s. Compare to *HOMO*.

Magnetic quantum number, m_ℓ: The *quantum number* that describes the spatial *orientation* of an *atomic orbital*. The number of values possible for a given *electron* (integers from $-\ell$ to $+\ell$) indicates the number of *orbitals* in a *subshell*.

Main group elements: *Elements* in columns 1, 2, 13-18 of the *periodic table*. The outermost *electron*s of these *element*s are in *s* or *p orbitals*.

Malleable: A property of *metal*s indicating that they can be hammered or pressed into various shapes without breaking or cracking.

Mass Number, A: The number of *protons* plus *neutrons* in a particular *atom*.

Mass spectrum (plural = spectra): A graph of the number of particles in a sample with particular mass-to-charge ratios. The result of using a *mass spectrometer*.

Mass spectrometer: An instrument used to measure the masses of particles in a sample by first *ionizing* the particles and then separating the particles by mass with a magnetic field.

Matter: Anything that has mass and occupies space.

Mechanical wave: Waves that are propagated by the movement of particles, such as sound waves and water waves.

Mechanism diagram: (or, just *mechanism*) A tool used by chemists to show the rearrangements of *electron*s during a *chemical change*. Double-headed, curved arrows show the movements of *electron* pairs.

Melting: The *phase change* from *solid* to *liquid*.

Meridional (mer) isomer: *Octahedral isomer* of a MY_3Z_3 complex in which three identical *ligand*s *(pronounced as in "pig")* are found on a central plane (*meridional* plane) slicing through the structure. Named after a meridian line, which connects a north and south pole; a *meridional* plane contains a meridian line. See also *facial isomer*.

Metabolism: The sum total of the biochemical reaction pathways responsible for the maintenance of life.

Metal: Any *element* having a particular set of characteristics including being a good conductor, having luster, being *malleable* and *ductile*. Most are *solid*s at room temperature.

Metallic bond: the usually strong attraction between neighboring *atom*s in *solid metal*s. Sometimes described as utilizing a sea of *valence electrons*.

Metallic crystal: a regularly repeating array of *metal atom*s in a *solid* piece of *metal*.

Metallic solid: See *Metallic crystal*.

Metalloid: Also called "semimetal." Any *element* having a set of characteristics intermediate to those of the *metals* and the *non-metals*. All are *solid*s at room temperature.

Metathesis: See *Double displacement*.

Microwave radiation: *Electromagnetic radiation* with *wavelength*s generally between 1 mm and 1.0 m, it is less energetic than *infrared radiation*. *Absorption* of *microwave* radiation by chemical *substance*s may cause *molecule*s to rotate.

Millimeters of mercury (mmHg): The extra pressure generated by a column of mercury that is one millimeter high. Historically arising from the widespread use of mercury column manometers and barometers. Currently, 1 mmHg is defined as 133.322387415 Pa. Essentially equivalent to 1 *torr*.

Minimally soluble: See *Essentially insoluble*.

Miscible: An adjective describing any *liquid*s that dissolve in one another at any relative concentrations.

Mitochondrial matrix: The gel-like *solution* inside the inner membrane of the mitochondria.

Mixture: Two or more intermingled *substance*s lacking a definite composition. Relative proportions of the *substance*s are not fixed. Can be *homogeneous* or *heterogeneous*.

Modulating protein: Any small *protein* that participates in a signal-transduction cascade and has a binding site for a *second messenger*. *Calmodulin* is an example; it binds the *second messenger*, Ca^{2+}.

Molality (m): A unit of *solution* concentration. *Mole*s of *solute* per kilogram of *solvent*.

Molar absorptivity: (ε) A measure of how well a particular *solute* absorbs a particular *wavelength* of *energy*, in units of L/mol·cm.

Molar mass: The mass, in grams, of one *mole* of a particular material.

Molar volume (of a gas): The volume required for 1.0 *mole* of *gas* at a particular pressure and temperature. At *STP*, the *molar volume* of a *gas* is 22.71 L.

Molarity: (M) A unit used for measuring the concentration of *solutions*. *Mole*s of *solute* per liter of *solution*.

Mole: The amount of material having a mass in grams equal to the *formula mass* of the *substance* in *atomic mass units*. For example, because one carbon-12 *atom* has the mass 12 u, a *mole* of carbon-12 *atom*s has a mass of 12 g. This amount of *substance* will consist of *Avogadro's number* of formula units.

Mole fraction: (chi, χ) A unit used for measuring the concentration of *solutions*. *Mole*s of one component per total *mole*s of all components.

Molecular crystal: A *molecular solid* whose composition displays a regularly repeating array of *molecule*s, such as crystalline sugar.

Molecular equation: See *Neutral formula equation*.

Molecular formula: The *chemical formula* of a molecular species. May be the same as the *empirical formula*, or a whole number multiple of the *empirical formula*.

Molecular mass: The sum of the *atomic masses* of the *atom*s of a *molecule*. Can be in *atomic mass* units or grams per *mole*. In the case of grams per *mole*, the average *molecular mass* will result.

Molecular orbital diagram: A graphical/pictorial representation of the energies and identities of the *molecular orbital*s of a multi-atom system.

Molecular orbital, MO: Three-dimensional region of space within a *molecule* or *polyatomic ion* in which a pair of *electron*s of the species may be found. Analogous to *atomic orbital* but tend to be much more *delocalized*.

Molecular shape: The geometric *shape* of a *molecule* that is related to its *electron pair geometry* but is named only for the positions of *atom*s, not the lone pairs.

Molecular solid: Any *solid* composed of a three-dimensional array of *molecule*s that attract each other via *intermolecular attractions*.

Molecular weight: The old term for "*molecular mass*." It is not strictly correct, but it is widely used.

Molecule: Covalently bonded, neutral collection of *atoms* having a particular composition and *shape*.

Monatomic: Structurally consists of single *atoms*.

Monodentate ligand: A *ligand (pronounced as in "pig")* forming one bonding attachment to the central *metal cation* or *atom*. Also called *unidentate*.

Monoisotopic element: Any of the 26 *elements* occurring as only one stable *isotope*. The *atomic masses* of these *elements* are NOT averages! Not to be confused with a *monoisotopic mass*.

Monomer: Any small *molecule* with at least two *functional groups* such that it can *bond* with other *molecules* like itself to create long, stringy structures called *polymers*.

Motif: A distinctive and/or recurring form or structure.

Multidentate ligands (pronounced as in "pig"): See *Polydentate ligands*.

Multiple interacting equilibria: Two or more reactions involving at least one species in common, and occurring simultaneously in the same container.

Multiplicity: (of *bonds*) The identity of a *bond* as single (2 bonding *electrons*), double (4 bonding *electrons*), or triple (6 bonding *electrons*), etc.

Myoglobin: A small *protein* of the *globin* family whose job is to store excess oxygen in the tissues. Is present in very high concentrations in ocean-dwelling mammals such as whales.

N-terminus: The end of a *peptide* or *protein polymer* that has an unbonded *amine group*.

Natural law: A statement that describes the most fundamental characteristics of nature.

Negative cooperativity: A rare type of biological *cooperativity*, wherein the binding of one *substrate* or *ligand* (pronounced *lye'-gand*) decreases the affinity for another *substrate* or *ligand*. Compare to *positive cooperativity*.

Negative effector: Any *effector* whose binding to a *protein* decreases the *protein*'s activity or decreases the *protein*'s ability to bind its *ligand* (*lye'-gand*) or *substrate*. Compare to *positive effector*.

Network solid: A *solid* that is not molecular in nature. Discreetly bonded sets of *atoms* are not present. Instead, a three-dimensional grid of bonded *atoms* exists in a material of unspecified size.

Net ionic equation: A *chemical equation* for an *ionic* reaction system that includes only the *ions* undergoing change. Non-reactive *ions* (*spectator ions*), though present in the system, are not included in the *net ionic equation*. Compare to *total equation* and *total ionic equation*.

Neutral formula (reaction) equation: Any reaction equation for a process that is written completely in terms of full, neutral formulas of each *substance*. No *ionic* formulas are present. Compare to *Ionic equation*.

Neutral (pH): An *aqueous solution* that is neither acidic, nor basic. The *hydronium ion* concentration and the *hydroxide ion* concentration are both $1.0 \times 10^{-7} M$ (at 25 °C).

Neutralization: The reaction of an acid and a base in *stoichiometric* quantities. With *strong acids* and bases the result is *salt* water with a pH of 7.0. For *weak acid-strong base* the result is a basic *solution* and for *weak base-strong acid* the result is an acidic *solution*.

Neutron: A *subatomic particle* that carries no charge. Found in the *nucleus* of an *atom*. Mass = 1.6749×10^{-27} kg.

Neutron capture: A nuclear reaction featuring the incorporation of a bombarding *neutron* into the *nucleus* of the *reactant nuclide*. The resulting *nuclide* is a heavier *isotope* of the parent. See also, *termination*.

Nitrogen-fixing bacteria: Bacteria with the somewhat rare capability of converting atmospheric nitrogen, N_2, into useable nitrogen for plants, such as NH_4^+. This is a biochemically difficult task because of the very high *bond* strength of the *triple bond* of N_2, which must be broken in the process.

Nitrogenous: An adjective indicating that a chemical species incorporates at least one nitrogen *atom*, as in the "*nitrogenous* bases of DNA."

Noble gas: Any of the *elements* of *Group* 18. So called because, as the nobility would not associate with the commoners, these *gases* did not react with other *substances*. Also called the *inert gases* even though they are not entirely *inert*.

Nodal surface: See *Node*.

Node: A surface at which the probability of finding a particular *electron* is zero. Can be *radial* or *angular*. See *angular node* and *radial node*.

Nomenclature: The scientific system for naming *substances* with unique and identifying names.

Nonbonding molecular orbital: Essentially, a *molecular orbital* that is an unchanged *atomic orbital* due to the impossibility of interaction with any *atomic orbital* on the neighboring *atom*(s).

Nonelectrolyte: Any molecular species that dissolves in water without producing *ions*.

Nonequivalent resonance structures: A set of possible *Lewis dot structures* for the same species that differ from one another in the *bond multiplicity* and/or *formal charge* assignments.

Nonmetal: Any *element* exhibiting a particular set of characteristics including being poor conductors, dull in appearance, and brittle as *solids*. Many are *gases* at room temperature.

Nonpolar: Characterized by the complete lack of charge separation.

Nonpolar bond: Any *covalent bond* between *atoms* of the same *electronegativity* (or very similar electronegativities.) *Covalent bonds* where the bonding *electrons* are shared evenly between the bonded nuclei.

Nonpolar molecule: A *molecule* having an even distribution of charge throughout, without centers of positive and negative charge.

Non-stoichiometric: A reaction system where one or more of the *reactants* is present in excess, so that a *limiting reagent* is present. A reaction system for which the amount of *product* formed is not easily determined from the amounts of *reactants* present because the reaction does not go to completion.

Nonsuperimposable: Two species that cannot be positioned in space in such a way that they exactly line up with one another (unless *bonds* are broken and re-assembled in a different *configuration*). Usually used to describe *isomers*. These species represent different chemical *substances*. Compare to *Superimposable*.

Normal boiling point, normal freezing point, etc.: The temperature at which the indicated *phase change* occurs when atmospheric pressure is 1.00 atm. See also *Standard boiling point*.

Nuclear binding energy: The amount of mass that is converted to *energy* (via $E = mc^2$) in the binding together of *protons* and *neutrons* to form a *nucleus*. The mass of a *nucleus* is less than the masses of the separated *protons* and *neutrons* from which it is made.

Nucleus: The central core of an *atom*, containing the *protons* and *neutrons*. Almost all of the mass of an *atom* is found in the *nucleus*.

Nuclide: Another name for "*atom*" that emphasizes the particular make-up of the *nucleus* in terms of numbers of *protons* and *neutrons*.

Octahedral: The geometry resulting from a *steric number* of six around the central *atom*. Characterized by 90° *bond* angles.

Octet: The eight *valence electrons* typically found around an *atom* in a bonded structure; see also *Duet*.

Optical isomerism: A type of *stereoisomerism* characterized by same set of *bond*s, but being *nonsuperimposable* mirror images. Compare to *geometrical isomerism*.

Optical isomers: *Nonsuperimposable* mirror images. *Molecule*s having identical *atom*s and identical *bond*s, but still not being superimposable because they are mirror images. Arise when *tetrahedral* centers have four different *group*s attached.

Orbit: A two-dimensional elliptical pathway that defines the movement of planets or other satellites in outer space. In chemistry: The two-dimensional circular pathway describing the path of an *electron* around the *nucleus* of a Bohr *atom*.

Orbital: The three-dimensional special region occupied by one or two *electrons* in a chemical entity, such as an *atom* or *molecule*. Not an *orbit*. See *Atomic orbitals* or *Molecular orbitals*.

Orbital diagram: A drawing that shows *electrons* as up-arrows and down-arrows on lines that represent specific *atomic orbitals*. *Orbital diagrams* offer more information than an *electron configuration* because the arrangement of *electrons* within a *subshell* is specified and the *electron* spins are denoted.

Orbital mixing: For *hybridization*: Mathematical rearrangements of two to six atomic *wave functions* from one *atom*, giving rise to new *wave function*s that define a new set of equivalent *atomic orbitals* called *hybrid atomic orbitals*.

Organic: An adjective indicating a carbon-based structure.

Organic chemistry: The study of *compounds* of carbon.

Orientation: The position or directionality of an object with respect to a particular reference.

Outer leaf: The layer of a phospholipid *bilayer* that is oriented away from the interior compartment of the cell or *vesicle*.

Oxidation: Any process by which an *atom* or *ion* loses *electrons*. Must occur simultaneously with a *reduction*.

Oxidation number: See "*Oxidation state*."

Oxidation-reduction reaction: Any reaction in which the *oxidation state* of at least one involved *atom* changes over the course of the reaction. There must be both an *oxidation* and a *reduction*.

Oxidation state: Also called "*oxidation number*." For a *monatomic ion*, the same as the charge on the *ion*. The charge associated with a particular *atom* in a *Lewis dot structure* after assigning lone pairs to the *atom* on which they reside and assigning bonding *electrons* to the more electronegative *atom* of the bonded pair.

Oxidized: A chemical species becomes *oxidized* when it loses *electrons* to some other chemical species.

Oxidizing agent: A *reactant* that takes *electrons* from another *reactant*. The *oxidizing agent* gets *reduced*, while being the agent of something else's *oxidation*.

Oxoacid: A *Bronsted-Lowry acid* wherein the transferable *proton*(s) are bonded to an oxygen *atom*.

Oxygenated conformation: The *tertiary structure* of the *hemoglobin tetramer* that is more favorable for oxygen bonding. Compare to *Deoxygenated conformation*.

Ozone: An *allotrope* of oxygen with formula O_3.

P_{50}: The *partial pressure* or *concentration* of a species required to half-fill the available binding spots in a *protein*. The special case of a *dissociation constant*, K_D, when the number of bonding sites filled is equal to the number unfilled.

p block element: Any *element* whose last ground state *electron* is in a *p orbital*. The *element*s found in *group*s 13-18 (3A-8A) of the *periodic table*, except for hydrogen and helium. These *element*s are *main group elements*.

Parallel spin: *Electron*s having the same value of the *spin quantum number*, m_s. In an *orbital diagram*, *electron*s denoted by an up-arrow have *parallel spin* with any other *electron* denoted by an up-arrow.

Paramagnetic: An adjective indicating that a species contains one or more unpaired *electron*s and thus is weakly attracted into an external magnetic field.

Paramagnetism: The property associated with being *paramagnetic*.

Parent nuclide: The *reactant nuclide* in any *radioactive* decay event; compare to *daughter nuclide*.

Partial double bond (character): A description of a *double bond* that is present in some *resonance* structures, but absent from at least one *resonance* contributor so that there is not enough *pi electron density* in a particular position to comprise full *double bond* strength.

Partial pressure: The pressure that is attributable to a particular *gas* in a *mixture* of *gas*es. The pressure that the *gas* would have if it were in the container alone.

Particulate: Of, or in the form of, discreet particles.

Pascal: (Pa) The SI unit of pressure, 100,000 Pa = 1 *bar*.

Path length: (ℓ) The inside dimension of a *cuvette*. The distance through which the light energy passes through the *solution*.

Pauli Exclusion Principle: The rule that states that no two *electron*s in the same *atom* can have the same set of four *quantum numbers*. This rule requires that two *electron*s in the same *orbital* must have different values of the *spin quantum number*.

Peptide: A relatively short *polymer* of *amino acids*, perhaps up to ~100 *residues*.

Peptide bond: The *bond* that forms between two *amino acids* as they polymerize to form *peptides* and/or *proteins*. This *bond* creates a new *amide group*.

Percent error: $\dfrac{measured\ value - true\ value}{true\ value} \times 100\%$.

Percent ionization: $\dfrac{amount\ ionized}{total\ amount} \times 100\%$.

Percent yield: A comparison of the *actual yield* of a *product* to the *theoretical yield* of the same product: $\%\ yield = \left(\dfrac{actual\ yield}{theoretical\ yield}\right) \times 100\%$.

Percentage composition: The mass percentage of each *element* of a *substance*.

Period: A row on the *periodic table*.

Periodic Table: A systematic arrangement, in two dimensions, of the known *elements*, such that *elements* with similar *chemical properties* are in vertical columns, and *elements* with outer *electrons* in the same "*shell*" are in the same horizontal rows.

Permeable: The adjective describing a *membrane* or other structure that allows at least some *substances* to pass through.

Perturbation: A deviation from a normal state caused by outside influences.

Phase: The physical form of a *substance*: *solid, liquid, gas, plasma, aqueous,* etc.

Phase change: Any *physical change* of state, such as *melting* or *sublimation*.

Phase tag: Parenthetical abbreviations in reaction equations that indicate physical *phases* of *reactants* and *products*.

pH: The power function describing the concentration of hydronium ion in an aqueous system, $pH = -\log [H_3O^+]$.

pH plot: A plot of the pH of the *solution* in the reaction flask (*y*-axis) of a *titration* versus the volume of *titrant* used (*x*-axis). These plots have characteristic shapes depending on the nature of the acid and base involved in the *titration*.

pH scale: A method by which to report the acid-base characteristics of an *aqueous* system. A *neutral solution* has a pH of 7.00. Acidic *solutions* have smaller pH values and basic *solutions* have larger pH values. $pH = -\log [H_3O^+]$.

Phosphorylation: Any *chemical reaction* resulting in the addition of a *phosphate group* to another *molecule*. The phosphate *group* often comes from *ATP*.

Photon: A discreet packet of *electromagnetic radiation*, sometimes thought of as a particle.

Physical change: A change that does not result in a new *substance*, but simply a change in form (temperature, volume, *solubility*, *phase*) of the original *substance*(s).

Physical phase: See *physical state*.

Physical property: Any property of *matter* that describes the *substance* without regard to its chemical reactivity. Color, density, *solubility*, and odor are examples.

Physical state: A fundamental form of *matter* indicating whether it exists as a *solid, liquid, gas, plasma,* or is in *solution*.

Physiological respiration: The result of action of the respiratory system. The delivery of oxygen to tissues and removal of *carbon dioxide* waste from the tissue and *gas* exchange of oxygen and *carbon dioxide* in the lungs.

P_i ("i" is a subscript here): An abbreviation used in biochemistry/biology to refer to any of the inorganic phosphate *ions*: PO_4^{3-} (phosphate), HPO_4^{2-} (hydrogen phosphate), $H_2PO_4^-$ (dihydrogen phosphate).

Pi (π) bond: A *pi interaction* involving *p orbitals* on just two neighboring *atoms* and populated with two *electrons*. One of the two bonding component of a covalent *double bond*, two of the three components of a *triple bond*.

Pi (π) electron: Any *electron* residing in a *pi bond*, *pi orbital*, or *pi system*.

Pi (π) interaction: The interaction of *atomic orbitals* on neighboring *atoms* that results in placing *electron density* outside of the (imaginary) line connecting the two nuclei. A "sideways" interaction of *orbitals*.

Pi (π) orbital: A *molecular orbital* arising from the overlap of *atomic orbitals* such that two regions of space, off to the side of the two nuclei, are available to the bonding *electron*s. A "sideways" overlap of *atomic orbitals*. *Electron density* of a *pi orbital* is not along the line connecting the two nuclei. Can be *bonding, antibonding,* or *nonbonding.*

Pi (π) stacking: A weak bonding interaction involving the *association* of *pi system*s on one *molecule* with those on another, often in a sandwich-like geometry.

Pi (π) system: A *pi interaction* of *p orbital*s on three of more neighboring *atom*s. Compare to *pi bond.*

pK$_a$: $-log\,K_a$.

pK$_b$: $-log\,K_b$.

pK$_w$: $pK_w = -\log K_w$.

Planar: Structures in which the *nuclei* of all *atom*s lie on the same plane.

Planck's constant, h: A constant of nature with units of *angular momentum* $\left(J \cdot s \text{ or } \frac{kg \cdot m^2}{s}\right)$. $h = 6.62606957 \times 10^{-34}$ J·s.

Plasma: A *physical state* much like a *gas*, but having a large proportion of ionized particles and a large energy content. The overall charge is essentially neutral. *Plasma*s glow as *electron*s release energy as they move closer to a *nucleus.*

pOH: $pOH = -\log [OH^-]$.

Polar: Characterized by the unequal distribution of charge so that there is a region of positive charge and a region of negative charge.

Polar (covalent) bond: A *covalent chemical bond* in which the bonding *electron*s are unevenly shared (due to *electronegativity* differences) so that one end of the *bond* has positive charge and the other end has negative charge.

Polar head group: The *polar* portion of an *amphiphile* such as a *fatty acid* (CO_2H) or phospholipid (*polar alcohol*).

Polar molecule: A *molecule* whose center of negative charge and center of positive charge do not coincide. There must be both *polar bonds* and a geometry such that the *polar bond*s do not cancel each other.

Polarity: The property of being *polar.*

Polarizability: The characteristic of being *polarizable.*

Polarizable: Having an *electron* cloud that is susceptible to *distortion*s resulting in *dipole* character. Larger species, with more *electron*s that are held more loosely are generally more *polarizable* than smaller species with tightly held *electron*s.

Polyatomic: Structurally consisting of more than one *atom.*

Polydentate ligand: Any *ligand (pronounced as in "pig")* having more than one point of attachment to the central *metal cation* or *atom.* Also called *chelating ligand, multidentate ligand.*

Polymer: A large bonded system with repeating structural units based on the *monomer* that was used to create the *polymer.* Can be linear or branched, a homo*polymer* or a co*polymer.* DNA is a *polymer* of nucleic acids and *protein*s are a *polymer* of *amino acid*s.

Polyprotic acid: A *Bronsted-Lowry acid* with more than one *acidic hydrogen atom.*

Polyunsaturated fat: *Triacylglycerol molecules* in which one or more of the long *hydrocarbon* chain has more than one *double bond.*

Porin: Any of a large number of membrane-spanning *proteins* that produce a pore in the *membrane bilayer* that allows the equilibration of relatively small water-soluble *molecules* on both sides of the membrane.

Porphyrin: A large *planar*, cyclic *organic molecule* that may serve as a *square planar*, *tetradentate ligand (pronounced as in "pig")* to *metal ions*. The structural basis of the *heme cofactor.*

Positive cooperativity: The most common type of biological *cooperativity*, wherein the binding of one *substrate* or *ligand (lye'-gand)* increases the affinity for another *substrate* or *ligand*. Compare to *negative cooperativity.*

Positive effector: Any *effector* whose binding to a *protein* increases the *protein*'s activity or increases the *protein*'s ability to bind its *ligand (lye'-gand)* or *substrate*. Compare to *negative effector.*

Positron, β^+: A high-energy *electron*-like particle, except that the charge is +1 instead of −1 that emanates from an unstable *nucleus* during some *radioactive* decay events.

Positron emission: *Radioactivity* characterized by the release of a *positron* from the *nucleus* of an *atom*. The result is a *proton* becoming a *neutron*; compare to *electron capture*. Often accompanied by the release of gamma rays.

Potential energy: Energy due to position.

Potential energy minimum: The smallest amount of *potential energy* that a system can have. The most stable arrangement of the system.

Precipitate: A *solid* that forms from *substances* that were previously dissolved.

Precipitation: The act of forming a *precipitate.*

Precision: A measure of the consistency, or reproducibility, within a set of data. The fineness to which an instrument can be read reliably and reproducibly. *Precision* is limited by *random errors*. Compare to *Resolution.*

Primary sequence: The order of *amino acid residues* in a *peptide* or *protein*; listed from the *N-terminus* to the *C-terminus.*

Primary standard: A well-behaved *reactant* used during an analytical procedure whose amount can be accurately determined by mass and upon which all calculations are based.

Primary structure: (of a *protein*) The structural aspects of a *protein* related to its *primary sequence.*

Principal quantum number, n: A *quantum number* describing the size of an *atomic orbital*, and therefore, giving an idea of the energy of any *electron* found in the *orbital.*

Product: Mathematics: The result of a multiplication event. Chemistry: Any species being formed during a *chemical reaction*. Any species found on the right side of a *chemical equation.*

Protein: A large *polymer* of *amino acids*, often used in the context of a naturally produced *polymer* utilizing a set of 20 naturally occurring *amino acids* and having a particular function within a living system.

Proton: A positively charged *subatomic particle* located in the *nucleus* of an *atom*. Mass = 1.6726×10^{-27} kg. An H^+ *ion*; because an H *atom* is one *proton* and one *electron*, an H^+ *ion* is simply a *proton.*

Proton acceptor: A *Bronsted-Lowry base* that uses a lone pair of *electrons* to make a new *bond* to an H^+ *ion* (a *proton*).

Proton transfer: The movement of an H^+ *ion* from one species to another. An acid-base reaction.

Pure: a single *substance* that is free of contamination and not mixed with any other *substance*.

Q: See "*Reaction Quotient*" entries.

Q axis: A number line of *reaction quotient* values on which a current Q value, the *standard state* Q value (exactly 1.0) and the K_{eq} value of a particular reaction at a particular temperature can be indicated. The direction that a reaction must *shift* (forward or reverse) may be indicated.

Quadratic formula: $x = \dfrac{-b \pm \sqrt{b^2 - 4ac}}{2a}$

A formula useful for solving equations of the form: $0 = ax^2 + bx + c$.

Quadruple bond: A *bond* arising from the sharing of eight *electrons* between two *metal atoms* utilizing *d orbital* interactions. It usually consists of one *sigma*, two *pi*, and one *delta bond*.

Qualitative: Having to do with non-numeric analyses, such as the identification of an unknown.

Quantitative: Having to do with numeric analyses, such as determining the amount of material present.

Quantization: The characteristic associated with any property that can only have a particular set of values.

Quantized: Of, or pertaining to, *quantization*.

Quantum number: Any of a set of four numbers (n, ℓ, m_ℓ, m_s) whose values are *quantized*, that describe a particular *electron* when included in the *Schrodinger wave equation*.

Quaternary structure: The highest level of *protein* architecture that relates to the *association* of multiple *protein* chains into a single working *molecule*. Not all working *proteins* utilize this structural characteristic. *Hemoglobin* is an example of a *protein* displaying *quaternary structure*.

Quintuple bond: A *bond* arising from the sharing of ten *electrons* between two *metal atoms* utilizing interactions of all five *d orbitals*. It consists of one *sigma*, two *pi*, and two *delta bonds*.

Radial function, R(r): A mathematical function involving *quantum numbers* that describes how the *electron*-wave changes as distance from the *nucleus* increases.

Radial node: Any spherical surface centered on the *nucleus* of an *atom* on which an *electron* cannot be found because the probability of finding it there is zero. A spherical surface around the *nucleus* of an *atom* at which the *amplitude* of an electron wave is zero.

Radial probability distribution: The *product* of the radial function and the surface area of a sphere, both at the same distance, r, from the *nucleus*. A measure of the probability of finding a particular *electron* on that spherical surface.

Radical: Also called a "free radical." In *chemistry*, a *radical* is any particle having an odd number of *electrons*. These species are particularly unstable and highly reactive. The superoxide *radical*, O_2^-, for instance, is the result of adding one *electron* to the O_2 *molecule*, which then has 17 total *electrons*.

Radioactive: An adjective used to describe a *nuclide* that undergoes spontaneous nuclear decay.

Radioactivity: The occurrence of various decay events from the *nucleus* of an unstable *atom*.

Radiotracer: A *molecule* in which one normal substituent is substituted with a *radioactive atom* for medical or scientific purposes.

Random error: Any unavoidable error in measuring related to *electrical* "noise" or other unknown and unpredictable errors. *Random errors* provide a normal distribution of values around the average value. *Random errors* limit the *precision* of a data set.

Rare earth metals: See "*Lanthanide.*"

Reactant: Any species serving as a starting material for a *chemical reaction.* Any species found on the left side of a *chemical equation.*

Reaction mechanism: A diagram showing how *electrons* rearrange to accomplish the transition from *reactants* to *products.*

Reaction position: The description of a reaction system by listing the current concentrations (of *solutes*) and/or *partial pressures* (of *gases*) for each chemical species except *pure solids* and *pure liquids.*

Reaction Quotient, Q: The description of a reaction system arrived at by dividing the *product* concentrations (for *solutes*) or *partial pressures* (for *gases*) (raised to the appropriate powers) by the *reactant* concentrations or *partial pressures* (raised to the appropriate powers). By convention, concentrations are entered in units of *molarity* and *partial pressures* are entered in units of *bar.* So,

for the reaction: $aA(g) + bB(aq) \rightleftharpoons cC(aq) + dD(g)$, $Q = \dfrac{[C]^c (P_D)^d}{(P_A)^a [B]^b}$. This version of the

reaction quotient is the thermodynamic definition that is favored in this textbook. Compare to the *reaction quotient, Q_c* and the *reaction quotient, Q_p.*

Reaction Quotient, Q_c: The description of a reaction system arrived at by dividing the *product* concentrations (raised to the appropriate powers) by the *reactant* concentrations (raised to the appropriate powers). Concentrations in *molarity* are used for both *solutes* and *gases.* So, for the

reaction: $aA(g) + bB(aq) \rightleftharpoons cC(aq) + dD(g)$, $Q_c = \dfrac{[C]^c [D]^d}{[A]^a [B]^b}$.

Reaction Quotient, Q_P: The description of a *gas-phase* reaction system arrived at by dividing the *product partial pressures* (raised to the appropriate powers) by the *reactant* concentrations (raised to the appropriate powers). So, for the reaction: $aA(g) + bB(g) \rightleftharpoons cC(g) + dD(g)$,

$Q_P = \dfrac{(P_C)^c (P_D)^d}{(P_A)^a (P_B)^b}$.

Reaction yield: Any of the various measurements of the amount of *product* expected or produced by a *chemical reaction,* including *actual yield, theoretical yield,* and *percent yield.*

Reagent: Another name for a *reactant.*

Redox: See "*Oxidation-reduction reaction.*"

Reduced: A chemical species is *reduced* when it has gained *electrons* from some other species.

Reduction: Any process during which an *atom* gains *electrons.* Must occur simultaneously with an *oxidation.*

Reducing agent: The *reactant* that gives *electrons* to another *reactant.* The *reducing agent* becomes *oxidized*; it is the agent of something else's *reduction.*

Replication: The cellular process by which the separation of *duplex DNA* strands occurs, allowing each strand to serve as a template for the synthesis of a new strand of DNA.

Residue: See *Amino acid residue.*

Resolution: The degree to which a difference in measurement can be detected; the fineness to which an instrument can be read. Compare to *Precision.*

Resonance hybrid: The structural view of a chemical species that results from consideration of the characteristics of all reasonable *resonance structures.*

Resonance: The concept of *electron delocalization* as portrayed by the drawing of multiple structures (differing in electron placement) for one species, and then "averaging" those pictures in one's mind.

Resonance stability: The extra stability gained by a chemical species that features *delocalized electron*s and possibly *delocalized* charge.

Resonance structures: Multiple *Lewis dot structures* for one chemical species that result from the repositioning of some *pi electrons*/lone pairs. *Resonance* structures always have *atom*s in the same places, but different placements of *valence electrons.* Sometimes *resonance* structures are equally likely and other times one is more or less likely than others. See also: *Resonance hybrid.* See also: *Formal charge.*

Respiration: See *physiological respiration* and/or *cellular respiration.*

Reversible: Any process that can relatively easily go forward or backwards, depending on local conditions.

Reversible reaction: A reaction whose reverse reaction competes, so that the forward reaction does not consume all of any *reagent.* A reaction with a moderate or small value of K_{eq}. A reaction that must be analyzed using the concept of an *equilibrium table.*

Rotation (molecular): The head-over-tail tumbling of a *molecule* that involves no change of *shape* of the *molecule.* Compare to *Internal rotation.*

Rounding numbers: Removing non-significant digits from a measured or calculated value in a way that fairly preserves information about *precision.*

Rydberg constant: $R_H = 2.179872171 \times 10^{-18}$ J. The energy difference between the ground *electronic* energy state and the infinite energy level for the hydrogen *atom electron.* R_H equals the *ionization energy* of the hydrogen *atom electron.*

s block element: Any *element* whose highest energy ground state *electron* is in an *s orbital.* The *element*s in *group*s 1 and 2 (1A and 2A) of the periodic table, plus helium. These *element*s are *main group elements.*

Salt: *Compounds* composed of *cations* and *anions* held together in three-dimensional networks by *electrostatic* forces called *ionic bonds.* *Ionic compound* and *salt* mean the same thing. The phrase "table salt" refers specifically to sodium chloride, NaCl.

Salt bridge: The interaction of *anionic* and *cationic* sites in a *protein* that helps to stablilize *tertiary structure.*

Saturated: With respect to *gases*: an *atmosphere* that is holding the maximum amount of a particular *gas* at a particular temperature. With respect to carbon chains: a carbon chain having the maximum number of bonded hydrogen *atom*s, and thus only *single bond*s between carbon *atom*s. With respect to *solutions*: A *solution* containing the maximum amount of a given *solute.* Can be either concentrated or *dilute*, depending on the *solubility* of the *solute.* With respect to *hemoglobin*: the state in which all oxygen-binding sites on all of the *hemoglobin molecule*s are filled.

Schrodinger wave equation: The mathematical description of an *electron* in terms of the *wave function.*

Scientific method: A statement of the process of asking questions and testing possible answers to those questions.

Scientific notation: The method of expressing any number as a number between 1 and 10 multiplied by some power of 10, such as 6.02×10^{23}.

Second messenger: Any *molecule* or *ion* released inside of a cell upon binding of a *first messenger* to the outer *membrane* of the cell.

Secondary structure: (of a *protein*) The structural aspects of a *protein* related to the *conformation* of sections of the *polymer* into regions of *alpha helix* or *beta strand*, etc.

Self-assembly: The assembly of multiple *molecules* into a working unit, driven by natural forces such as the *hydrophobic effect*.

Self-ionization: See *Autoionization*.

Self-seal: The closing of a self-assembled *bilayer* into a spherical unit, driven by natural forces such as the *hydrophobic effect*.

Semi-metal: See "*metalloid*."

Semi-solid: A physical *phase* characterized by the ability of the *substance* to maintain its own shape, but also the ability to take the shape of its container when minimal pressure is applied.

Sequester: to isolate, or hide away.

Serial dilution: This is not adding more milk to your Cheerios™. A set of modest, consecutive *dilution*s designed to provide for an overall drastic *dilution* is a way that minimizes the error associated with drastic *dilution*s. Usually the set of *dilution*s share the same *concentration factor*.

Shape: See *Molecular shape*.

Shell: In atomic structure: A *shell* is composed of *orbital*s of roughly the same size and energy as one another. A *shell* is designated by the principle *quantum number*, *n*. The first *shell* of *orbital*s has $n = 1$. The second *shell* has $n = 2$, etc. Compare to *subshell*. See also *hydration shell* or *solvation shell*.

Shift: The reaction that occurs when a *stressed equilibrium* system reacts in one direction or the other in order to reestablish *equilibrium*.

Shift left: The occurrence of reverse reaction aimed at returning a system to *equilibrium* status by increasing the amount of *reactant* present.

Shift right: The occurrence of forward reaction aimed at returning a system to *equilibrium* status by increasing the amount of *products* present.

Sickle cell anemia: A debilitating genetic disease in individuals with two sickle cell genes that is characterized by a single mutation in the code for the beta-chains of *hemoglobin* resulting in a surface valine *residue* instead of a glutamic acid *residue*.

Side chains: (of *amino acids*) The set of *atom*s bonded to the *alpha-carbon* of a naturally occurring *amino acid* and giving it its identity.

Sigma (σ) bond: A *sigma interaction* involving two *electron*s on neighboring *atom*s. The usual component of a single covalent *bond*, one of the two components of a *double bond*, and one of the three components of a *triple bond*.

Sigma (σ) framework: A picture of a *molecule*'s skeleton showing only sticks for *sigma bond*s (one stick per *single bond*, *double bond*, and *triple bond*.

Sigma (σ) interaction: The interaction of *atomic orbitals* on neighboring *atoms* that results in placing *electron density* directly on the line connecting the two nuclei. A "head-on" interaction of *orbitals*.

Sigma (σ) orbital: A *molecular orbital* arising from the overlap of *atomic orbitals* such that one region of space, in between the two nuclei, is available to the bonding *electrons*. A "head-on" overlap of *atomic orbitals*. The *electron density* of a *sigma orbital* is centered on the line connecting the two nuclei. Can be *bonding*, *antibonding* or *nonbonding*.

Signal transduction: A method of *molecule*-to-*molecule* communication within and between cells that generally relies upon *shape* changes induced in *molecules* upon binding to signaling species.

Signal transduction cascade: A *signal transduction* process that amplifies the original signal as subsequent steps occur so that a large biological response can be made to the original signal.

Significant figures: Also called "significant digits." The reproducible digits of a measured value given by the measuring device. Occasionally a measuring device provides some non-reproducible digits as well; these are NOT significant.

Single bond: A *bond* resulting from the sharing of two *electrons*. Usually a *sigma bond*.

Slater shielding rules: An outdated method for assigning values of *effective nuclear charge* to specific *electrons* in an *atom*. Emphasizes the idea that *electrons* in the same *shell* provide relatively poor shielding compared to *electrons* that are closer to the *nucleus*.

Slightly soluble: See *Essentially insoluble*.

Sodium-potassium adenosine triphosphatase (Na⁺-K⁺ ATPase): A membrane-spanning *enzyme* responsible for maintaining the *concentration gradients* of Na^+ and K^+ across the cell membrane. Couples the transport of these *ions* with *ATP hydrolysis*.

Solid: One of the common states, or *phases*, of *matter*, characterized by having a shape that is independent of its container with particles in a rigid, three-dimensional array that prohibits them from moving in any way other than vibrating in place.

Solubility Product Constant, K_{sp}: An *equilibrium constant* for the dissolution of an *essentially insoluble ionic compound* in water.

Solute: The minor component of a *solution*, said to be dissolved in the *solvent*.

Solution: Any *homogeneous mixture*. Most commonly thought of as a *solid* dissolved in a *liquid*, but *mixtures* of *gases* and *alloys* are also examples of *solutions*.

Solvation shell: The layer of *solvent molecules* closest to a *solute* particle. May be called a *hydration shell* when the *solvent* is water.

Solvent: The major component of a *solution*.

sp hybrid orbitals: *Hybrid atomic orbitals* that arise from the mathematical mixing of an *s* and *p* valence *atomic orbital* on the same *atom* to give two equivalent *hybrid orbitals* aiming at 180° to one another.

sp² hybrid orbitals: *Hybrid atomic orbitals* that arise from the mathematical mixing of an *s* and two *p* valence *atomic orbital* on the same *atom* to give three equivalent *hybrid orbitals* aiming at 120° to one another.

sp³ hybrid orbitals: *Hybrid atomic orbitals* that arise from the mathematical mixing of an *s* and three *p* valence *atomic orbital* on the same *atom* to give four equivalent *hybrid orbitals* aiming at 109.5° to one another.

sp³d hybrid orbitals: *Hybrid atomic orbital*s that arise from the mathematical mixing of an *s*, three *p* and one *d* valence *atomic orbital* on the same *atom* to give five equivalent *hybrid orbital*s aiming at the corners of a regular trigonal bipyramid.

sp³d² hybrid orbitals: *Hybrid atomic orbital*s that arise from the mathematical mixing of an *s*, three *p* and two *d* valence *atomic orbital* on the same *atom* to give six equivalent *hybrid orbital*s aiming at the corners of a regular octahedron.

Spectator ion: The non-reacting *ion*s in an *ionic* system undergoing an overall change.

Spectral lines: The *emission* lines (often used in conjunction with *visible emission* lines) of a chemical species that occur when *electron*s move from *excited state*s to lower energy states.

Spectrochemical series: A listing of *ligands (pronounced as in "pig")* in order of their ability to split the energies of the t_{2g} and e_g *orbital*s. *Ligand*s "high" in the series produce a large split (large Δ_o) and *ligand*s "low" in the series produce small splits (small Δ_o).

Spectrophotometry: An experiment in which the amount of radiation (*visible*, *infrared*, *ultraviolet*, *microwave*, etc.) absorbed by a chemical species is measured. The instruments used are called spectrophotometers.

Speed of light, c: A misnomer for the speed of *electromagnetic radiation*, only a small part of which is *visible* light.

Speed of propagation: The rate of travel of a wave. Most often applied to the rate of travel of *electromagnetic radiation*, c, all types of which travel at a rate of 2.998×10^8 m/s in a vacuum. See *Speed of light*.

Speed of sound: The rate at which a sound wave travels through a *substance*, much more variable than the *speed of light*.

Spin quantum number, m_s: The *quantum number* that differentiates between the two *electron*s in the same *orbital*; only two values are allowed: $+\frac{1}{2}$ and $-\frac{1}{2}$. Chemists think about this *quantum number* as describing either a clockwise or counterclockwise rotation of the *electron* on its axis.

Spontaneous fission: A type of *radioactive* decay that features the splitting of an unstable *nucleus* into two smaller nuclei (occasionally a third much lighter daughter as well). This process occurs naturally, without an induction event. It almost always results in the release of one or more high energy *neutron*s as well. This type of decay can only occur for very heavy *nuclide*s with a high number of *neutron*s. Compare to *induced fission*.

Square planar: A *molecular shape* usually characterized by an *octahedral electron pair geometry* and the presence of two lone pairs. The central *ion* lies at the center of a square, with an attached atom at every corner of the square, so that all five *atom*s are coplanar. In *coordination chemistry*, one of the geometries associated with a *coordination number* of four.

Stability Constant, K_s: An *equilibrium constant* for the *dissociation* of a *complex ion* into its component *ion*s. The reciprocal of the *formation constant*. Larger values imply a less stable *complex ion*.

Staggered conformation: A *conformation* in which the *atom*s bonded to one *atom* are exactly between the *atom*s bonded to a neighboring *atom* when viewed along the *bond* axis. Compare to *Eclipsed conformation*.

Standard boiling point, standard freezing point, etc.: The temperature at which the indicated *phase change* occurs when atmospheric pressure is 1.00 *bar*. See also ***normal boiling point***.

Standard solution: A *solution* whose concentration is accurately known either because it was made by carefully weighing out a sample of the *solute* and dissolving to a known total volume, or because it was determined by some technique such as *titration*. *Standard solutions* are used during *titration*s, often as the *titrant*.

Standard state: The state of a *substance* that is present when the pressure is exactly 1 *bar*. The *standard state* of a *gas* is its state at a pressure of exactly 1 *bar* at any temperature. The *standard state* of a *solute* is its state at a concentration of exactly 1 M at any temperature. Compare to *Standard Pressure and Temperature*.

Standard Temperature and Pressure: (*STP*) A temperature of exactly 0 °C and a pressure of exactly 1 *bar*.

Steady state: Any chemical system, including a living cell, in which the overall levels of particular *substances* is not changing in noticeable ways. Essentially, a *chemical equilibrium*.

Stereoisomerism: One of two main categories of *isomerism*, the other being *structural isomerism*. *Stereoisomerism* involves spatial differences rather than bonding differences.

Stereoisomers: *Isomers* that differ only in the spatial arrangement of groups; having the same *bond*s, but different spatial *orientation*s of particular *bond*s. *Geometric isomers* (such as *cis* and *trans*) and *optical isomers* are both *stereoisomers*.

Steric effect: Any effect on a *molecule*'s structure or reactivity that arises from the fact that *atom*s occupy space and therefor may get in each other's way.

Steric number, SN: The total number of positions occupied around a particular *atom* in a *Lewis dot structure*. The sum of the number of *atom*s plus the number of lone pairs around a central *atom* in a *Lewis dot structure*.

Stoichiometric: Having to do with the arithmetic of balanced *chemical reaction* equations for reaction systems that can be treated as "going to completion." A reaction is "*stoichiometric*" when the *reactant*s have been added together in amounts that can react without leaving leftovers. See also *non-stoichiometric* and *sub-stoichiometric*.

Stoichiometry: The study or use of *quantitative* relationships between amounts of *reactant*s and the amounts of *product*s in a *chemical reaction*. *Stoichiometry* depends on the coefficients of *reactant*s and *product*s as well as the subscripts in the formulas of *reactant*s and *product*s.

Stoichiometry table: A tool for use in the determination of the results of a limiting *reagent*s type problem. The *stoichiometry* table makes use of the arithmetic associated with the coefficients of the balanced *chemical reaction* equation. This tool is used to analyze reaction systems that can be treated as if they go to completion. Table entries are in units of "*moles*".

STP: See *Standard Temperature and Pressure*.

Straight chain: The characteristic of a *polymer* that has no branching points, so there are only two ends to the long *molecule*. Compare to *Branched chain*. In organic chemistry: the characteristic of a string of carbon atoms with no branch points. "Straight" in this context does NOT indicate 180° bond angles, it just indicates the absence of branch points.

Stress: An event that renders a system at *equilibrium* no longer at *equilibrium*. There are two main categories of *stress*es: changes in temperature and changes in amounts or concentrations or partial pressures of material.

Strong acid: A *Bronsted-Lowry acid* that *transfer*s 100% of its acidic *proton*s to water, thus generating a *stoichiometric* amount of *hydronium ion*.

Strong acid solution: An *aqueous solution* whose pH is governed by the presence of a *strong acid*, regardless of what other species (especially *weak acid*s) might be present.

Strong base: A *Bronsted-Lowry base* that releases a *stoichiometric* number of *hydroxide ions* into *solution* when dissolved in water, or that releases a *stoichiometric* number of oxide *ions* that react with water to produce *hydroxide ion*s.

Strong base solution: An *aqueous solution* whose pH is governed by the presence of a *strong base*, regardless of what other species (especially *weak base*s) might be present.

Strong electrolyte: A species that releases a *stoichiometric* number of *ions* into *solution* when dissolved in water. No intact formula units exist in *solution*. Examples include *strong acids*, *strong bases* and *soluble salts*.

Strong field ligand: *Ligand*s *(pronounced as in "pig")* that give rise to a large splitting of the t_{2g} and e_g *orbital*s.

Structural isomerism: One of the two main categories of *isomer*ism, the other being *stereoisomerism*. In *structural isomerism*, the two species with the same formula have different sets of *bond*s.

Structure-function relationship: A biochemical principle that emphasizes the strong connection between the structure of a *molecule* or *polymer* and its biological function.

Subatomic particle: Any particle that is part of an *atom*. The three primary *subatomic particle*s are *protons*, *neutrons* and *electrons*.

Sublimation: The *phase change* from *solid* to *gas*.

Subshell: Groups of *atomic orbital*s of similar shapes, all with the same principle *quantum number*, but having different *angular momentum quantum number*s (ℓ). *Electron*s in 2p (or 3s, or 5d, etc.) *orbital*s of an *atom* are in the same *subshell*.

Substance: *Homogeneous matter* having a definite composition.

Substitutional alloy: A *solid homogeneous solution* of two or more similarly sized *metal atom*s such that all of the *atom*s take up primary positions (not *interstitial positions*) in the *solid* matrix.

Substoichiometric: Any *product* present in smaller amount than would be expected based on a reaction going to completion. Or, a *reagent* that is present in less than *stoichiometric* amounts, so that it will be the limiting *reagent*.

Substrate: In biochemistry, the *reactant* that binds to an *enzyme* in order to undergo a chemical transformation.

Subunit: One of a set of *protein polymer* chains that fold as individual *molecule*s and then associate with weak bonding interactions into a single working *molecule*. The *association* of multiple *subunits* is called the *quaternary structure* of the *protein*.

Superimposable: Any species that can be positioned in space to exactly line up with one another without the need to break any *bond*s. These species represent the same chemical *substance*, even if a structural picture is drawn with a different *orientation* or *conformation*. Compare to *Nonsuperimposable*.

Supernatent: The *liquid* (or *solution*) above a settled *solid*.

Systematic error: The repeated occurrence of an error such that all measurements made are too high or too low. These can commonly be attributed to mal-functioning instruments or the incorrect use of an instrument.

Temperature Dependent: Any measurement or characteristic that changes at different temperatures. *Equilibrium constants* are temperature dependent.

Termination: Any nuclear event that occurs during a *chain reaction* that results in the loss of particles that sustain the *chain reaction*, such as *neutron capture*.

Tertiary structure: A level of *protein* architecture that has to do with how strands of *secondary structure* fold up to achieve a globular form (often).

Tetradentate: A *ligand (pronounced as in "pig")* that makes four simultaneous *coordinate covalent bonds* to a central *metal ion*, often in *square planar* geometry. See *porphyrin* and *heme*.

Tetrahedral: The geometry resulting from a *steric number* of four around the central *atom*. Characterized by 109.5° *bond* angles.

Theoretical yield: The mass of *product* expected based on the amount of *limiting reactant* available.

Theory: Models that explain natural phenomena on a more broadly based level than hypotheses.

Titrant: The *solution* that is slowly added to another *solution* during a *titration*. Usually a *standard solution* delivered via a buret.

Titration: The *quantitative* analytical tool employing the slow addition of one *reagent* to another, in an attempt to determine the amount of one of the *reagent*s present.

Torr: A unit of pressure equal to one millimeter of mercury, 760 *torr* = 1 atm. The name honors Evangelista Torricelli.

Total equation: See *Neutral formula equation*.

Total ionic equation: See *Ionic equation*.

Trans: An adjective used in *chemistry* to indicate that similar structural features are opposite of each other in spatial positioning. Often in reference to *isomers*.

Trans bilayer movement: Also called "*flip-flop*." The movement of a membrane phospholipid from one leaf to the other, which requires that the *polar head group* move through the *nonpolar* interior of the membrane layer, and thus is not a favorable movement.

Trans fat: Any *triacylglycerol molecule* that has at least one long *hydrocarbon* chain with a non-naturally occurring *trans double bond*.

Transcription: The cellular process by which the separation of *duplex DNA* strands from one another occurs, allowing one of the strands to serve as a template for the synthesis of a messenger RNA.

Transfer: The concept of a portion of a chemical species being un-bound from its original species and bound to a new species, instead. One *bond* is broken and another *bond* is made. For example, a *proton transfer* occurs when a *proton* comes off a *Bronsted-Lowry acid* and then binds to a water *molecule*, instead.

Transition metal: Any *element* in *group*s 3-12 of the *periodic table*, sometimes described as the *d block elements*.

Transmission: The flow of *electromagnetic radiation* through a medium such as a *solution* or window, with the radiation coming out the other side.

Transmitted light: *Electromagnetic radiation* (often *visible* light) that passes through a *transparent* material or *solution* by virtue of not being *absorbed*.

Transparent: A characteristic of a *solution* or material meaning that it is see-through, not cloudy or opaque. *Transparent* materials can be colorless (water) or colored (green glass).

Triacylglycerol: A biologically important *molecule* with a glycerol backbone and three long *hydrocarbon* chains that originate as *fatty acid molecules*. These *substance*s are called fats when they are *solid* at room temperature and oils when they are *liquid*s at room termperature.

Tridentate ligand *(pronounced as in "pig"):* Any *polydentate ligand* forming three simultaneous bonding attachments to the central *metal cation* or *atom*.

Trigonal bipyramidal: The geometry resulting from a *steric number* of five around the central *atom*. Characterized by 120° and 90° bond angles.

Trigonal (or Trigonal planar): The geometry resulting from a *steric number* of three around the central *atom*. Characterized by 120° *bond* angles.

Trigonal pyramidal: The *molecular shape* associated with a *tetrahedral* geometry of *electron* pairs when one of those pairs is a lone pair.

Triple bond: A *bond* arising from the sharing of six *electrons*. Usually one sigma and two *pi bonds*.

Triprotic acid: A *Bronsted-Lowry acid* with three acidic *protons*.

Ultraviolet (UV) radiation: *Electromagnetic radiation* with *wavelengths* generally between 100 nm and 400 nm, it is more energetic than *visible radiation*. *Absorption* of *ultraviolet radiation* by chemical *substances* may excite *electrons* and cause *bond* breakage.

Unbranched: Carbon chains in which each carbon *atom* is bonded to exactly two other carbon *atoms*, except for the ends of the chain, in which the carbons are bonded to only one other carbon *atom*. Also referred to as "straight chains" even though the bond angles are NOT 180°.

Unidentate ligand *(pronounced as in "pig"):* See *Monodentate ligand*.

Unit cell: The smallest portion of a *crystal* necessary to show the repeating structural geometry.

Valence electrons: Usually the *electrons* having the highest *principle quantum number* in an *atom*, but can also refer to *d electrons* that are beyond the *noble gas* core. The outermost *electrons*. Often the *electrons* shown in a dot symbol, or *Lewis dot structure*. The *electrons* involved in *chemical bonds* are *valence electrons*.

Valence orbital potential energy: A measure of the average *potential energy* of an *electron* within an *atomic orbital*.

Valence Shell Electron Pair Repulsion (VSEPR): The *theory* centered on the concept that *electron* pairs will repel each other as much as possible, leading to a method for the determination of the three-dimensional *shapes* of *molecules* and *ions*.

Vapor pressure: The *partial pressure* of a *gas* that is in *equilibrium* with its *condensed phase* (*solid*, *liquid*, or *solution*) at a specific temperature.

Van der Waals force: Same as *London dispersion force*.

Vesicle: A laboratory-formed spherical *bilayer* of *phospholipids* (and perhaps other minor components) that can mimic aspects of a cell membrane.

Visible absorption spectrum: A graph of the results of a *visible spectrophotometry* experiment in terms of *absorbance* vs. *wavelength*.

Visible radiation (Vis): *Electromagnetic radiation* with *wavelengths* generally between 400 nm and 700 nm, it is less energetic than *ultraviolet radiation*. *Absorption* of *visible* radiation (light) by chemical *substances* may cause *electrons* to become excited, especially if the structure contains *conjugated double bonds*. Because some *visible wavelengths* are *absorbed*, these materials and *substances* appear colored.

Visible spectrophotometry: An experiment (utilizing an instrument called a *visible* spectrophotometer) to determine which *wavelengths* of *visible radiation* are *absorbed* by a *transparent* material or *solution*.

Volatile: Easily *evaporated* under normal conditions. Easily moves into the *gas phase*. In other contexts, can also mean that a substance is prone to change rapidly and/or unpredictably, as in an explosion.

Volatility: The characteristic of being *volatile*.

VSEPR: See *Valence Shell Electron Pair Repulsion*.

Water of hydration: The water *molecule*s that are tightly associated with a *crystal* structure of another *substance*, but are not covalently bonded.

Wave function: (ψ) A complicated, mathematical function that describes the *amplitude* of the *electron* wave at different points in space. Each possible value of ψ for an *atom* is known as an *orbital*.

Wave-particle: A species having characteristics of both waves and particles, often described as having a *dual nature*. Applies to both *electromagnetic radiation* and very small particles such as the *electron*.

Wavelength, λ: The peak-to-peak distance for crests of any wave, often used particularly in the case of *electromagnetic radiation*.

Weak acid: A *Bronsted-Lowry acid* that, when dissolved in water, is capable of transferring only a small percent of its acidic *protons* (H^+) to water *molecule*s, and thus, produces a *substoichiometric* number of *hydronium ions*. A *weak acid* is a *weak electrolyte*.

Weak base: A *Bronsted-Lowry base* that, when dissolved in water, is capable of taking only a small number of *protons* (H^+) from water *molecule*s, and thus, produces a *substoichiometric* number of *hydroxide ions*. A *weak vase* is a *weak electrolyte*.

Weak electrolyte: A species that releases fewer than a *stoichiometric* number of *ions* into *solution* when dissolved in water. Usually approximately 90% of the formula units of a *weak electrolyte* remain unionized.

Weak field ligand (pronounced as in "pig"): *Ligand*s that give rise to a small splitting of the t_{2g} and e_g *orbital*s.

Zwitterion: Any covalently bonded species having more than one simultaneously ionized site, at least one of which is negatively charged and another is positively charged. The overall charge on the *zwitterion* is the sum of the charges of the ionized sites. *Zwitterions* may have a net charge of zero at a particular *pH*, or range of *pH*'s, even though multiple sites are *ionized*. *Amino acids* are a good example.

ANSWERS TO EXERCISES

CHAPTER 12 ANSWERS TO EXERCISES

Exercise 12-1

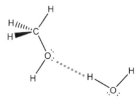

The donor and acceptor roles have been reversed.

Exercise 12-2

a. $Ba(OH)_2(s) \longrightarrow Ba^{2+}(aq) + 2OH^-(aq)$

b. $NiSO_4(s) \longrightarrow Ni^{2+}(aq) + SO_4^{2-}(aq)$

c. $HI(aq) + H_2O(\ell) \longrightarrow I^-(aq) + H_3O^+(aq)$

d. $Na_2S_2O_3(s) \longrightarrow 2Na^+(aq) + S_2O_3^{2-}(aq)$

Exercise 12-3

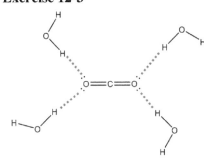

Each water molecule is a hydrogen bond donor. The oxygen atoms of CO_2 are the hydrogen bond acceptors. Note the linearity around the bridging hydrogen atoms; they have a steric number of 2.

Exercise 12-4

a. sodium chromate = Na_2CrO_4 and has a molar mass of 161.973 g/mol

$$\text{concentration} = \frac{1.2344\,g\,Na_2CrO_4}{500.0\,mL} \times \frac{1000\,mL}{L} \times \frac{1\,mol\,Na_2CrO_4}{161.973\,g\,Na_2CrO_4} = 1.524 \times 10^{-2}\,M\,Na_2CrO_4$$

b. molar mass (including waters of hydration) = 249.686 g/mol

$$\text{concentration} = \frac{0.3269\,g\,salt}{250.0\,mL} \times \frac{1000\,mL}{L} \times \frac{1\,mol\,salt}{249.686\,g\,salt} = 5.237 \times 10^{-3}\,M\,CuSO_4 \cdot 5H_2O$$

Exercise 12-5

a. $KMnO_4$ and has a molar mass of 158.034 g/mol

$$2.000\,L \times \frac{0.500\,mol\,KMnO_4}{1\,L} \times \frac{158.034\,g\,KMnO_4}{1\,mol\,KMnO_4} = 158\,g\,KMnO_4$$

b. $Ni(NO_3)_2$ and has a molar mass of 182.703 g/mol

$$100.0\,mL \times \frac{0.800\,mol\,Ni(NO_3)_2}{1000\,mL} \times \frac{182.703\,g\,Ni(NO_3)_2}{1\,mol\,Ni(NO_3)_2} = 14.6\,g\,Ni(NO_3)_2$$

Exercise 12-6

a. $Sr(ClO_3)_2$ $\quad 0.0989\,M\,Sr(ClO_3)_2 \times \dfrac{1\,M\,Sr^{2+}}{1\,M\,Sr(ClO_3)_2} = 0.0989\,M\,Sr^{2+}$

$\qquad\qquad\qquad 0.0989\,M\,Sr(ClO_3)_2 \times \dfrac{2\,M\,ClO_3^-}{1\,M\,Sr(ClO_3)_2} = 0.198\,M\,ClO_3^-$

b. $Hg_2(NO_3)_2$ $\quad 0.0552\,M\,Hg_2(NO_3)_2 \times \dfrac{1\,M\,Hg_2^{2+}}{1\,M\,Hg_2(NO_3)_2} = 0.0552\,M\,Hg_2^{2+}$

$\qquad\qquad\qquad 0.0552\,M\,Hg_2(NO_3)_2 \times \dfrac{2\,M\,NO_3^-}{1\,M\,Hg_2(NO_3)_2} = 0.110\,M\,NO_3^-$

c. 0.120 mol $K_2C_2O_4$ produces 0.240 mol K^+ and 0.120 mol $C_2O_4^{2-}$
0.080 mol KCl produces 0.080 mol K^+ and 0.080 mol Cl^-

$\left[C_2O_4^{2-}\right] = \dfrac{0.120\,mol}{0.7500\,L} = 0.160\,M \qquad \left[Cl^-\right] = \dfrac{0.080\,mol}{0.7500\,L} = 0.11\,M \qquad \left[K^+\right] = \dfrac{(0.240+0.080)\,mol}{0.7500\,L} = 0.427\,M$

Exercise 12-7

$250.0\,mL \times \dfrac{0.500\,mol\,HNO_3}{1000\,mL} = 0.125\,mol\,HNO_3\ needed$

$0.125\,mol\,HNO_3 \times \dfrac{1\,L}{1.2293\,mol\,HNO_3} \times \dfrac{1000\,mL}{L} = 102\,mL\,stock\,solution$

Exercise 12-8

$25.00\,mL \times \dfrac{0.106\,mol}{1\,mL} = 2.65\times10^{-3}\,mol$ (was found in 5.00 mL of the unknown solution)

concentration of unknown solution $= \dfrac{2.65\times10^{-3}\,mol}{5.00\,mL} \times \dfrac{1000\,mL}{L} = 0.530\,M$

Exercise 12-9

a. $3.60\,M \times \dfrac{1000\,mM}{1\,M} = 3.60\times10^3\,mM$ each dilution is $\times\dfrac{1}{5}$, so will require four dilution steps.

b. $3.60\times10^3\,mM \times \left(\dfrac{10\,mL}{50\,mL}\right)^4 = 5.76\,mM$

Exercise 12-10 $HNO_3(aq) + OH^-(aq) \longrightarrow NO_3^-(aq) + H_2O(\ell)$

$0.02468\,L \times \dfrac{0.1066\,mol\,OH^-}{1\,L} \times \dfrac{1\,mol\,HNO_3}{1\,mol\,OH^-} = 2.6309\times10^{-3}\,mol\,HNO_3$

$\left[HNO_3\right] = \dfrac{2.6309\times10^{-3}\,mol}{0.03000\,L} = 8.770\times10^{-2}\,M\,HNO_3$

Exercise 12-11

$$5.76\,mL\,Na_2SO_4\,solution \times \frac{1\,L}{1000\,mL} \times \frac{0.200\,mol\,Na_2SO_4}{1\,L} = 1.152 \times 10^{-3}\,mol\,Na_2SO_4$$

$$1.152 \times 10^{-3}\,mol\,Na_2SO_4 \times \frac{1\,mol\,SO_4^{2-}}{1\,mol\,Na_2SO_4} \times \frac{2\,mol\,Ag^+}{1\,mol\,SO_4^{2-}} = 2.304 \times 10^{-3}\,mol\,Ag^+$$

$$\left[Ag^+\right]_{original} = \frac{2.304 \times 10^{-3}\,mol\,Ag^+}{25.00\,mL} \times \frac{1000\,mL}{1\,L} = 9.22 \times 10^{-2}\,M\,Ag^+$$

Exercise 12-12

a.

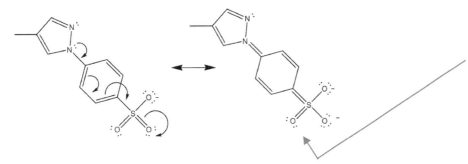

Negative charge could be on this oxygen, just as well as the other.

b. There are many choices, some of which are pictured below.

Exercise 12-13

When 1% is absorbed, I = 1 when I_o = 100. $A = \log\left(\frac{I_o}{I}\right)$ $A = \log\left(\frac{100}{1}\right) = 2.00$

Exercise 12-14

$$\lambda = 700 \qquad A_{700} = \left(0\frac{L}{mol \cdot cm} \right)(1.00\,cm)\left(0.0010\frac{mol}{L} \right) = 0$$

$$A_{700} = \log\left(\frac{100}{100} \right) = 0$$

$$\lambda = 550 \qquad A_{550} = \left(1000\frac{L}{mol \cdot cm} \right)(1.00\,cm)\left(0.0010\frac{mol}{L} \right) = 1.0$$

$$A_{550} = \log\left(\frac{100}{10} \right) = 1.0$$

$$\lambda = 500 \qquad A_{500} = \left(400\frac{L}{mol \cdot cm} \right)(1.00\,cm)\left(0.0010\frac{mol}{L} \right) = 0.40$$

$$A_{500} = \log\left(\frac{100}{40} \right) = 0.40$$

Exercise 12-15

$$A_{402} = \left(\varepsilon_{402} \right)\left(\ell \right)\left(c \right)$$

$$0.020 = \left(0.038\frac{L}{mol \cdot cm} \right)(10.00\,cm)(c)$$

$$c = 5.3 \times 10^{-2}\frac{mol}{L}$$

CHAPTER 13 ANSWERS TO EXERCISES

Exercise 13-1
a. element   **b.** mixture   **c.** mixture

d. compound (ideally, although water is not usually pure)

e. compound   **f.** solution

Exercise 13-2
a. chemical   **b.** physical   **c.** physical   **d.** chemical

Exercise 13-3
The water and glass get cold. The dissolving process for urea is endothermic, so heat is taken from the surroundings, making the surroundings cold.

Exercise 13-4
a. Add water to the mixture and stir. The sugar will dissolve, but not the sand. Pour the resulting mixture through a filter so that the dissolved sugar and water pass through but the sand is retained. Drying the sand and evaporating the water from the sugar solution will result in separated sugar and sand. Throughout this process, neither the formula of the sugar, nor that of the sand, changes.
b. Stir the mixture with the pole of a magnet. The iron filings will stick but the sand will not. Formulas remain unchanged throughout this process.
c. The salt contains Na^+ and Cl^- while the elements are $Na(s)$ and $Cl_2(g)$. In order to obtain the elements from the salt, formulas have to change, meaning that a chemical reaction must occur.

Exercise 13-5

a. $P_4 + 6H_2 \longrightarrow 4PH_3$

b. $3Fe_2O_3 + C \longrightarrow 2Fe_3O_4 + CO$

c. $2S_2O_3^{2-} + I_2 \longrightarrow S_4O_6^{2-} + 2I^-$

d. $4HCl + MnO_2 \longrightarrow MnCl_2 + Cl_2 + 2H_2O$

Exercise 13-6

a. $CS_2 + 3O_2 \longrightarrow CO_2 + 2SO_2$

b. $Cr_2O_7^{2-} + H_2O \rightleftharpoons 2HCrO_4^-$

c. $I_2 + 3XeF_2 \rightleftharpoons 2IF_3 + 3Xe$

d. $2KNO_3 + S + 3C \longrightarrow K_2S + 3CO_2 + N_2$

Exercise 13-7

$Ca \longrightarrow Ca^{2+} + 2e^-$

$Cl_2 + 2e^- \longrightarrow 2Cl^-$

Exercise 13-8

$Mg \longrightarrow Mg^{2+} + 2e^-$

$Zn \longrightarrow Zn^{2+} + 2e^-$

a. $\underline{S + 2e^- \longrightarrow S^{2-}}$

b. $\underline{Cl_2 + 2e^- \longrightarrow 2Cl^-}$

$Mg(s) + S(s) \longrightarrow MgS(s)$

$Zn(s) + Cl_2(g) \longrightarrow ZnCl_2(s)$

Exercise 13-9

$4Li(s) + O_2(g) \longrightarrow 2Li_2O(s)$

$2Na(s) + O_2(g) \longrightarrow Na_2O_2(s)$

$K(s) + O_2(g) \longrightarrow KO_2(s)$

Exercise 13-10

a. $C_4H_{10} + \dfrac{13}{2}O_2 \longrightarrow 4CO_2 + 5H_2O$ or $2C_4H_{10} + 13O_2 \longrightarrow 8CO_2 + 10H_2O$

b. $(CH_3)_2 CO + 4O_2 \longrightarrow 3CO_2 + 3H_2O$

c. $2Al + \dfrac{3}{2}O_2 \longrightarrow Al_2O_3$ or $4Al + 3O_2 \longrightarrow 2Al_2O_3$

Exercise 13-11

$Ag^+(aq) + Cl^-(aq) \longrightarrow AgCl(s)$

$Ag^+(aq) + I^-(aq) \longrightarrow AgI(s)$

$Pb^{2+}(aq) + 2I^-(aq) \longrightarrow PbI_2(s)$

$Ni^{2+}(aq) + 2OH^-(aq) \longrightarrow Ni(OH)_2(s)$

Exercise 13-12

a. $Ba^{2+}(aq) + SO_4^{2-}(aq) \longrightarrow BaSO_4(s)$ spectators $= Na^+$ and Cl^-

b. $H_3O^+(aq) + OH^-(aq) \longrightarrow 2H_2O(\ell)$ spectators $= K^+$ and NO_3^-

c. $3Ag^+(aq) + PO_4^{3-}(aq) \longrightarrow Ag_3PO_4(s)$ spectators $= K^+$ and NO_3^-

Exercise 13-13

a. $2Fe^{3+}(aq)+3S^{2-}(aq)\longrightarrow Fe_2S_3(s)$ spectators $=Na^+$ and Cl^-

b. $Ni^{2+}(aq)+2OH^-(aq)\longrightarrow Ni(OH)_2(s)$ spectators $=K^+$ and SO_4^{2-}

c. $Hg_2^{2+}(aq)+2Cl^-(aq)\longrightarrow Hg_2Cl_2(s)$ spectators $=H_3O^+$ and NO_3^-

d. $Pb^{2+}(aq)+CrO_4^{2-}(aq)\longrightarrow PbCrO_4(s)$ spectators $=K^+$ and ClO_4^-

e. No reaction occurs. All possible products are soluble ($KClO_4$ and $NaNO_3$). All we did was create a mixture of aqueous ions: $K^+(aq)$, $Na^+(aq)$, $ClO_4^-(aq)$, $NO_3^-(aq)$.

Exercise 13-14

a. Fe^{3+} gets reduced to Fe^{2+}, Cu^+ gets oxidized to Cu^{2+}

b. Fe^{3+} gets reduced to Fe^{2+}, I^- gets oxidized to I_2

c. Cu metal gets oxidized to Cu^{2+}, Cl_2 gets reduced to $2\ Cl^-$

d. Al metal gets oxidized to Al^{3+}, O_2 gets reduced to O^{2-}

e. P_4 gets oxidized (to the partial positive charge of P in PCl_3),
   Cl_2 gets reduced (to the partial negative charge of Cl in PCl_3).

CHAPTER 14 ANSWERS TO EXERCISES

Exercise 14-1

Three equivalencies are found in the problem: 4.5×10^3 molecules $H_2 = 1$ L of atmosphere
$$0.60\ L = 1\ breath$$
$$\text{about 4 breaths} = 1\ min$$
In addition, we need to know that: $60\ min = 1\ h$
Starting a "sentence" of dimensional analysis with a number that is not a ratio often works out well. This problem is about a 1 hour time period.
Solving:

$$1\,h\times\frac{60\,min}{1\,h}\times\frac{\sim 4\,breaths}{1\,min}\times\frac{0.60\,L\,atmosphere}{1\,breath}\times\frac{4.5\times10^3\,molecules\,H_2}{L\,atmosphere}\approx 6\times10^5\,molecules\,H_2\,in\,one\,hour$$

Alternatively, because we know the answer features units of molecules of H_2 in the numerator, it would be safe to begin the sentence of dimensional analysis with a ratio based on the first equivalence in the list above.

$$\frac{4.5\times10^3\,molecules\,H_2}{L\,atmosphere}\times\frac{0.60\,L\,atmosphere}{1\,breath}\times\frac{\sim 4\,breaths}{1\,min}\times\frac{60\,min}{1\,h}\approx 6\times10^5\,\frac{molecules\,H_2}{h}$$

Exercise 14-2

Any multiple of the empirical formula will work.

$1\times C_3H_6O = C_3H_6O$ $2\times C_3H_6O = C_6H_{12}O_2$ $3\times C_3H_6O = C_9H_{18}O_3$ etc.

Exercise 14-3

We make the calculations a little easier by assuming 100 g of glucose. Based on the mass percents, this mass of glucose would contain 40.00 g carbon, 53.29 g oxygen, and 6.71 g hydrogen. We convert these masses into moles:

$$40.00\,g\,C\times\frac{1\,mol\,C}{12.0107\,g\,C}=3.33\,mol\,C \qquad 53.29\,g\,O\times\frac{1\,mol\,O}{15.9994\,g\,O}=3.33\,mol\,O$$

$$6.71\,g\,H\times\frac{1\,mol\,H}{1.0079\,g\,H}=6.66\,mol\,H$$

This is a 1:1:2 ratio. Formulas of organic compounds are usually given in the order C-H-other atoms alphabetically. This empirical formula is CH_2O.

Exercise 14-4

The unaccounted-for mass must be the sulfur. 100%-25.5%-6.42% = 68.1% S. We convert mass information into mole information, basing our calculations on a 100.0 g sample:

$$25.5\,g\,C \times \frac{1\,mol\,C}{12.0107\,g\,C} = 2.08\,mol\,C$$

$$6.42\,g\,H \times \frac{1\,mol\,H}{1.0079\,g\,H} = 6.37\,mol\,H$$

$$68.1\,g\,S \times \frac{1\,mol\,S}{32.066\,g\,S} = 2.12\,mol\,S$$

We divide each mole amount by the smallest one, looking for whole number results.
2.08/2.08 = 1 mol C
6.37/2.08 = 3.06 ~ 3 mol H
2.12/2.08 =1.02 ~ 1 mol S
empirical formula = CH_3S

Exercise 14-5

The NaOH trap can trap both CO_2 and H_2O. This experiment depends on trapping them separately. Therefore the trap for H_2O must come first.

Exercise 14-6

CH_2O formula mass = 30 g/mol

glucose = $\dfrac{180\,g\,/\,mol}{30\,g\,/\,mol}$ = 6, thus we should multiply the empirical formula by 6 = $C_6H_{12}O_6$.

Exercise 14-7

CH_3S formula mass ~ 47 g/mol

Compound C = $\dfrac{94.2\,g\,/\,mol}{47\,g\,/\,mol}$ ~ 2, thus we multiply the empirical formula by 2 = $C_2H_6S_2$

Exercise 14-8

Balanced reaction equation $\qquad 2\,NF_3(g) \longrightarrow N_2(g) + 3\,F_2(g)$

$$0.50\,mol\,NF_3 \times \frac{1\,mol\,N_2}{2\,mol\,NF_3} = 0.25\,mol\,N_2$$

$$0.50\,mol\,NF_3 \times \frac{3\,mol\,F_2}{2\,mol\,NF_3} = 0.75\,mol\,F_2$$

Exercise 14-9

Balanced reaction equation $\qquad P_2S_5 + 3\,PCl_5 \longrightarrow 5\,PSCl_3$

$$1.00\,mol\,PCl_5 \times \frac{1\,mol\,P_2S_5}{3\,mol\,PCl_5} = 0.333\,mol\,P_2S_5\ used$$

$$1.00\,mol\,PCl_5 \times \frac{5\,mol\,PSCl_3}{3\,mol\,PCl_5} = 1.67\,mol\,PSCl_3\ made$$

Exercise 14-10

$$1.000\,g\,Ni(PF_3)_4 \times \frac{1\,mol\,Ni(PF_3)_4}{410.57\,g\,Ni(PF_3)_4} \times \frac{1\,mol\,Ni}{1\,mol\,Ni(PF_3)_4} \times \frac{58.6934\,g\,Ni}{1\,mol\,Ni} = 0.1430\,g\,Ni$$

Exercise 14-11

a. The balanced reaction equation shows that one mole P_4 requires 6 mol Cl_2, thus 10 mol Cl_2 is excess Cl_2 and the P_4 is the limiting reagent. We can form 4 mol PCl_3.

b. $2\,mol\,P_4 \times \dfrac{6\,mol\,Cl_2}{1\,mol\,P_4} = 12\,mol\,Cl_2\,required$. Thus, 8 mol Cl_2 is limiting.

$8\,mol\,Cl_2 \times \dfrac{4\,mol\,PCl_3}{6\,mol\,Cl_2} = 5.3\,mol\,PCl_3\,formed$

c. $1.3\,mol\,P_4 \times \dfrac{6\,mol\,Cl_2}{1\,mol\,P_4} = 7.8\,mol\,Cl_2\,required$. Thus, 8 mol Cl_2 is excess and P_4 limits.

$1.3\,mol\,P_4 \times \dfrac{4\,mol\,PCl_3}{1\,mol\,P_4} = 5.2\,mol\,PCl_3\,formed$

Exercise 14-12

Write a balanced reaction equation $\quad 3S + P_4 \longrightarrow P_4S_3$. We need an S/P_4 mole ratio of 3.

We have $\dfrac{10.0\,g\,S}{12.0\,g\,P_4} \times \dfrac{1\,mol\,S}{32.065\,g\,S} \times \dfrac{123.895\,g\,P_4}{1\,mol\,P_4} = 3.22\,\dfrac{mol\,S}{mol\,P_4}$ Thus, S is excess and P_4 is limiting.

$12.0\,g\,P_4 \times \dfrac{1\,mol\,P_4}{123.9\,g\,P_4} \times \dfrac{1\,mol\,P_4S_3}{1\,mol\,P_4} \times \dfrac{220.09\,g\,P_4S_3}{1\,mol\,P_4S_3} = 21.3\,g\,P_4S_3\,expected$

Exercise 14-13 Ethylene is the limiting reagent.

a. $20.00\,g\,C_2H_4 \times \dfrac{1\,mol\,C_2H_4}{28.053\,g\,C_2H_4} \times \dfrac{1\,mol\,C_2H_4Br_2}{1\,mol\,C_2H_4} \times \dfrac{187.86\,g\,C_2H_4Br_2}{1\,mol\,C_2H_4Br_2} = 133.9\,g\,C_2H_4Br_2\,expected$

b. $\dfrac{110.6\,g\,C_2H_4Br_2\,obtained}{133.9\,g\,C_2H_4Br_2\,expected} \times 100\% = 82.60\%\,yield$

Exercise 14-14

In glucose there are about 1.2 C-O bonds per carbon atom. In pyruvate there are 5 C-O bonds per 3 carbon atoms for a ratio of 1.7 C-O bonds per carbon atom. Pyruvate is the final product of glycolysis.

The citric acid cycle generates CO_2 (O=C=O) from the carbon atoms that enter as pyruvate. There are 4 C-O bonds per carbon atom. This is the maximum number of C-O bonds to a carbon atom.

As the number of bonds to oxygen increases, the carbon atoms lose electron density due to the higher electronegativity of oxygen. Thus, there is a moderate oxidation of carbon during glycolysis and the citric acid cycle completes the oxidation of carbon atoms.

CHAPTER 15 ANSWERS TO EXERCISES

Exercise 15-1

Gas	Abundance	×	Mass (g/mol)	=	Component of molar mass (g/mol)
N_2	0.7808	×	28.01	=	21.8702
O_2	0.2094	×	32.00	=	6.7008
Ar	0.00934	×	39.95	=	0.3731
CO_2	0.000409	×	44.01	=	0.0180
Ne	0.000018	×	20.18	=	0.000361
				Sum=	28.9625

We add the values in the right-most column to obtain the average molar mass of air (based on these 5 components). Significant digits of the first five values are in black. The vertical line marks the least precise decimal place, and thus informs us of how many decimal places we can report in the sum. Thus, the average molar mass of air is 28.96 g/mol.

Exercise 15-2

$$0.0831446\frac{L\cdot bar}{mol\cdot K}\times\frac{100,000\,Pa}{1\,bar}\times\frac{1\,kPa}{1000\,Pa}\times\frac{1\times10^{-6}\,\mu L}{1\,L}\times\frac{1\,mol}{1000\,mmol}=8314.46\frac{\mu L\cdot kPa}{mmol\cdot K}$$

$$0.0831446\frac{L\cdot bar}{mol\cdot K}\times\frac{1000\,mL}{1\,L}\times\frac{750.6\,torr}{1\,bar}=6.2363\times10^4\frac{mL\cdot torr}{mol\cdot K}$$

Exercise 15-3

$$PV=nRT \qquad T=\frac{PV}{nR}=\frac{(2.00\,bar)(2.500\,L)}{(0.100\,mol)\left(0.083145\frac{L\cdot bar}{mol\cdot K}\right)}=601K\quad(328°C)$$

Exercise 15-4

$$PV=nRT \qquad V=\frac{nRT}{P}=\frac{(1\,mol,\text{exactly})\left(0.083145\frac{L\cdot bar}{mol\cdot K}\right)(273.15\,K)}{1\,bar\,(\text{exactly})}=22.711\,L$$

Exercise 15-5
Density is mass per volume. Determination of mol/volume would be a good start for obtaining mass/volume because we have a molar mass for air. We must convert the temperature in degrees Fahrenheit to Kelvins before using the ideal gas law.

Convert temp to Kelvin $\frac{5}{9}\left(-34°F-32°F\right)=-36.7°C$ $-36.7°C+273.15=236.5\,K$

$$\frac{P}{RT}=\frac{\left(742\,torr\times\dfrac{1\,bar}{750.06\,torr}\right)}{\left(0.083145\dfrac{L\cdot bar}{mol\cdot K}\right)\left(236.5\,K\right)}=5.0308\times10^{-2}\frac{mol}{L}\qquad 5.0308\times10^{-2}\frac{mol}{L}\times\frac{28.96\,g}{mol}=1.46\frac{g}{L}$$

OR, one could use PM = dRT (but then you need to either remember or derive this relationship)

$$d=\frac{PM}{RT}=\frac{\left(742\,torr\times\dfrac{1\,bar}{750.06\,torr}\right)\left(28.96\dfrac{g}{mol}\right)}{\left(0.083145\dfrac{L\cdot bar}{mol\cdot K}\right)\left(236.5\,K\right)}=1.46\frac{g}{L}$$

Exercise 15-6

$$M=\frac{dRT}{P}=\frac{\left(1.78\dfrac{g}{L}\right)\left(0.083145\dfrac{L\cdot bar}{mol\cdot K}\right)\left(298\,K\right)}{\left(1.00\,bar\right)}=44.1\frac{g}{mol}$$

This molar mass is a good match to the molar mass of CO_2.

Exercise 15-7
nR is a constant in this problem, so

$$\frac{P_1V_1}{T_1}=\frac{P_2V_2}{T_2}\qquad \frac{\left(0.983\,bar\right)\left(4.25\,L\right)}{296\,K}=\frac{\left(P_2\right)\left(17.0\,L\right)}{255\,K}\qquad P_2=0.212\,bar$$

Exercise 15-8
0.0018% is the fraction = 0.000018; $P_{Ne}=0.000018(0.988\ bar)=1.8\times10^{-5}$ bar

Exercise 15-9

a. $k_B=\dfrac{R}{N_A}=\dfrac{8.3144598\dfrac{J}{mol\cdot K}}{6.02214\times10^{23}\dfrac{1}{mol}}=1.38065\times10^{-23}\dfrac{J}{K}$

b. $k_B=\dfrac{R}{N_A}=\dfrac{0.083144598\dfrac{L\cdot bar}{mol\cdot K}}{6.02214\times10^{23}\dfrac{1}{mol}}=1.38065\times10^{-25}\dfrac{L\cdot bar}{K}$

Exercise 15-10

$$V = \frac{Nk_B T}{P} \qquad V = \frac{\left(3.68 \times 10^{22}\right)\left(1.3807 \times 10^{-25} \frac{L \cdot bar}{K}\right)(315\,K)}{2.0\,bar} = 0.80\,L$$

$$3.68 \times 10^{22}\ particles \times \frac{1\,mol}{6.02214 \times 10^{23}\ particles} = 6.11 \times 10^{-2}\,mol$$

$$V = \frac{nRT}{P} = \frac{\left(6.11 \times 10^{-2}\,mol\right)\left(0.083145 \frac{L \cdot bar}{mol \cdot K}\right)(315\,K)}{2.0\,bar} = 0.80\,L$$

Exercise 15-11

$$R = \frac{J}{mol \cdot K} = \frac{kg \cdot m^2}{s^2 \cdot mol \cdot K};\ T = K;\ M = \frac{g}{mol} \qquad \sqrt{\frac{kg \cdot m^2}{s^2 \cdot mol \cdot K} \times K \times \frac{mol}{g} \times \frac{1000\,g}{kg}} = \sqrt{\frac{m^2}{s^2}} = \frac{m}{s}$$

Exercise 15-12

$$\frac{rate_{H_2}}{rate_{Kr}} = \sqrt{\frac{83.80 \frac{g}{mol}}{2.016 \frac{g}{mol}}} = 6.447$$

H_2 molecules travel at an average rate that is 6.447 times faster than that of Kr atoms.

Exercise 15-13

$$k_H = 41.73 \frac{mg}{L \cdot bar} \times \frac{1\,bar}{100,000\,Pa} = 4.173 \times 10^{-4} \frac{mg}{L \cdot Pa}$$

$$k_H = 41.73 \frac{mg}{L \cdot bar} \times \frac{1\,bar}{750.06\,torr} \times \frac{1\,g}{1000\,mg} \times \frac{1\,mol\,O_2}{32.00\,g\,O_2} = 1.739 \times 10^{-6} \frac{mol}{L \cdot torr}$$

Exercise 15-14

a. $k_{H(gas\,B)} \times 1.55 = k_{H(gas\,A)} = 1.9 \times 10^{-4} \frac{mol}{L \cdot bar}$ $\qquad k_{H(gas\,B)} = 1.2 \times 10^{-4} \frac{mol}{L \cdot bar}$

b. $d[B] = k_{H(gas\,B)} \times P_{gas\,B}$ $\qquad 0.0034 \frac{mol}{L} = 1.2 \times 10^{-4} \frac{mol}{L \cdot bar} \times P_{gas\,B}$ $\qquad P_{gas\,B} = 28\,bar$

Exercise 15-15

Binding curves for myoglobin (blue) and hemoglobin (green). Myoglobin's $P_{50} \sim 3$ torr, while hemoglobin's $P_{50} \sim 26$ torr. At every P_{O_2} other than zero, the myoglobin curve is above the hemoglobin curve, indicating that at any given pressure of oxygen gas, myoglobin displays a higher affinity for the oxygen.

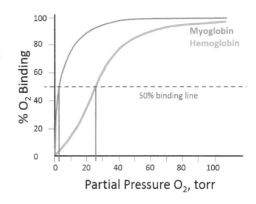

Exercise 15-16

Myoglobin sequesters oxygen away from potential reducing agents and maintains tissues at a very low concentration of free oxygen, thus minimizing the formation of the damaging species such as superoxide and hydrogen peroxide.

CHAPTER 16 ANSWERS TO EXERCISES

Exercise 16-1
The rates stop changing when they are equal. When *rate forward* = *rate reverse*, the concentration of $FeSCN^{2+}$ stops changing. Prior to that moment, the forward reaction has been making $FeSCN^{2+}$ faster than the reverse reaction has been decomposing it, so it's concentration has been going up. Because it is the reactant for the reverse reaction, the reverse reaction has been speeding up. On the other hand, in the time that the forward reaction has been going faster than the reverse reaction, the concentrations of Fe^{3+} and SCN^- have been decreasing. Because these are the reactants for the forward reaction, it has been slowing down. When the rates of the forward and reverse reaction equalize, concentrations stop changing which means that the rates of the reactions will also stop changing.

Exercise 16-2
Q cannot have a negative value because concentrations cannot have negative values.

Exercise 16-3

The form of the Q expression for this reaction equation is $Q = \dfrac{\left[Cd^{2+}\right]\left[HCN\right]^4\left[OH^-\right]^4}{\left[Cd(CN)_4^{2-}\right]}$.

Temperatures are unimportant to the calculation of the value of Q.

a. $Q = \dfrac{(2.0)(2.0)^4(2.0)^4}{(2.0)} = 2^8 = 256$ **b.** $Q = \dfrac{(0.143)(0.143)^4(0.143)^4}{(0.143)} = (0.143)^8 = 1.75 \times 10^{-7}$

c. $Q = \dfrac{(1.0)(1.0)^4(1.0)^4}{(1.0)} = 1.0$

Exercise 16-4
There are many ways of accomplishing this conversion. One very good way is to use exact equivalencies:

1.0 atm = 1.01325 bar and 1.0 bar = 1.0×10^5 Pa.

$$R = 0.082057 \frac{L \cdot atm}{mol \cdot K} \times \frac{1.01325\,bar}{1\,atm} \times \frac{1 \times 10^5\,Pa}{1\,bar} = 8314.4 \frac{L \cdot Pa}{mol \cdot K}$$

Exercise 16-5

The ideal gas law tells us that $\dfrac{P}{RT} = \dfrac{n}{V}$. Because we either know P or $\dfrac{n}{V}$ and wish to know the other, we need only apply the conversion factor of RT. We can choose various units for R. *(Can you convert one value of R to any of the others?)* The temperature in each case in 298 K.

a. $\dfrac{n}{V} = \dfrac{P}{RT} = \dfrac{0.00454\ atm}{\left(0.08206\ \dfrac{L \cdot atm}{mol \cdot K}\right)(298K)} = 1.86 \times 10^{-4}\ \dfrac{mol}{L}$ (*or* M)

b. $\dfrac{n}{V} = \dfrac{P}{RT} = \dfrac{804\ mmHg}{\left(62.36\ \dfrac{L \cdot mmHg}{mol \cdot K}\right)(298\ K)} = 4.33 \times 10^{-2}\ \dfrac{mol}{L}$ (*or* M)

c. $\dfrac{n}{V} = \dfrac{P}{RT} = \dfrac{0.044\ bar}{\left(0.08314\ \dfrac{L \cdot bar}{mol \cdot K}\right)(298\ K)} = 1.78 \times 10^{-3}\ \dfrac{mol}{L}$ (*or* M)

d. $P = \dfrac{n}{V}(RT) = 0.65\dfrac{mol}{L} \times \left(0.08314\dfrac{L \cdot bar}{mol \cdot K}\right)(298\ K) = 16\ bar$ or

$0.65\dfrac{mol}{L} \times \left(62.36\dfrac{mmHg \cdot L}{mol \cdot K}\right)(298\ K) = 1.2 \times 10^{4}\ mmHg$

Exercise 16-6

Determine the concentration of NO_2: $\dfrac{n}{V} = \dfrac{0.980\ bar}{\left(0.08314\ \dfrac{L \cdot bar}{mol \cdot K}\right)(298\ K)} = 3.955 \times 10^{-2}\ M$

Determine the concentration of N_2O_4: $\dfrac{n}{V} = \dfrac{0.122\ bar}{\left(0.08314\ \dfrac{L \cdot bar}{mol \cdot K}\right)(298\ K)} = 4.924 \times 10^{-3}\ M$

Substitute these values into the Q_c expression: $Q_c = \dfrac{\left[N_2O_4\right]}{\left[NO_2\right]^2} = \dfrac{4.924 \times 10^{-3}}{\left(3.955 \times 10^{-2}\right)^2} = 3.15$

Exercise 16-7

a. $CaCO_3(s) + H_2O(\ell) + CO_2(g) \rightleftharpoons Ca^{2+}(aq) + 2HCO_3^{2-}(aq)$ $K_{eq} \neq K_c$ and K_p is undefined

b. $Fe_2O_3(s) + 3H_2(g) \rightleftharpoons 2Fe(s) + 3H_2O(g)$ $K_{eq} = K_p$ but $K_{eq} \neq K_c$

c. $2CH_4(g) + 2NH_3(g) + 3O_2(g) \rightleftharpoons 2HCN(g) + 6H_2O(g)$ $K_{eq} = K_p$ but $K_{eq} \neq K_c$

d. $2\ H_2O_2(aq) \underset{}{\overset{catalase\ enzyme}{\rightleftharpoons}} 2\ H_2O(\ell) + O_2(aq)$ $K_{eq} = K_c$ and K_p is undefined

Exercise 16-8 Important points about this equilibrium system:

i. The color is due to reactants, not products.

ii. Thus, the darker color present in the first photo (at the left) indicates that more reactant is present.

iii. The temperature of the system in the first photo (at the left) is the highest temperature.

Putting these thoughts together, we can say that the reactants are favored more as the temperature is raised. Thus, the equilibrium constant decreases as the temperature is raised and the plot shows a negative slope.

Exercise 16-9

a.

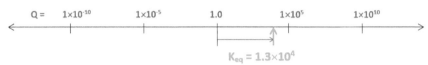

Remember that these number lines are logarithmic, so the length of the horizontal (purple) arrow shows how many factors of 10 are changing. For example, consider that the same length arrow would represent moving from a Q of 10^{-2} to 10^{-1} and from a Q of 10^{1} to 10^{2}. The first of these represents a change in Q of 0.09 while the second represents a change in Q of 90.

b. 1.50 bar $ClNO_2$, 1.62 bar NO, 0.010 bar NO_2 and 0.025 bar ClNO

$$\text{The initial Q value is } Q = \frac{\left(P_{NO_2}\right)\left(P_{ClNO}\right)}{\left(P_{NO}\right)\left(P_{ClNO_2}\right)} = \frac{(0.010)(0.025)}{(1.62)(1.50)} = 1.0 \times 10^{-4}$$

Exercise 16-10

The strategy to use here is to calculate Q and then compare it to K.

a. $Q = \dfrac{\left(P_{N_2O_4}\right)}{\left(P_{NO_2}\right)^2} = \dfrac{0.13}{(0.45)^2} = 0.64$. So Q < K_{eq} (6.8). For Q to increase, its numerator needs to get

bigger and its denominator needs to get smaller. This will occur if the forward reaction proceeds.

$2NO_2(g) \rightleftharpoons N_2O_4(g)$ at 298 K

b.

$$Q_c = \frac{\left[NH_3\right]^2}{\left[N_2\right]\left[H_2\right]^3} = \frac{(0.129)^2}{(0.221)(0.342)^3} = 1.88$$. So Q_c > K_c (0.060). For Q_c to decrease, its numerator

must decrease and its denominator must increase. This will occur if the reverse reaction proceeds.

$N_2(g) + 3H_2(g) \rightleftharpoons 2NH_3(g)$ at 500 °C

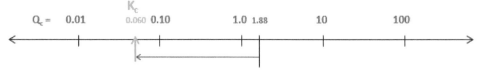

The arrow always runs from Q to K!

Exercise 16-11
If the initial reaction position IS the equilibrium reaction position, there is no purple arrow to draw because no net reaction will occur. The K_{eq} point is the beginning and the end!

Exercise 16-12
The given initial conditions are $P_{NO_2} = 1.00$ bar; $P_{N_2} = 0.50$ bar; $P_{O_2} = 1.00$ bar
and result in atom partial pressures as follows:

1.00 bar NO_2 implies: 1.00 bar N atoms and 2.00 bar O atoms
0.50 bar N_2 implies: 1.00 bar N atoms
1.00 bar O_2 implies: 2.00 bar O atoms
                          2.00 bar N atoms   4.00 bar O atoms (which is identical to 2.00 bar NO_2)

Exercise 16-13 Here are the reactions under consideration:

a. $A(g) + 2B(g) \rightleftharpoons 3C(g)$

b. $3A(g) \rightleftharpoons 2B(g)$

c. $A(s) + 2B(g) \rightleftharpoons 3C(g)$

d. $A(g) + 2B(g) \rightleftharpoons 2C(g) + D(g)$

e. $A(g) + 2B(s) \rightleftharpoons C(g)$

We look for coefficients that place the same number of moles of gas on each side of the reaction arrow. Reactions a, d, and e fit this criteria. Remember not to include pure solids and pure liquids in your analysis because these particles do not appear in the K_{eq} expression.

Exercise 16-14   Here are the reactions under consideration:

a. $A(s) + 2B(aq) \rightleftharpoons 3C(aq)$

b. $3A(aq) \rightleftharpoons 2B(aq) + C(aq)$

c. $A(aq) + B(aq) \rightleftharpoons 2C(aq)$

d. $A(aq) + 2B(aq) \rightleftharpoons 2C(aq) + D(s)$

e. $A(aq) + 2B(s) \rightleftharpoons C(aq)$

We look here for coefficients that place the same number of dissolved solute particles on each side of the reaction arrow. Reactions b, c, and e fit this criteria. Remember not to include pure solids and pure liquids in your analysis because these particles do not appear in the K_{eq} expression.

Exercise 16-15

a. $\left(K_1\right)^2 = K_2$ or $K_1 = \sqrt{K_2}$

b. $\dfrac{1}{K_3} = K_4$ or $K_3 = \dfrac{1}{K_4}$

c. $\left(K_5\right)^3 = K_6$ or $K_5 = \left(K_6\right)^{1/3}$ or $K_5 = \sqrt[3]{K_6}$

Exercise 16-16
Here we must find a way to manipulate the given reactions (and their K's) so that they can be summed to produce the reaction in question.

a. *reverse* 1: $\quad 2\,BrCl(g) \rightleftharpoons Cl_2(g) + Br_2(g)$ $\qquad\qquad K_{1(rev)} = \dfrac{1}{2.2} = 0.45$

$\quad$ *keep* 2: $\quad Br_2(g) + I_2(g) \rightleftharpoons 2\,IBr(g)$ $\qquad\qquad K_2 = 0.051$

$\quad\quad\quad\quad$ ———————————————————

$\quad\quad 2\,BrCl(g) + I_2(g) \rightleftharpoons 2\,IBr(g) + Cl_2(g)$ $\qquad K = K_{1(rev)} \times K_2 = 0.023$

b. *keep* 1: $\quad Br_2(g) + N_2(g) + O_2(g) \rightleftharpoons 2\,NOBr(g)$ $\qquad K_1 = 1.3 \times 10^{-29}$

$\quad$ *reverse* 2: $\qquad\qquad 2\,NO(g) \rightleftharpoons N_2(g) + O_2(g)$ $\qquad K_{2(rev)} = \dfrac{1}{4.3 \times 10^{-31}} = 2.3 \times 10^{30}$

$\quad\quad\quad\quad$ ————————————————

$\quad\quad 2\,NO(g) + Br_2(g) \rightleftharpoons 2\,NOBr(g)$ $\qquad\qquad K = K_1 \times K_{2(rev)}$

$\qquad\qquad\qquad\qquad\qquad\qquad\qquad\qquad\qquad\qquad = 1.3 \times 10^{-29} \times 2.3 \times 10^{30} = 3.0 \times 10^{1}$

Exercise 16-17
a. The products are "aqueous" and the reactants are "solid."
b. K_f, the formation constant.
c. The formation constant and the stability constant are reciprocals of one another.
d. The hydronium ion, H_3O^+, is always made by the ionization of a weak acid.
e. The hydroxide ion, OH^-, is always made by the ionization of a weak base.
f. No, K_a and K_b are not reciprocals (the reactions are not reverse reactions). K_a includes the hydronium ion concentration while K_b includes the hydroxide ion concentration.

Exercise 16-18
$K_D = 3.4 \times 10^{-6}$ $\quad$ We write a <u>dissociation</u> equation: H = hormone and R = receptor

$$H{\cdot}R \rightleftharpoons H + R \qquad K_D = \frac{[H][R]}{[H{\cdot}R]}$$

A small value of K_D means that there is very little product. So the association is STRONG.

CHAPTER 17 ANSWERS TO EXERCISES

Exercise 17-1
This problem is looking for reactions whose K_{eq} values will increase when the temperature increases. A K_{eq} value increases when more product, and less reactant, is present. An endothermic process will shift toward products with an increase in temperature, so we are looking for endothermic processes.

a. Bond-making processes release energy. They are exothermic. This reaction will have a K_{eq} value that <u>decreases</u> with an increase in temperature.
b. There is a loss of bonding in the forward process. As a liquid becomes a gas most of its intermolecular associations must be broken. Bond-breaking processes are endothermic. This process' K_{eq} value will <u>increase</u> with an increase in temperature. This one makes intuitive sense: more water will vaporize at higher temperatures!
c. This is an energy producing (exothermic) reaction. It will have a K_{eq} value that <u>decreases</u> with an increase in temperature.
d. This is an energy utilizing (endothermic) reaction. Its K_{eq} value will <u>increase</u> with an increase in temperature.

Exercise 17-2

a. We are told that the process is endothermic so we can write: $3Al_2Cl_6(g) + heat \rightleftharpoons 2Al_3Cl_9(g)$.

Cooler temperatures will result in a shift to try to produce more heat. This system will shift to the left at cooler temperatures. More reactant will be made.

b. Higher temperatures will cause a shift to the right; more product will be made. Product is in the numerator, so K_{eq} values will increase at higher temps.

Exercise 17-3

When the volume of the gas system is increased, all concentrations decrease. The gas phase system under consideration:

$$2NO_2(g) \rightleftharpoons N_2O_4(g)$$

responds to this stress by shifting to the left because there are more moles of gas on the left. By providing a larger number of gas particles, a shift to the left can fill the added volume.

Exercise 17-4

When the total pressure of the gas system is decreased, the partial pressures of each component also decrease. The gas phase system under consideration:

$$2NO_2(g) \rightleftharpoons N_2O_4(g)$$

will respond to this stress by shifting to the left because there are more moles of gas on the left. The pressure of the system is increase via a shift that produces a larger number of gas particles.

Exercise 17-5

This is simply another way to increase the volume of the gas phase system. The system components find themselves in a larger space, and therefore smaller partial pressures and smaller concentrations.

a. This system will shift left in order to increase the total number of gas particles in the system.

b. This system will not be stressed by the volume change because there are 2 moles of gas on each side of the reaction arrow.

c. This system will shift right in order to increase the total number of gas particles in the system.

Exercise 17-6

Adding additional solvent increases the volume of the system. Systems will see this as a stress if there are different numbers of dissolved particles on each side of the reaction arrow.

a. This system will shift to the left, more lead iodide will dissolve to fill the additional volume of water available.

b. This system will shift to the left. There are three moles of dissolved particles on the left and only two on the right.

Exercise 17-7

a. This system does not experience a stress from an increase in pressure because none of the system components are gases.

b. This system loses volume as solvent is removed. This will stress the system by causing higher concentrations of dissolved ions. (The system will shift to try to alleviate the crowding of ions so the system will shift toward the solid lead(II) sulfate. Precipitation will occur.)

c. Any reaction is either exothermic or endothermic and will therefore be stressed by changes in temperature. Remember, K_{eq} values are temperature dependent. (This reaction is probably endothermic in the forward direction—a larger molecule breaking into three smaller molecules—with loss of bonding. It will shift toward the left if the temperature is decreased.)

d. Adding a catalyst never stresses a system. (Interestingly, this particular reaction is so slow that without the catalyst the reactants will not be able to reach equilibrium and product will not form.)

Exercise 17-8

First, generate a balanced chemical reaction for the process described in the problem:

$$2SO_3(g) \rightleftharpoons 2SO_2(g) + O_2(g)$$

This helps us to identify the K_{eq} expression:

$$K_{eq} = \frac{\left(P_{SO_2}\right)^2 \left(P_{O_2}\right)}{\left(P_{SO_3}\right)^2}$$

With this groundwork done we are ready to construct our equilibrium table. We will use entries of partial pressures (in units of bars) for this table so that the entries can be substituted into the K_{eq} expression.

	$2SO_3(g)$ $\rightleftharpoons$	$2SO_2(g)$ +	$O_2(g)$
Initial pressure (bar)	1.50	0	0
Changes in pressure (bar)	-2x	+2x	+x
Equilibrium pressure (bar)	1.50 - 2x	2x	x

Substitute the equilibrium partial pressure expressions into the K_{eq} expression:

$$K_{eq} = 0.293 = \frac{\left(P_{SO_2}\right)^2 \left(P_{O_2}\right)}{\left(P_{SO_3}\right)^2} = \frac{(2x)^2 (x)}{(1.50 - 2x)^2}$$

We enter this equation into the solver of our calculator and determine that $x = 0.3566$ (carrying an extra digit to avoid rounding errors). We can use this value of x to determine the partial pressures of each gas at equilibrium:

  Partial pressure of SO_3 = 1.50 − 2x = 1.50 − 2(0.3566) = 0.787 bar.
  Partial pressure of SO_2 = 2x = 2(0.3566) = 0.713 bar.
  Partial pressure of O_2 = x = 0.357 bar.

NOTE: It might be instructive to try to solve for x by assuming that $2x$ is much smaller than 1.50. Do you expect this method to work on this problem? Is the result of your work sensible? (Using this method the value calculated for x is 0.5483, nothing would immediately suggest that this is ridiculous.) Does the value for x found by this method pass the 5% rule (is $2x$ less than 5% of 1.50)? (This value of x certainly does not pass the 5% rule, 5% of 1.50 is 0.075. This makes the value suspect. We are not surprised that the value of x found by the solver is different.) Finally, can you substitute this x value of 0.5483 into the original K_{eq} expression and obtain 0.293 for the K_{eq} value?

$$K_{eq} = \frac{(2 \times 0.5483)^2 (0.5483)}{(1.50 - 2 \times 0.5483)^2} = 4.05 \quad \boxed{not\ 0.293}$$

A similar check on the value from the solver: $$K_{eq} = \frac{(2 \times 0.3566)^2 (0.3566)}{(1.50 - 2 \times 0.3566)^2} = 0.293$$

Exercise 17-9
Consider the language of "positive homotropic effector."
Positive means that binding one will help the binding of another; that is true for oxygen.
Homotropic means the effector is the normal ligand/substrate of the protein; that is true for oxygen.
An *effector* molecule is simply a molecule that controls the activity of the protein; that is true for oxygen!
(Note that we cannot say that oxygen is a positive homotropic *allosteric* effector, because part of "allosteric" is binding at a site that is not the normal active site, and oxygen only binds to the heme.)

CHAPTER 18 ANSWERS TO EXERCISES

Exercise 18-1

    a. $HBr(aq) + H_2O(\ell) \rightleftharpoons H_3O^+(aq) + Br^-(aq)$

    b. $HClO_4(aq) + H_2O(\ell) \rightleftharpoons H_3O^+(aq) + ClO_4^-(aq)$

    c. $HOCl(aq) + H_2O(\ell) \rightleftharpoons H_3O^+(aq) + OCl^-(aq)$

    d. $C_6H_5CO_2H(aq) + H_2O(\ell) \rightleftharpoons H_3O^+(aq) + C_6H_5CO_2^-(aq)$

Exercise 18-2

    a. $NO_2^-(aq) + H_2O(\ell) \rightleftharpoons HNO_2(aq) + OH^-(aq)$

    b. $CH_3CO_2^-(aq) + H_2O(\ell) \rightleftharpoons CH_3CO_2H(aq) + OH^-(aq)$

    c. $CH_3NH_2(aq) + H_2O(\ell) \rightleftharpoons CH_3NH_3^+(aq) + OH^-(aq)$

    d. $C_6H_5O^-(aq) + H_2O(\ell) \rightleftharpoons C_6H_5OH(aq) + OH^-(aq)$

Exercise 18-3

    a. $HNO_2(aq) + H_2O(\ell) \rightleftharpoons NO_2^-(aq) + H_3O^+(aq)$

    b. $H_3O^+(aq) + OCl^-(aq) \rightleftharpoons H_2O(\ell) + HOCl(aq)$

    c. $HBr(aq) + NH_3(aq) \rightleftharpoons Br^-(aq) + NH_4^+(aq)$

    d. $HNO_2(aq) + OCl^-(aq) \rightleftharpoons NO_2^-(aq) + HOCl(aq)$

Exercise 18-4
    In a nutshell, if a species is able to serve as both an acid and a base, it is unlikely that it will be particularly good at either one. Acids and bases are opposite in character with respect to proton binding. A good proton acceptor must be a poor proton donor; if a species wants more protons, it won't give its own protons away. A good proton donor must be a poor proton acceptor; if a species likes to give its own protons away, it won't want to take protons from other species. Thus, an amphoteric substance (like water) can be both a poor acid and a poor base, but not a good acid and a good base.

Exercise 18-5

At room temperature it is always true in an aqueous solution that $[H_3O^+]_{eq}[OH^-]_{eq} = 1.008 \times 10^{-14}$.

a. $\left[OH^-\right]_{eq} = \dfrac{K_w}{\left[H_3O^+\right]_{eq}} = \dfrac{1.008 \times 10^{-14}}{3.7 \times 10^{-6}} = 2.7 \times 10^{-9} \ M$

b. $\left[H_3O^+\right]_{eq} = \dfrac{K_w}{\left[OH^-\right]_{eq}} = \dfrac{1.008 \times 10^{-14}}{9.2 \times 10^{-3}} = 1.1 \times 10^{-12} \ M$

c. $\left[OH^-\right]_{eq} = \dfrac{K_w}{\left[H_3O^+\right]_{eq}} = \dfrac{1.008 \times 10^{-14}}{2.8 \times 10^{-11}} = 3.6 \times 10^{-4} \ M$

d. $\left[H_3O^+\right]_{eq} = \dfrac{K_w}{\left[OH^-\right]_{eq}} = \dfrac{1.008 \times 10^{-14}}{6.6 \times 10^{-9}} = 1.5 \times 10^{-6} \ M$

Exercise 18-6

a. At room temperature $K_w = 1.008 \times 10^{-14}$.

$\left[OH^-\right]_{eq} = \dfrac{K_w}{\left[H_3O^+\right]_{eq}} = \dfrac{1.008 \times 10^{-14}}{3.1 \times 10^{-7}} = 3.3 \times 10^{-8} \ M$

This solution is acidic because $[H_3O^+]_{eq} > [OH^-]_{eq}$.

b. At 60 °C $K_w = 9.6 \times 10^{-14}$.

$\left[OH^-\right]_{eq} = \dfrac{K_w}{\left[H_3O^+\right]_{eq}} = \dfrac{9.6 \times 10^{-14}}{3.1 \times 10^{-7}} = 3.1 \times 10^{-7} \ M$

This solution is neutral because $[H_3O^+]_{eq} = [OH^-]_{eq}$.

Exercise 18-7

a. between pH 0 and pH 1   **b.** between pH 9 and pH 10   **c.** between pH 6 and pH 7
d. between pH 2 and pH 3   **e.** between pH −1 and pH 0

Exercise 18-8

a. $pH = -\log[H_3O^+]_{eq} = -\log(2.8 \times 10^{-6}) = 5.55$
b. $[H_3O^+]_{eq} = 10^{-pH} = 10^{-10.65} = 2.2 \times 10^{-11} \ M$
c. $[H_3O^+]_{eq} = 10^{-pH} = 10^{-3.92} = 1.2 \times 10^{-4} \ M$
d. $pH = -\log[H_3O^+]_{eq} = -\log(4.2 \times 10^{-1}) = 0.38$

Exercise 18-9

a. $[H_3O^+]_{eq} = 10^{-pH} = 10^{-4.13} = 7.4131 \times 10^{-5}\ M = 7.4 \times 10^{-5}\ M$ and

$$\left[OH^-\right]_{eq} = \frac{K_w}{\left[H_3O^+\right]_{eq}} = \frac{1.008 \times 10^{-14}}{7.4131 \times 10^{-5}} = 1.4 \times 10^{-10}\ M$$

b. $$\left[H_3O^+\right]_{eq} = \frac{K_w}{\left[OH^-\right]_{eq}} = \frac{1.008 \times 10^{-14}}{9.4 \times 10^{-3}} = 1.1 \times 10^{-12}\ M$$

$pH = -\log[H_3O^+]_{eq} = -\log(1.0723 \times 10^{-12}) = 11.97$

c. $pH = -\log[H_3O^+]_{eq} = -\log(5.7 \times 10^{-6}) = 5.24$

$$\left[OH^-\right]_{eq} = \frac{K_w}{\left[H_3O^+\right]_{eq}} = \frac{1.008 \times 10^{-14}}{5.7 \times 10^{-6}} = 1.8 \times 10^{-9}\ M$$

Exercise 18-10

Temperature ($^{\circ}$C)	K_w value $K_w = [H_3O^+]_{eq}[OH^-]_{eq}$	pK_w	$[H_3O^+]_{eq}$ in pure water	$[OH^-]_{eq}$ in pure water
0	1.2×10^{-15}	**14.92**	3.5×10^{-8}	3.5×10^{-8}
24	1.000×10^{-14}	**14.0000**	1.000×10^{-7}	1.000×10^{-7}
25	1.008×10^{-14}	**13.9965**	1.004×10^{-7}	1.004×10^{-7}
60	9.6×10^{-14}	**13.02**	3.1×10^{-7}	3.1×10^{-7}
100	6.1×10^{-13}	**12.21**	7.8×10^{-7}	7.8×10^{-7}
200	5.0×10^{-12}	**11.30**	2.2×10^{-6}	2.2×10^{-6}

Exercise 18-11

Row Number	$[H_3O^+]_{eq}$	Same $[H_3O^+]_{eq}$ (as only an exponent of 10)	pH	$[OH^-]_{eq}$	pOH
1	$2.3 \times 10^{-1}\ M$	$10^{-0.64}\ M$	0.64	*4.4 × 10⁻¹⁴*	*13.36*
2	$3.1 \times 10^{-3}\ M$	$10^{-2.51}\ M$	2.51	*3.3 × 10⁻¹²*	*11.49*
3	$4.6 \times 10^{-4}\ M$	$10^{-3.34}\ M$	3.34	*2.2 × 10⁻¹¹*	*10.66*
4	$5.4 \times 10^{-6}\ M$	$10^{-5.27}\ M$	5.27	*1.9 × 10⁻⁹*	*8.73*
5	$4.6 \times 10^{-7}\ M$	$10^{-6.34}\ M$	6.34	*2.2 × 10⁻⁸*	*7.66*
6	$7.9 \times 10^{-8}\ M$	$10^{-7.10}\ M$	7.10	*1.3 × 10⁻⁷*	*6.90*
7	$8.5 \times 10^{-10}\ M$	$10^{-9.07}\ M$	9.07	*1.2 × 10⁻⁵*	*4.93*
8	$9.7 \times 10^{-11}\ M$	$10^{-10.01}\ M$	10.01	*1.0 × 10⁻⁴*	*3.99*
9	$4.6 \times 10^{-12}\ M$	$10^{-11.34}\ M$	11.34	*2.2 × 10⁻³*	*2.66*

Exercise 18-12

a. HCl is a strong acid. So $HCl(aq) + H_2O(\ell) \longrightarrow H_3O^+(aq) + Cl^-(aq)$ goes essentially to completion. If a solution is 2.4×10^{-3} M in HCl then $[H_3O^+]_{eq} = 2.4 \times 10^{-3}$ M and pH $= -\log[H_3O^+]_{eq} = -\log(2.4 \times 10^{-3}) = 2.62$ (2 sig figs).

b. NaOH is a strong base. So $NaOH(aq) \longrightarrow Na^+(aq) + OH^-(aq)$ goes essentially to completion. If a solution is 0.0032 M in NaOH then $[OH^-]_{eq} = 0.0032$ M and pOH $= -\log[OH^-]_{eq} = -\log(0.0032) = 2.49485$ and pH $= 14.00 - 2.49485 = 11.51$ (2 sig figs).

c. HClO₄ is a strong acid. So $HClO_4(aq) + H_2O(\ell) \longrightarrow H_3O^+(aq) + ClO_4^-(aq)$ goes essentially to completion. If a solution is 0.100 M in HClO₄ then $[H_3O^+]_{eq} = 0.100$ M and pH $= -\log[H_3O^+]_{eq} = -\log(0.100) = 1.000$ (3 sig figs).

d. Ba(OH)₂ is a strong base, so $Ba(OH)_2(aq) \longrightarrow Ba^{2+}(aq) + 2OH^-(aq)$ goes essentially to completion. If a solution is 4.51×10^{-5} M in Ba(OH)₂ then $[OH^-]_{eq} = 2 \times (4.51 \times 10^{-5}\ M) = 9.02 \times 10^{-5}$ M and pOH $= -\log[OH^-]_{eq} = -\log(9.02 \times 10^{-5}) = 4.04479$ and pH $= 14.000 - 4.04479 = 9.955$ (3 sig figs).

e. K₂O is a strong base. The following reaction occurs between the oxide ion and water: $O^{2-}(aq) + H_2O(\ell) \longrightarrow 2OH^-(aq)$. If a solution is 5.1×10^{-4} M in K₂O, then $[OH^-]_{eq} = 2 \times (5.1 \times 10^{-4}\ M) = 1.02 \times 10^{-3}$ M, and pOH $= -\log(1.02 \times 10^{-3}) = 2.9914$ and pH $= 14.00 - 2.9914 = 11.01$ (2 sig figs).

CHAPTER 19 ANSWERS TO EXERCISES

Exercise 19-1

The first two reactions involve the pair: H_3O^+ / H_2O.
The second two reactions involve the pair: H_2O / OH^-.

Exercise 19-2

a. percent ionization $= \dfrac{80,000,000}{1,000,000,000} \times 100\% = 8.0\%$

b. percent ionization $= \dfrac{4.73 \times 10^{21}}{6.022 \times 10^{23}} \times 100\% = 0.785\%$

c. percent ionization $= \dfrac{0.0063}{0.44} \times 100\% = 1.4\%$

Exercise 19-3

a. percent ionization $= \dfrac{4.9 \times 10^{13}}{3.0 \times 10^{15}} \times 100\% = 1.6\%$

b. percent ionization $= \dfrac{0.00521}{0.265} \times 100\% = 1.97\%$

c. percent ionization $= \dfrac{2.2 \times 10^{-4}}{\left(0.0021 + 2.2 \times 10^{-4}\right)} \times 100\% = 9.5\%$

Exercise 19-4

a. $9.3\% = \dfrac{x}{0.14} \times 100\%$

$x = 1.302 \times 10^{-2} = \left[H_3O^+\right]$

$pH = -\log(1.302 \times 10^{-2}) = 1.89$

b. $6.5\% = \dfrac{x}{0.032} \times 100\%$

$x = 2.08 \times 10^{-3} = \left[H_3O^+\right]$

$pH = -\log(2.08 \times 10^{-3}) = 2.68$

c. $9.3\% = \dfrac{x}{0.032} \times 100\%$

$x = 2.976 \times 10^{-3} = \left[H_3O^+\right]$

$pH = -\log(2.976 \times 10^{-3}) = 2.53$

d. Both the concentration and the percent ionization are important. We calculated the pH of two 0.032 M solutions, one that was 9.3% ionized and one that was 6.5% ionized. They have different pH values. The one that is more ionized has a smaller pH.

Part **c** (here) and Example 19-2 share the same mathematics for a weak base and a weak acid. One generates a pH of 2.53 and the other a pOH of 2.53. So we see that when the percent ionization and the concentrations are the same, we get analogous results.

Part **a** (here) and Example 19-1 both worked with solutions that were 0.14 M. The calculated pH values are not the same because the percent ionizations are different.

We could also look at parts **a** and **c** (here). Both problems involve the same percent ionization, but if you apply it to a large concentration you get more ions, so the pH values are different.

Exercise 19-5

a. $6.6\% = \dfrac{x}{0.045} \times 100\%$

$x = 2.97 \times 10^{-3} = \left[OH^-\right]$

$pOH = -\log(2.97 \times 10^{-3}) = 2.527$

$pH = 14.00 - 2.527 = 11.47$

b. $10.0\% = \dfrac{x}{0.28} \times 100\%$

$x = 2.80 \times 10^{-2} = \left[OH^-\right]$

$pOH = -\log(2.80 \times 10^{-2}) = 1.553$

$pH = 14.00 - 1.553 = 12.45$

Exercise 19-6

Acid ionization reaction equation
$HA(aq) + H_2O(\ell) \rightleftharpoons A^-(aq) + H_3O^+(aq)$
$HIO_3(aq) + H_2O(\ell) \rightleftharpoons IO_3^-(aq) + H_3O^+(aq)$
$HF(aq) + H_2O(\ell) \rightleftharpoons F^-(aq) + H_3O^+(aq)$
$HNO_2(aq) + H_2O(\ell) \rightleftharpoons NO_2^-(aq) + H_3O^+(aq)$
$HCO_2H(aq) + H_2O(\ell) \rightleftharpoons HCO_2^-(aq) + H_3O^+(aq)$
$CH_3CO_2H(aq) + H_2O(\ell) \rightleftharpoons CH_3CO_2^-(aq) + H_3O^+(aq)$
$HClO(aq) + H_2O(\ell) \rightleftharpoons ClO^-(aq) + H_3O^+(aq)$
$HCN(aq) + H_2O(\ell) \rightleftharpoons CN^-(aq) + H_3O^+(aq)$
$NH_4^+(aq) + H_2O(\ell) \rightleftharpoons NH_3(aq) + H_3O^+(aq)$

Exercise 19-7

Base ionization reaction equation
$B: (aq) + H_2O(\ell) \rightleftharpoons BH^+(aq) + OH^-(aq)$
$NH_3(aq) + H_2O(\ell) \rightleftharpoons NH_4^+(aq) + OH^-(aq)$
$CN^-(aq) + H_2O(\ell) \rightleftharpoons HCN(aq) + OH^-(aq)$
$ClO^-(aq) + H_2O(\ell) \rightleftharpoons HClO(aq) + OH^-(aq)$
$CH_3CO_2^-(aq) + H_2O(\ell) \rightleftharpoons CH_3CO_2H(aq) + OH^-(aq)$
$HCO_2^-(aq) + H_2O(\ell) \rightleftharpoons HCO_2H(aq) + OH^-(aq)$
$NO_2^-(aq) + H_2O(\ell) \rightleftharpoons HNO_2(aq) + OH^-(aq)$
$F^-(aq) + H_2O(\ell) \rightleftharpoons HF(aq) + OH^-(aq)$
$IO_3^-(aq) + H_2O(\ell) \rightleftharpoons HIO_3(aq) + OH^-(aq)$

Exercise 19-8

Expect that the stronger base is the anion having fewer resonance opportunities: ClO^-.

Exercise 19-9

Acid structures	Conjugate base structures

We see that HIO_3, HNO_2, HCO_2H, and CH_3CO_2H all have conjugate bases with multiple resonance structures.

Exercise 19-10

a. HIO_3 b. H_2SeO_4 c. HF_2C-CO_2H

Exercise 19-11

$CF_3CO_2^-$ should be a poorer base than $CH_3CO_2^-$ because of the electronegativity of the fluorine atoms. The negative charge on $CF_3CO_2^-$ is stabilized by the presence, nearby, of such highly electronegative atoms.

Exercise 19-12

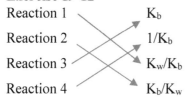

Reaction 1 — K_b

Reaction 2 — $1/K_b$

Reaction 3 — K_w/K_b

Reaction 4 — K_b/K_w

Exercise 19-13

a. $K_b = K_w/K_a = 9.9 \times 10^{-13}$

b. $1/K_a = 1.3 \times 10^8$

c. $1/K_b = K_a/K_w = 3.2 \times 10^7$

d. $K_a = 2.5 \times 10^{-5}$

Exercise 19-14

The reaction in 19-13b has a strong acid reactant and the reaction in 19-13c has a strong base reactant. These two reactions have large K_{eq} values and go essentially to completion.

Exercise 19-15

a.

	$HIO_3(aq)$	$+$ $H_2O(\ell)$	$\rightleftharpoons$ $IO_3^-(aq)$	$+$ $H_3O^+(aq)$
Initial M	0.34		0	0
Changes in M	$-x$	Pure liquid	$+x$	$+x$
Equilibrium M	$0.34 - x$		x	x

$$K_a = 1.6 \times 10^{-1} = \frac{[IO_3^-][H_3O^+]}{[HIO_3]}$$ substitution yields $$1.6 \times 10^{-1} = \frac{x^2}{0.34 - x}$$

Using an equation solver yields: $x = 0.166 = [H_3O^+]$, pH $= -\log(0.166) = 0.78$

b.

	$HIO_3(aq)$	$+$ $H_2O(\ell)$	$\rightleftharpoons$ $IO_3^-(aq)$	$+$ $H_3O^+(aq)$
Initial M	0.034		0	0
Changes in M	$-x$	Pure liquid	$+x$	$+x$
Equilibrium M	$0.034 - x$		x	x

$$K_a = 1.6 \times 10^{-1} = \frac{[IO_3^-][H_3O^+]}{[HIO_3]}$$ substitution yields $$1.6 \times 10^{-1} = \frac{x^2}{0.034 - x}$$

Using an equation solver yields: $x = 0.0288 = [H_3O^+]$, pH $= -\log(0.0288) = 1.54$

c.

	$NH_4^+(aq)$	+ $H_2O(\ell)$	$\rightleftharpoons$	$NH_3(aq)$	+ $H_3O^+(aq)$
Initial M	0.12			0	0
Changes in M	$-x$	Pure liquid		$+x$	$+x$
Equilibrium M	$0.12 - x$			x	x

$$K_a = 5.6 \times 10^{-10} = \frac{\left[NH_3\right]\left[H_3O^+\right]}{\left[NH_4^+\right]} \quad \text{substitution yields} \quad 5.6 \times 10^{-10} = \frac{x^2}{0.12 - x}$$

Using an equation solver yields: $x = 8.20 \times 10^{-6} = [H_3O^+]$, $\quad$ pH $= -\log (8.20 \times 10^{-6}) = 5.09$

Exercise 19-16

a.

	$NH_3(aq)$	+ $H_2O(\ell)$	$\rightleftharpoons$	$NH_4^+(aq)$	+ $OH^-(aq)$
Initial M	0.15			0	0
Changes in M	$-x$	Pure liquid		$+x$	$+x$
Equilibrium M	$0.15 - x$			x	x

$$K_b = 1.8 \times 10^{-5} = \frac{\left[NH_4^+\right]\left[OH^-\right]}{\left[NH_3\right]} \qquad 1.8 \times 10^{-5} = \frac{x^2}{0.15 - x}$$

Using an equation solver yields: $\quad x = 0.00163 = [OH^-]$
pOH $= -\log (0.00163) = 2.787$, $\quad$ pH $= 14.00 - 2.787 = 11.21$

b.

	$HCO_2^-(aq)$	+ $H_2O(\ell)$	$\rightleftharpoons$	$HCO_2H(aq)$	+ $OH^-(aq)$
Initial M	0.080			0	0
Changes in M	$-x$	Pure liquid		$+x$	$+x$
Equilibrium M	$0.080 - x$			x	x

$$K_b = 5.7 \times 10^{-11} = \frac{\left[HCO_2H\right]\left[OH^-\right]}{\left[HCO_2^-\right]} \qquad 5.7 \times 10^{-11} = \frac{x^2}{0.080 - x}$$

Using an equation solver yields: $x = 2.135 \times 10^{-6} = [OH^-]$
pOH $= -\log (2.135 \times 10^{-6}) = 5.671$, $\quad$ pH $= 14.00 - 5.671 = 8.33$

Exercise 19-17

$$\text{percent ionization} = \frac{1.11 \times 10^{-6}}{0.068} \times 100\% = 0.0016\%$$

Exercise 19-18

This solution should behave exactly like the solution in Example 19-7. The 0.020 M HCl replaces the first ionization of sulfuric acid. The hydrogen sulfate ion is dissolved in a solution that is already 0.020 M in H_3O^+. The pH should be the same.

Exercise 19-19

Carbonic acid has only two ionizable protons, so it does not have a third ionization equilibrium constant.

CHAPTER 20 ANSWERS TO EXERCISES

Exercise 20-1

a. strong base will react with the weak acid buffer component, HCN

$$HCN(aq) + OH^-(aq) \longrightarrow CN^-(aq) + H_2O(\ell)$$

b. strong acid will react with the weak base buffer component, CN^-

$$CN^-(aq) + H_3O^+(aq) \longrightarrow HCN(aq) + H_2O(\ell)$$

c. strong base will react with the weak acid buffer component, CH_3CO_2H

$$CH_3CO_2H(aq) + OH^-(aq) \longrightarrow CH_3CO_2^-(aq) + H_2O(\ell)$$

d. strong acid will react with the weak base buffer component, $HPO_4{}^{2-}$

$$HPO_4^{2-}(aq) + H_3O^+(aq) \longrightarrow H_2PO_4^-(aq) + H_2O(\ell)$$

Exercise 20-2

a. This is a weak acid and its conjugate base at a ratio of 1.2, so it is a buffer.

b. This is a weak base and its conjugate acid at a ratio of 33, so it is not a buffer, the concentrations are not balanced enough.

c. This is a weak acid and a weak base, but they are not conjugates, so this is not a buffer.

d. This is a weak acid and its conjugate base at a ratio of 8, so it is a buffer.

Exercise 20-3

a. $pH = pK_a = 5.00$

b. $\left[H_3O^+ \right] = K_a \times \dfrac{\left[HA \right]_{eq}}{\left[A^- \right]_{eq}}$

$\left[H_3O^+ \right] = 1.0 \times 10^{-5} \times \dfrac{10}{1} = 1.0 \times 10^{-4}$ $\qquad pH = -log\left(1.0 \times 10^{-4}\right) = 4.00$

c. $\left[H_3O^+ \right] = K_a \times \dfrac{\left[HA \right]_{eq}}{\left[A^- \right]_{eq}}$

$\left[H_3O^+ \right] = 1.0 \times 10^{-5} \times \dfrac{1}{10} = 1.0 \times 10^{-6}$ $\qquad pH = -log\left(1.0 \times 10^{-6}\right) = 6.00$

Exercise 20-4

a. $\left[H_3O^+\right]=K_a\times\dfrac{\left[HA\right]_{eq}}{\left[A^-\right]_{eq}}$

$\left[H_3O^+\right]=4.0\times10^{-8}\times\dfrac{0.42}{0.42}=4.0\times10^{-8}$

$pH=-log\left(4.0\times10^{-8}\right)=7.40$

b. $\left[H_3O^+\right]=K_a\times\dfrac{\left[HA\right]_{eq}}{\left[A^-\right]_{eq}}$

$\left[H_3O^+\right]=4.0\times10^{-8}\times\dfrac{0.20}{0.15}=5.33\times10^{-8}=5.3\times10^{-8}$

$pH=-log\left(5.33\times10^{-8}\right)=7.27$

c. $\left[H_3O^+\right]=K_a\times\dfrac{\left[HA\right]_{eq}}{\left[A^-\right]_{eq}}$

$\left[H_3O^+\right]=1.8\times10^{-4}\times\dfrac{0.060}{0.060}=1.8\times10^{-4}$

$pH=-log\left(1.8\times10^{-4}\right)=3.74$

d. $\left[H_3O^+\right]=K_a\times\dfrac{\left[HA\right]_{eq}}{\left[A^-\right]_{eq}}$

$\left[H_3O^+\right]=1.8\times10^{-4}\times\dfrac{0.060}{0.14}=7.71\times10^{-5}=7.7\times10^{-5}$

$pH=-log\left(7.71\times10^{-5}\right)=4.11$

Exercise 20-5

a. $HA=HClO$ and $A^-=ClO^-$

$pH=pK_a+log\left(\dfrac{\left[A^-\right]}{\left[HA\right]}\right)$

$pH=7.40+log\left(\dfrac{0.20}{0.24}\right)$

$pH=7.32$

b. $pH=pK_a+log\left(\dfrac{\left[A^-\right]}{\left[HA\right]}\right)$

$6.50=pK_a+log\left(\dfrac{2}{1}\right)$

$pK_a=6.50-log\left(2\right)=6.209$

$K_a=10^{-6.209}=6.2\times10^{-7}$

c. $HA=NH_4^+$ with $pK_a=9.24$ and $A^-=NH_3$

$pH=pK_a+log\left(\dfrac{moles\ A^-}{moles\ HA}\right)$

$pH=9.24+log\left(\dfrac{0.0020}{0.0032}\right)$

$pH=9.04$

d. (i) $HA=hisH^+$ with $pK_a=6.1$ and $A^-=his$

$7.4=6.1+log\left(\dfrac{moles\ his}{moles\ hisH^+}\right)$

$1.3=log\left(\dfrac{moles\ his}{moles\ hisH^+}\right)$

$19.95=\dfrac{moles\ his}{moles\ hisH^+}=\dfrac{19.95}{1}$ means that for every 1 $hisH^+$ there are 19.95 his.

(ii) % $hisH^+=\dfrac{\#\ hisH^+}{total\ His\ residues}\times100\%=\dfrac{1}{(19.95+1)}\times100\%=5\%$

Exercise 20-6

a. The added OH⁻ will react with the HCO₂H.

$$moles\ HCO_2H = 0.1000\ L \times \frac{0.35\ mol}{L} = 0.035\ mol\ HCO_2H$$

$$moles\ HCO_2^- = 0.1000\ L \times \frac{0.15\ mol}{L} = 0.015\ mol\ HCO_2^-$$

Stoichiometry Table:

	$OH^-(aq)$	$+$	$HCO_2H(aq)$	$\longrightarrow$	$HCO_2^-(aq)$	$+$	$H_2O(\ell)$
initial moles :	0.0010		0.035		0.015		
change :	−0.0010		−0.0010		+0.0010		
final moles :	0		0.034		0.016		

A buffer solution

This solution will remain a buffer, because the limiting reagent in the buffering reaction is the strong base. This buffer will have a higher pH due to a larger proportion of the weak base component (and smaller proportion of the weak acid component).

b. The added H₃O⁺ will react with the CH₃CO₂⁻.

$$moles\ CH_3CO_2H = 0.0250\ L \times \frac{0.035\ mol}{L} = 0.000875\ mol\ CH_3CO_2^-$$

$$moles\ CH_3CO_2^- = 0.0250\ L \times \frac{0.010\ mol}{L} = 0.00025\ mol\ CH_3CO_2^-$$

Stoichiometry Table:

	$H_3O^+(aq)$	$+$	$CH_3CO_2^-(aq)$	$\longrightarrow$	$CH_3CO_2H(aq)$	$+$	$H_2O(\ell)$
initial moles :	0.0010		0.00025		0.000875		
change :	−0.00025		−0.00025		+0.00025		
final moles :	0.00075		0		0.001125		

A strong acid solution

The resulting solution is a strong acid solution. Expect a lower pH.

Exercise 20-7

a. The pK$_a$ values of possible weak acids from the table are 3.20 (HF), 3.25 (HNO₂), and 3.75 (HCO₂H). The one that is closest to 3.40 is HNO₂ at 3.25. Therefore, a good buffer system would be HNO₂/NO₂⁻.

b. The pK$_a$ values of possible weak acids from the table are 7.40 (HClO), 9.25 (NH₄⁺), and 9.21 (HCN). The one that is closest to 9.30 is NH₄⁺ at 9.25. Therefore, a good buffer system would be NH₄⁺/ NH₃.

Exercise 20-8

Choose a weak acid buffering component with a pK_a close to 7.00. The best choice from Table 19-6 is HClO. Therefore a good buffer system would be HClO/ ClO⁻. Because salts are usually easier to use, start with the weak base component. The salt NaClO has a molar mass of 74.44 g/mol. (Other hypochlorite salts could also be used!) Calculate the amount of salt necessary to make 500 mL of 0.15 M solution:

$$500. \, mL \times \frac{0.15 \, mol \, ClO^-}{1000 \, mL} \times \frac{1 \, mol \, NaClO}{1 \, mol \, ClO^-} \times \frac{74.44 \, g \, NaClO}{mol \, NaClO} = 5.583 \, g \, NaClO = 5.6 \, g \, NaClO$$

Dissolve the sodium hypochlorite in water to make a little less than 500 mL solution. Add a concentrated H_3O^+ solution, with stirring, until a pH meter reads 7.00. (This step results in establishing a buffer solution containing both ClO⁻ and HClO at the desired pH.) Finish diluting to 500. mL with deionized water, adjusting pH if necessary.

Exercise 20-9

The strong acid reacts with the weak base, HCO_2^-. First determine the moles of reactants:

$$0.0030 \, L \times \frac{12 \, mol \, H_3O^+}{L} = 0.036 \, mol \, H_3O^+$$

$$0.100 \, L \times \frac{0.070 \, mol \, HCO_2^-}{L} = 0.015 \, mol \, HCO_2^-$$

Set up the stoichiometry table:

	$H_3O^+(aq)$	+	$HCO_2^-(aq)$	$\longrightarrow$	$HCO_2H(aq)$	+	$H_2O(\ell)$
initial moles :	0.036		0.0070		0.0070		
change :	− 0.0070		− 0.0070		+ 0.0070		
final moles :	0.029		0		0.0140		

Determine the pH:

A strong acid solution

Here we have a strong acid solution. We need to calculate the final [H₃O⁺].

$$\left[H_3O^+ \right] = \frac{0.029 \, mol}{total \, volume \, (L)} \, ; \text{ and the total volume is 103.0 mL (0.1030 L)}$$

$$\left[H_3O^+ \right] = \frac{0.029 \, mol}{0.1030 \, L} = 0.28 \, M$$

$$pH = -\log(0.28) = 0.55$$

Exercise 20-10

Determine the moles H_3O^+ used in the titration:

$$20.64 \, mL \, H_3O^+ \, sln \times \frac{1 L}{1000 \, mL} \times \frac{1.093 \, mol \, H_3O^+}{1 \, L \, H_3O^+ \, sln} = 0.02256 \, mol \, H_3O^+$$

The titration reaction is:

$$H_3O^+(aq) + OCl^-(aq) \longrightarrow HOCl(aq) + H_2O(\ell)$$

So, 0.02256 mol OCl⁻ must have been present to react with the 0.02256 mol H₃O⁺ used. The original volume of the NaOCl solution was 25.00 mL, so the concentration of NaOCl must have been:

$$[NaOCl]_{orig} = \frac{0.02256 \, mol}{0.02500 \, L} = 0.9024 \, M$$